TEACHER'S EDITION Le[illegible]

MCP Mathematics

Richard Monnard • Royce Hargrove

TEACH THE COVER: There are 8 bowling pins. 3 are knocked down. How many are left?

ISBN 0-7652-6059-X
Printed in the United States of America
15 18

Project Staff

Art & Design: Robert Dobaczewski, Kathleen Ellison, Senja Lauderdale, David Mager, Jim O'Shea, Angel Weyant

Editorial: Stephanie P. Cahill, Gina Dalessio, Phyllis Dunsay, Mary Ellen Gilbert, Dena Kennedy, Theresa McCarthy, Marilyn Sarch

Marketing: Doug Falk, Clare Harrison

Production/ Manufacturing: Irene Belinsky, Lawrence Berkowitz, Louis Campos, Diane Fristachi, Pamela Gallo, Leslie Greenberg, Suellen Leavy, Ruth Leine, Karyn Mueller, Michele Uhl

Publishing Operations: Carolyn Coyle, Richetta Lobban

1-800-321-3106
www.pearsonlearning.com

MCP Mathematics

About the Program This comprehensive math program will help students in Grades K to 6 develop a solid mathematics background. It is designed to encourage critical-thinking skills, active participation, and mastery of skills within the context of problem-solving situations. The program's developmental sequence introduces and extends skills taught in most mathematics curricula, such as number sense, operations, algebra, geometry, data collection and analysis, logic, and probability.

A Research-Based Approach

The program offers a strong pedagogical approach that is research based. First, students are provided a developed model that introduces the lesson concept. Then, students are given guided practice opportunities to get started. Next, abundant practice is provided for mastery. Finally, students can apply their skills to problem-solving and enrichment activities. An overview of this approach follows.

- **Direct Instruction**
  Each lesson begins with a developed model that demonstrates the algorithm or concept in a problem-solving situation and gets students actively involved in the situation. . . . *Students taught using direct instruction were found to perform better on tests of computation and year-end tests (Crawford and Snider 2000).**

- **Guided Practice**
  A Getting Started section provides samples of the concept or skill being taught and allows you to guide and observe students as they begin to apply the skills learned. *When low-achieving students were taught using such direct instruction methods as . . . guided practice, . . . they showed improved mastery of basic skills, solved computation and word problems correctly in less time, and had higher self-ratings of academic motivation (Kame´enui, Carnine, Darch, and Stein 1986; Din 1998; Ginsburg-Block and Fantuzzo 1998).**

- **Independent Practice**
  The Practice section can be used to develop and master basic skills by allowing students to independently practice the algorithms and to apply learning from the lesson or from previous lessons. *Research indicates that providing students with extended practice appears to serve two purposes: re-teaching of the skill for students who had not yet mastered it and relating of the previously learned skill to new skills, resulting in the formation of interrelationships among concepts that improved retention and yielded higher achievement test results (Hett 1989).**

- **Higher-Order Thinking Skills**
  A collection of real-life word problems in the Problem Solving section provides application opportunities related to the lesson concepts. *Frequent practice with word problems is associated with higher-order skill development (Coy 2001). This finding is especially true when the word problems present familiar real life situations (Coy 2001).**

- **Problem-Solving Strategies**
  Once per chapter, a special lesson introduces students to the techniques of problem solving using Polya's four-step model. The Apply activities in these lessons allow students to use problem-solving strategies in everyday situations. *Students who received instruction in problem-solving processes showed better performance on tests of skills, tasks, and problem solving, as well as on a measure of the transfer of learning (Durnin et al. 1997).**

- **Calculator Usage**
  Calculator lessons in Grades 3 to 6 teach students the functions and the skills needed to use calculators intelligently after they've developed a foundation of competence in pencil-and-paper computation. *. . . Students who used calculators in mathematics instruction had more positive attitudes toward mathematics and a higher math self-concept. . . . A special curriculum developed around calculators has been shown to improve mathematics achievement (Hembree and Dessart 1986).**

- **Frequent and Cumulative Assessment**
  Chapter Tests provide both students and teachers with a checkpoint that tests all the skills taught in a chapter. You will find Alternate Chapter Tests based on the same objectives in the Teacher's Edition. *Assessment has been found to be most effective when it is a frequent and well-integrated aspect of mathematics instruction (Brosnan and Hartog 1993).* Cumulative Assessments maintain skills that have been taught in all previous chapters. A standardized test format is used starting at the middle of the second-grade text. The Teacher's Edition also contains Alternate Cumulative Assessments. . . . *Frequent cumulative tests result in higher levels of achievement than do infrequent tests or tests related only to content since the last test (Dempster 1991).**

- **Remedying Common Errors**
  The comprehensive Teacher's Edition provides abundant additional help for teachers, including a four-step lesson plan that walks the teacher through the lesson, pointing out common errors and providing intervention strategies. *Curricula with an error correction component were found to result in higher scores for computation, math concepts, and problem solving (Stefanich and Rokusek 1992; Crawford and Snider 2000).**

* *Research compiled by PRES Associates, Inc. (2004). Research Support for* MCP Mathematics *(unpublished).*

Using the Student Edition

Use the First Page of a Lesson for Direct Instruction

Each two-page lesson focuses on one main objective. The first page begins with a developed model that students can actively work on as you walk them through it.

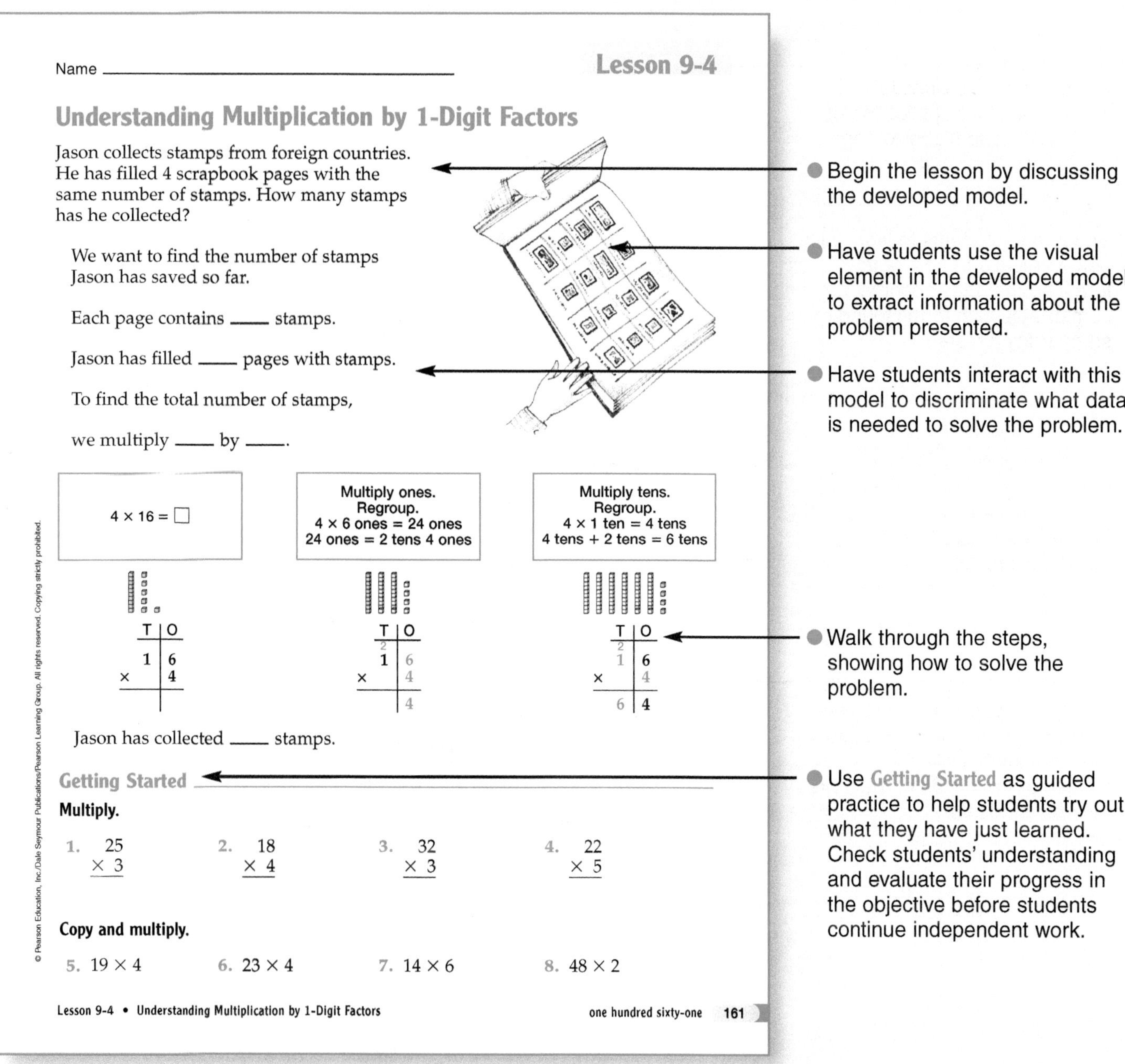

Name ______________________ **Lesson 9-4**

Understanding Multiplication by 1-Digit Factors

Jason collects stamps from foreign countries. He has filled 4 scrapbook pages with the same number of stamps. How many stamps has he collected?

We want to find the number of stamps Jason has saved so far.

Each page contains ____ stamps.

Jason has filled ____ pages with stamps.

To find the total number of stamps,

we multiply ____ by ____.

$4 \times 16 = \square$	Multiply ones. Regroup. 4×6 ones = 24 ones; 24 ones = 2 tens 4 ones	Multiply tens. Regroup. 4×1 ten = 4 tens; 4 tens + 2 tens = 6 tens
T O: 1 6 × 4	T O: (2) 1 6 × 4 = 4	T O: (2) 1 6 × 4 = 6 4

Jason has collected ____ stamps.

Getting Started

Multiply.

1. 25 × 3
2. 18 × 4
3. 32 × 3
4. 22 × 5

Copy and multiply.

5. 19 × 4
6. 23 × 4
7. 14 × 6
8. 48 × 2

- Begin the lesson by discussing the developed model.
- Have students use the visual element in the developed model to extract information about the problem presented.
- Have students interact with this model to discriminate what data is needed to solve the problem.
- Walk through the steps, showing how to solve the problem.
- Use Getting Started as guided practice to help students try out what they have just learned. Check students' understanding and evaluate their progress in the objective before students continue independent work.

Using the Student Edition

Assign Practice From the Second Page of a Lesson

The second page of a lesson provides practice and extension of the lesson's objective. You can begin the process of individual mastery by assigning Practice exercises that students can work on independently.

- Have students Practice independently to provide opportunities for application of basic skills and higher-order thinking.
- Encourage students to work with both vertical and horizontal forms so that they become comfortable with forms found on standardized tests.
- Check students' abilities to assemble an algorithm and give them practice in transferring information by assigning **Copy and . . .** exercises.
- Use Now Try This! activities to extend the basic skill work and to make learning the concepts fun. Use the activities to challenge the minds of the more capable students.

Practice

Multiply.

1. 35 × 2
2. 24 × 3
3. 16 × 5
4. 47 × 2
5. 33 × 3
6. 27 × 3
7. 19 × 4
8. 12 × 5
9. 26 × 3
10. 18 × 4
11. 49 × 1
12. 19 × 3
13. 13 × 4
14. 24 × 4
15. 37 × 2
16. 14 × 6
17. 24 × 2
18. 12 × 7
19. 38 × 2
20. 12 × 8

Copy and multiply.

21. 47 × 2
22. 36 × 2
23. 14 × 7
24. 16 × 3
25. 23 × 4
26. 17 × 4
27. 31 × 1
28. 11 × 5
29. 18 × 3
30. 12 × 6
31. 14 × 5
32. 42 × 2

Now Try This!

Study the following pattern.

47 × 2 = 40 twos + 7 twos = 80 + 14 = 94

Use the pattern to help you complete the rest of the multiplications.

1. 24 × 3 = ____ threes + ____ threes = ____ + ____ = ____
2. 37 × 2 = ____ twos + ____ twos = ____ + ____ = ____
3. 17 × 4 = ____ fours + ____ fours = ____ + ____ = ____
4. 12 × 7 = ____ sevens + ____ sevens = ____ + ____ = ____

Teach Problem Solving and Calculators in Every Chapter

Problem Solving lessons focus on different problem-solving strategies using the chapter concepts and skills. Calculator lessons teach students to use the technology while reinforcing chapter content.

- **It's Algebra!** indicates lessons that will help students prepare for algebra.
- Discuss the problem and the visual with students. Every problem-solving step is organized so that students truly understand how to arrive at the solution.
- Follow the steps with students as they first learn to understand the question and find the information they need under **SEE**.
- Help students plan a method for solving the problem by reviewing the example under **PLAN**.
- Have students find the answer by completing **DO**.
- Have students use **CHECK** to ensure accuracy.
- Use the Apply activities to allow students to stretch their use of the problem-solving strategy.
- Use Calculator lessons to introduce students to basic calculator skills and terms and to have students practice the new skills.

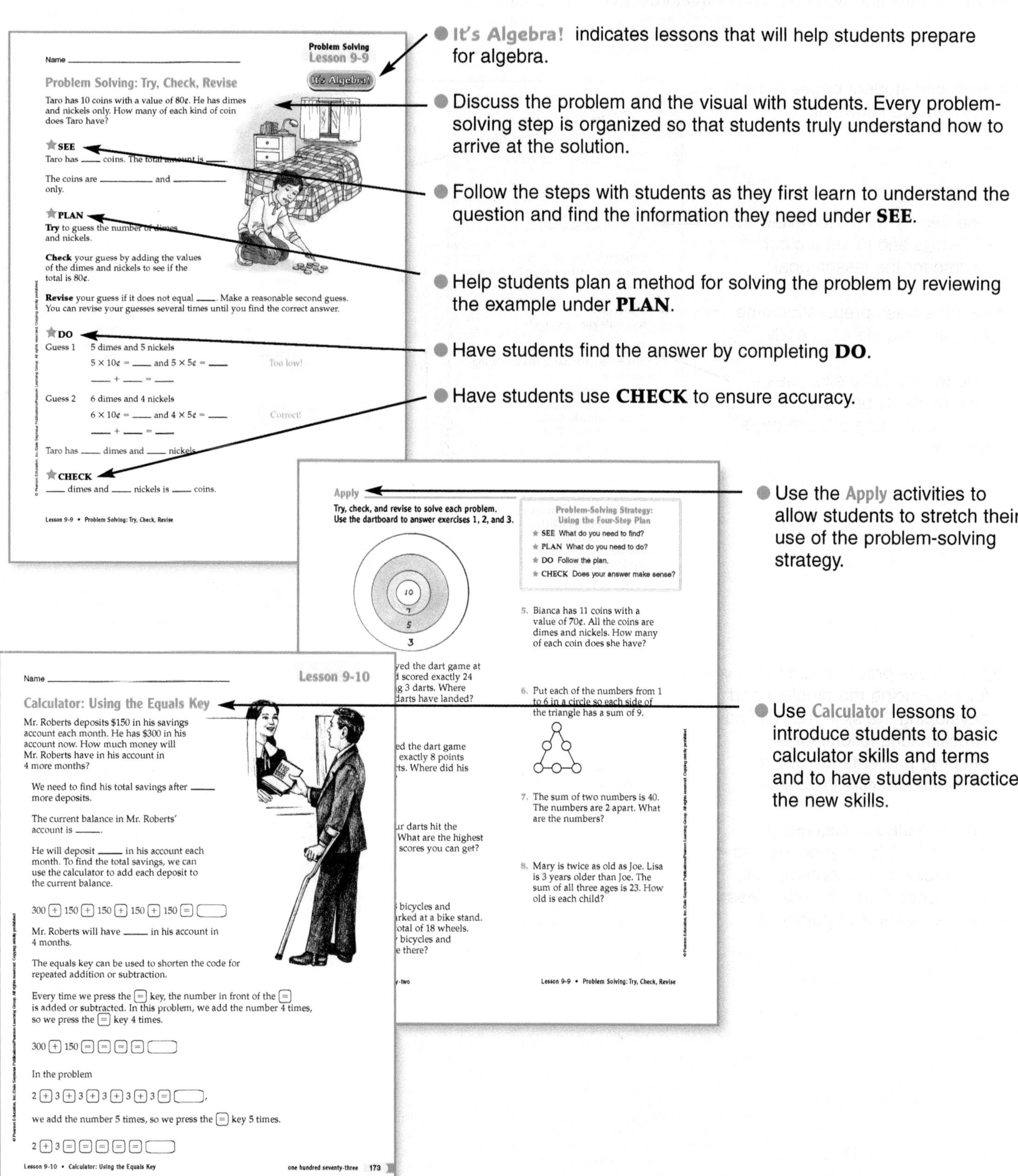

Name ____________ Problem Solving Lesson 9-9

It's Algebra!

Problem Solving: Try, Check, Revise

Taro has 10 coins with a value of 80¢. He has dimes and nickels only. How many of each kind of coin does Taro have?

SEE
Taro has ___ coins. The total amount is ___.
The coins are ___ and ___ only.

PLAN
Try to guess the number of dimes and nickels.
Check your guess by adding the values of the dimes and nickels to see if the total is 80¢.
Revise your guess if it does not equal ___. Make a reasonable second guess. You can revise your guesses several times until you find the correct answer.

DO
Guess 1 5 dimes and 5 nickels
5 × 10¢ = ___ and 5 × 5¢ = ___ Too low!
___ + ___ = ___
Guess 2 6 dimes and 4 nickels
6 × 10¢ = ___ and 4 × 5¢ = ___ Correct!
___ + ___ = ___
Taro has ___ dimes and ___ nickels.

CHECK
___ dimes and ___ nickels is ___ coins.

Lesson 9-9 • Problem Solving: Try, Check, Revise

Apply
Try, check, and revise to solve each problem. Use the dartboard to answer exercises 1, 2, and 3.

Problem-Solving Strategy: Using the Four-Step Plan
SEE What do you need to find?
PLAN What do you need to do?
DO Follow the plan.
CHECK Does your answer make sense?

5. Bianca has 11 coins with a value of 70¢. All the coins are dimes and nickels. How many of each coin does she have?
6. Put each of the numbers from 1 to 6 in a circle so each side of the triangle has a sum of 9.
7. The sum of two numbers is 40. The numbers are 2 apart. What are the numbers?
8. Mary is twice as old as Joe. Lisa is 3 years older than Joe. The sum of all three ages is 23. How old is each child?

Lesson 9-9 • Problem Solving: Try, Check, Revise

Name ____________ Lesson 9-10

Calculator: Using the Equals Key

Mr. Roberts deposits $150 in his savings account each month. He has $300 in his account now. How much money will Mr. Roberts have in his account in 4 more months?

We need to find his total savings after ___ more deposits.
The current balance in Mr. Roberts' account is ___.
He will deposit ___ in his account each month. To find the total savings, we can use the calculator to add each deposit to the current balance.
300 [+] 150 [+] 150 [+] 150 [+] 150 [=] [ ]
Mr. Roberts will have ___ in his account in 4 months.
The equals key can be used to shorten the code for repeated addition or subtraction.
Every time we press the [=] key, the number in front of the [=] is added or subtracted. In this problem, we add the number 4 times, so we press the [=] key 4 times.
300 [+] 150 [=] [=] [=] [=] [ ]
In the problem
2 [+] 3 [+] 3 [+] 3 [+] 3 [+] 3 [=] [ ],
we add the number 5 times, so we press the [=] key 5 times.
2 [+] 3 [=] [=] [=] [=] [=] [ ]

Lesson 9-10 • Calculator: Using the Equals Key one hundred seventy-three 173

Using the Teacher's Edition

Instruct Using a Four-Step Lesson Plan

The Teacher's Edition is designed and organized with you in mind. Consistent four-step lesson plans on two pages will help you make efficient use of your planning time and will help you deliver effective instruction.

- Reduced student pages provide point-of-use information.
- Use Getting Started to review the Objectives and to set a clear course for the lesson goal.
- Reduce class preparation time by gathering Materials early.
- Use the Warm Up exercises to help students brush up on skills at the beginning of each day's lesson.
- Teach gives practical suggestions for introducing the problem and developing the skill. You will find specific suggestions for an effective presentation of the model in **Introduce the Lesson.**
- **Develop Skills and Concepts** gives suggestions for presenting and developing the algorithm, skill, or concept. Some include ideas for the use of manipulatives.

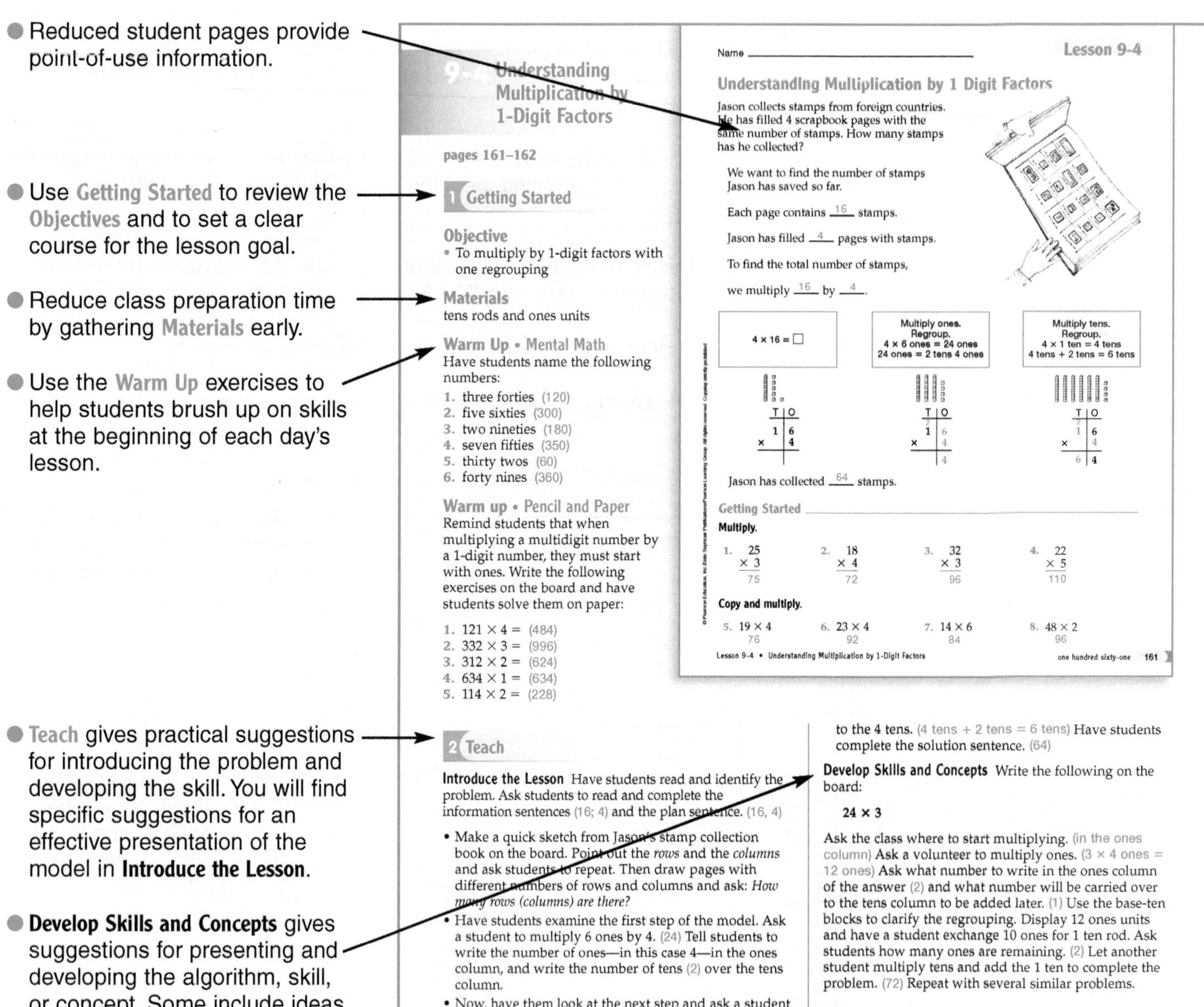

9-4 Understanding Multiplication by 1-Digit Factors

pages 161–162

1 Getting Started

Objective
- To multiply by 1-digit factors with one regrouping

Materials
tens rods and ones units

Warm Up • Mental Math
Have students name the following numbers:
1. three forties (120)
2. five sixties (300)
3. two nineties (180)
4. seven fifties (350)
5. thirty twos (60)
6. forty nines (360)

Warm up • Pencil and Paper
Remind students that when multiplying a multidigit number by a 1-digit number, they must start with ones. Write the following exercises on the board and have students solve them on paper:
1. 121 × 4 = (484)
2. 332 × 3 = (996)
3. 312 × 2 = (624)
4. 634 × 1 = (634)
5. 114 × 2 = (228)

Name ______ Lesson 9-4

Understanding Multiplication by 1 Digit Factors

Jason collects stamps from foreign countries. He has filled 4 scrapbook pages with the same number of stamps. How many stamps has he collected?

We want to find the number of stamps Jason has saved so far.
Each page contains 16 stamps.
Jason has filled 4 pages with stamps.
To find the total number of stamps,
we multiply 16 by 4.

4 × 16 = □

Multiply ones. Regroup. 4 × 6 ones = 24 ones 24 ones = 2 tens 4 ones

Multiply tens. Regroup. 4 × 1 ten = 4 tens 4 tens + 2 tens = 6 tens

Jason has collected 64 stamps.

Getting Started
Multiply.
1. 25 × 3 = 75 2. 18 × 4 = 72 3. 32 × 3 = 96 4. 22 × 5 = 110

Copy and multiply.
5. 19 × 4 = 76 6. 23 × 4 = 92 7. 14 × 6 = 84 8. 48 × 2 = 96

Lesson 9-4 • Understanding Multiplication by 1-Digit Factors one hundred sixty-one 161

2 Teach

Introduce the Lesson Have students read and identify the problem. Ask students to read and complete the information sentences (16; 4) and the plan sentence. (16, 4)
- Make a quick sketch from Jason's stamp collection book on the board. Point out the *rows* and the *columns* and ask students to repeat. Then draw pages with different numbers of rows and columns and ask: *How many rows (columns) are there?*
- Have students examine the first step of the model. Ask a student to multiply 6 ones by 4. (24) Tell students to write the number of ones—in this case 4—in the ones column, and write the number of tens (2) over the tens column.
- Now, have them look at the next step and ask a student to tell the product of 4 × 1 ten. (4) Point out that the 2 tens left from the one's multiplication must be added to the 4 tens. (4 tens + 2 tens = 6 tens) Have students complete the solution sentence. (64)

Develop Skills and Concepts Write the following on the board:

24 × 3

Ask the class where to start multiplying. (in the ones column) Ask a volunteer to multiply ones. (3 × 4 ones = 12 ones) Ask what number to write in the ones column of the answer (2) and what number will be carried over to the tens column to be added later. (1) Use the base-ten blocks to clarify the regrouping. Display 12 ones units and have a student exchange 10 ones for 1 ten rod. Ask students how many ones are remaining. (2) Let another student multiply tens and add the 1 ten to complete the problem. (72) Repeat with several similar problems.

T161

Practice

Multiply.

1. 35 × 2 = 70	2. 24 × 3 = 72	3. 16 × 5 = 80	4. 47 × 2 = 94	5. 33 × 3 = 99
6. 27 × 3 = 81	7. 19 × 4 = 76	8. 12 × 5 = 60	9. 26 × 3 = 78	10. 18 × 4 = 72
11. 49 × 1 = 49	12. 19 × 3 = 57	13. 13 × 4 = 52	14. 24 × 4 = 96	15. 37 × 2 = 74
16. 14 × 6 = 84	17. 24 × 2 = 48	18. 12 × 7 = 84	19. 38 × 2 = 76	20. 12 × 8 = 96

Copy and multiply.

21. 47 × 2 = 94	22. 36 × 2 = 72	23. 14 × 7 = 98	24. 16 × 3 = 48
25. 23 × 4 = 92	26. 17 × 4 = 68	27. 31 × 1 = 31	28. 11 × 5 = 55
29. 18 × 3 = 54	30. 12 × 6 = 72	31. 14 × 5 = 70	32. 42 × 2 = 84

Now Try This!

Study the following pattern.

47 × 2 = 40 twos + 7 twos = 80 + 14 = 94

Use the pattern to help you complete the rest of the multiplications.

1. 24 × 3 = 20 threes + 4 threes = 60 + 12 = 72
2. 37 × 2 = 30 twos + 7 twos = 60 + 14 = 74
3. 17 × 4 = 10 fours + 7 fours = 40 + 28 = 68
4. 12 × 7 = 10 sevens + 2 sevens = 70 + 14 = 84

3 Practice

Have students solve all the exercises on the page. Remind them to start multiplying in the ones column, and write any tens over the tens column and add them in last.

Now Try This! Discuss with the students how multiplying by decades helps to do problems mentally. Have students complete the exercises.

4 Assess

Ask students where they must begin multiplying a two-digit number. (at the ones)

For Mixed Abilities

Common Errors • Intervention

When students multiply the ones, they may not regroup but write both digits in the answer.

INCORRECT	CORRECT
38 × 2 = 616	38 × 2 = 76 (regrouped 1)

Have them work with partners and base-ten blocks to model the problem.

Enrichment • Measurement

Have students think about the 8- and 6-hour clocks they made in the Enrichment on page T160. Ask them to explain the problem with these clocks. (The clock is in the same configuration 3 or 4 times a day.) Ask each student to devise a different way of distinguishing one part of the day from another, as our use of A.M. and P.M. does.

More to Explore • Measurement

Have the students make a simple rain gauge. Ask them to mark off a glass or plastic jar in quarter-inches. Have students place the jar in a safe but open place at home or school. Ask the students to take measurements each time it rains or snows and record the results for a two-week period. Have students make a bar graph to show the amount of rainfall for the two weeks. Have the class compare their results with the official measurements given by the TV weather report or the newspaper.

ESL/ELL STRATEGIES

Make a quick sketch on the board of a page from Jason's stamp collection book. Point out the *rows* and *columns* and ask students to repeat the words. Then, draw pages with different numbers of rows and columns and ask: *How many rows (columns) are there?*

T162

- Use the Common Errors • **Intervention** feature to explore a common error pattern and to provide remediation to struggling students. Collectively, all the Common Errors features in any chapter constitute a complete set of the common errors that students are likely to make when working in that chapter.
- Enrichment activities are a direct extension of the skills being taught. Some students may do these activities on their own while you work with those students who need more help.
- More to Explore activities are challenging and independent, expanding the mathematical experiences of the students. The More to Explore section encompasses a wide variety of activities and projects and introduces and extends skills taught in the normal curriculum—including data collection and analysis, logic, and probability.
- ESL/ELL Strategies are offered twice per chapter. These activities will help you provide insights into English vocabulary and increase comprehension of mathematical concepts. Specific techniques cited ensure that learning is taking place. The techniques also remove potential language barriers for English-language learners at beginning levels of proficiency.
- Practice offers you guidelines to assist your students as they practice independently.
- Assess provides you with a short question or activity that can be used to quickly evaluate if students have grasped the main objective of the lesson.

Assessment

Assess Often With Chapter and Cumulative Tests

A variety of assessments help you track your students' mastery of algorithms, basic skills, and problem solving.

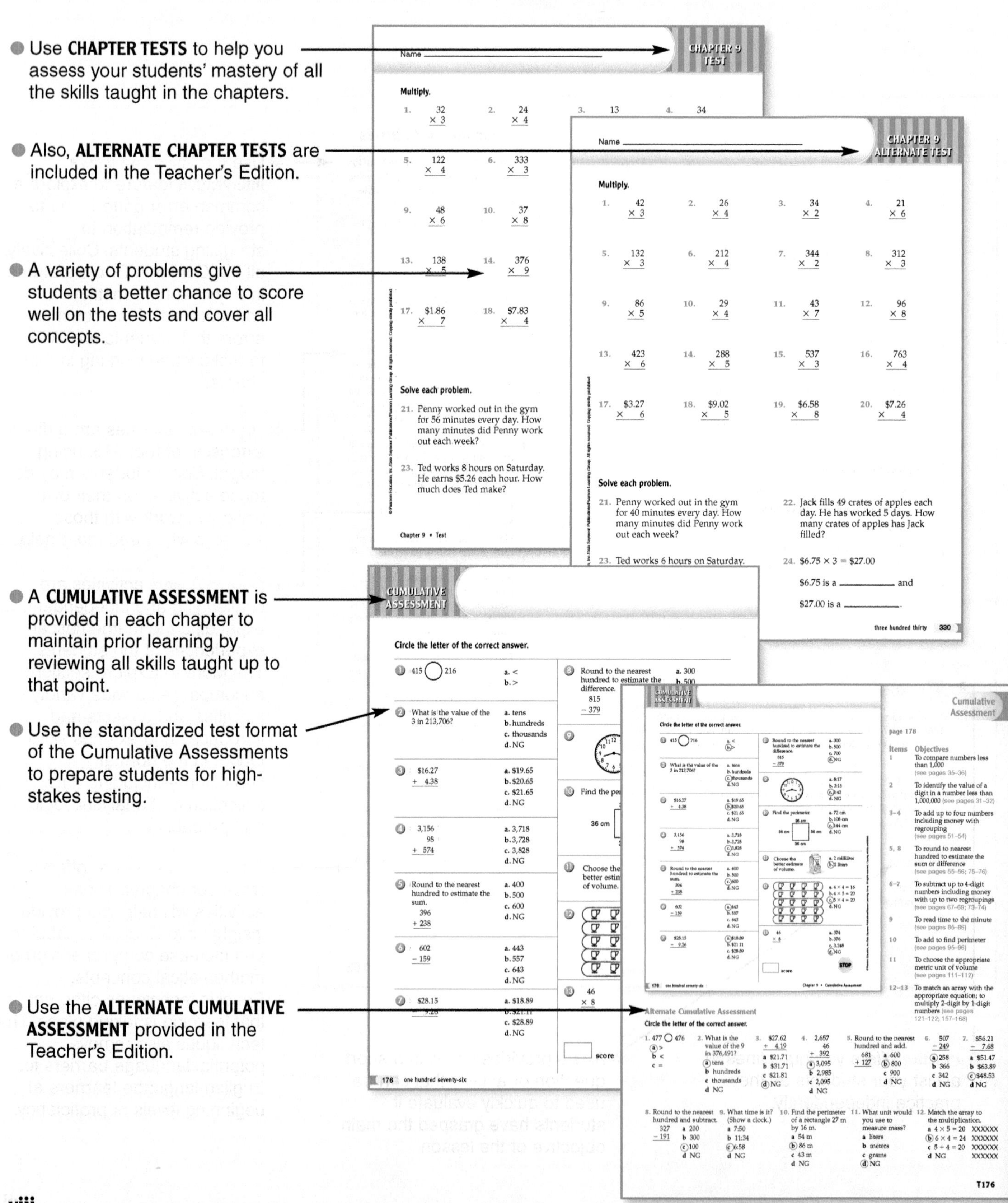

- Use **CHAPTER TESTS** to help you assess your students' mastery of all the skills taught in the chapters.
- Also, **ALTERNATE CHAPTER TESTS** are included in the Teacher's Edition.
- A variety of problems give students a better chance to score well on the tests and cover all concepts.
- A **CUMULATIVE ASSESSMENT** is provided in each chapter to maintain prior learning by reviewing all skills taught up to that point.
- Use the standardized test format of the Cumulative Assessments to prepare students for high-stakes testing.
- Use the **ALTERNATE CUMULATIVE ASSESSMENT** provided in the Teacher's Edition.

Scope and Sequence

Levels	K	A	B	C	D	E	F
Readiness							
Using attributes of size, shape, and color	●	●	●				
Sorting and classifying	●	●					
Spatial relationships	●						
Numeration							
One-to-one correspondence	●						
Understanding numbers	●	●	●	●	●	●	●
Writing numbers	●	●					
Counting objects	●	●	●				
Sequencing numbers	●	●	●	●	●		
Numbers before and after	●	●	●	●	●		
Ordering numbers	●	●	●	●	●	●	●
Comparing numbers	●	●	●	●	●	●	●
Grouping numbers	●	●	●	●	●		
Ordinal numbers	●	●	●	●			
Number words		●	●	●	●	●	●
Expanded numbers				●	●	●	●
Place value	●	●	●	●	●	●	●
Skip-counting	●	●	●	●	●		
Roman numerals			●	●			●
Rounding numbers			●	●	●	●	●
Squares and square roots							●
Primes and composites				●	●	●	●
Multiples			●	●	●	●	●
Least common multiples						●	●
Greatest common factors						●	●
Exponents						●	●
Addition							
Addition facts	●	●	●	●	●	●	●
Fact families		●	●	●	●	●	●
Missing addends		●	●	●	●	●	●
Adding money	●	●	●	●	●	●	●
Column addition		●	●	●	●	●	●
Two-digit addends		●	●	●	●	●	●
Multidigit addends			●	●	●	●	●
Addition with regrouping		●	●	●	●	●	●
Basic properties of addition				●	●	●	●
Estimating sums			●	●	●	●	●
Addition of fractions				●	●	●	●

Scope and Sequence

Levels	K	A	B	C	D	E	F
Addition *(continued)*							
Addition of mixed numbers				●	●	●	●
Addition of decimals				●	●	●	●
Addition of customary measures						●	●
Addition of integers						●	●
Subtraction							
Subtraction facts	●	●	●	●	●	●	●
Fact families		●	●	●	●	●	●
Missing subtrahends		●	●	●	●		
Subtracting money	●	●	●	●	●	●	●
Two-digit numbers		●	●	●	●	●	●
Multidigit numbers			●	●	●	●	●
Subtraction with regrouping		●	●	●	●	●	●
Zeros in the minuend			●	●	●	●	●
Basic properties of subtraction				●	●	●	●
Estimating differences			●	●	●	●	●
Subtraction of fractions				●	●	●	●
Subtraction of mixed numbers						●	●
Subtraction of decimals				●	●	●	●
Subtraction of customary measures						●	●
Subtraction of integers						●	●
Multiplication							
Multiplication facts			●	●	●	●	●
Fact families			●	●	●	●	●
Missing factors				●	●	●	●
Multiplying money				●	●	●	●
Multiplication by powers of ten				●	●	●	●
Multidigit factors				●	●	●	●
Multiplication with regrouping				●	●	●	●
Basic properties of multiplication			●	●	●	●	●
Estimating products				●	●	●	●
Multiples				●	●	●	●
Least common multiples						●	●
Multiplication of fractions						●	●
Factorization						●	●
Multiplication of mixed numbers						●	●
Multiplication of decimals					●	●	●
Exponents						●	●
Multiplication of integers						●	●

Scope and Sequence

Levels	K	A	B	C	D	E	F
Division							
Division facts			●	●	●	●	●
Fact families			●	●	●	●	●
Divisibility rules				●	●	●	●
Two-digit quotients				●	●	●	●
Remainders				●	●	●	●
Multidigit quotients					●	●	●
Zeros in quotients					●	●	●
Division by multiples of ten					●	●	●
Two-digit divisors					●	●	●
Properties of division					●	●	●
Averages					●	●	●
Greatest common factors						●	●
Division of fractions						●	●
Division of mixed numbers						●	●
Division of decimals						●	●
Division of integers							●
Money							
Counting pennies	●	●	●	●	●		
Counting nickels	●	●	●	●	●		
Counting dimes	●	●	●	●	●		
Counting quarters		●	●	●	●		
Counting half-dollars		●	●	●	●		
Counting dollar bills		●	●	●	●		
Writing dollar and cent signs		●	●	●	●	●	●
Matching money with prices	●	●	●				
Determining amount of change		●	●	●	●		
Determining sufficient amount		●	●				
Determining which coins to use		●	●				
Addition	●	●	●	●	●	●	●
Subtraction	●	●	●	●	●	●	●
Multiplication				●	●	●	●
Division				●	●	●	●
Estimating amounts of money			●	●	●	●	●
Rounding amounts of money			●	●	●	●	●
Buying from a table of prices		●	●	●	●	●	●
Fractions							
Understanding equal parts	●	●	●	●			
One-half	●	●	●	●	●		

Scope and Sequence

Levels	K	A	B	C	D	E	F
Fractions *(continued)*							
One-fourth	●	●	●	●	●		
One-third	●	●	●	●	●		
Identifying fractional parts of figures	●	●	●	●	●	●	●
Identifying fractional parts of sets		●	●	●	●	●	●
Finding unit fractions of numbers				●	●		
Equivalent fractions				●	●	●	●
Comparing and ordering fractions				●	●	●	●
Simplifying fractions					●	●	●
Mixed numbers				●	●	●	●
Addition of fractions				●	●	●	●
Subtraction of fractions				●	●	●	●
Addition of mixed numbers					●	●	●
Subtraction of mixed numbers						●	●
Multiplication of fractions						●	●
Multiplication of mixed numbers						●	●
Division of fractions						●	●
Division of mixed numbers						●	●
Renaming fractions as decimals				●	●	●	●
Renaming fractions as percents						●	●
Decimals							
Place value				●	●	●	●
Reading decimals				●	●	●	●
Writing decimals				●	●	●	●
Converting fractions to decimals					●	●	●
Writing parts of sets as decimals				●	●	●	●
Comparing decimals				●	●	●	●
Ordering decimals				●	●	●	●
Addition of decimals				●	●	●	●
Subtraction of decimals				●	●	●	●
Rounding decimals					●	●	●
Multiplication of decimals					●	●	●
Division of decimals						●	●
Renaming decimals as percents						●	●
Geometry							
Polygons	●	●	●	●	●	●	●
Sides and vertices of polygons		●	●	●	●	●	●
Faces, edges, and vertices		●	●	●	●	●	●
Solid figures	●	●	●	●	●	●	●

Scope and Sequence

Levels	K	A	B	C	D	E	F
Geometry *(continued)*							
Symmetry	●	●	●	●	●	●	●
Lines and line segments				●	●	●	●
Rays and angles				●	●	●	●
Measuring angles						●	●
Transformations			●	●	●	●	●
Congruency				●	●	●	●
Similar figures					●	●	●
Circles					●	●	●
Triangles				●	●	●	●
Quadrilaterals				●	●	●	●
Measurement							
Nonstandard units of measure	●	●					
Customary units of measure		●	●	●	●	●	●
Metric units of measure		●	●	●	●	●	●
Renaming customary measures				●	●	●	●
Renaming metric measures				●	●	●	●
Selecting appropriate units		●	●	●	●		
Estimating measures		●	●	●	●		
Perimeter by counting		●	●				
Perimeter by formula				●	●		●
Area of polygons by counting		●	●	●	●		
Area of polygons by formula					●	●	●
Volume by counting				●	●	●	
Volume by formula					●	●	●
Addition of measures						●	●
Subtraction of measures						●	●
Circumference of circles							●
Area of circles							●
Surface area of space figures							●
Estimating temperatures				●	●	●	●
Reading temperature scales		●	●	●	●	●	●
Time							
Ordering events	●						
Calendars	●	●	●	●	●		
Telling time to the hour	●	●	●	●	●		
Telling time to the half-hour		●	●	●	●		
Telling time to the five-minutes		●	●	●	●		
Telling time to the minute			●	●	●		

Scope and Sequence

Levels	K	A	B	C	D	E	F
Time *(continued)*							
Understanding A.M. and P.M.				●	●	●	●
Elapsed time			●	●	●	●	●
Graphing							
Tallies	●	●	●	●	●	●	
Bar graphs		●	●	●	●	●	●
Picture graphs	●	●	●	●	●		
Line graphs				●	●	●	●
Circle graphs						●	
Line plots			●			●	
Stem-and-leaf plots						●	●
Histograms							●
Ordered pairs			●	●	●	●	●
Statistics and Probability							
Understanding probability			●	●	●	●	●
Listing outcomes					●	●	●
Mean, median, and mode				●	●	●	●
Writing probabilities				●	●	●	●
Compound probability							●
Making predictions							●
Tree diagrams					●	●	●
Ratios and Percents							
Understanding ratios					●	●	●
Equal ratios						●	●
Proportions						●	●
Scale drawings						●	●
Ratios as percents						●	●
Percents as fractions						●	●
Fractions as percents						●	●
Finding the percents of numbers						●	●
Integers							
Understanding integers						●	●
Addition of integers						●	●
Subtraction of integers						●	●
Multiplication of integers							●
Division of integers							●
Graphing integers on coordinate planes							●

Scope and Sequence

Levels	K	A	B	C	D	E	F
Problem Solving							
Act it out	●	●	●	●	●	●	●
Choose a strategy	●	●	●	●	●		
Choose the correct operation	●	●	●	●	●		
Collect and use data		●	●	●	●	●	●
Determine missing or extra data		●	●	●	●		
Draw a picture or diagram	●	●	●	●	●	●	●
Identify a subgoal						●	●
Look for a pattern	●	●	●	●	●	●	●
Make a graph	●	●	●	●	●	●	●
Make a list		●	●	●	●	●	●
Make a model					●		
Make a table		●	●	●		●	●
Make a tally graph						●	
Restate the problem					●	●	●
Solve a simpler but related problem				●	●	●	●
Solve multistep problems				●	●	●	●
Try, check, and revise	●	●	●	●	●	●	●
Use a formula						●	●
Use a four-step plan				●	●	●	●
Use an exact answer or an estimate				●	●		
Use logical reasoning		●	●	●	●		●
Work backward				●	●	●	●
Write a number sentence		●	●	●	●		
Calculators							
Calculator codes				●	●	●	●
Equals key				●	●	●	●
Addition/subtraction keys				●	●	●	●
Multiplication/division keys				●	●	●	●
Clear key				●	●		
Calculators: Real-World Applications							
Averages						●	●
Formulas						●	●
Money					●	●	●
Percents						●	●
Repeating decimals						●	●
Statistics						●	●

Scope and Sequence

Levels	K	A	B	C	D	E	F
Algebra							
Patterns	●	●	●	●	●	●	●
Completing number sentences	●	●	●	●	●	●	●
Properties of numbers				●	●	●	●
Numerical expressions				●	●	●	●
Evaluating numerical expressions					●	●	●
Algebraic expressions						●	●
Evaluating algebraic expressions						●	●
Order of operations				●	●	●	●
Integers						●	●
Addition and subtraction of integers						●	●
Multiplication and division of integers							●
Ordered pairs			●	●	●	●	●
Function tables				●	●	●	●
Graphing a rule or an equation						●	●
Variables				●	●	●	●
Equations				●	●	●	●
Solve addition and subtraction equations						●	●
Solve multiplication and division equations						●	●
Model problem situations with equations						●	●
Solve inequalities							●
Formulas						●	●
Properties of equality						●	●

Contents

1-1 Numbers 0 Through 10

pages 1–2

1 Getting Started

Objectives

- To read numbers and number names 0 through 10
- To count 0 through 10 and write the number

Warm Up • Mental Math

Have students name the number that

1. tells their age
2. tells how many people are in their family
3. tells how many children are in their family
4. rhymes with eleven (7)
5. names no objects (0)
6. rhymes with sticks (6)

Warm Up • Number Sense

Have students count in unison from 0 to 10. Now, have a student name a number from 0 to 10. Have students begin with that number and count on through 10. Repeat for more review of counting on to 10. Repeat the exercise to have students write the numbers on the board.

Name ______________________________

Chapter 1

Basic Facts Through 10

Lesson 1-1

Match the set to the number.
Match the number to the number name.

	Set	Number	Number name
1		1	two
2		9	one
3		2	four
4		4	nine
5		3	ten
6		0	five
7		10	three
8		5	zero
9		7	seven
10		8	six
11		6	eight

2 Teach

Develop Skills and Concepts Draw six circles on the board. Ask students to tell how many circles are drawn. Write **6** and **six** on the board and have students read the number and the number word. Write **four** on the board and have a student draw circles and write the number. (4)

- Continue for the other numbers from 0 to 10. When all numbers have been represented on the board, have students locate the numbers and number names on the board as you say them in random order.

3 Practice

Using page 1 Have students count the objects in the first group and trace the line to the 2. Tell students to trace the line from the number 2 to its number name. (two) Tell students that they are to draw a line from each group to the number that tells how many objects are in the group. Tell students they are then to draw a line from the number to its number name. Have students complete the exercises independently.

Using page 2 Tell students to write in each box the number that tells how many objects there are for Exercises 1–11. For Exercise 12, tell students to begin at start and connect the dots in order from 1 to 10. Have students complete the exercises independently.

Write the numbers.

1. 1
2. 0
3. 2
4. 5
5. 4
6. 9
7. 3
8. 7
9. 10
10. 8
11. 6

12. Connect the dots.

START

4 Assess

Give each student a pair of number and number-name cards for 0 through 10. Draw three circles on the board and have students hold up the correct number card. Repeat this exercise with the numbers 7 and 10. Then, draw six squares on the board and have students hold up the correct number-name card. Repeat this exercise with the numbers 2 and 5.

For Mixed Abilities

Common Errors • Intervention

Watch for students who write numbers backward. Write the numbers on the board and have students dip their pointing fingers in a cup of water and trace over the numbers, one at a time, with slippery fingers.

Enrichment • Number Sense

1. Have students cut pictures of objects from catalogs or magazines to show each number from 0 to 10. They should then write the number beside each group.
2. Ask students to make a dot-to-dot picture for the numbers 0 through 10. Then, tell them to have a friend connect the dots.
3. Have students play a matching game with a friend. They should lay all number and number-name cards for 0 through 10 facedown. Students will take turns turning over the cards and matching the numbers to their names.

More to Explore • Application

Play Simon Says using directions that require counting movements a specified number of times. For example, say, *Simon says jump 10 times,* and have students count aloud. Then, say, *Simon says clap 8 times. Hold up 4 fingers.* Students holding up fingers would be out of the game because it was not prefaced with "Simon says." Continue playing and counting until only one person remains.

As a variation, do a movement such as touching shoulders many times in succession while children count silently. Have a student imitate the movement the same number of times while students count aloud. Continue having one student lead the movements a number of times and another student try to duplicate the movements.

1-2 Sums Through 5

pages 3–4

1 Getting Started

Objective
- To review addition facts for sums through 5

Vocabulary
sum, + (plus sign), = (equals sign), addition

Materials
*number and number-name cards for 0 through 10

Warm Up • Mental Math
Have students name the number that
1. comes before 6 (5)
2. follows 9 (10)
3. comes first in their phone number
4. comes last in their phone number
5. is 1 more than 8 (9)
6. comes before 1 (0)
7. rhymes with late (8)
8. is at the bottom of a clock face (6)

Warm Up • Number Sense
Combine number and number-name cards for 0 through 10. Have a student pick a card and illustrate the number on the board by drawing Xs, circles, or other objects. Continue until all students have participated.

Name ______________________

We started with 3 fish.
We bought 2 more.
How many fish do we have in all? 5

3 + 2 = 5

$$\begin{array}{r} 3 \\ +\ 2 \\ \hline 5 \end{array}$$

Add.

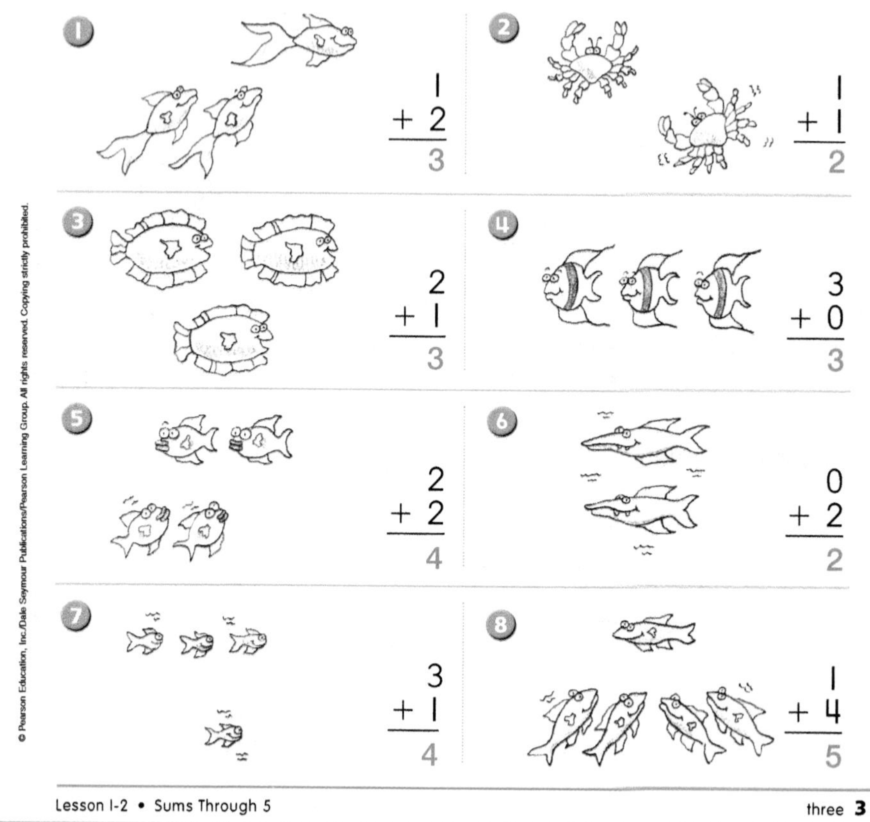

---

2 Teach

Develop Skills and Concepts Write **3 and 1 more is 4** on the board. Then, write **3 + 1 = 4** on the board. Make sure that when you write the number sentence, the addition sign is directly under the word *and* and the equals sign is directly under the word *is*.

- Tell students this is a number sentence and is a shorter way to write 3 and 1 more is 4. Point to each part of the number sentence as you read it to students, *3 plus 1 equals 4*. Tell students the equals sign tells us that 3 + 1 is the same as 4.
- Write **4 and 1 more is 5** on the board and ask a volunteer to write the number sentence. (4 + 1 = 5) Have students read this number sentence with you. (4 plus 1 equals 5.) Repeat this activity for "2 and 3 more is 5."

*indicates teacher demonstration materials

3 Practice

Using page 3 Have students tell about the picture at the top of the page. Read the first sentence telling how many fish we started with. Have students trace the 3. Continue reading with students as they trace the 2 and the 5. Help students read the number sentence and vertical problem. Then, have them trace the 5 in each. Tell students to write the sum for each problem on the page. Have students complete the exercises independently.

Using page 4 Have students complete the number sentences to find all the ways to show a sum of 1, 2, 3, 4, and 5. Tell students to find the sums for each problem in Exercises 6 and 7. Have students complete the exercises independently.

Add.

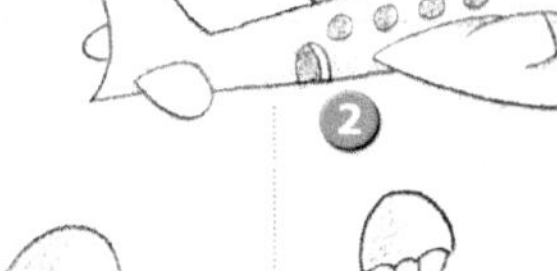

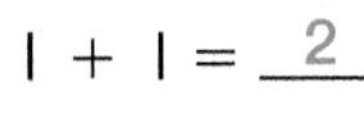

1. 1 + 0 = 1
   0 + 1 = 1

2. 2 + 0 = 2
   1 + 1 = 2
   0 + 2 = 2

3. 3 + 0 = 3
   2 + 1 = 3
   1 + 2 = 3
   0 + 3 = 3

4. 4 + 0 = 4
   3 + 1 = 4
   2 + 2 = 4
   1 + 3 = 4
   0 + 4 = 4

5. 2 + 3 = 5
   1 + 4 = 5
   0 + 5 = 5
   3 + 2 = 5
   4 + 1 = 5
   5 + 0 = 5

6.
$\begin{array}{r}2\\+1\\\hline 3\end{array}$ $\begin{array}{r}3\\+0\\\hline 3\end{array}$ $\begin{array}{r}1\\+1\\\hline 2\end{array}$ $\begin{array}{r}2\\+2\\\hline 4\end{array}$ $\begin{array}{r}1\\+2\\\hline 3\end{array}$ $\begin{array}{r}2\\+3\\\hline 5\end{array}$

7.
$\begin{array}{r}3\\+2\\\hline 5\end{array}$ $\begin{array}{r}1\\+3\\\hline 4\end{array}$ $\begin{array}{r}4\\+1\\\hline 5\end{array}$ $\begin{array}{r}1\\+4\\\hline 5\end{array}$ $\begin{array}{r}3\\+1\\\hline 4\end{array}$ $\begin{array}{r}0\\+4\\\hline 4\end{array}$

4 Assess

Tell students that there are 2 cats sitting on a fence. Three more cats join them. Ask, *How many cats are there now?* (5) Have students write the number sentence. (2 + 3 = 5)

For Mixed Abilities

Common Errors • Intervention

Some students may have difficulty with the concept of addition. Have 3 students stand. Have another student join the 3. Ask, *How many are there in all?* (4) Write **3 + 1 = 4** on the board. Have 2 of the students stand apart from the other 2. Write **2 + 2 = 4** on the board. Ask students how the 4 students could be grouped other ways into 2 groups to model more number sentences where the sum is 4. (1 + 3 = 4, 4 + 0 = 4, 0 + 4 = 4) Write the number sentences on the board as students answer.

Enrichment • Number Sense

1. Have students use number names to write six different addition sentences for the sum of 5.
2. Tell students to cut pictures of objects from catalogs or magazines to illustrate five different addition sentences for the sum of 4.

More to Explore • Number Sense

Have students draw pictures of a creature by following these directions:

It has 2 legs and 2 more.

It has 4 spots and 1 more.

It has 1 eye and 2 more.

It has 3 wings and 1 more.

You may wish to write directions on the board for students to follow.

1-3 Sums Through 10

pages 5–6

1 Getting Started

Objective
- To review addition facts for sums through 10

Materials
10 counters

Warm Up • Mental Math
Ask students who is older.

1. Ted is 18, Ned is 19. (Ned)
2. Rick is 16, Nick is 15. (Rick)
3. Mary is 2, Teri is 8. (Teri)
4. Darin is 13, Taryn is 12. (Darin)
5. Kyle is 11, Lyle is 14. (Lyle)
6. Juan is 8, Jon is 18. (Jon)
7. Phil is 27, Lil is 37. (Lil)
8. Kara is 21, Sarah is 11. (Kara)

Warm Up • Pencil and Paper
Organize the class into groups of three or four students. Have each group write as many addition facts for the sum of 5 as they can. (5 + 0, 4 + 1, 3 + 2, 2 + 3, 1 + 4, 0 + 5) Give each group five counters to assist them.

Name ______________________ **Lesson 1-3**

Add.

1. 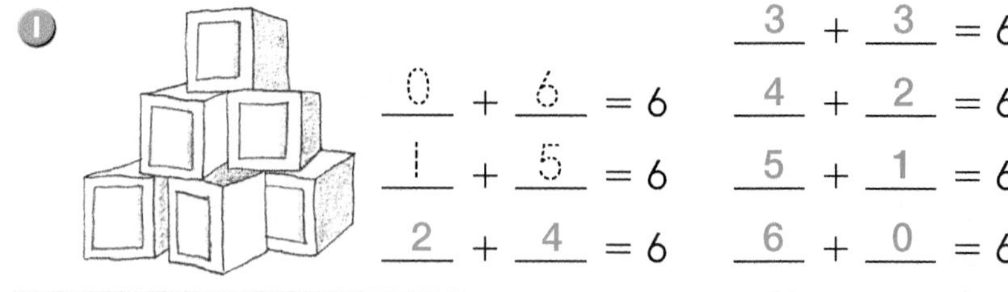

	3 + 3 = 6
0 + 6 = 6	4 + 2 = 6
1 + 5 = 6	5 + 1 = 6
2 + 4 = 6	6 + 0 = 6

2. 1 + 1 = 2   4 + 4 = 8   4 + 2 = 6
3. 2 + 2 = 4   5 + 5 = 10   5 + 2 = 7
4. 3 + 3 = 6   3 + 4 = 7   6 + 2 = 8

5.

8	0	4	7	1	9	3
+ 1	+ 2	+ 0	+ 1	+ 6	+ 1	+ 5
9	2	4	8	7	10	8

6.

2	4	5	3	2	5	6
+ 7	+ 3	+ 4	+ 6	+ 8	+ 3	+ 4
9	7	9	9	10	8	10

Solve.

7. Jim saw 4. [4]
Jan saw 5. (+) [5]
They saw 9. [9]

8. Maria picked 5. [5]
Lynn picked 3. (+) [3]
They picked 8. [8]

2 Teach

Develop Skills and Concepts Give each student 6 counters. Have students lay out their counters in two groups. Stress that the groups do not have to be equal. For example, students can put 5 counters in one group and 1 in the other. Ask students how many are in each group as you develop all seven addition facts for 6. Have a student write each fact on the board as it is developed.

- Repeat this activity with 7 counters and then with 8.

3 Practice

Using page 5 Have students cover all of the blocks on the top of the page with their hand or a sheet of paper and tell how many blocks there are. (0) Have students remove the cover and tell how many blocks are shown. (6) Ask students the sum of 0 and 6. (6) Have students trace the 0 and the 6 and read the number sentence. Repeat for 1 + 5 = 6. Tell students that they are to complete the facts for a sum of 6 and then work the number sentences below those facts.

- Remind students that a fact can be written vertically. Tell students to work the two rows of vertical problems.
- Work through the first story problem with students and have them trace the numbers and the addition sign, and write the answer in the problem and in the solution statement. Tell students they are to write the addition sign in the circle of the second problem. Help students complete the problem.

Using page 6 Tell students to find the sum of each problem in the first three rows. Now, have students look at the first table at the bottom of the page. Tell students that if we have 2 and add 3 more, we have 5 altogether. Have students trace the 5. Ask students to tell the sum if we have 4 and add 3 more. (7) Have students write **7**. Tell students that the next table asks them to give the sum if 4 is added, and in the last table, they are to add 5 to each number. Have students complete all three tables.

Add.

1.

1	3	4	1	6	3	2
+ 9	+ 6	+ 2	+ 2	+ 1	+ 7	+ 2
10	9	6	3	7	10	4

2.

3	6	4	5	2	5	1
+ 2	+ 2	+ 1	+ 2	+ 6	+ 1	+ 8
5	8	5	7	8	6	9

3.

2	7	2	4	1	8	3
+ 1	+ 2	+ 8	+ 6	+ 7	+ 2	+ 1
3	9	10	10	8	10	4

Complete each table.

4.

Add 3.	
2	5
4	7
1	4
3	6
6	9
5	8
7	10

5.

Add 4.	
1	5
3	7
0	4
2	6
6	10
5	9
4	8

6.

Add 5.	
3	8
0	5
2	7
5	10
1	6
4	9

4 Assess

Draw the following table on the board.

Add 2.	
4	
8	
6	
5	
7	

Have volunteers go to the board and fill in the answers.
(6, 10, 8, 7, 9)

For Mixed Abilities

Common Errors • Intervention

Make two sets of flashcards with the addends for a fact on one side and the other side blank. Have students work in pairs with the cards. Tell them to lay the cards facedown in an array. Have one partner turn one card over and tell the sum. This partner then tries to turn over another card with the same sum. A match wins both cards and another turn. If there is no match, both cards are returned to the array facedown and the other partner tries for a match.

Enrichment • Number Sense

1. Tell students to draw pictures to show an addition fact that tells how many animals they and a friend have altogether.
2. Tell students that they have 10¢ to buy 2 items. Have them list all the possible prices of the items they could buy.

More to Explore • Number Sense

Review double facts such as 3 + 3 and 4 + 4. Have students connect 3 blue interlocking cubes together to represent the first addend. Have them connect 3 red interlocking cubes together to represent the second addend. Students connect the two trains of 3 to form the sum 6. Be sure students see that the two addends are equal. Separate the sum back into two groups of 3. Add one cube onto the blue group to change the addend to 4. Connect the group of 4 and the group of 3, representing the problem 4 + 3. Ask students what the sum is. (7) Point out that this is one more than the first sum of 6. Discuss why. Repeat the activity using 4 + 4 followed by 4 + 5. Repeat as many times as needed. Be sure that students observe that whenever the two addends are neighboring or consecutive numbers they have a double-plus-1 situation and can get the sum by just adding one to the doubles sum.

1-4 Subtracting From 5 and Less

pages 7–8

1 Getting Started

Objective

- To review subtraction facts for minuends through 5

Vocabulary

minuend, – (minus sign), subtraction

Materials

*addition fact cards for sums through 10; 5 counters

Warm Up • Mental Math

Have students give the following numbers:

1. numbers on a clock face (12)
2. digits on a clock face (15)
3. days in a week (7)
4. 0 + 0 (0)
5. 4 + 0 (4)
6. 3 and 2 more (5)
7. 6 plus 4 (10)
8. add 3 and 6 (9)

Warm Up • Number Sense

Have students give the sum of addition facts as you show them addition cards in random order. As the sum of each fact is given, have students place fact cards in groups of common sums. For example, put all sums of 8 in a group.

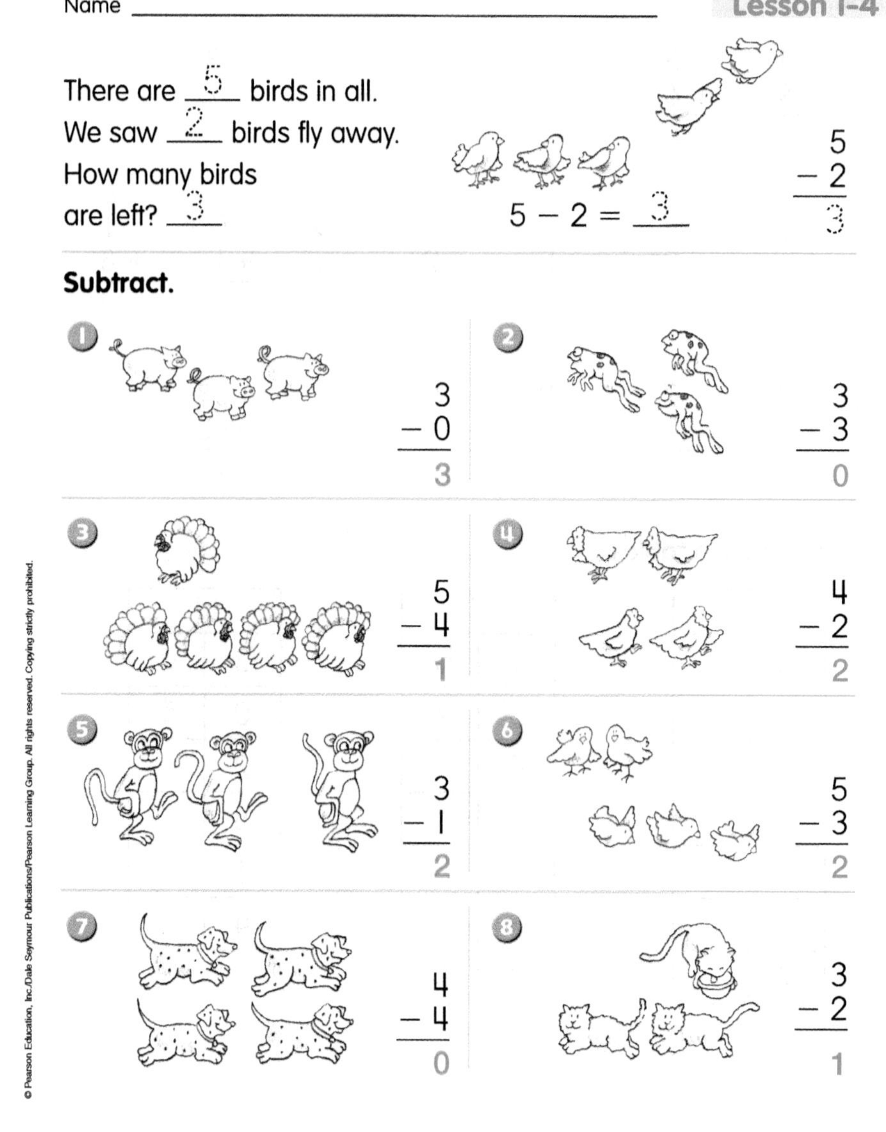

Name ______________________ Lesson 1-4

There are 5 birds in all.
We saw 2 birds fly away.
How many birds are left? 3

$5 - 2 = 3$

$$\begin{array}{r} 5 \\ -\ 2 \\ \hline 3 \end{array}$$

Subtract.

1. $\begin{array}{r} 3 \\ -\ 0 \\ \hline 3 \end{array}$
2. $\begin{array}{r} 3 \\ -\ 3 \\ \hline 0 \end{array}$
3. $\begin{array}{r} 5 \\ -\ 4 \\ \hline 1 \end{array}$
4. $\begin{array}{r} 4 \\ -\ 2 \\ \hline 2 \end{array}$
5. $\begin{array}{r} 3 \\ -\ 1 \\ \hline 2 \end{array}$
6. $\begin{array}{r} 5 \\ -\ 3 \\ \hline 2 \end{array}$
7. $\begin{array}{r} 4 \\ -\ 4 \\ \hline 0 \end{array}$
8. $\begin{array}{r} 3 \\ -\ 2 \\ \hline 1 \end{array}$

2 Teach

Develop Skills and Concepts Have students lay out 5 counters. Tell students to group the counters into two groups with 3 in one group and 2 in the other. Write **3 + 2 = 5** on the board. Have students remove the group of 2 counters and tell how many are left. (3) Write **5 take away 2 is 3** on the board. Tell students that we can write this sentence a shorter way as you write **5 – 2 = 3** on the board. Have students replace the 2 counters and take the group of 3 away. Write **5 take away 3 is 2** and **5 – 3 = 2** on the board. Tell students that take-away problems are called subtraction.

- Continue to develop the subtraction facts for the minuend 5 and then have students find facts for the minuends 4, 3, 2, and 1. Have students write the number sentences on the board as facts are found.

3 Practice

Using page 7 Have students tell about the picture at the top of the page. Help students count the birds and read the sentence telling how many birds in all. Have students trace the 5. Continue reading with students as they trace the 2 and the 3. Help students read the number sentence and vertical problem. Then, have them trace the 3 in each.

- Tell students to find the number of animals left in each box and write the number under the problem. Have students solve the exercises independently.

Using page 8 Ask students how many there are in all in Exercise 1. (5) Have students draw a line through 1 object to show that 1 object is to be subtracted. Ask how many are left. (4) Have students trace the 4. Work through Exercise 2 with students. Then, have students complete the remaining exercises independently.

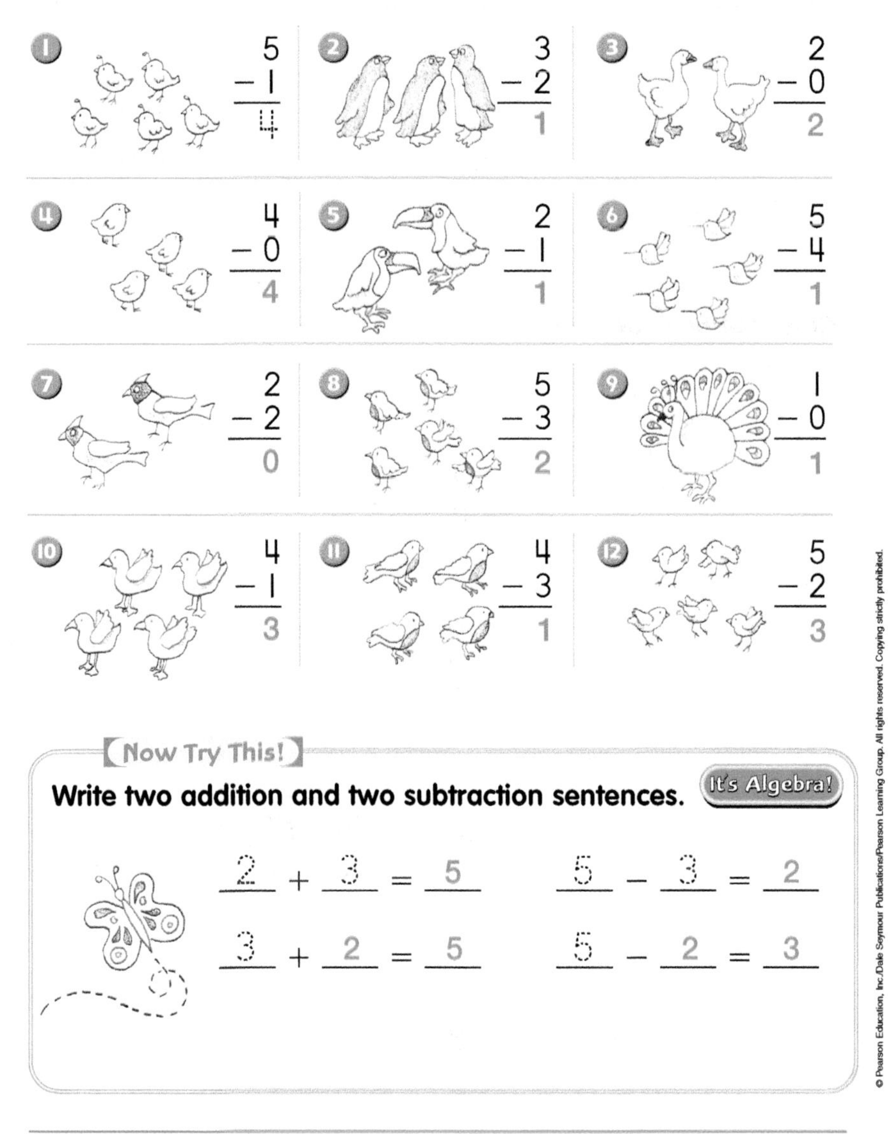

Subtract.

1. 5 − 1 = 4
2. 3 − 2 = 1
3. 2 − 0 = 2
4. 4 − 0 = 4
5. 2 − 1 = 1
6. 5 − 4 = 1
7. 2 − 2 = 0
8. 5 − 3 = 2
9. 1 − 0 = 1
10. 4 − 1 = 3
11. 4 − 3 = 1
12. 5 − 2 = 3

Now Try This!

Write two addition and two subtraction sentences. It's Algebra!

2 + 3 = 5   5 − 3 = 2

3 + 2 = 5   5 − 2 = 3

Now Try This! Teach fact families with interlocking cubes. Have students connect four red cubes and three blue cubes. On the board, write **4 + 3 = 7**. Turn the train around to show **3 + 4 = 7**. Break off the blue section. Write **7 − 3 = 4** to show what was done. Reconnect the cubes and break off the red section. Write **7 − 4 = 3**. Students should see that the four number sentences all come from the numbers 3, 4, and 7 and represent a fact family. Help students complete the activity.

It's Algebra! The concepts of this activity prepare students for algebra.

4 Assess

Tell students, *There are 4 apples sitting on a counter. Jimmy comes by and eats 1 apple. How many apples are left?* (3) Have students write the number sentence. (4 − 1 = 3)

For Mixed Abilities

Common Errors • Intervention

Some students may have difficulty understanding subtraction. Have 4 students stand together. Have 1 student move away. Ask, *How many are left if 1 is taken away from 4?* (3) Write **4 − 1 = 3** on the board. Have the 4 students stand together again. Now, have 2 students move away. Ask, *How many are left if 2 students are taken away from 4?* (2) Write **4 − 2 = 2** on the board. Have students think of more subtraction number sentences starting with 4. (4 − 3 = 1, 4 − 0 = 4, 4 − 4 = 0) Write the sentences on the board and have students model each of them.

Enrichment • Number Sense

1. Have students write two addition and two subtraction sentences to show four objects in all.
2. Have students draw pictures to show four ways they could share 5 cookies with a friend. Tell students they would not be sharing if they kept all 5 or gave away all 5.

More to Explore • Number Sense

Cut out 13 footprints and label them 0 to 12. Possibly have students make them by tracing around one of their shoes. Tape the footprints to the floor about 6 inches apart to create a number line. Have students use the number line to solve addition and subtraction problems by acting out the problems, moving back and forth along the number line.

ESL/ELL STRATEGIES

Clarify the difference between *fly* and *fly away* by explaining that *fly away* means the bird "disappears and doesn't come back." Introduce the phrase *go away* when describing the actions shown in the other exercises on page 7.

1-5 Subtracting From 10 and Less

pages 9–10

1 Getting Started

Objective
- To review subtraction facts for minuends through 10

Materials
*addition fact cards for sums through 10; *subtraction fact cards for minuends through 10

Warm Up • Mental Math
Ask students to count backward from

1. 20 to 10
2. 13 to 0
3. 22 to 11
4. 19 to 9
5. 10 to 0
6. 24 to 12
7. 12 to 2
8. 18 to 4

Warm Up • Number Sense
Have students give the answers as you show them addition and subtraction fact cards in random order. As the sum or difference is given, have students place fact cards in groups of fact families.

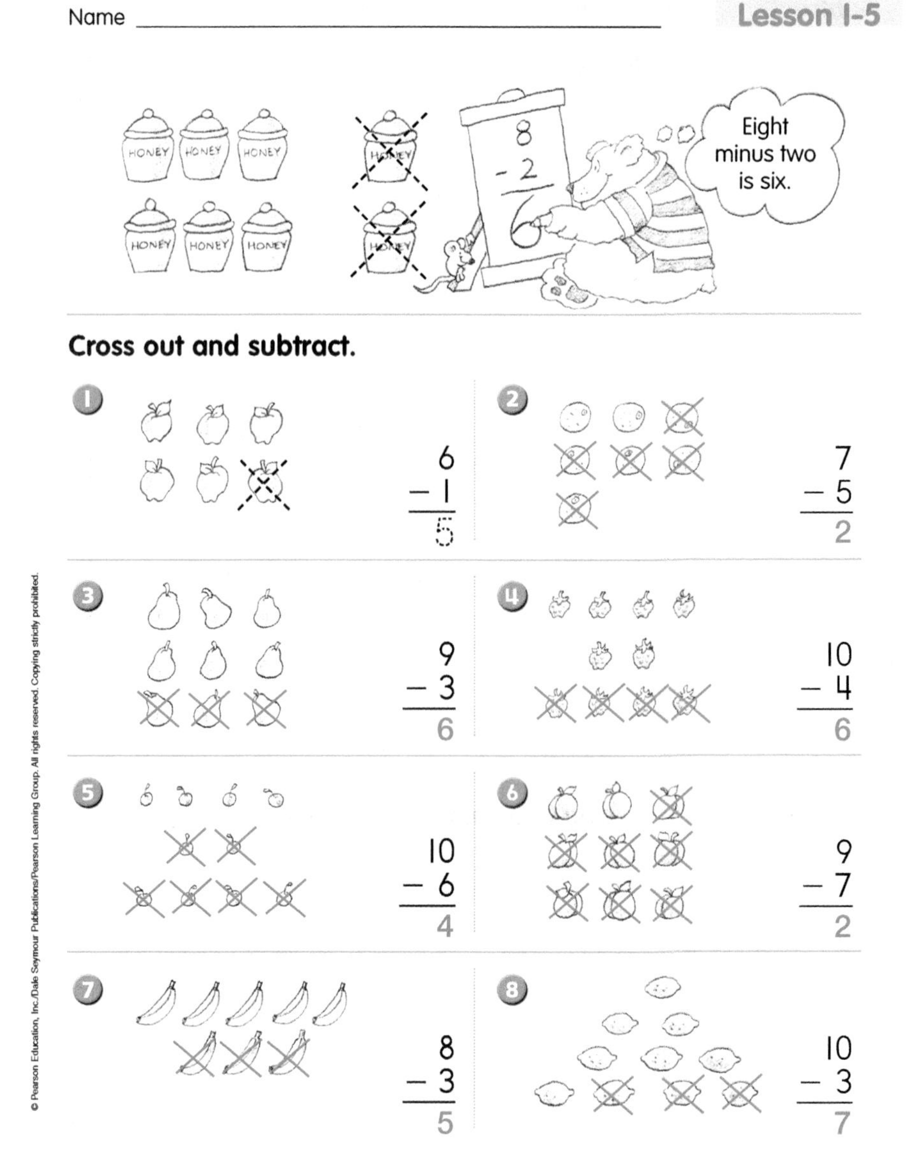

2 Teach

Develop Skills and Concepts Remind students that **8 + 2 = 10** as you write the number sentence on the board. Ask students how many would be left if 2 were taken away from 10. (8) Write **10 − 2 = 8** on the board.

- Now, ask how many would be left if 8 were taken away from 10. (2) Have a student write the number sentence or vertical problem on the board. (10 − 8 = 2)
- Continue to develop more subtraction facts for 10 and some of the facts for 6, 7, 8, and 9.

3 Practice

Using page 9 Have students tell about the picture at the top of the page and trace the lines through the 2 objects to show that 2 are taken away from 8. Have students tell the number left. (6)

- Work Exercise 1 with students and then have them complete the remaining exercises independently.

Using page 10 Remind students that subtraction problems can be written as number sentences or as vertical problems. Tell students they will work problems of both kinds on this page.

- Have students look at the first table at the bottom of the page. Ask what number is left if we have 5 and take 2 away. (3) Have students trace the 3. Repeat for the first problem in the next table and then tell students to complete the exercises independently.

Subtract.

1. $10 - 3 = \underline{7}$ $8 - 2 = \underline{6}$ $8 - 6 = \underline{2}$
2. $7 - 4 = \underline{3}$ $6 - 3 = \underline{3}$ $10 - 9 = \underline{1}$
3. $10 - 5 = \underline{5}$ $9 - 4 = \underline{5}$ $8 - 7 = \underline{1}$
4. $8 - 5 = \underline{3}$ $10 - 6 = \underline{4}$ $7 - 2 = \underline{5}$
5. $8 - 4 = \underline{4}$ $10 - 1 = \underline{9}$ $6 - 5 = \underline{1}$
6. $9 - 5 = \underline{4}$ $9 - 3 = \underline{6}$ $10 - 2 = \underline{8}$

7.

6	9	7	6	10	9	7
− 6	− 8	− 5	− 2	− 8	− 6	− 0
0	1	2	4	2	3	7

8.

8	6	9	7	10	9	8
− 3	− 4	− 2	− 3	− 4	− 7	− 0
5	2	7	4	6	2	8

Complete each table.

9.

Subtract 2.	
5	3
7	5
8	6

10.

Subtract 3.	
7	4
9	6
6	3

11.

Subtract 5.	
8	3
6	1
10	5

4 Assess

Have students write three subtraction problems using the minuend 10. Have them switch papers with a classmate to answer.

For Mixed Abilities

Common Errors • Intervention

Some students may have difficulty remembering subtraction facts for minuends through 10. Give each student a number from 6 to 10. Have students write a subtraction sentence using that number as a minuend, another number for the subtrahend, and a blank line for the answer. They can then take turns writing their facts on the board with other students supplying the answers.

Enrichment • Number Sense

1. Have students use a spinner with numbers 0 through 10. Tell them to take turns with a friend giving one addition and one subtraction fact for each number they spin.
2. Have students name as many situations as they can in which subtraction is used. For example, if they have 9 pencils and 4 are not sharpened, they have 5 sharp pencils.

More to Explore • Algebra

Draw the following group of sets on the board: 2 triangles, 3 circles, 4 squares, 6 stars, and 5 rectangles. From this group of sets, have students identify the set that has the fewest objects; the most objects; one more than the squares; two less than the circles; more than the triangles, but less than the stars; and more than the circles and the squares.

Now, have some of the students ask their classmates to identify these sets by properties. Ask, *Are any of the sets equivalent?* Have students draw a set that is equivalent to the triangles.

ESL/ELL STRATEGIES

As you encounter them, discuss with students all the words and phrases that tell them to subtract numbers. These items include *minus, subtract*, and *How many . . . are left?* Model examples on the board using each word or phrase.

1-6 Mixed Practice

pages 11–12

1 Getting Started

Objectives

- To practice addition facts for sums through 10
- To practice subtraction facts for minuends through 10

Materials

10 counters; *addition fact cards for sums through 10; *subtraction fact cards for minuends through 10

Warm Up • Mental Math

Have students name a subtraction fact related to

1. 4 + 5 = 9 (9 − 5 = 4, 9 − 4 = 5)
2. 3 + 7 = 10 (10 − 3 = 7, 10 − 7 = 3)
3. 2 + 6 = 8 (8 − 6 = 2, 8 − 2 = 6)
4. 4 + 6 = 10 (10 − 4 = 6, 10 − 6 = 4)

Have them name an addition fact related to

5. 10 − 2 = 8 (8 + 2 = 10, 2 + 8 = 10)
6. 6 − 4 = 2 (4 + 2 = 6, 2 + 4 = 6)
7. 10 − 5 = 5 (5 + 5 = 10)
8. 9 − 0 = 9 (9 + 0 = 9, 0 + 9 = 9)

Warm Up • Number Sense

Write **4 + 5 = ____** on the board. Have students show the problem with counters and give the sum. Have a student write the sum on the board. Repeat for more facts for sums and minuends through 10.

Name ______________________

Add.

1	2 + 2 = 4	1 + 1 = 2	5 + 2 = 7	3 + 2 = 5	6 + 1 = 7	1 + 4 = 5	7 + 2 = 9
2	4 + 1 = 5	6 + 3 = 9	2 + 6 = 8	5 + 1 = 6	3 + 7 = 10	4 + 2 = 6	1 + 9 = 10
3	0 + 4 = 4	3 + 3 = 6	8 + 1 = 9	1 + 6 = 7	5 + 0 = 5	2 + 1 = 3	4 + 5 = 9
4	1 + 2 = 3	8 + 0 = 8	4 + 3 = 7	2 + 8 = 10	7 + 1 = 8	6 + 4 = 10	2 + 5 = 7
5	3 + 4 = 7	5 + 3 = 8	1 + 8 = 9	5 + 5 = 10	6 + 2 = 8	8 + 2 = 10	3 + 1 = 4
6	7 + 3 = 10	4 + 4 = 8	2 + 3 = 5	3 + 5 = 8	0 + 7 = 7	1 + 3 = 4	9 + 1 = 10
7	2 + 4 = 6	3 + 6 = 9	1 + 5 = 6	4 + 6 = 10	1 + 7 = 8	5 + 4 = 9	2 + 7 = 9

2 Teach

Develop Skills and Concepts Shuffle the addition and subtraction fact cards. Show the cards one at a time and ask students if we add or subtract. Then, have another student give the sum or difference. Continue until each student has given several correct answers.

3 Practice

Using page 11 Tell students to find the sum of each exercise on this page. Allow students to use counters if they need help. Have students complete the page independently.

Using page 12 Tell students to subtract in all the exercises on this page. Allow students to use counters if they need help. Have students complete the page independently.

Subtract.

1	5 − 1 = 4	9 − 3 = 6	8 − 6 = 2	6 − 5 = 1	10 − 3 = 7	6 − 2 = 4	10 − 1 = 9
2	8 − 2 = 6	6 − 3 = 3	9 − 8 = 1	7 − 6 = 1	5 − 5 = 0	3 − 1 = 2	9 − 4 = 5
3	7 − 3 = 4	8 − 5 = 3	9 − 1 = 8	10 − 5 = 5	5 − 2 = 3	10 − 2 = 8	4 − 3 = 1
4	10 − 7 = 3	8 − 4 = 4	4 − 0 = 4	8 − 3 = 5	7 − 7 = 0	4 − 1 = 3	10 − 9 = 1
5	6 − 4 = 2	9 − 6 = 3	6 − 1 = 5	10 − 6 = 4	8 − 7 = 1	9 − 5 = 4	9 − 7 = 2

Now Try This!

Write the missing numbers. It's Algebra!

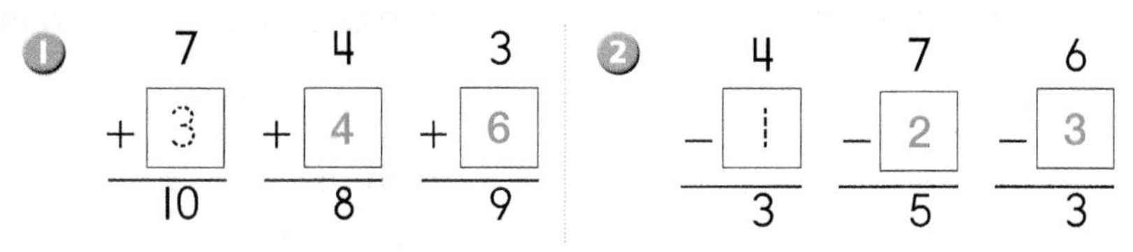

Now Try This! Write **2 + ____ = 5** on the board and ask students what number needs to be added to 2 to have a sum of 5. (3) Have a student write the number. Repeat for more problems for sums through 10. Now, write **10 − ____ = 4** vertically on the board and ask students what number is subtracted from 10 to have 4 left. (6) Have a student write the number. Repeat for more sentences for minuends through 10. Remind students to look at the sign in each problem. Have students complete the problems independently.

It's Algebra! The concepts of this activity prepare students for algebra.

4 Assess

Use addition and subtraction fact cards to hold a class math bee.

For Mixed Abilities

Common Errors • Intervention

Some students may need practice with their facts. Have them work with partners with addition and subtraction fact cards. They can take turns showing each other a fact card and asking for the answer, identifying it as a sum or difference. Be sure students read aloud all parts of each fact.

Enrichment • Number Sense

1. Tell students to write a story about 4 cats and 5 cats. They should then write a subtraction or addition problem that goes with the story.
2. Have students work in pairs. Tell one student to affix an addition or subtraction fact to the back of a partner. The student should then tell a story as a clue for the partner to guess the fact.

More to Explore • Number Sense

Distribute six 5-in. square tagboard cards to each student. Students work with partners. Each pair decides on a number greater than 10 and less than 30. Both students draw a set with that number on one of their cards. For example, if one pair chooses 16 as its first number, each partner draws a set with 16 objects on his or her card. The students continue selecting a number and drawing matching sets on the cards. When all six cards have matching, equivalent sets, the two students shuffle their cards and place them facedown on the table. Students take turns playing a matching game by turning over two cards and counting to see if the numbers are equivalent. If they match, the student keeps the cards and takes another turn.

1-7 Problem Solving: Write a Number Sentence

pages 13–14

1 Getting Started

Objectives
- To write a number sentence
- To add or subtract to solve money problems

Materials
10 real or play pennies; *addition fact cards for sums through 10; *subtraction fact cards for minuends through 10

Warm Up • Mental Math
Ask students which is more?
1. 5 + 3 or 9 − 2 (5 + 3)
2. 8 − 2 or 7 + 2 (7 + 2)
3. 3 + 3 or 3 + 5 (3 + 5)
4. 6 − 0 or 5 − 4 (6 − 0)

Ask which is less?
5. 8 − 2 or 5 + 0 (5 + 0)
6. 4 + 5 or 6 + 4 (4 + 5)
7. 8 − 3 or 9 − 5 (9 − 5)
8. 10 − 3 or 10 − 4 (10 − 4)

Warm Up • Number Sense
Have students give the sum or difference as you randomly show addition and subtraction fact cards.

Name ______________________

Problem Solving
Lesson 1-7

It's Algebra!

Solve.

1. Mark bought a 4¢ and a 3¢. How much did both cost? 7 ¢
4¢ + 3¢ = 7 ¢

2. Sam bought a 5¢ and a 2¢. How much did both cost? 7 ¢
5¢ + 2¢ = 7 ¢

3. Mary bought a 8¢ and a 1¢. How much did both cost? 9 ¢
8¢ + 1¢ = 9 ¢

4. Andy bought a 3¢ and a 7¢. How much did both cost? 10 ¢
3¢ + 7¢ = 10 ¢

5. Ann bought a 7¢ and a 2¢. How much did both cost? 9 ¢
7 ¢ + 2 ¢ = 9 ¢

6. Meg bought a 4¢ and a 4¢. How much did both cost? 8 ¢
4 ¢ + 4 ¢ = 8 ¢

7. Frank bought a 6¢ and a 4¢. How much did both cost? 10 ¢
6 ¢ + 4 ¢ = 10 ¢

8. Sue bought a 3¢ and a 5¢. How much did both cost? 8 ¢
3 ¢ + 5 ¢ = 8 ¢

2 Teach

Develop Skills and Concepts Students can use a four-step plan to solve word problems or any exercises in a Problem Solving lesson. This plan helps students break the problem down into parts. The four steps are SEE, PLAN, DO, and CHECK.

- In SEE, students read the problem and look at the given art or graphs for information. Then, they list all the information.
- In PLAN, students think about how to use the information to solve the problem. Students then list the operations to be used with the information in order.
- In DO, students complete the computation as planned.
- In CHECK, students work backward to make sure the computation is correct.

3 Practice

Using page 13 Read Exercise 1 with students.

- Now, apply the four-step plan. For SEE, ask, *What are you asked to do?* (find out how much a baseball glove sticker and a butterfly sticker cost together) *What information are you given?* (A baseball glove sticker costs 4¢ and a butterfly sticker costs 3¢.) For PLAN, ask students how they will solve the problem. (add) For DO, have students trace the 7 in the problem and solution statement. For CHECK, have students use real or play pennies to verify the answer.
- Ask students to tell the price of each of the items in Exercise 2. (5¢ and 2¢) Have a student read the story problem. Ask students to answer the question. (7) Have students look at Exercise 5 to see that they are to write the addends and plus signs in each of the last four exercises. Have students complete the page independently.

Solve.

1. Aaron had 7¢.
He bought a [pencil] 4¢.
How much was left? 3 ¢
7¢ − 4¢ = 3 ¢

2. Dawn had 9¢.
She bought a [barrette] 3¢.
How much was left? 6 ¢
9¢ − 3¢ = 6 ¢

3. Tina had 8¢.
She bought a [stamp] 5¢.
How much was left? 3 ¢
8¢ − 5¢ = 3 ¢

4. Rex had 9¢.
He bought a [key ring] 4¢.
How much was left? 5 ¢
9¢ − 4¢ = 5 ¢

5. Randy had 8¢.
He bought a [toy mouse] 7¢.
How much was left? 1 ¢
8 ¢ ⊖ 7 ¢ = 1 ¢

6. Juan had 9¢.
He bought a [ball] 3¢.
How much was left? 6 ¢
9 ¢ ⊖ 3 ¢ = 6 ¢

7. Tom had 10¢.
He bought a [sticker] 4¢.
How much was left? 6 ¢
10 ¢ ⊖ 4 ¢ = 6 ¢

8. Tracy had 10¢.
She bought a [heart] 3¢.
How much was left? 7 ¢
10 ¢ ⊖ 3 ¢ = 7 ¢

Using page 14 Tell students to subtract in each exercise to find the amount of money left. Work through the first exercise with the students. Have them look at Exercise 5 as you tell them that they are to write the problem and the minus sign in the last four problems. Have students complete the page independently.

4 Assess

Tell students that you want to buy a pencil for 4¢ and an eraser for 3¢. Ask how much do you need. (7¢) Then, tell students you have 9¢. Ask how much will you have left over if you buy the pencil and eraser for 7¢. (2¢)

For Mixed Abilities

Common Errors • Intervention

Some students may have difficulty adding and subtracting with money. Have students work with partners and 9 real or play pennies. Tell them to pay 4¢ for a sheet of paper and count to tell how much is left. (5¢) Write **9¢ − 4¢ = 5¢** on the board. Repeat for other subtraction problems. Then, tell them to pay out 4¢ for one paper and 3¢ for another and count to tell how much they spent in all. (7¢) Write **4¢ + 3¢ = 7¢** on the board. Repeat for other addition problems.

Enrichment • Application

1. Have students draw a picture of themselves at a store purchasing 2 items for a total of 10¢ or less.
2. Have students draw pennies to show that they have 10¢ and spend 7¢.

More to Explore • Estimation

Take an inventory in the classroom. Have students compile a list of things to count, for example, chairs, desks, pieces of chalk, windows, reading books, electrical outlets, clocks, and blue pencils. Have students guess how many of each object is in the room. Then, have students count the number of objects. Students may work independently or in small groups to complete the tally. Count together to check for accuracy when the count is complete.

Chapter 1 Test

page 15

Items	Objectives
1	To read numbers and number names (see pages 1–2)
2–8	To review addition facts for sums through 10 (see pages 3–16)

Alternate Chapter Test

You may wish to use the Alternate Chapter Test on page 315 of this book for further review and assessment.

Name ______________________________

Chapter 1 Test

Match.

1.

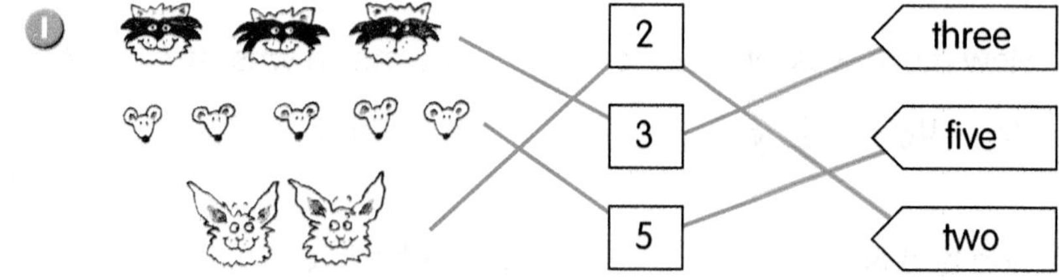

Add.

2.

1	3	4	3	2	4	1
+ 1	+ 1	+ 5	+ 0	+ 7	+ 3	+ 4
2	4	9	3	9	7	5

3.

2	5	2	3	3	2	3
+ 8	+ 1	+ 5	+ 3	+ 7	+ 4	+ 6
10	6	7	6	10	6	9

4.

2	5	0	5	3	7	6
+ 2	+ 5	+ 4	+ 2	+ 5	+ 2	+ 3
4	10	4	7	8	9	9

5. 7 + 0 = 7   7 + 3 = 10   5 + 3 = 8

6. 3 + 4 = 7   5 + 4 = 9   0 + 8 = 8

7. 2 + 3 = 5   4 + 4 = 8   8 + 1 = 9

8. 1 + 7 = 8   1 + 9 = 10   4 + 6 = 10

Subtract.

9

3	2	4	7	6	8	5
− 1	− 0	− 2	− 4	− 3	− 6	− 3
2	2	2	3	3	2	2

10

6	9	10	6	9	8	10
− 4	− 2	− 1	− 2	− 5	− 3	− 5
2	7	9	4	4	5	5

11 10 − 2 = 8   10 − 3 = 7   6 − 6 = 0

12 8 − 4 = 4   7 − 0 = 7   10 − 6 = 4

Solve.

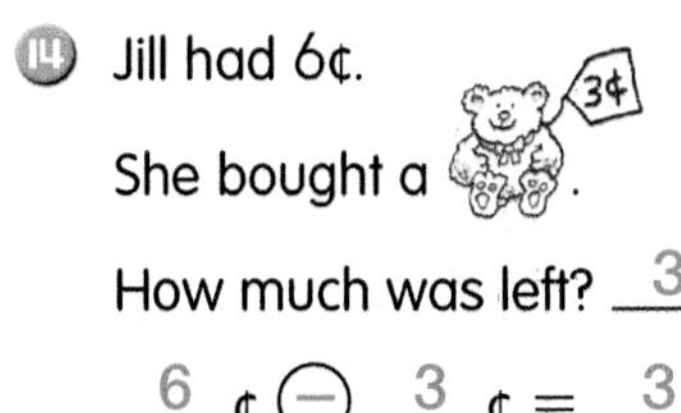

13 Ruth had 6¢.
She bought a [2¢].
How much was left? 4 ¢
6 ¢ ⊖ 2 ¢ = 4 ¢

14 Jill had 6¢.
She bought a [3¢].
How much was left? 3 ¢
6 ¢ ⊖ 3 ¢ = 3 ¢

15 Hal bought a [5¢] and a [5¢]. How much did both cost? 10 ¢
5 ¢ ⊕ 5 ¢ = 10 ¢

16 Rose had 8¢.
She bought a [2¢].
How much is left? 6 ¢
8 ¢ ⊖ 2 ¢ = 6 ¢

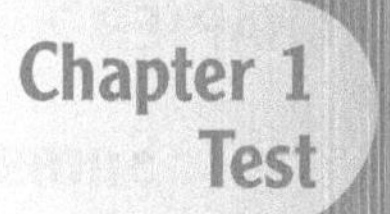

Chapter 1 Test

page 16

Items	Objectives
9–12	To review subtraction facts for minuends through 10 (see pages 7–10)
13–16	To add or subtract to solve money problems (see pages 13–14)
	To write number sentences (see pages 13–14)

CHAPTER 2

2-1 Sums Through 12

pages 17–18

1 Getting Started

Objective
- To review addition facts for sums through 12

Materials
12 counters

Warm Up • Mental Math
Have students give the sum or difference.

1. 3 + 5 (8)
2. 6 − 2 (4)
3. 5 + 0 (5)
4. 9 − 2 (7)
5. 6 + 3 (9)
6. 4 − 2 (2)
7. 7 + 3 (10)
8. 9 − 3 (6)

Warm Up • Algebra
Write on the board addition or subtraction facts such as **7 ◯ 3 = 4** and have students write the sign in the circle that makes the fact true.

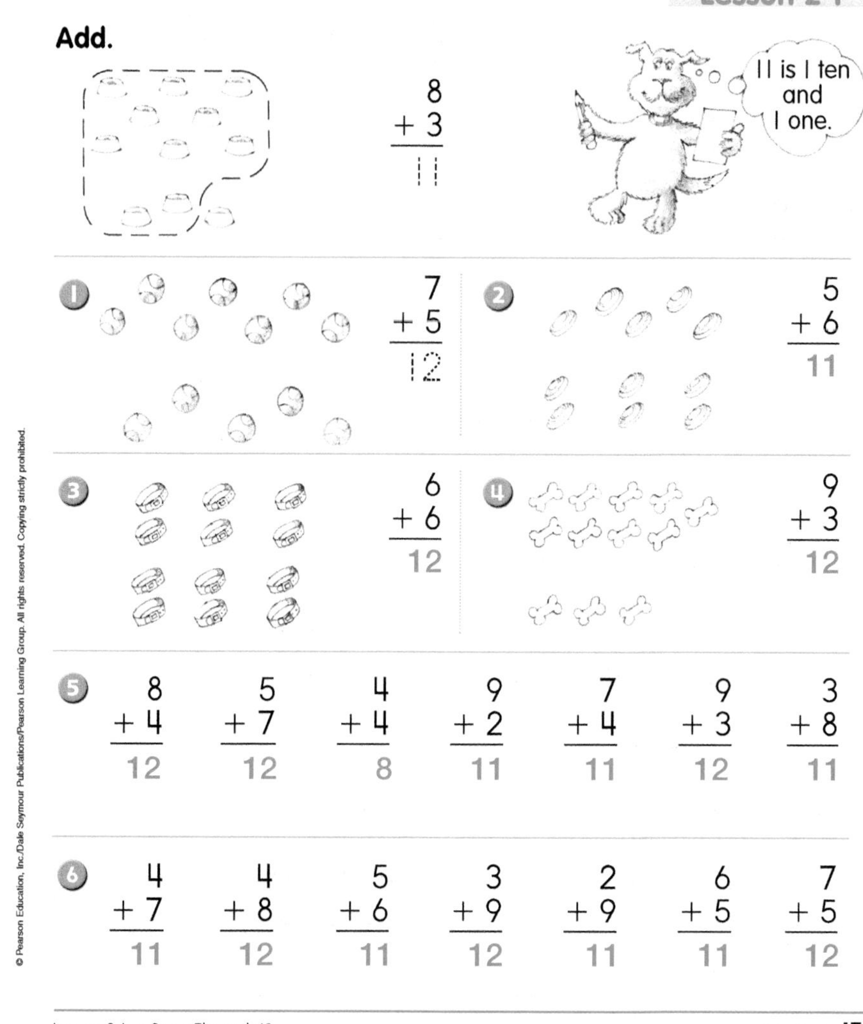

Name ______________________

Basic Facts Through 12

Chapter 2

Lesson 2-1

Add.

8 + 3 = 11	
① 7 + 5 = 12	② 5 + 6 = 11
③ 6 + 6 = 12	④ 9 + 3 = 12

⑤	8 + 4 = 12	5 + 7 = 12	4 + 4 = 8	9 + 2 = 11	7 + 4 = 11	9 + 3 = 12	3 + 8 = 11
⑥	4 + 7 = 11	4 + 8 = 12	5 + 6 = 11	3 + 9 = 12	2 + 9 = 11	6 + 5 = 11	7 + 5 = 12

2 Teach

Develop Skills and Concepts Write the numbers 0 through 12 along a number line on the board. Draw 11 triangles on the board. Have a student count the triangles and tell how many there are. (11) Have a student circle 10 of the triangles to form a group. Ask how many tens and ones there are. (1 tens, 1 ones) Repeat for 12 triangles. (1 ten 2 ones)

- Write **3 + 8** vertically on the board and have a student find 3 on the number line and go forward 8 more to tell the sum. (11) Repeat for **2 + 9** and **4 + 7**. Now, write **3 + 9** on the board and repeat the activity to have students find the sum. (12) Continue for sums of 11 and 12 until all sums are found.

3 Practice

Using page 17 Tell students to trace the circle around the group of ten bowls at the top of the page and trace the 11 to show that the sum of 8 and 3 is 1 ten 1 one, or 11.

- Tell students to circle the group of ten in each of the next four exercises and then work the two rows of exercises at the bottom. Allow students to use counters if needed. Have students complete the page independently.

Using page 18 Have students find the 3 in the center of the first wheel. Tell students that they will begin with 3 and add a number in the next ring to write a sum in the outer ring. Have students add 3 + 3 and trace the 6. Have students work 3 + 6 and record the sum of 9. Tell students to begin with 5 in the second wheel and add the numbers to write the sums.

- Have students complete the rest of the page independently.

Complete each wheel.

1

Add.

2	7 + 2 = 9	9 + 1 = 10	8 + 4 = 12	5 + 5 = 10	4 + 7 = 11	6 + 6 = 12	9 + 3 = 12
3	4 + 5 = 9	6 + 3 = 9	2 + 7 = 9	8 + 2 = 10	3 + 9 = 12	7 + 5 = 12	3 + 6 = 9
4	8 + 3 = 11	5 + 6 = 11	4 + 6 = 10	7 + 4 = 11	3 + 8 = 11	6 + 4 = 10	9 + 2 = 11
5	4 + 8 = 12	6 + 5 = 11	3 + 7 = 10	5 + 4 = 9	7 + 3 = 10	2 + 8 = 10	5 + 7 = 12

4 Assess

Ask students to write five number sentences for the sum of 12. (Accept any five of the following: 9 + 3, 8 + 4, 7 + 5, 6 + 6, 5 + 7, 4 + 8, 3 + 9)

For Mixed Abilities

Common Errors • Intervention

Some students may have difficulty working with sums greater than 10. Have them work with partners and counters. Have them use the counters to model problems for sums of 11 (9 + 2 = 11, 2 + 9 = 11, 8 + 3 = 11, 3 + 8 = 11, 7 + 4 = 11, 4 + 7 = 11, 6 + 5 = 11, 5 + 6 = 11) and sums of 12 (9 + 3 = 12, 3 + 9 = 12, 8 + 4 = 12, 4 + 8 = 12, 7 + 5 = 12, 5 + 7 = 12, 6 + 6 = 12). They can use counters to model each addend, join them, and count to find the sum. Then, they can write the fact.

Enrichment • Number Sense

1. Have students write and solve problems of doubles from 0 + 0, 1 + 1, and so on as far as they can.
2. Have students use an egg carton and counters or plastic eggs to find all the ways to use addition to make 1 dozen.
3. Tell students to draw a clock face and write the numbers in place. They should then write addition problems such as 1 + 11 = 12, 2 + 10 = 12, and so on until a pattern is seen. Have them tell about the pattern for finding two addends whose sum is 12.

More to Explore • Auditory Learning

Clap-count math facts. For example, clap 10 times, pause, and state **plus** or **minus**. Then, clap 6 more times. Have a student clap the correct answer. (16) Invite students to take turns clapping their own math problems and ask another student to indicate the correct answer. If a student gives the correct answer, then that student is the next clapper. Variations can include stamping feet and humming.

2-2 Practice Sums Through 12

pages 19–20

1 Getting Started

Objectives
- To practice addition for sums through 12
- To add for sums through 12 to solve problems

Materials
12 counters; *addition fact cards for sums through 12

Warm Up • Mental Math
Have students give the sum.

1. 0 + 1 + 2 (3)
2. 9 + 0 + 1 (10)
3. 6 + 2 + 1 (9)
4. 2 + 2 + 3 (7)
5. 3 + 4 + 1 (8)
6. 1 + 0 + 3 (4)
7. 2 + 1 + 3 (6)
8. 2 + 2 + 1 (5)

Warm Up • Algebra
Write addition and subtraction problems on the board such as 3 ◯ 9 = 12 or 8 ◯ 3 = 5 and have students write the correct sign in the circle. Use subtraction problems for minuends only through 10 at this time.

Name ______________________

Add.

1 9 + 1 = 10; 7 + 3 = 10; 5 + 4 = 9; 8 + 2 = 10; 6 + 5 = 11; 3 + 7 = 10; 4 + 8 = 12

2 5 + 7 = 12; 8 + 4 = 12; 2 + 8 = 10; 3 + 6 = 9; 7 + 4 = 11; 2 + 9 = 11; 6 + 4 = 10

Complete each table.

3

Add 6.	
2	8
4	10
6	12
3	9
5	11

Add 4.	
4	8
5	9
7	11
8	12
6	10

Add 3.	
5	8
7	10
4	7
9	12
6	9

Add 5.	
5	10
7	12
4	9
6	11
3	8

Solve.

4 Ken has 9 shells. He finds 3 more. How many shells does Ken have?

9 + 3 = 12

12 shells

5 Megan picks 5 flowers. Rich picks 6 flowers. How many flowers do they have?

5 + 6 = 11

11 flowers

2 Teach

Develop Skills and Concepts Tell students to lay out 7 counters to show that Pete fed 7 carrots to his rabbits in the morning. Tell students that Pete fed his rabbits 4 more carrots that evening. Ask students to lay out 4 counters to show the rabbits' evening meal. Ask how many carrots the rabbits ate that day. (11) Continue acting out story problems for students to practice sums of 11 and 12.

- Have students make up a story problem where 5 and 7 more are to be added. Then, have students create more story problems for sums of 11 and 12.

3 Practice

Using page 19 Tell students that they are to write the sums for the exercises at the top of the page. Have students look at the tables in the middle of the page. Ask what is to be done in such a table. (Add 6 to each number in the first table, add 4 to each number in the next table, then add 3 and 5 in the last two tables.)

- Help students read the story problems if necessary. Remind students to write the sum of the problem in the box and in the solution statement. Have students complete the page independently.

Using page 20 Tell students to write the sum in each vertical problem and in each number sentence. Have students complete the exercises independently.

Add.

1	7 + 2 = 9	1 + 9 = 10	4 + 6 = 10	3 + 8 = 11	6 + 4 = 10	5 + 4 = 9	1 + 8 = 9
2	6 + 6 = 12	8 + 2 = 10	7 + 3 = 10	3 + 7 = 10	5 + 6 = 11	9 + 1 = 10	4 + 7 = 11

3. 1 + 1 = 2   8 + 4 = 12   2 + 8 = 10

4. 2 + 2 = 4   7 + 5 = 12   9 + 3 = 12

5. 3 + 3 = 6   6 + 5 = 11   8 + 3 = 11

6. 4 + 4 = 8   5 + 7 = 12   9 + 2 = 11

7. 5 + 5 = 10   2 + 9 = 11   4 + 8 = 12

Now Try This!

It's Algebra!

Circle pairs of numbers.

1.

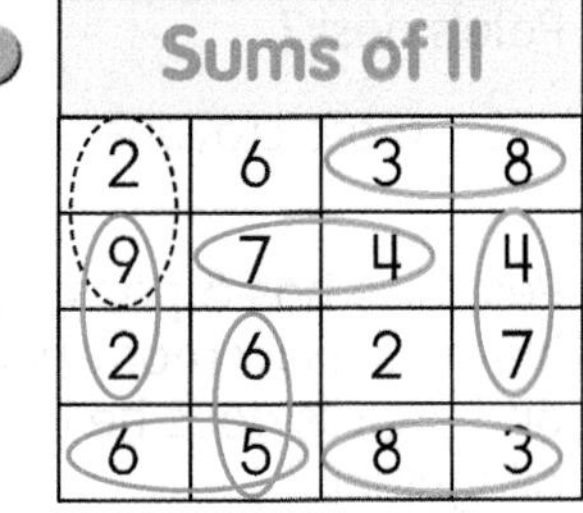

Sums of 11			
2	6	3	8
9	7	4	4
2	6	2	7
6	5	8	3

(There are 8 pairs.)

2.

Sums of 12			
4	8	2	5
9	3	8	7
8	9	6	6
4	7	7	5

(There are 7 pairs.)

Now Try This! Write the following on the board:

2	4	6	1
8	1	5	5
0	9	3	2
6	3	7	4

Tell students to circle two numbers next to each other whose sum is 10. Circle the pair of 5s as you tell students that 5 plus 5 more equals 10. Have students circle other pairs of numbers until six pairs are found. (4 and 6, 2 and 8, 5 and 5, 1 and 9, 3 and 7, and 3 and 7)

Then, have students trace the circle in the first exercise. Ask how many pairs are in each exercise. (8, 7) Tell students that some pairs may share a number. Have students complete the activity independently.

4 Assess

Show students addition fact cards and have them give you the answers. Continue until all students have answered at least one correctly.

For Mixed Abilities

Common Errors • Intervention

For students who need additional practice with sums of 11 and 12, write the following on the board:

2 + 9 = □
3 + 8 = □
4 + 7 = □
5 + □ = □
6 + □ = □
7 + □ = □
8 + □ = □
9 + □ = □

Discuss the pattern of "one more" and "one less" in the pairs of addends. Then, starting with 3 + 9 = □, repeat the activity to practice with sums of 12. Finally, have students copy the sentences and write numbers for the boxes to make the sentences true.

Enrichment • Number Sense

1. Have students draw 2 hens with a total of 12 eggs so that 1 hen has 4 eggs.
2. Have one student point to two 1-digit numbers on a clock face and have another give the sum. Have them take turns pointing to the numbers.

More to Explore • Logic

Duplicate matrix squares, such as the following, for students.

+	0 1 2 3 4 . . . 9
0	0 1 2 3 4 . . .
1	1 2 3 4 5 . . .
2	2 3 4 5 6 . . .
3	3 4 5 6 7 . . .
4	4 5 6 7 8 . . .
.	
.	
.	
9	9 10 11 12 13 . . .

Explain that the numbers across the top and down the left side are the addends. To find a sum of two addends, tell students to find one addend along the top and to follow down the row to match the second addend on the left. The number marking their match point is the sum. Give students several addition problems to solve using the matrix.

2-3 Problem Solving: Make and Use a Table

pages 21–22

1 Getting Started

Objective

- To make and use a table to answer questions

Vocabulary

tally

Warm Up • Mental Math

Have students give the sum or difference.

1. 5 + 3 (8)
2. 4 + 6 (10)
3. 2 + 5 (7)
4. 11 − 6 (5)
5. 10 − 8 (2)

Warm Up • Number Sense

Write the following on the board:

5 + 4 = (9)	11 − 7 = (4)
7 + 4 = (11)	12 − 8 = (4)
12 − 3 = (9)	3 + 7 = (10)
6 + 6 = (12)	11 − 5 = (6)

Have a student circle the sign that tells them to add or subtract and then write the answer.

Name ________________________

Problem Solving
Lesson 2-3

These items were found on Pete's desk.

Make a tally mark | for each item. 𝍸 stands for 5 items.

Item	Tally	Number
Pencil	𝍸	5
Eraser	|||	3
Crayon	||||	4
Marker	||	2

Use the table to answer each question.

1. How many erasers are on Pete's desk?
   3 erasers

2. How many more crayons than markers are on Pete's desk?
   2 more crayons

3. Which item does Pete have the most of?
   pencils

4. Pete also has 6 pens on his desk. How many pens and pencils does he have altogether?
   11 pens and pencils

2 Teach

Develop Skills and Concepts Ask students to count the number of boys and girls in the class. Write the following table on the board:

Students in Our Class	
Boys	Girls

Use the information students gathered to fill in the table.

3 Practice

Using page 21 Have students look at the tally table. Ask students what tally represents 1. (|) Ask students what tally represents 5. (𝍸)

- Now, apply the four-step plan to the example. For SEE, ask, *What are you being asked to do?* (find how many of each item Pete has on his desk) Then, *What information is given?* (a diagram with pencils, erasers, crayons, and markers) For PLAN, ask students how many tally marks they will write for each item. (pencil, 5; eraser, 3; crayon, 4; and marker, 2) For DO, have students complete the tally table. For CHECK, have them count how many tally marks were used in their completed tally tables. (14) Ask, *Does this match the number of objects in the diagram?* (yes)
- Have students complete Exercises 1 through 4 independently.

Using page 22 Have students look at the diagram of the fruit at the top of the page. Ask students for the title of the table. (Pieces of Fruit at a Picnic) Then, ask them how to represent six items. (𝍸|) Have students count the number of bananas shown in the diagram and then write the number 5 using tally marks. (𝍸) Have students complete Exercise 1 independently.

Make a table about the fruit in the picture. Then use the table to answer each question.

Pieces of Fruit at a Picnic		
Fruit	**Tally**	**Number**
Apples	𝍸 I	6
Bananas	𝍸	5
Pears	III	3
Watermelon	I	1

1. How many bananas are there?

   5 bananas

2. How many more apples are there than pears?

   3 more apples

3. Which fruit has the fewest pieces?

   watermelon

4. Which fruit has the most pieces?

   apples

5. There are 3 more strawberries than apples. How many strawberries are there?

   9 strawberries

6. Lisa counted the apples. Mike counted the bananas. Who counted more pieces of fruit?

   Lisa

- For Exercise 2, have students write the number sentence needed to answer what they are being asked to find. Ask, *How many apples are there?* (6) *How many pears are there?* (3) *What operation do you need to solve the problem?* (subtraction) Have students use 6 − 3 = 3 to find how many more apples there are than pears. Have students complete the remaining exercises independently.

4 Assess

Have students work in groups of three. Give groups some red, blue, and green crayons so that they have ten crayons in all. Have each group create a tally table labeled "Our Crayons."

For Mixed Abilities

Common Errors • Intervention

If students are having difficulty interpreting the information from the tally table, have them count and record the number for each category beside each row of the table.

Enrichment • Data Collection

1. Have students work with a partner. Give each pair a mix of red, blue, and green crayons so that there are ten crayons in all. Students will take turns counting crayons to make a tally table. Then, have them take turns asking questions about the number of crayons that they have.
2. Have students ask ten people what their favorite pet is: dog, cat, hamster, or bird. Then, construct a tally table to display the class results.

More to Explore • Probability

Divide the class into groups of four. Give each group one number cube. Ask students how many sides are on each number cube. (6) Ask how many sides have a 2. (1) Then, tell students that you believe that out of every 6 rolls, only 1 of those will be a 2. Tell a recorder to print each number from 1 through 6 in a tally table. Then, each student in the group rolls the number cube 6 times. The recorder keeps a tally after each roll. The group should compare the results to the teacher's prediction.

ESL/ELL STRATEGIES

Call on volunteers to explain the meaning of *fewest* (the smallest number of items) and *most* (the largest number of items). Ask students to use the words in sentences as they describe things in the classroom.

2-4 Subtracting From 12 and Less

pages 23–24

1 Getting Started

Objective

- To subtract from minuends through 12

Materials

12 counters

Warm Up • Mental Math

Have students give the sums.

1. 7¢ + 2¢ (9¢)
2. 4¢ + 2¢ (6¢)
3. 3¢ + 4¢ + 7¢ (14¢)
4. 4¢ + 8¢ (12¢)
5. 9¢ + 8¢ (17¢)
6. 6¢ + 2¢ − 1¢ (7¢)

Warm Up • Pencil and Paper

Dictate the following problems for students to write down and solve:

7 − 4 = (3), 10 − 2 = (8), 7 + 4 = (11), 9 + 3 = (12), 9 − 6 = (3), 6 + 6 = (12), 5 + 7 = (12), 10 − 4 = (6), 9 − 4 = (5)

Allow students to write the problems in vertical or horizontal form. Vary the dictation to include the different ways to denote addition and subtraction, for example, *minus, take away, and 6 more, plus,* and so on.

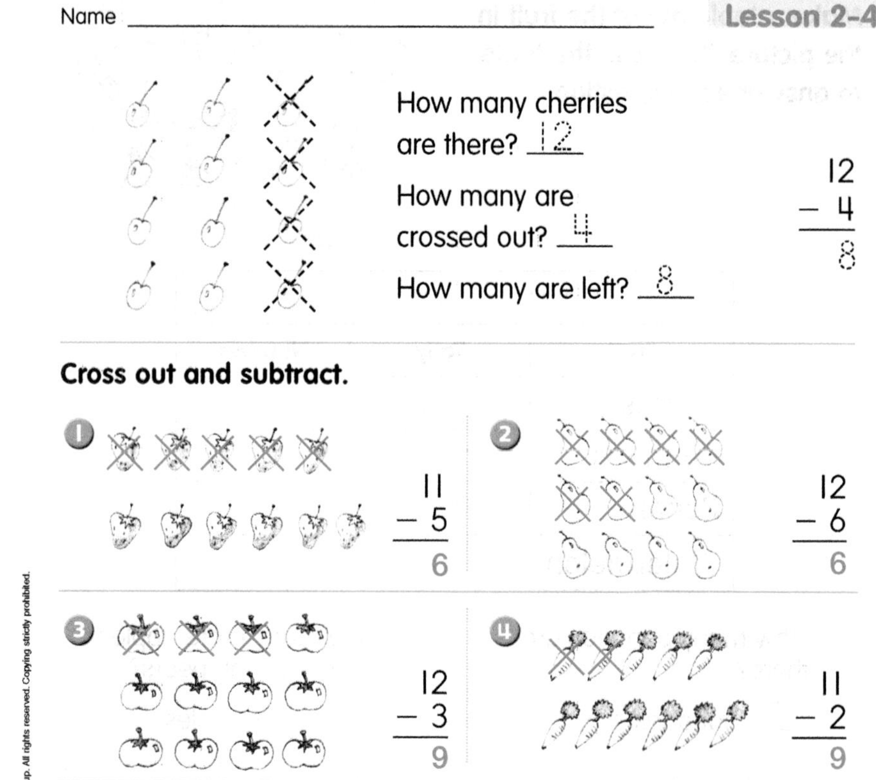

Name ______________________ Lesson 2-4

How many cherries are there? 12

How many are crossed out? 4

How many are left? 8

12 − 4 = 8

Cross out and subtract.

1. 11 − 5 = 6
2. 12 − 6 = 6
3. 12 − 3 = 9
4. 11 − 2 = 9

Subtract.

5. 11 − 3 = 8; 11 − 8 = 3; 11 − 7 = 4; 11 − 4 = 7; 12 − 3 = 9; 12 − 9 = 3; 12 − 6 = 6

6. 11 − 5 = 6; 11 − 6 = 5; 12 − 5 = 7; 12 − 7 = 5; 11 − 9 = 2; 12 − 4 = 8; 12 − 8 = 4

2 Teach

Develop Skills and Concepts Draw 10 objects on the board. Write **10 − 7 =** on the board and have a student cross out 7 of the objects and tell how many are left. (3) Repeat for more subtraction problems for minuends through 10. Now, draw 12 objects on the board and have students tell how many there are. (12) Write **12 − 4 =** on the board and have a student cross out 4 of the objects and tell how many are left. (8) Repeat for more problems with minuends of 11 and 12.

3 Practice

Using page 23 Read each question at the top of the page with students as they trace the answers. Tell students to cross out the number of objects to be taken away and then write the number left in the problem. Tell students to complete all the exercises on the page. Allow use of counters as needed.

Using page 24 Have students complete the page independently. Allow use of counters as needed.

Subtract.

1. $8 - 1 = 7$ $\quad 11 - 6 = 5$ $\quad 10 - 1 = 9$
2. $10 - 2 = 8$ $\quad 9 - 1 = 8$ $\quad 12 - 8 = 4$
3. $11 - 4 = 7$ $\quad 12 - 7 = 5$ $\quad 8 - 2 = 6$
4. $9 - 0 = 9$ $\quad 10 - 9 = 1$ $\quad 10 - 4 = 6$
5. $11 - 5 = 6$ $\quad 8 - 7 = 1$ $\quad 12 - 5 = 7$
6. $10 - 3 = 7$ $\quad 12 - 6 = 6$ $\quad 8 - 3 = 5$

7.

9	10	9	11	9	11	8
− 2	− 8	− 9	− 3	− 4	− 8	− 6
7	2	0	8	5	3	2

8.

9	10	8	9	12	10	9
− 8	− 5	− 4	− 3	− 4	− 6	− 7
1	5	4	6	8	4	2

9.

8	11	9	10	12	8	11
− 8	− 7	− 6	− 7	− 3	− 5	− 9
0	4	3	3	9	3	2

4 Assess

Have each student write a subtraction story problem. Then, have students switch papers and solve each other's problems.

For Mixed Abilities

Common Errors • Intervention

If students have difficulty subtracting from 11 and 12, have them write related addition sentences. For a subtraction sentence such as

$11 - 6 = \square$

have them write

$\square + 6 = 11$

and find the addend that makes the number sentence true. Encourage students to model these sentences with markers. Once they know that $5 + 6 = 11$, then they should know that $11 - 6 = 5$.

Enrichment • Number Sense

1. Working in pairs, have one student point to 1 on a clock face. The other student should point to the number that is 12 take away 1. Tell them to continue through 12 take away 11.
2. Have one student give a related addition fact for each subtraction fact card that another student shows.
3. Have students make a subtraction fact table for minuends through 12.

More to Explore • Logic

Duplicate a matrix square, such as the one on page T20 for students:

Remind students about the addition problems they used the matrix for in the More to Explore activity on page T20. Now, have students do the following and look for patterns:

1. Count by 1s from the top.
2. Count by 1s from the left side.
3. Count by 2s diagonally, left to right.
4. Trace the diagonal from right to left.
5. Look for other patterns.

2-5 Practice Subtracting From 12 and Less

pages 25–26

1 Getting Started

Objective

- To practice subtraction from minuends through 12

Materials

unlined index cards; *subtraction fact cards for minuends through 12; *addition fact cards for sums through 12

Warm Up • Mental Math

Have students name the number.

1. 1 ten 2 ones (12)
2. 2 tens 1 one (21)
3. 1 ten 6 ones (16)
4. 9 ones (9)
5. 2 tens 0 ones (20)
6. 1 ten 5 ones (15)

Warm Up • Number Sense

Group subtraction fact cards into minuends through 8, minuends 9 through 12, and facts related to doubles. Select several facts from the first group and have students work problems at the board. Help students see that all the facts are related to sums through 8. Repeat for facts related to sums of 9 through 12 and facts related to doubles. Use addition fact cards if necessary.

Name ______________________

Subtract.

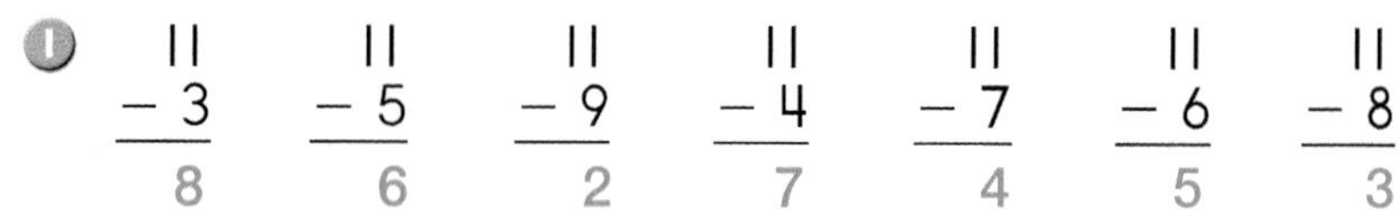

1.

11	11	11	11	11	11	11
− 3	− 5	− 9	− 4	− 7	− 6	− 8
8	6	2	7	4	5	3

2.

12	12	12	12	12	12	12
− 3	− 5	− 6	− 8	− 4	− 7	− 9
9	7	6	4	8	5	3

Complete each wheel.

Solve.

5. Janice has 11 [books]. She read 5 of them. How many books are left to read? (−)
11
5
6
6 books

6. Jim had 12 [grapes]. He ate 7 of them. How many grapes are left? (−)
12
7
5
5 grapes

2 Teach

Develop Skills and Concepts Have students create their own subtraction fact cards on unlined index cards. On one side of the card, students will write a problem, and on the other side, they will write the answer. Review all cards to make sure students' arithmetic is correct, and then use the cards to hold a class math bee.

3 Practice

Using page 25 Tell students that they are to write the answer to each subtraction fact in the two rows of exercises.

- Ask students if they can tell what they will do with the two wheels. Have students tell the number left when 8 is taken away from 12. (4) Have students trace the 4 and then help students work another problem and one problem on the second wheel if necessary.
- Have students read through the two story problems and give help if needed. Have students then complete the page independently.

Using page 26 Tell students to complete the three columns of problems independently.

Subtract.

1	10 − 3 = 7	8 − 2 = 6	10 − 8 = 2
2	9 − 1 = 8	11 − 3 = 8	11 − 5 = 6
3	11 − 4 = 7	10 − 4 = 6	9 − 3 = 6
4	10 − 7 = 3	12 − 3 = 9	12 − 5 = 7
5	8 − 7 = 1	10 − 5 = 5	12 − 6 = 6
6	11 − 2 = 9	12 − 8 = 4	10 − 2 = 8
7	12 − 4 = 8	10 − 9 = 1	11 − 6 = 5
8	10 − 1 = 9	11 − 7 = 4	12 − 9 = 3
9	11 − 8 = 3	12 − 7 = 5	10 − 6 = 4

Now Try This!

Use these numbers to write four number sentences. It's Algebra!

5 11 6	4 12 8
5 + 6 = 11	4 + 8 = 12
6 + 5 = 11	8 + 4 = 12
11 − 6 = 5	12 − 4 = 8
11 − 5 = 6	12 − 8 = 4

Now Try This! Write **2, 6, 4** on the board and tell students that we can use these three numbers to write four number sentences. Write **2 + 4 = 6** on the board and help students develop and write three more number sentences. (4 + 2 = 6, 6 − 2 = 4, 6 − 4 = 2) Repeat the activity for four sentences using the numbers 2, 5, and 3. (2 + 3 = 5, 3 + 2 = 5, 5 − 2 = 3, 5 − 3 = 2) Have students trace the numbers in the first problem and then complete the activity independently.

It's Algebra! The concepts in this activity prepare students for algebra.

4 Assess

Tell students that there are 12 eggs in a dozen. Say, *Luis has a dozen eggs. His family ate 7 eggs for breakfast. How many eggs are left?* Have students write and solve a number sentence for this problem. (12 − 7 = 5)

For Mixed Abilities

Common Errors • Intervention

Some students may need more practice subtracting from the minuends 11 and 12. Have them practice with partners and fact cards with minuends of 11 and 12. They can take turns showing each other the fact cards, asking for the answers. They should repeat more often those facts that their partner has difficulty remembering.

Enrichment • Number Sense

1. Have students sort subtraction fact cards into a group having answers that are even and a group having answers that are odd numbers.
2. Tell students to write all the subtraction facts that are related to sums of 11 and 12.

More to Explore • Application

Have a Mystery Day. Have students write answers to a brief numerical questionnaire about themselves. Sample questions might include the following: How many buttons are on a dress or shirt? How many missing teeth do you have? How many pockets do you have? How old are you? and so on. Collect the completed questionnaires and read them aloud. Have students guess each mystery student. Provide more counting practice by having students count the letters in their first and last names. Have them discover whose name has the most letters. Then, have them count how many of each letter are in the names of the entire class, and record the number next to each letter on an alphabet chart. Have students write their names with crayons and incorporate them into colorful designs to be displayed.

2-6 Mixed Practice

pages 27–28

1 Getting Started

Objective
- To practice addition and subtraction

Materials
*addition fact cards through sums of 12; *subtraction fact cards through minuends of 12

Warm Up • Mental Math
Have students count on to 19 from
1. 6 (7, . . . , 19)
2. 11
3. 9
4. 14
5. 10
6. 12
7. 8
8. 4

Warm Up • Pencil and Paper
Write the following on the board and have students copy them:

4 + 6	9
3 + 6	8
12 − 6	11
6 + 5	12
11 − 3	3
5 + 7	10
12 − 9	6

Have students draw a line from the problem to its answer.

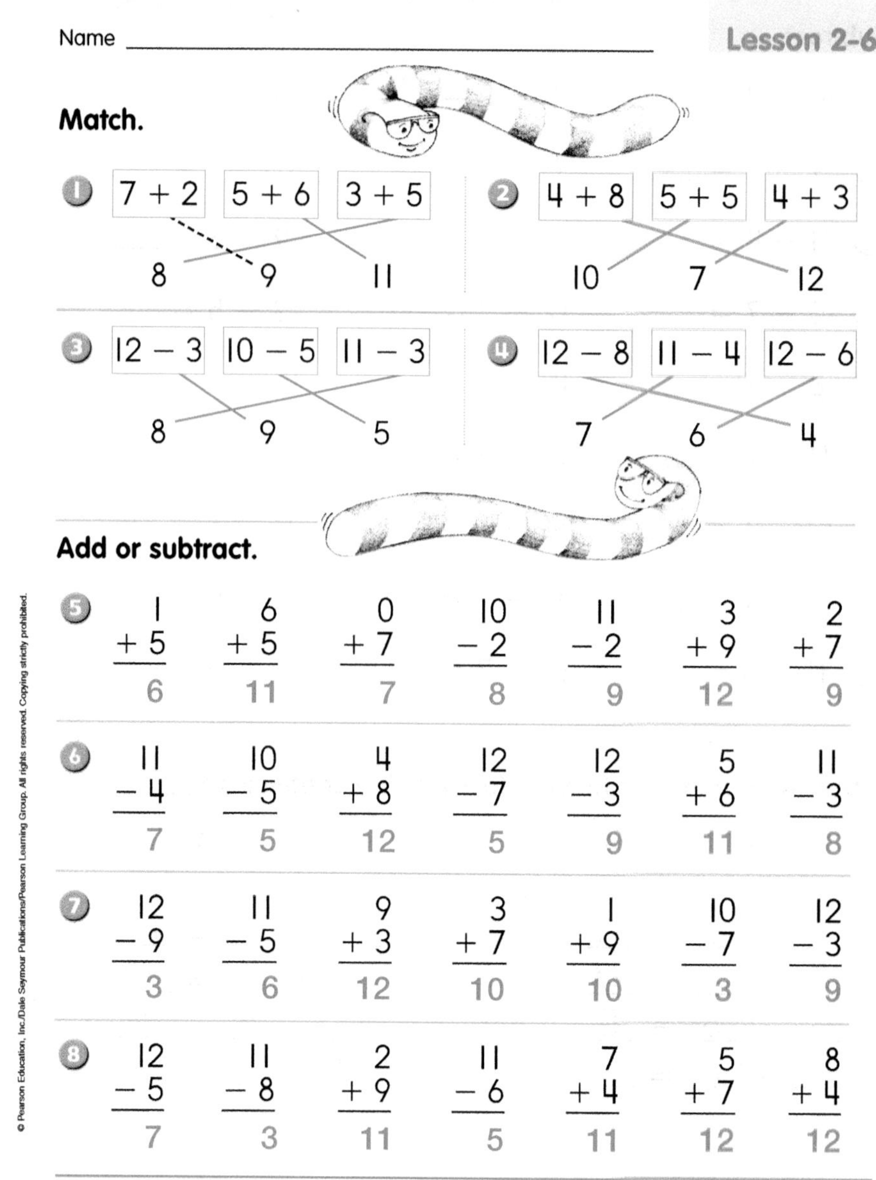

Name ______________________ Lesson 2-6

Match.

1. 7 + 2, 5 + 6, 3 + 5 — 8, 9, 11
2. 4 + 8, 5 + 5, 4 + 3 — 10, 7, 12
3. 12 − 3, 10 − 5, 11 − 3 — 8, 9, 5
4. 12 − 8, 11 − 4, 12 − 6 — 7, 6, 4

Add or subtract.

5	1 + 5 = 6	6 + 5 = 11	0 + 7 = 7	10 − 2 = 8	11 − 2 = 9	3 + 9 = 12	2 + 7 = 9
6	11 − 4 = 7	10 − 5 = 5	4 + 8 = 12	12 − 7 = 5	12 − 3 = 9	5 + 6 = 11	11 − 3 = 8
7	12 − 9 = 3	11 − 5 = 6	9 + 3 = 12	3 + 7 = 10	1 + 9 = 10	10 − 7 = 3	12 − 3 = 9
8	12 − 5 = 7	11 − 8 = 3	2 + 9 = 11	11 − 6 = 5	7 + 4 = 11	5 + 7 = 12	8 + 4 = 12

Lesson 2-6 • Mixed Practice twenty-seven 27

2 Teach

Develop Skills and Concepts Discuss the following or other situations in which students use addition or subtraction: Wanting 10 players to begin a game of soccer and having only 6, collecting 12 students' papers and counting only 9 so far, having a group of 8 students join a group of 4 students, and so on. Have students tell which operation they would use in each situation.

3 Practice

Using page 27 Tell students that they are to find the answer to the problem in each box at the top of the page and draw a line from the box to the answer. Have students work the first exercise and trace the line to the 9.

- Tell students to write the answer to each problem in the next section. Remind students to look at the sign in each problem to see if they are to add or subtract. Have students complete the page independently.

Using page 28 Remind students to look at the sign in each problem before beginning to work the problem. Have students complete the page independently.

Add or subtract.

1. 2 + 9 = 11
2. 5 + 7 = 12
3. 8 + 3 = 11
4. 10 − 1 = 9
5. 11 − 4 = 7
6. 12 − 6 = 6
7. 7 + 5 = 12
8. 8 + 2 = 10
9. 4 + 7 = 11
10. 10 − 5 = 5
11. 12 − 9 = 3
12. 6 + 5 = 11

13. 9 + 1 = 10; 4 + 8 = 12; 11 − 9 = 2; 3 + 8 = 11
14. 6 + 4 = 10; 12 − 7 = 5; 11 − 5 = 6; 12 − 8 = 4
15. 12 − 3 = 9; 3 + 7 = 10; 9 + 3 = 12; 5 + 5 = 10
16. 8 + 4 = 12; 10 − 6 = 4; 12 − 5 = 7; 11 − 3 = 8
17. 10 − 8 = 2; 3 + 9 = 12; 11 − 7 = 4; 6 + 6 = 12

Now Try This!

It's Algebra!

Write the correct sign.

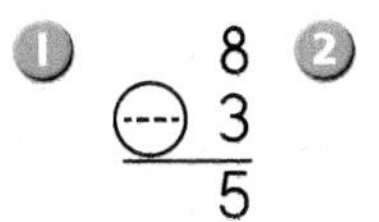

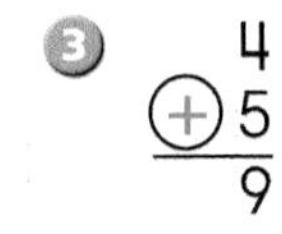
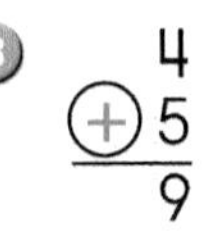
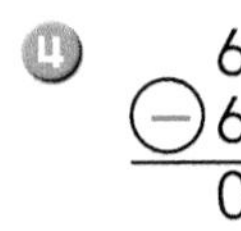
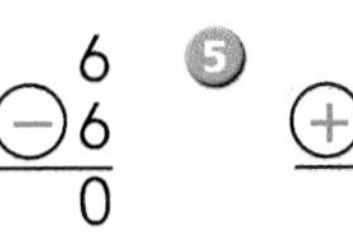

1. 8 − 3 = 5
2. 12 − 7 = 5
3. 4 + 5 = 9
4. 6 − 6 = 0
5. 7 + 4 = 11

Now Try This! Tell students that they are to write a plus or minus sign in each circle to make the exercise true. Have students complete the exercise independently.

It's Algebra! The concepts of this activity prepare students for algebra.

4 Assess

Use addition and subtraction fact cards to hold a class math bee.

For Mixed Abilities

Common Errors • Intervention

If students continue to have difficulty mastering their addition or subtraction facts through the number 12, have them create fact families with fact cards. Have students work in pairs. Give them the fact cards mixed up for five fact families and have them form the fact families by placing the related fact cards in groups. After the five groups are correctly formed, encourage students to read each set aloud to see the relationships.

Enrichment • Number Sense

1. Tell one student to say a number. Have another student silently add or subtract a number and give the sum or difference. Tell the first student to guess the number and tell if it had been added or subtracted to the first number.
2. Have students write rebus word problems with the minuend 12.

More to Explore • Algebra

Make a bulletin board that illustrates the intersection and union of sets. Use different colors of yarn to outline large shapes. The regions should overlap each other. For example:

Cut out stars and place them at random across the board. Use 30 to 50 stars, depending on the size of the board. Ask students to tell how many stars are in the heart set, the circle set, in the union of half-oval and heart, and in the intersection of circle and rectangle. Have students create questions to ask other students.

2-7 Problem Solving: Act It Out

pages 29–30

1 Getting Started

Objectives
- To act out math problems to find a solution
- To add or subtract to solve money problems with sums and minuends through 12¢

Vocabulary
nickel

Materials
2 real or play nickels; 12 real or play pennies

Warm Up • Mental Math
Tell students to name the number that comes

1. before 26
2. before 12
3. after 19
4. between 10 and 12
5. before 16
6. between 19 and 21

Warm Up • Number Sense
Draw a number line on the board and write **5, 10, 15, 20,** and **25** in their respective places. Have students count with you by 5s through 25. Have students write in the missing numbers from 0 through 24. Point to the 8 and have students begin at 5 and count on to 8 to tell the number. Repeat for other points on the number line, having students count by 5s through 20, for example, and then count on by 1s to 23.

Name ____________________

1 nickel — 5 cents — 5¢

1 penny — 1 cent — 1¢

Five, six, seven, eight, nine. I have 9 cents.

9 ¢

Use the coins to answer each problem.

	I have this much.	I saved this much.	How much do I have?
1	7 ¢	4 ¢	7 ¢ + 4 ¢ = 11 ¢
2	6 ¢	6 ¢	6 ¢ + 6 ¢ = 12 ¢
3	9 ¢	3 ¢	9 ¢ + 3 ¢ = 12 ¢

2 Teach

Develop Skills and Concepts Have students lay out 2 nickels. Ask students how many pennies are in 1 nickel. (5) Ask students to tell the total amount in 2 nickels. (10¢) Write **5¢ + 5¢ = 10¢** vertically on the board. Have students lay out 1 nickel and 6 pennies. Ask students what money problem they can write to find the sum of these coins. (5¢ + 6¢ =) Have a student write and solve the problem on the board. (11¢) Now, draw two groups of coins on the board to show 8¢ + 4¢ and have students tell the amount of money in each group. (8¢, 4¢) Have a student write and solve the problem on the board. (8¢ + 4¢ = 12¢) Repeat for more examples of two amounts through totals of 12¢. Now, have students lay out 11¢. Tell students to remove 6¢ and tell how much money is left. (5¢) Have a student write and solve the problem on the board. (11¢ − 6¢ = 5¢) Repeat for more subtraction problems of minuends through 12¢.

3 Practice

Using page 29 Have students look at the example at the top of the page.

- Now, apply the four-step plan. For SEE, ask, *What are you asked to do?* (count the money) Then, *What information is given?* (1 nickel, 4 pennies) For PLAN, ask students how they plan to count the money. (start with the nickel, and then count the pennies) For DO, have students count the money. For CHECK, have students add 5¢ and 4¢. (5¢ + 4¢ = 9¢) Then, have students trace the 9.
- Work through Exercise 1 with students. Then, have them complete the page.

Use the coins to answer each problem.

I have this much.	I spent this much.	How much is left?
1 11¢	5¢	11¢ − 5¢ = 6¢
2 10¢	7¢	10¢ − 7¢ = 3¢
3 12¢	8¢	12¢ − 8¢ = 4¢
4 11¢	7¢	11¢ − 7¢ = 4¢

Using page 30 Remind students that 1 nickel is 5¢ so they should count by 5s and count on by 1s to find how much money in all. Have students count the coins in the first exercise and trace the 11. Ask students the cost of the item in the first exercise. (5¢) Have students trace the 5. Tell students they have 11¢ and spend 5¢. They need to find out how much money is left. Have students trace the numbers in the exercise to find the answer. Have students complete the remaining exercises independently.

4 Assess

Put 3¢ price tags on crayons. Give students 1 nickel and 2 pennies and ask how much change they would have left if they bought the crayons. (4¢) Repeat the activity by giving students 1 nickel and 4 pennies, 2 nickels, and 2 nickels and 2 pennies.

For Mixed Abilities

Common Errors • Intervention

Some students may add or subtract money incorrectly because they have difficulty counting money. For a group of coins, such as 1 nickel and 3 pennies, have them start with the coin that has the greater value, the nickel, and count on the 3 pennies—5¢, 6¢, 7¢, 8¢—to find the total value of the group. They can write this amount as one of the addends in the problem. Then, they should count in a similar manner to find the value of the second group of coins and write the other addend.

Enrichment • Number Sense

1. Have students draw three objects and their price tags of 4¢, 6¢, and 2¢. Tell them to write and solve a problem to find the total cost of all three objects.
2. Have students write subtraction facts for minuends of 11 or 12 whose answers are 7 or more. Then, tell them to write two related addition facts for each subtraction fact.

More to Explore • Application

Take a counting walk outside. Make each group of students responsible for counting specific items such as houses, cars, traffic lights, telephone poles, dogs, lines in sidewalks, and so on. Have students write their results on the board and compare. Have groups count how many steps from the door to the wastebasket, how many times a student can jump in 1 minute, how many days until vacation, and so on. Compare results tallied by different groups to see how much they differ.

ESL/ELL STRATEGIES

Use paraphrasing to clarify the meaning of *spent this much.* (How much money did you pay?) and *How much is left?* (How much money did you have after paying?)

Chapter 2 Test

page 31

Items	Objectives
1–2	To review addition facts for sums through 12 (see pages 17–20)
3–4	To review subtraction facts for minuends through 12 (see pages 23–26)
5–6	To add or subtract to solve money problems (see pages 29–30)

Name ______________________________

Chapter 2 Test

Add.

1.

1	8	8	5	3	3	5
+ 9	+ 4	+ 3	+ 6	+ 9	+ 7	+ 7
10	12	11	11	12	10	12

2.

6	9	4	2	6	7	3
+ 5	+ 3	+ 8	+ 9	+ 6	+ 4	+ 8
11	12	12	11	12	11	11

Subtract.

3.

11	11	10	10	11	11	12
− 2	− 9	− 7	− 3	− 5	− 6	− 6
9	2	3	7	6	5	6

4.

12	12	11	11	12	11	12
− 4	− 8	− 7	− 4	− 5	− 3	− 7
8	4	4	7	7	8	5

Solve.

5. Kay had 11¢. She spent 6¢. How much money does she have left? 5 ¢

11 ¢
− 6 ¢
5 ¢

6. Dan bought a ruler for 7¢ and an eraser for 5¢. How much money did he spend? 12 ¢

7 ¢
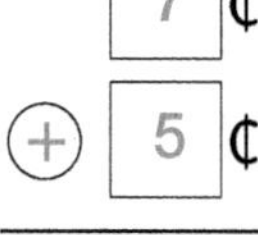
+ 5 ¢
12 ¢

Alternate Chapter Test

You may wish to use the Alternate Chapter Test on page 316 of this book for further review and assessment.

Add or subtract.

1. $1 + 2 = \underline{3}$ $9 - 3 = \underline{6}$ $1 + 5 = \underline{6}$
2. $7 - 4 = \underline{3}$ $8 - 2 = \underline{6}$ $3 + 3 = \underline{6}$
3. $2 + 4 = \underline{6}$ $6 - 1 = \underline{5}$ $9 + 3 = \underline{12}$
4. $5 + 3 = \underline{8}$ $7 + 5 = \underline{12}$ $6 + 4 = \underline{10}$

5. $9 - 4 = 5$ $4 + 4 = 8$ $2 + 7 = 9$ $5 + 5 = 10$ $8 - 5 = 3$ $9 - 6 = 3$ $10 - 5 = 5$

6. $11 - 3 = 8$ $12 - 5 = 7$ $10 - 2 = 8$ $9 + 1 = 10$ $6 + 3 = 9$ $11 - 6 = 5$ $12 - 8 = 4$

7. $5 - 5 = 0$ $8 + 3 = 11$ $6 + 5 = 11$ $4 + 8 = 12$ $3 + 7 = 10$ $10 - 7 = 3$ $12 - 9 = 3$

Solve.

8. Adam had 4¢ and saved 5¢. How much money did Adam have altogether? 9 ¢

4 ¢
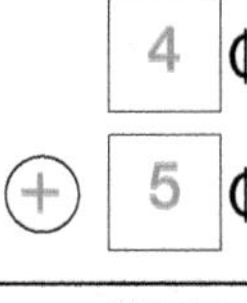
\+ 5 ¢
9 ¢

9. Molly had 11¢. She spent 4¢. How much money did Molly have left? 7 ¢

11 ¢
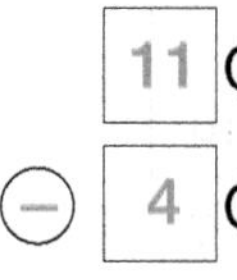
− 4 ¢
7 ¢

page 32

Items	Objectives
1–4	To review addition and subtraction facts with sums and minuends through 10 (see pages 2–10)
5–7	To review addition and subtraction facts with sums and minuends through 12 (see pages 17–28)
8	To review addition through sums of 10¢ (see pages 13–14)
9	To review subtraction facts with minuends through 12¢ (see pages 29–30)

CHAPTER 3

3-1 Numbers Through 19

pages 33–34

1 Getting Started

Objectives

- To read and write numbers and number names through 19
- To add 1 ten and ones for sums through 19

Materials

blank addition table

Warm Up • Mental Math

Ask students what number is added to

1. 10 to have a sum of 15 (5)
2. 12 to have a sum of 12 (0)
3. 9 to have a sum of 12 (3)
4. 15 to have a sum of 20 (5)

Ask students what number is subtracted from

5. 12 to have 3 left (9)
6. 15 to have 10 left (5)
7. 20 to have 15 left (5)

Warm Up • Number Sense

Draw a number line on the board and have students fill in the numbers 0 through 19. Have students circle every other number from 0 to 18. Have students read the circled numbers to count by 2s. Have students read the odd numbers in order.

Name ______________________

Addition Facts Through 18

Chapter 3

Lesson 3-1

Write the numbers.

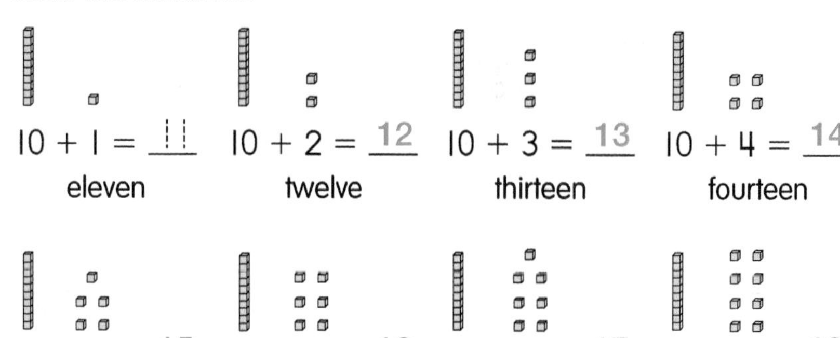

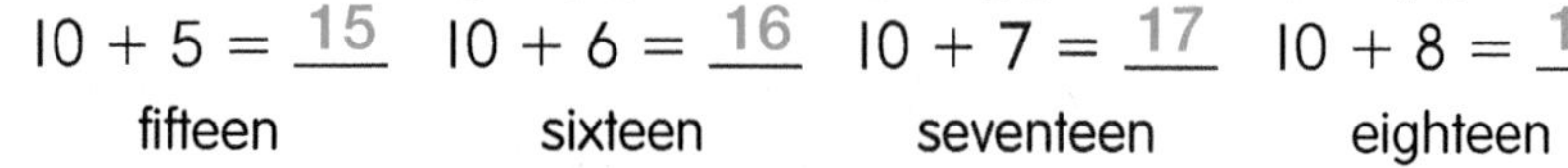

Match.

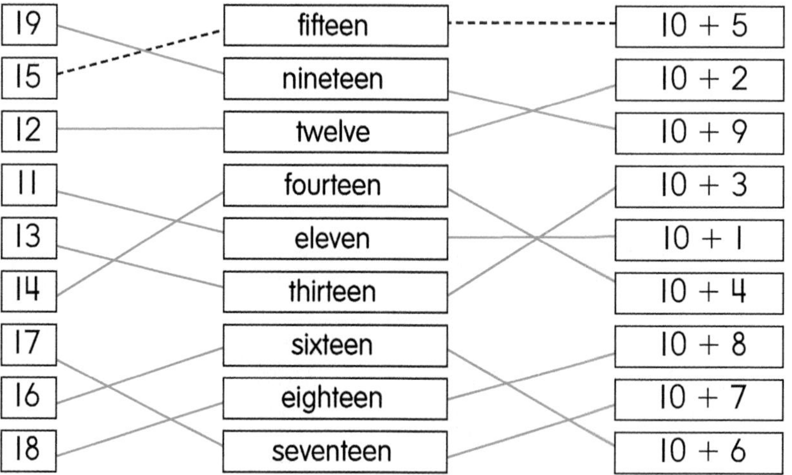

2 Teach

Develop Skills and Concepts Write **8 + 3 =** on the board and have a student write the sum. (11) Have a student draw 11 objects on the board and circle 10 of them. Ask students how many tens are in 11. (1) Ask how many ones. (1) Write **10 + 1 =** on the board and have a student write the sum. (11) Write **eleven** on the board and remind students that this is the number name for 11. Repeat the activity to develop more numbers from 12 through 19 and write the number name for each number. Have students write the sums through 12 on the addition table. Have students then count the blank squares to find out how many addition facts have sums of more than 10. (36)

3 Practice

Using page 33 Tell students to count the tens and ones and write the sum for each exercise at the top of the page. Have students complete the first exercise and trace the 11.

- On the second half of the page, tell students to draw a line from the number name in the middle column to its number on the left. Have students trace the line to match 15 to fifteen. Then, tell students to match the number name to the box on the right that tells the number of tens and ones in the number. Have students trace the line from fifteen to 10 + 5. Have students complete the page independently.

Using page 34 Have students read the word *eleven* and trace the number. Tell students to read the number name and write its number on the line in each exercise in this section.

Write each number.

1. eleven 11
2. eighteen 18
3. fourteen 14
4. twelve 12
5. ten 10
6. seventeen 17
7. nineteen 19
8. thirteen 13
9. sixteen 16
10. fifteen 15
11. zero 0
12. nine 9

Add. Color by answers.

 red

11 red	12 blue	13 green
14 black	15 orange	16 brown
17 yellow	18 purple	19 pink

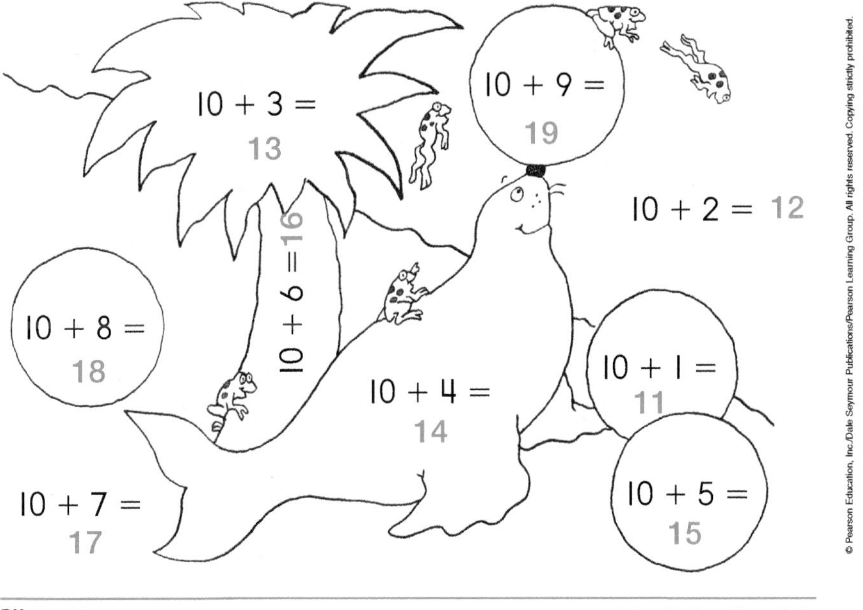

- Then, have students read the number and color pairs. Tell them to find the sum for each exercise, match each sum to a color, and color that part of the picture with that color.

4 Assess

Have students create their own color-by-number pictures, similar to the one on the bottom of page 34. Tell them to create a color key and use addition facts to code their drawing. When their drawings are complete, have them exchange papers with another student to color.

For Mixed Abilities

Common Errors • Intervention

Some students may have difficulty with the numbers 11 through 19. Have them work with partners to model these numbers. For example, have them use a tens rod and a ones cube to model eleven, writing 10 + 1 = 11 to show what they have done. Then, have them continue in this manner with the numbers in order through 19. Encourage students to also count out an array of single counters to match each number.

Enrichment • Number Sense

1. Have students write the numbers and number names from 0 to 19 on cards. Tell them to match the numbers to their names with a partner.
2. Have students use grid paper and crayons to make a tens strip and strips of 1 to 9 squares. Tell them to cut out the strips and then lay out a number from 11 to 19 for a friend to name their number.

More to Explore • Writing

Ask students to think about the way they use numbers every day. Write their ideas on the board. Then, ask students to think about what life would be like without a numbering system. Tell students to draw a picture showing one way the absence of numbers would make a difference in their lives. Have them write a few sentences to describe their picture on the back. Have students explain their picture to the rest of the class. Put all the pages together, add a cover and title, and share the book with other classes.

ESL/ELL STRATEGIES

To review the pronunciation of the numbers 13 through 19, write them on the board in word form, capitalizing the stressed syllable, which is always *-teen,* for example: thir-TEEN. Say each number and ask students to repeat the word.

3-2 Review Sums Through 12

pages 35–36

1 Getting Started

Objective
- To review and practice sums through 12

Vocabulary
dozen

Materials
*addition fact cards for sums through 12; 1 egg carton; 12 counters

Warm Up • Mental Math
Ask students which day comes before

1. Monday (Sunday)
2. Thursday (Wednesday)
3. Friday (Thursday)
4. Tuesday(Monday)
5. Sunday (Saturday)
6. Wednesday (Tuesday)
7. Saturday (Friday)

Warm Up • Number Sense
Show addition fact cards that are doubles and doubles plus 1 in random order. (5 + 5, 5 + 6) Have students give the sum of each and place them in a doubles or doubles plus 1 group. Now, show the doubles fact cards and have students find the doubles plus 1 fact. Then, show a doubles plus 1 fact for students to find the doubles fact.

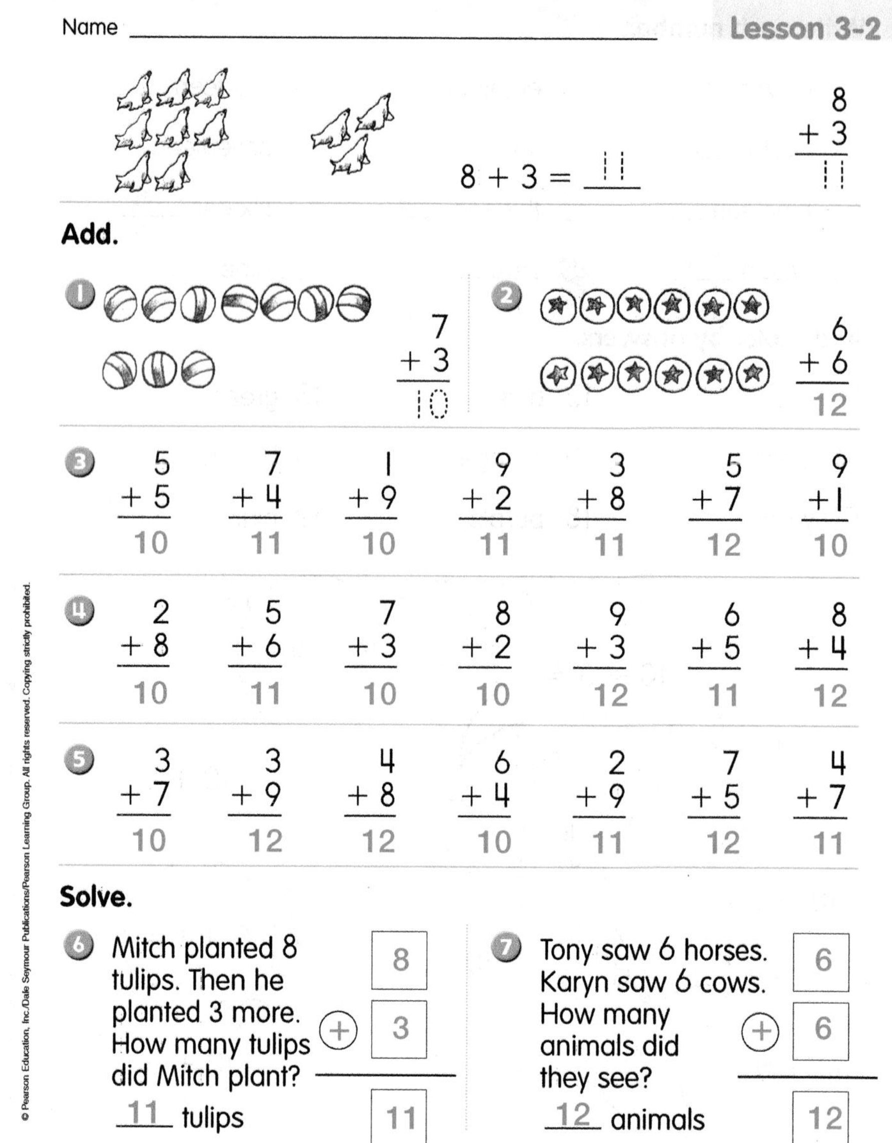

Name ______ Lesson 3-2

8 + 3 = 11

8
+ 3
11

Add.

1. 7 + 3 = 10
2. 6 + 6 = 12

3	5 + 5 = 10	7 + 4 = 11	1 + 9 = 10	9 + 2 = 11	3 + 8 = 11	5 + 7 = 12	9 + 1 = 10
4	2 + 8 = 10	5 + 6 = 11	7 + 3 = 10	8 + 2 = 10	9 + 3 = 12	6 + 5 = 11	8 + 4 = 12
5	3 + 7 = 10	3 + 9 = 12	4 + 8 = 12	6 + 4 = 10	2 + 9 = 11	7 + 5 = 12	4 + 7 = 11

Solve.

6. Mitch planted 8 tulips. Then he planted 3 more. How many tulips did Mitch plant?
11 tulips
8 + 3 = 11

7. Tony saw 6 horses. Karyn saw 6 cows. How many animals did they see?
12 animals
6 + 6 = 12

2 Teach

Develop Skills and Concepts Have students place 1 counter in each compartment of an egg carton. Ask students how many counters there are in all. (12) Tell students that 12 of anything can be called a dozen. Discuss buying eggs by the dozen. Have students remove all counters and then place 1 counter in each of 3 compartments. Ask how many more counters will make 1 dozen. (9) Have a student write **3 + 9 = 12** on the board. Continue to review the facts for 11 and 12 in this way.

3 Practice

Using page 35 Have students count how many seals there are in each group in the example and tell the total. (11) Have students trace the 11 in both problems. Ask students to tell the number of objects there are in each group in Exercise 1. (7, 3) Ask students how many objects there are in all. (10) Remind students there are 1 ten 0 ones in 10 as they draw a circle around the 10 objects. Repeat the procedure for Exercise 2 and have students complete the next set of exercises.

- Read through the two story problems with students if necessary. Remind students that they must write the sign in each problem and record the answer in the solution statement when they complete it.

Using page 36 Have students complete the four rows of exercises independently.

Add.

1	3 + 9 = 12	5 + 5 = 10	3 + 6 = 9	8 + 2 = 10	5 + 3 = 8	9 + 1 = 10	8 + 4 = 12
2	5 + 7 = 12	1 + 9 = 10	7 + 3 = 10	6 + 5 = 11	4 + 8 = 12	3 + 3 = 6	7 + 5 = 12
3	3 + 4 = 7	7 + 4 = 11	8 + 3 = 11	4 + 5 = 9	7 + 2 = 9	4 + 4 = 8	2 + 9 = 11
4	6 + 6 = 12	9 + 3 = 12	4 + 7 = 11	5 + 3 = 8	2 + 8 = 10	9 + 2 = 11	4 + 6 = 10

Now Try This!

Write the missing numbers. It's Algebra!

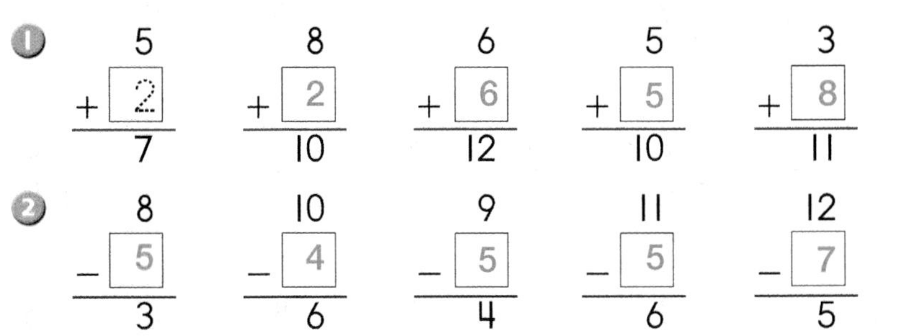

1	5 + [2] = 7	8 + [2] = 10	6 + [6] = 12	5 + [5] = 10	3 + [8] = 11
2	8 − [5] = 3	10 − [4] = 6	9 − [5] = 4	11 − [5] = 6	12 − [7] = 5

Now Try This! Remind students that they have worked exercises like this before. Ask students what number is added to 5 to have a sum of 7. (2) Have students trace the 2. Ask what operation is to be used in each problem in the first row. (addition) Ask what operation they will use in the second row. (subtraction) Have students complete the exercises independently.

It's Algebra! The concepts of this activity prepare students for algebra.

4 Assess

Tell students, *Marc has 8 marbles. Annie has 4. How many marbles do they have altogether?* Have students write and solve a number sentence for this problem. (8 + 4 = 12)

For Mixed Abilities

Common Errors • Intervention
Some students may need additional practice with sums through 12. Have students work in pairs. Give each pair a card with a number from 8 to 12 on it. Each pair looks at its card and the partners take turns writing on a separate sheet of paper a fact whose sum is the number on the card. When all the facts for the number are written correctly, the pair trades cards with another pair, continuing in this manner until all the facts are practiced.

Enrichment • Number Sense

1. Tell students to have a friend guess the addition fact they are thinking of if the sum is 11 and one of the numbers is 2.
2. Tell students to roll two dice and give the sum and have a friend roll the dice and give a sum. The higher sum wins a point. The first player to earn 10 points wins.

More to Explore • Estimation
Place different numbers of objects with interesting shapes in ten small paper bags. Select a student to find the bag that has the number of objects in it from 1 to 10 that you name. Have students feel the bags to determine which one holds the specified number of objects. Students may not look inside the bags. When students think they have found the correct bag, empty the bag and have students count the objects. Mix the order of the bags and repeat the activity several times.

ESL/ELL STRATEGIES

Use examples to explain instructions. Explain *match* by pointing to a sample answer and saying, *Things that match are the same.* For *missing number,* point to an empty box on page 36 and say, *There is no number here. It is a missing number.*

3-3 Sums Through 14

pages 37–38

1 Getting Started

Objective
- To add for sums through 14

Materials
addition fact cards for sums through 14; 14 counters

Warm Up • Mental Math
Have students give the sum.

1. 4 + 3 + 2 (9)
2. 1 + 9 + 6 (16)
3. 4 + 8 + 3 (15)
4. 2 + 2 + 6 (10)
5. 5 + 5 + 5 (15)
6. 2 + 5 + 7 (14)
7. 4 + 0 + 8 (12)

Warm Up • Number Sense
Have students name the sum of each addition fact for sums through 12 when shown addition fact cards in random order. A correct sum earns the card. When all cards have been earned, write the following across the board: **Doubles, Doubles Plus 1, Sum of 0 Through 8, Sum of 0 Through 12**. Have students place their cards on the chalk tray under the proper headings.

2 Teach

Develop Skills and Concepts Write **9 + 3 =** on the board and have a student write the sum. (12) Have a student draw a group of 9 Xs and a group of 3 Xs on the board. Have another student circle a group of ten and tell how many tens and ones are in 12. (1, 2) Draw another X on the board in the group of 3 Xs and ask students how many tens and ones in all. (1, 3) Write **13** on the board. Ask students what two numbers have a sum of 13. (10 and 3 or 9 and 4) Help students develop other facts for sums of 13 by drawing 13 Xs and ask students to circle two groups of Xs. Repeat the procedure to develop sums of 14.

3 Practice

Using page 37 Have students tell the two numbers that are to be added. (7, 6) Ask students to name the sum and trace the 13. Have students draw a circle around ten beads and tell how many tens and ones are in 13. (1, 3) Repeat for Exercise 2. Tell students to find the sums of Exercises 3 to 6 and circle a group of ten where necessary. Then, have them write the sums for the last section of exercises.

Using page 38 Encourage students to work the column of exercises first. Have students complete the page independently.

Add.

1. 5 + 5 = 10
2. 8 + 2 = 10
3. 5 + 6 = 11
4. 3 + 7 = 10
5. 3 + 9 = 12
6. 7 + 4 = 11
7. 4 + 7 = 11
8. 8 + 6 = 14
9. 7 + 5 = 12
10. 4 + 6 = 10
11. 6 + 6 = 12
12. 5 + 9 = 14

13	9 + 2 = 11	3 + 8 = 11	7 + 7 = 14	4 + 9 = 13
14	5 + 7 = 12	6 + 8 = 14	8 + 5 = 13	9 + 3 = 12
15	6 + 7 = 13	6 + 5 = 11	8 + 3 = 11	1 + 9 = 10
16	2 + 8 = 10	9 + 5 = 14	5 + 8 = 13	6 + 4 = 10
17	8 + 4 = 12	2 + 9 = 11	4 + 8 = 12	9 + 4 = 13

Now Try This!

Use these numbers to write addition sentences.

1. 8 6 4 2

   6 + 2 = 8

   4 + 2 = 6

2. 9 5 14 4

   9 + 5 = 14

   5 + 4 = 9

Now Try This! Have a student read the four numbers in the first exercise. Tell students that they are to use all four numbers to write two addition sentences. Have students trace the numbers in the first sentence as they read aloud with you. Have students complete the next sentence and then work the second exercise independently.

4 Assess

Have students list all addition facts for the sum of 14. (9 + 5, 8 + 6, 7 + 7, 6 + 8, 5 + 9)

For Mixed Abilities

Common Errors • Intervention

If students have difficulty with the new facts for sums of 13 and 14, have them work in pairs with counters to model the following problems and count to find the sum:

4 + 9 = 13, 5 + 8 = 13, 6 + 7 = 13, 7 + 6 = 13, 8 + 5 = 13, 9 + 4 = 13, 5 + 9 = 14, 6 + 8 = 14, 7 + 7 = 14, 8 + 6 = 14, and 9 + 5 = 14.

Encourage students to discuss the "one more" and "one less" patterns that they see.

Enrichment • Number Sense

1. Tell students to write the facts whose sums are even numbers less than 14 and then circle the doubles.
2. Tell students to write the facts whose sums are odd numbers less than 14 and circle the doubles plus 1 facts.

More to Explore • Logic

Have a special place on the board to write a daily riddle that involves mathematical concepts or numbers in general. Put an envelope beneath it.

Tell students to solve the riddle before the end of the day, write their solution on a sheet of paper, and put it in the envelope. Read all the answers aloud, giving a point to each student giving the correct one. Here are some examples:

1. What has eight legs and sings? (4 canaries)
2. If two's company and three's a crowd, what's four and five? (nine)
3. What grows larger each time you take something from it? (a hole)

After you have done this activity for several days, ask students to bring in daily math riddles to share with the class.

3-4 Money Sums Through 14¢

pages 39–40

1 Getting Started

Objective

- To add money amounts through 14¢

Materials

*5 classroom items with price tags of 2¢, 6¢, 3¢, 8¢, and 7¢; 2 real or play nickels; 12 real or play pennies

Warm Up • Mental Math

Have students count backward to 0 from the following numbers:

1. 12 (12, 11, . . . , 0)
2. 16
3. 20
4. 11
5. 9
6. 15
7. 17
8. 13

Warm Up • Pencil and Paper

Have students display coins in two groups for a sum of 11¢. Have students write addition problems to tell about their coin groups. Repeat for other sums through 12¢.

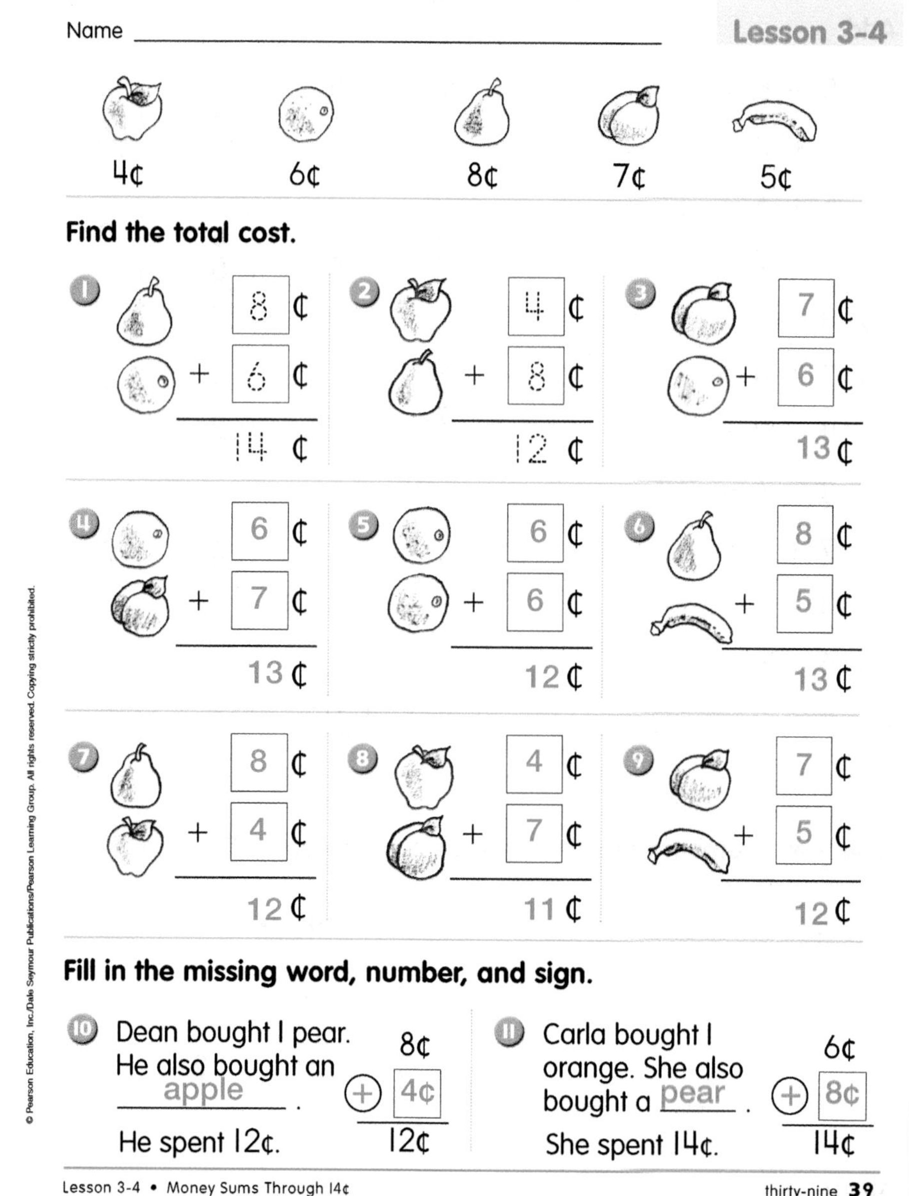

Name ______________________ Lesson 3-4

4¢ 6¢ 8¢ 7¢ 5¢

Find the total cost.

1. 8¢ + 6¢ = 14¢
2. 4¢ + 8¢ = 12¢
3. 7¢ + 6¢ = 13¢
4. 6¢ + 7¢ = 13¢
5. 6¢ + 6¢ = 12¢
6. 8¢ + 5¢ = 13¢
7. 8¢ + 4¢ = 12¢
8. 4¢ + 7¢ = 11¢
9. 7¢ + 5¢ = 12¢

Fill in the missing word, number, and sign.

10. Dean bought I pear. He also bought an apple. He spent 12¢. 8¢ + 4¢ = 12¢
11. Carla bought I orange. She also bought a pear. She spent 14¢. 6¢ + 8¢ = 14¢

© Pearson Education, Inc./Dale Seymour Publications/Pearson Learning Group. All rights reserved. Copying strictly prohibited.

Lesson 3-4 • Money Sums Through 14¢ thirty-nine 39

2 Teach

Develop Skills and Concepts Attach price tags of 2¢, 6¢, 3¢, 8¢, and 7¢ to five classroom items. Show students the five priced items. Ask a student to write and solve a problem on the board to find the sum of any two of the items. Continue to have students write and solve problems until each item has been paired with another. Give students nickels and pennies. Have students put out coins to show each purchase of two items.

3 Practice

Using page 39 Have students name each item across the top of the page and tell its price. Tell students that they are to write the price of each item in the box next to the item and find the total cost of the two items.

- Have students trace the numbers in the first exercise and write the sum. Repeat for the second exercise. Tell students that the cent sign is written beside each price and each sum so that anyone would know the problem is about money.
- Now, have students read the first story problem. Ask students what item Dean would buy from the top of the page if he paid 12¢ in all. (apple) Have students write the word and its cost in the problem. Help students complete the next exercise if necessary.

Using page 40 Have students find the sum for each exercise. Then, read through the first story problem with them and ask what operation they will use to solve it. (addition) Have students write the plus sign in the circle. Ask students what numbers will be added and have them write the numbers in the boxes and find the sum. Accept 9 + 4 or 4 + 9 and discuss why either order is correct. Have students write the sum in the solution statement. Have students complete the second story problem independently.

Add.

1. 5¢ + 5¢ = 10¢ 4¢ + 6¢ = 10¢ 7¢ + 4¢ = 11¢
2. 2¢ + 8¢ = 10¢ 8¢ + 4¢ = 12¢ 6¢ + 4¢ = 10¢
3. 5¢ + 4¢ = 9¢ 1¢ + 9¢ = 10¢ 5¢ + 6¢ = 11¢
4. 4¢ + 7¢ = 11¢ 6¢ + 5¢ = 11¢ 1¢ + 9¢ = 10¢

5	6¢ + 8¢ = 14¢	8¢ + 3¢ = 11¢	7¢ + 5¢ = 12¢	7¢ + 6¢ = 13¢	5¢ + 7¢ = 12¢	8¢ + 5¢ = 13¢	4¢ + 9¢ = 13¢
6	5¢ + 9¢ = 14¢	9¢ + 3¢ = 12¢	3¢ + 7¢ = 10¢	8¢ + 6¢ = 14¢	9¢ + 2¢ = 11¢	6¢ + 7¢ = 13¢	7¢ + 3¢ = 10¢
7	4¢ + 8¢ = 12¢	9¢ + 4¢ = 13¢	3¢ + 9¢ = 12¢	5¢ + 8¢ = 13¢	9¢ + 5¢ = 14¢	7¢ + 7¢ = 14¢	3¢ + 8¢ = 11¢

Solve.

8. Lauren has 9¢. Becky has 4¢. How much do the girls have altogether?

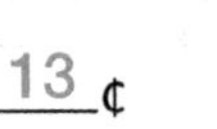

13 ¢

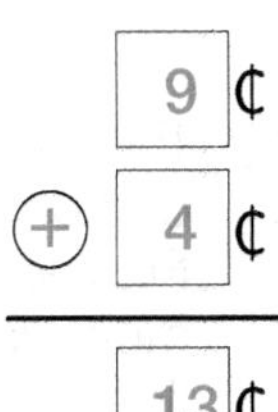

9 ¢ + 4 ¢ = 13 ¢

9. Mike bought a ball for 7¢ and a sticker for 7¢. How much did he spend?

14 ¢

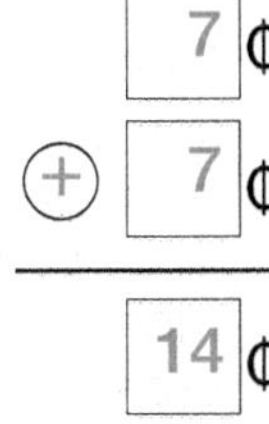

7 ¢ + 7 ¢ = 14 ¢

4 Assess

Tell students, *One week, Karen saved 4¢. The next week, she saved 9¢. How much did she save altogether?* (13¢)

For Mixed Abilities

Common Errors • Intervention

If students have difficulty adding amounts of money, have them work in pairs, using pennies to model each problem. Help them see the facts in pairs; for example, if 3¢ + 9¢ = 12¢, then 9¢ + 3¢ is also equal to 12¢.

Enrichment • Number Sense

1. Tell students to write and solve four different addition or subtraction problems using the numbers 6, 7, and 13.
2. Have students write and solve addition problems to show all the total costs if they could buy only two items at a time of things priced 6¢, 5¢, 8¢, and 4¢.
3. Tell students to suppose they have 14¢ and buy an item for 6¢ and another item for 7¢. Ask if they would have enough left to buy gum that costs 3¢.

More to Explore • Logic

Have students work with partners to count to a specified number. The first player in each pair begins counting and says either one or two numbers. The other player begins where the first player left off and may also say one or two numbers. Players continue counting until one of the players wins by counting to the specified number. Strategy is required to determine whether a student will say one or two numbers at each turn in an effort to be the student who says the final number.

As a variation, students can count by even or odd numbers, by 5s, 10s, or in fractional increments of $\frac{1}{4}$ ($\frac{1}{4}$, $\frac{1}{2}$, $\frac{3}{4}$, 1, $1\frac{1}{4}$, and so on), depending on their skill level.

3-5 Sums Through 16

pages 41–42

1 Getting Started

Objective
- To add for sums through 16

Materials
16 counters

Warm Up • Mental Math
Have students name the number.

1. 2 tens 6 ones (26)
2. 4 tens 0 ones (40)
3. 1 ten 1 one (11)
4. 7 tens 5 ones (75)
5. 3 tens 3 ones (33)
6. 2 tens 4 ones (24)
7. 5 tens 0 ones (50)
8. 0 tens 9 ones (9)

Warm Up • Number Sense
Write groups of four addition facts such as **4 + 9, 3 + 6, 6 + 7,** and **8 + 5** on the board. Have a volunteer circle all the facts in the group that have the same sum. Repeat for more groups of four facts in which students are asked to find facts having sums of 13 or 14.

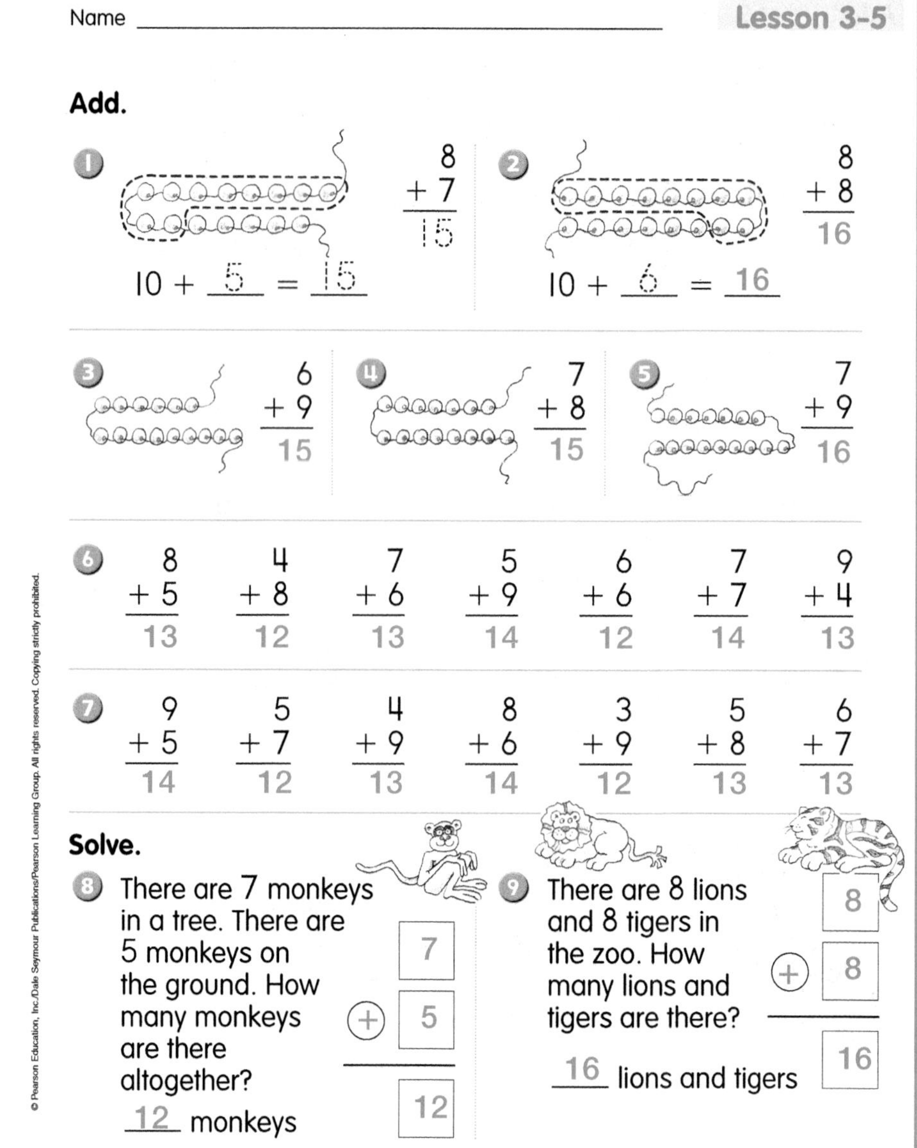

Name ______________________ Lesson 3-5

Add.

1. 8 + 7 = 15; 10 + 5 = 15
2. 8 + 8 = 16; 10 + 6 = 16
3. 6 + 9 = 15
4. 7 + 8 = 15
5. 7 + 9 = 16

6.

8	4	7	5	6	7	9
+ 5	+ 8	+ 6	+ 9	+ 6	+ 7	+ 4
13	12	13	14	12	14	13

7.

9	5	4	8	3	5	6
+ 5	+ 7	+ 9	+ 6	+ 9	+ 8	+ 7
14	12	13	14	12	13	13

Solve.

8. There are 7 monkeys in a tree. There are 5 monkeys on the ground. How many monkeys are there altogether?
7 + 5 = 12
12 monkeys

9. There are 8 lions and 8 tigers in the zoo. How many lions and tigers are there?
8 + 8 = 16
16 lions and tigers

2 Teach

Develop Skills and Concepts Have students display a group of 9 counters and another group of 5. Ask how many counters there are in all. (14) Have students add 1 counter to the group of 5 and tell how many are in each group now. (9 and 6) Have a student write **9 + 6** on the board. Ask students how many counters there are in all. (15) Have a student write the sum on the board. Tell students that they have found one addition fact for 15.

- Ask students how many tens and ones are in 15. (1 ten, 5 ones) Have students group the counters as 1 ten and 5 ones. Have a student write **10 + 5 = 15** on the board. Ask students how many of the 15 counters would be in one group if they had 8 in the other. (7) Have a student write **8 + 7 = 15** on the board.
- Continue to develop facts for 15 and then repeat the procedure to develop the facts for 16.

3 Practice

Using page 41 Ask students how many objects are in each group in the first exercise. (8 and 7) Have students circle ten of the objects and then trace the numbers to complete the exercise. Repeat for the next exercise and have students write the sums. Tell students to circle ten objects where necessary in each of the exercises and write the sums for the rest of the page. Then, help students read the story problems and remind them to write in the sign of operation. Have students complete the story problems independently.

Using page 42 Remind students to write the sign of operation in each story problem and record the answer in the solution statement. Have students complete the page independently.

Add.

1	9 + 2 = 11	8 + 3 = 11	7 + 5 = 12	9 + 3 = 12	7 + 7 = 14	5 + 9 = 14	5 + 5 = 10
2	7 + 4 = 11	6 + 6 = 12	8 + 5 = 13	4 + 7 = 11	3 + 9 = 12	8 + 8 = 16	9 + 5 = 14
3	6 + 5 = 11	9 + 4 = 13	4 + 8 = 12	7 + 6 = 13	3 + 8 = 11	7 + 4 = 11	6 + 9 = 15

4. 8 + 6 = 14 7 + 8 = 15 6 + 8 = 14
5. 4 + 9 = 13 6 + 5 = 11 5 + 7 = 12
6. 6 + 7 = 13 8 + 7 = 15 9 + 6 = 15
7. 8 + 4 = 12 5 + 8 = 13 7 + 9 = 16

Solve.

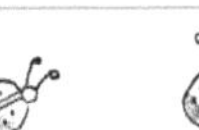
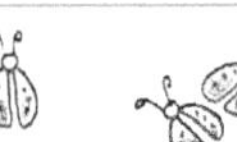

8. There are 9 children playing tag. There are 6 more playing kickball. How many children are playing?

9 + 6 = 15

15 children

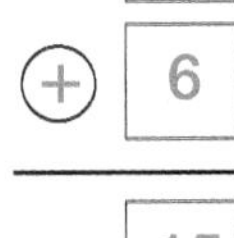
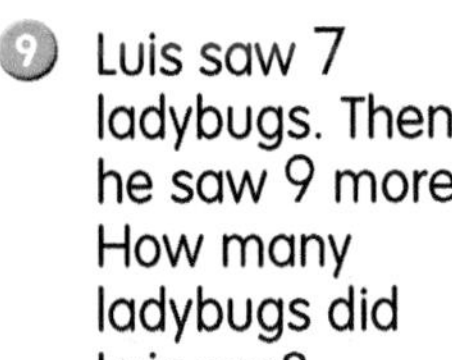
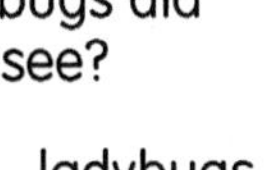

9. Luis saw 7 ladybugs. Then he saw 9 more. How many ladybugs did Luis see?

7 + 9 = 16

16 ladybugs

4 Assess

Write **9 + ____ = 16, 6 + ____ = 15,** and **8 + ____ = 16** on the board. Have students copy the problems and fill in the blanks. (7, 9, 8)

For Mixed Abilities

Common Errors • Intervention

To help students who have difficulty with sums of 15 and 16, have them work in pairs. On a sheet of paper, have them draw 9 Xs in one group and 7 Xs in another. Have one partner circle a group of ten Xs and the other partner tell how many more Xs there are. (6) Ask, *What number is 1 ten and 6 ones?* (16) Have students write **9 + 7 = 16** on the paper beneath the Xs. Continue with other sums of 15 and 16.

Enrichment • Number Sense

1. Tell students to work with a partner to put the addition fact cards for sums of 10 through 16 facedown. Have them draw two cards. A match of the same sum earns the cards and another turn. Tell students to play until all cards are earned.
2. Tell students to write all facts for sums through 16 where one of the addends is 8 or 9.

More to Explore • Logic

Write these number sentences on the board and have students write true or false after each one: **2 + 4 = 6** (true), **2 + 3 = 6** (false), **5 + 0 = 5** (true). Explain that number sentences can be true or false in the same way that statements like "I am 2 inches tall" can be true or false. Have students copy the following number sentences and write *T* (true) or *F* (false) after each one.

1. 3 + 7 = 11 (F)
2. 9 − 2 = 7 (T)
3. 10 − 1 = 8 (F)
4. 5 + 6 = 11 (T)
5. 7 + 1 = 8 (T)
6. 2 − 0 = 2 (T)
7. 3 + 0 = 4 (F)
8. 5 + 8 = 12 (F)
9. 3 + 7 = 10 (T)
10. 12 − 2 = 10 (T)
11. 8 − 1 = 6 (F)
12. 14 − 4 = 10 (T)
13. 9 + 4 = 14 (F)
14. 7 + 7 = 17 (F)

3-6 Sums Through 18

pages 43–44

1 Getting Started

Objective
- To add for sums through 18

Materials
addition facts table; 18 counters

Warm Up • Mental Math
Ask students how much money is in the following:

1. 2 nickels (10¢)
2. 2 nickels and 1 penny (11¢)
3. 4 nickels and 6 pennies (26¢)
4. 1 nickel and 2 pennies (7¢)
5. 2 nickels and 9 pennies (19¢)
6. 1 nickel and 8 pennies (13¢)
7. 3 nickels (15¢)
8. 5 nickels (25¢)

Warm Up • Pencil and Paper
Have students fill in all sums through 16 on an addition facts table. Have students note that only three facts are missing.

Name ____________________

Add.

1. 8 + 9 = 17; 10 + 7 = 17
2. 9 + 9 = 18; 10 + 8 = 18

3. 8 + 8 = 16
4. 7 + 9 = 16
5. 9 + 8 = 17

6	9 + 5 = 14	7 + 5 = 12	8 + 5 = 13	9 + 3 = 12	4 + 8 = 12	8 + 8 = 16	7 + 9 = 16
7	7 + 8 = 15	3 + 9 = 12	9 + 6 = 15	6 + 7 = 13	8 + 4 = 12	9 + 4 = 13	6 + 8 = 14
8	6 + 6 = 12	8 + 6 = 14	5 + 7 = 12	9 + 8 = 17	8 + 9 = 17	7 + 6 = 13	4 + 9 = 13
9	5 + 9 = 14	8 + 7 = 15	7 + 7 = 14	9 + 9 = 18	5 + 8 = 13	9 + 7 = 16	6 + 9 = 15

2 Teach

Develop Skills and Concepts Write 9 + 8 = and 9 + 9 = on the board and tell students that these are two of the remaining three facts to complete the addition table from the Warm Up • Pencil and Paper activity. Have students think of the sum of the double 8 + 8 and count on 1 to tell the sum of 9 + 8. Have a student write the sum. (17) Have students tell the number of tens and ones in 17. (1 ten, 7 ones) Have students think of the doubles plus 1 fact of 9 + 8 and count on 1 to tell the sum of 9 + 9. Have a student write the sum. (18) Have students tell the number of tens and ones in 18. (1 ten, 8 ones) Ask students what one more fact is known if 9 + 8 = 17. (8 + 9 = 17) Have students write the sums of 17 and 18 in the correct place on the facts table.

3 Practice

Using page 43 Discuss the number of objects in Exercise 1 and have students draw a circle around ten of them. Have students trace the numbers. Repeat for the second exercise and have students write the sum. Have students complete the page independently.

Using page 44 Remind students that they have completed wheels and tables before. Ask students what they will do in the wheels. (add the number in the second ring to the number in the center and write the sum in the outer ring)

- Ask what they will do in the tables. (add 6 to each number and write the sum, then add 5 to each number in the next table and add 8 to each number in the last table)
- Ask students what they will do in the story problems. By this time, students should remember to write the sign of operation and record the answer in the solution statement. Have students complete the page independently.

Complete each wheel.

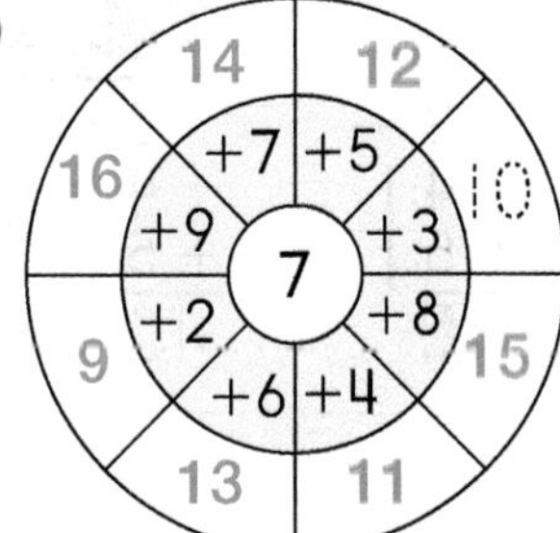

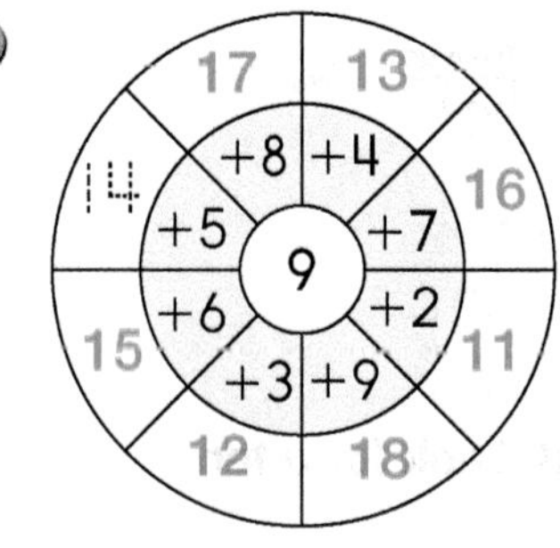

Complete each table.

3

Add 6.	
3	9
7	13
4	10
9	15
2	8

4

Add 5.	
3	8
7	12
8	13
9	14
5	10

Add 8.	
3	11
7	15
6	14
9	17
8	16

Solve.

6 Joe saw 7 red roses and 9 yellow roses. How many roses did Joe see?

16 roses

7
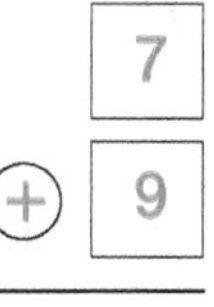
16

7 Rita has 8 pennies. Kim has 6 pennies. How many pennies do they have altogether?

14 pennies

8
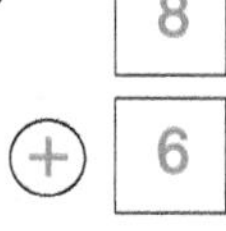
14

4 Assess

Write ____ + ____ = 17 and ____ + ____ = 18 on the board. Have students complete the number sentences. (9 + 8 = 17, 8 + 9 = 17, 9 + 9 = 18)

For Mixed Abilities

Common Errors • Intervention

Encourage students who have difficulty with some of the sums through 18 to use the doubles and doubles-plus-1 strategies to help them remember their facts.

Doubles	Doubles Plus 1
5 + 5 = 10	5 + 6 = 10 + 1, or 11
6 + 6 = 12	6 + 7 = 12 + 1, or 13
7 + 7 = 14	7 + 8 = 14 + 1, or 15
8 + 8 = 16	8 + 9 = 16 + 1, or 17

Enrichment • Number Sense

1. Tell students to write all facts that are doubles or doubles plus 1 for sums through 18.
2. Have students make their own set of addition fact cards for sums through 18.
3. Tell students to draw a picture to help them remember each fact they cannot quickly recall.

More to Explore • Application

Prepare four gameboards for students to play Button Toss Addition and Subtraction. Divide the board into 11 rectangles and mark each with a number, 0 through 10. Divide the class into four groups, each group getting a gameboard and each having two buttons. Each player in a group takes a turn tossing the two buttons onto the board and subtracts the smaller number landed on from the larger number. That is the score. Have students take several turns and add all individual scores to get a total and a winner. You can extend the activity by using numbers 9 through 18 on the boards.

3-7 Column Addition

pages 45–46

1 Getting Started

Objective

- To add three or four 1-digit numbers for sums through 18

Materials

*addition fact cards for sums of 9 through 18; *interlocking cubes

Warm Up • Mental Math

Tell students to count to 100 by 10s from:

1. 40 (50, 60, . . . , 100)
2. 10
3. 60
4. 30
5. 70
6. 20
7. 50
8. 0

Warm Up • Number Sense

Display all fact cards for sums of 9 through 18 on the chalk tray. Group students in pairs and assign each pair a number from 9 to 18. Tell students that they are to collect all the fact cards that have their number as a sum. When all cards are collected, have groups trade cards to check each other's work.

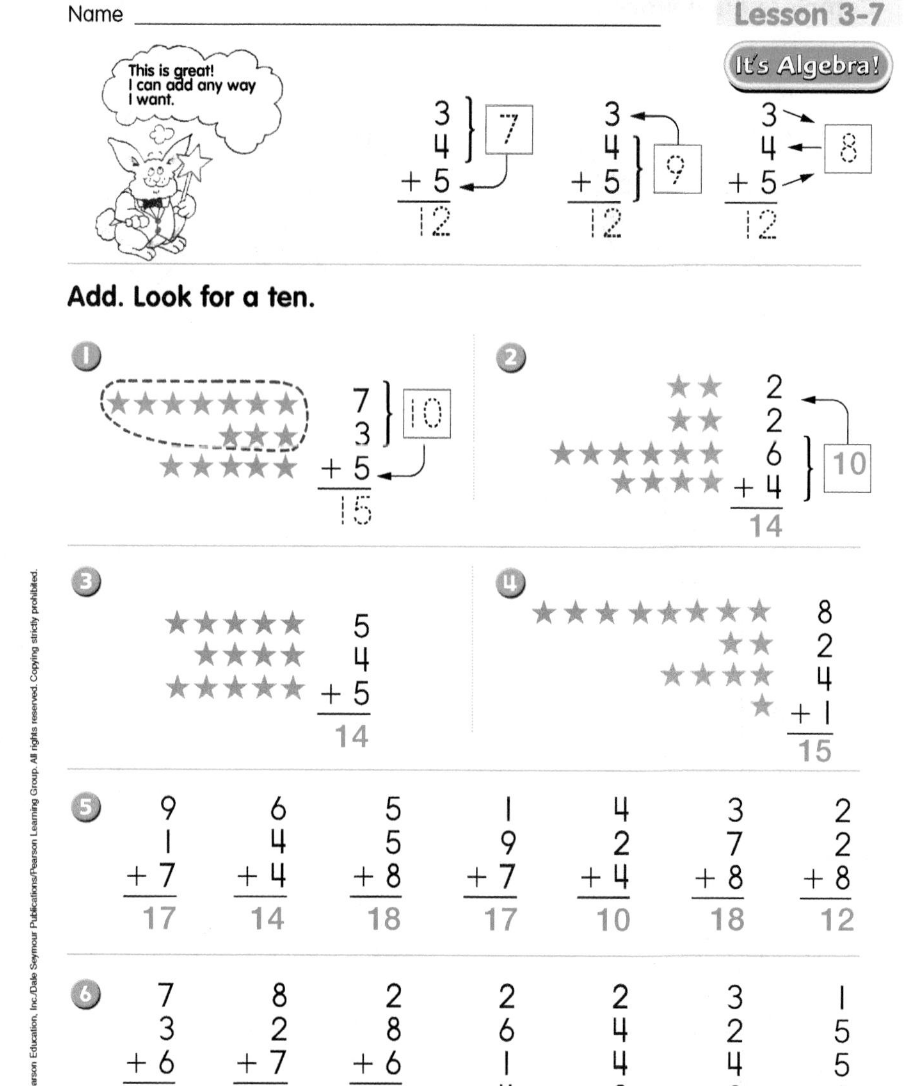

2 Teach

Develop Skills and Concepts To help students understand that 2 + 3 = 3 + 2, use interlocking cubes to represent the problem. Connect two red cubes together and three blue cubes together. Show the addition by connecting the two sets. Be sure students see it represents 2 + 3. Now, turn the train around so that the blue cubes come first. Students should see it as 3 + 2 but still the same train. This demonstration illustrates the Commutative Property of Addition.

- To illustrate the Associative Property of Addition, use three different colors of interlocking cubes. For example, two red, three blue, and four green can be connected by first connecting the red and blue, and then connecting that train to green to represent (2 + 3) + 4. You could also connect the blue and green together, and then the red, giving 2 + (3 + 4). In either case, the length of the train, which represents the sum, is the same.

It's Algebra! The concepts of this lesson prepare students for algebra.

3 Practice

Using page 45 Have students add 3 and 4 and trace the 7, then add 5 and trace the sum of 12. Remind students they can add the numbers in any order. Point out that the next two examples are the same but are to be added in a different order. Have students write the sum of 4 and 5 in the box (9) and then add 3 and trace the sum. (12) Have students compare the sums to check their work. Have students complete the third example. Remind students to add up the column to check their work. Have students complete the page independently.

Using page 46 Remind students to look for a ten although every exercise may not have one. Remind students to check each exercise by adding up the column. Have students complete the page independently.

Add.

1

2	2	3	3	7	7	1
3	7	2	7	2	3	1
+ 7	+ 3	+ 7	+ 2	+ 3	+ 2	+ 1
12	12	12	12	12	12	3

2

2	3	4	5	6	7	8
2	3	4	5	6	3	2
+ 2	+ 3	+ 4	+ 5	+ 4	+ 7	+ 8
6	9	12	15	16	17	18

3

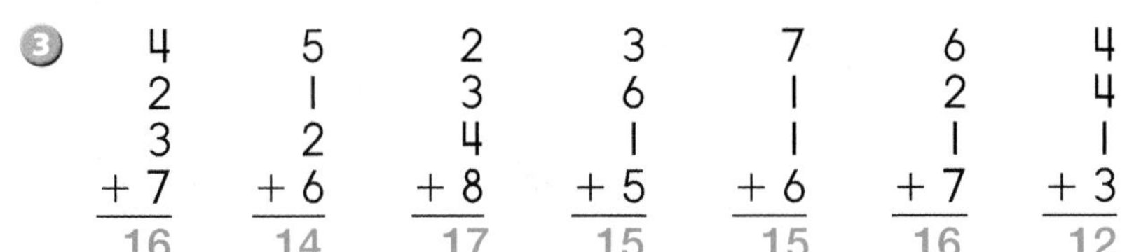

4	5	2	3	7	6	4
2	1	3	6	1	2	4
3	2	4	1	1	1	1
+ 7	+ 6	+ 8	+ 5	+ 6	+ 7	+ 3
16	14	17	15	15	16	12

Now Try This!

Write two addition number sentences using each number only once.

1  1 2 3 4 5 7

1 + 3 = 4

2 + 5 = 7

2  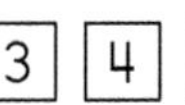 2 3 4 5 6 8

2 + 4 = 6

3 + 5 = 8

Now Try This! Have students read the six numbers in the first exercise. Tell students to use each of the six numbers one time to write two addition sentences. Have students trace the numbers as they read aloud with you and then complete the next sentence independently. Have students write two number sentences for the second exercise independently and then talk through the solution together. Now, have students use each set of six numbers to write more addition and subtraction sentences.

4 Assess

Have students write story problems with three addends and a sum of 18.

For Mixed Abilities

Common Errors • Intervention

Some students may forget to add the third or fourth addend when working with column addition. Have them practice using counters to represent each addend in the problem. Have them join the counters and then regroup them into a ten and ones and write the sum.

Enrichment • Number Sense

1. Tell students to write a problem to find the third number if three numbers are added together for a sum of 18 and two of the numbers are 6s.
2. Have students draw a picture that shows that three numbers from 1 to 9 can be added in any order.
3. Tell students to write three different problems of three addends whose sum is 17. Can they write another? And another?

More to Explore • Classification

Fill a large paper bag with several objects. The objects should belong to one set, for example, things with lids, wooden things, round things, red things, flat things, and so on. Label the bag with the name of the set. Have students take everything out of the bag and separate the objects into subsets according to any characteristics they choose. Tell students to make a list of the subsets and then place the objects back in the bag. After all students have had a chance to make subsets, have them compare their lists. Record how many different subsets were found. Have students make a list of attributes or properties that describe the subsets.

3-8 Money Sums Through 18¢

pages 47–48

1 Getting Started

Objective

- To add money through sums of 18¢

Materials

3 real or play nickels; 18 real or play pennies

Warm Up • Mental Math

Have students give the sum or number.

1. 2 + 3 + 2 (7)
2. 1 + 5 + 4 (10)
3. 10 + 4 (14)
4. 1 ten 2 ones (12)
5. 2 tens 6 ones (26)
6. 5¢ + 4¢ (9¢)
7. 8 + 8 + 2 (18)

Warm Up • Money

Draw a nickel and 4 pennies on the board and ask students to tell the amount. (9¢) Have students show another way to make 9¢ with coins. (9 pennies) Have students show other amounts through 18¢ in one or two ways, with coins available. Then, have students put 18¢ in three groups of coins and write and solve a 3-addend problem on the board.

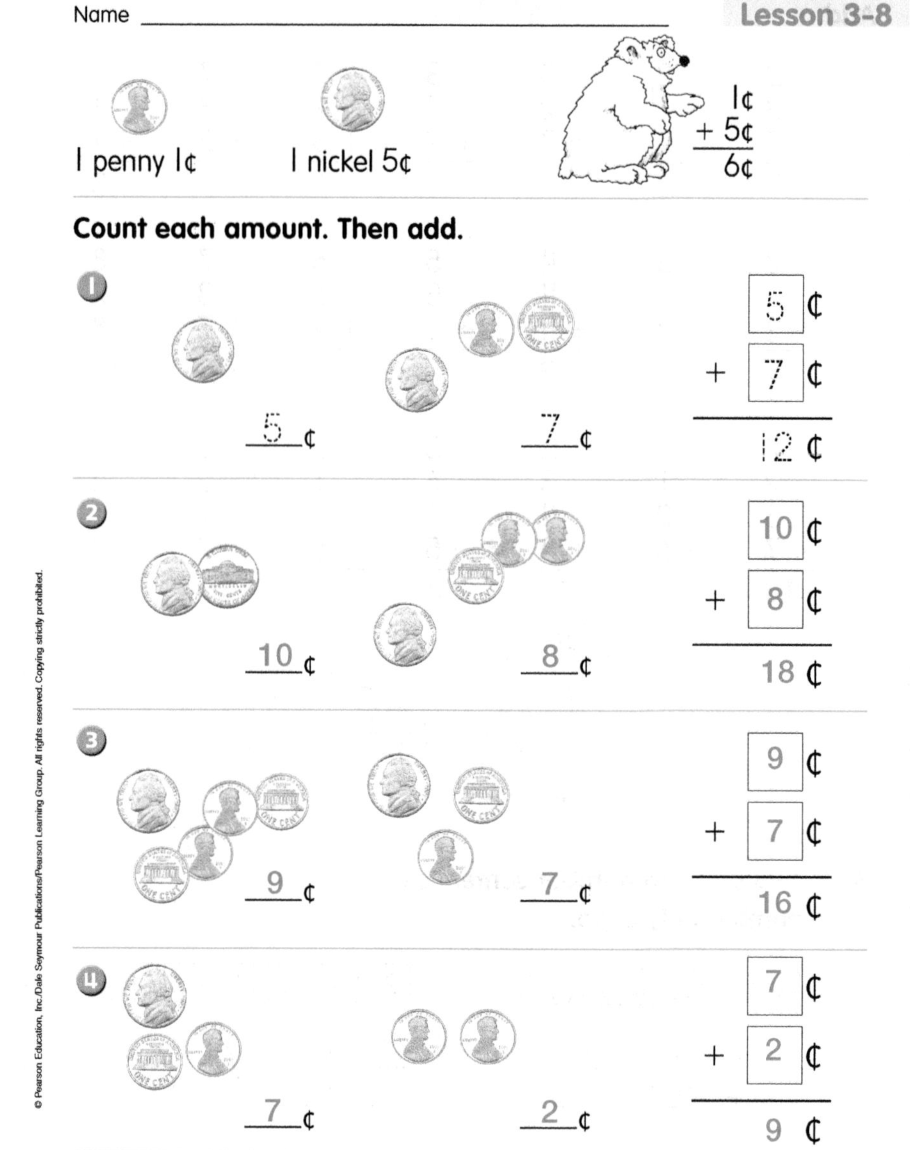

2 Teach

Develop Skills and Concepts Have students put out a nickel and 3 pennies in one group and a nickel and 4 pennies in another. Tell a student to write and solve a problem to add the amount of money in each group, remembering the cent signs. (8¢ + 9¢ = 17¢) Repeat for a group of 2 nickels and a group of 1 nickel and 1 penny. (10¢ + 6¢ = 16¢) Tell students that the cent sign must be written when we are talking about cents. Now, repeat for three groups of coins for a 3-addend problem of 1-digit amounts whose sum is 18¢ or less.

3 Practice

Using page 47 Call students' attention to the example at the top of the page. Explain that a nickel is worth 5¢, or 5 pennies. Have students read the problem the bear is writing. (1¢ + 5¢ = 6¢)

- Have students trace the 5¢, 7¢, and the sum of 12¢ in Exercise 1. Have students complete the page independently.

Using page 48 Have students tell the name of each sticker at the top of the page and its price. For Exercise 1, tell them to trace the 8¢ for the price of the cat, 6¢ for the price of the seal, and 14¢ for the total amount spent. Have students complete the page independently.

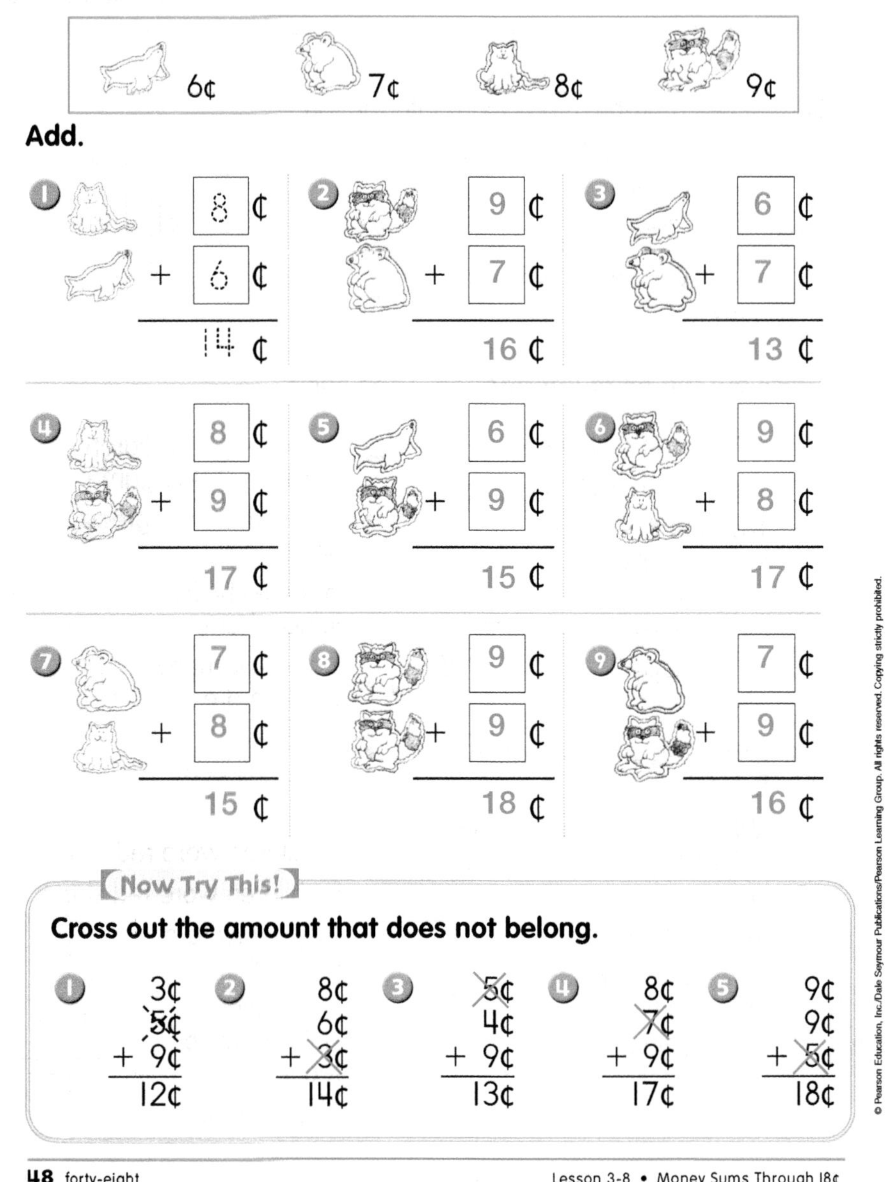

6¢ 7¢ 8¢ 9¢

Add.

1. 8¢ + 6¢ = 14¢
2. 9¢ + 7¢ = 16¢
3. 6¢ + 7¢ = 13¢
4. 8¢ + 9¢ = 17¢
5. 6¢ + 9¢ = 15¢
6. 9¢ + 8¢ = 17¢
7. 7¢ + 8¢ = 15¢
8. 9¢ + 9¢ = 18¢
9. 7¢ + 9¢ = 16¢

Now Try This!

Cross out the amount that does not belong.

1. 3¢, ~~5¢~~, + 9¢ = 12¢
2. 8¢, 6¢, + ~~3¢~~ = 14¢
3. ~~5¢~~, 4¢, + 9¢ = 13¢
4. 8¢, ~~7¢~~, + 9¢ = 17¢
5. 9¢, 9¢, + ~~5¢~~ = 18¢

Now Try This! Ask students to tell the sum of the first exercise. (12¢) Tell students that one of the addends does not belong in the problem. Ask students to find which two addends have a sum of 12¢. (3¢ and 9¢) Tell students to cross out the 5¢. Help students complete the next exercise before assigning the rest of the exercises to be completed independently.

4 Assess

Have students refer to the sticker animals on top of page 48. Tell them that you have 15¢ to spend. What two combinations of stickers can you buy for 15¢? (the seal for 6¢ and the raccoon for 9¢, the bear for 7¢ and the cat for 8¢)

For Mixed Abilities

Common Errors • Intervention

Some students may have difficulty with adding money. Have them work in pairs with real coins or play money. Each partner puts out an amount of money equal to 9¢ or less. The partners count each other's money, join the amounts, and find the sum. They can repeat the activity with other amounts of money less than 10¢.

Enrichment • Number Sense

1. Have students draw coins to show three equal amounts whose total sum is 18¢. Then, have them draw 18¢ in two equal amounts.
2. Tell students to write the addition problem that shows how much money there is in a club treasury if there were 5 members and each paid 3¢ dues.
3. Tell students to make an illustration to explain why they and a friend each have 9¢, but their coins are not the same.

More to Explore • Kinesthetic Learning

Draw a triangle, circle, square, and rectangle on the floor with chalk or tape. Make the shapes large enough for a student to stand inside and bounce a ball. Tell four students to choose their home shape. Tell students that when you clap your hands they are to start bouncing the ball. They can continue as long as they stay within their shapes. If they do not, they must take a seat. As they bounce the ball, they count. The winner is the student who has the highest number of bounces and stays within his or her shape. Continue playing until all students have had a turn.

3-9 Problem Solving: Too Much Information

pages 49–50

1 Getting Started

Objectives

- To eliminate extraneous information from a story problem
- To solve problems using sums through 18

Warm Up • Mental Math

Ask students which is more.

1. 13 or 31 (31)
2. 26 or 62 (62)
3. 45 or 15 (45)
4. 16 or 61 (61)
5. 11 or 21 (21)
6. 33 or 23 (33)
7. 24 or 34 (34)

Warm Up • Algebra

Write **5 + 7 =** on the board and have a student write the sum. (12) Write **12 = ____ + 2** on the board and have a student complete the sentence. (10) Write **5 + 7 = 10 + 2** on the board and tell students that 5 of the group of 7, joined the 5 to make 10 and left only 2 of the 7. Have students act out this movement from 1 group to the other. Repeat the procedure for 8 + 7 and 9 + 8.

Name ____________________

Problem Solving
Lesson 3-9

Sometimes a problem has extra information.
There are 8 cars in the parking lot.
~~6 of the cars are green.~~
Then 2 more cars drove in.
How many cars are now in the parking lot?
10 cars

8 + 2 = 10

Cross out the extra information. Then solve.

1. Sally found 8 shells. Trudy found 7 shells. ~~They put the shells in 2 buckets.~~ How many shells did they find?
15 shells
8 + 7 = 15

2. There were 6 children playing a video game. ~~3 children wore green shirts.~~ 5 more children joined them. Now how many children are playing?
11 children
6 + 5 = 11

3. ~~2 children were on line to buy tickets.~~ Mike used 5 tickets for the roller coaster. He used 9 tickets for the rocket. How many tickets did Mike use?
14 tickets
5 + 9 = 14

4. 6 children wore red shirts. 9 children wore red shirts. ~~Mr. Hull wore a green shirt.~~ How many children wore red shirts?
15 children
6 + 9 = 15

2 Teach

Develop Skills and Concepts Tell students a story of having 8 days off from school for vacation and then 2 snow days off. Tell students that 16 students built snowmen while off from school. Ask what operation should be used to find how many days the school was closed for vacation and weather conditions. (addition) Ask, *Is there any extra information in the story that will not help you solve the problem?* (Sixteen students built snowmen.) Have a student write a number sentence to solve the problem on the board. (8 + 2) Have students check to see if the problem is written correctly to answer the question and then have a student solve the problem. (10 days)

3 Practice

Using page 49 Have students look at the example at the top of the page.

- Now apply the four-step plan. For SEE, ask, *What are you asked to do?* (find how many cars are in the parking lot) Then, *What information is given?* (Eight cars are in the parking lot; six of the cars are green; two more cars drive into the parking lot.) Ask students, *Is there any information that will not help you solve the problem? If so, cross it out.* (Six of the cars are green.) Have students trace over the cross out that is over the second sentence. For PLAN, ask students how they will solve the problem. (add 8 and 2) For DO, have students add 8 and 2. (10) For CHECK, have students check that they used only relevant information. Ask, *What do 8 and 2 stand for in this problem?* (Eight cars were in the parking lot; two more cars drove in.) Ask, *Do these help you answer the question?* (yes; we want to know how many cars are in the parking lot.)

Cross out the extra information. Then solve.

1. There are 7 dogs on the grass.
~~There are 3 orange cats.~~
5 more dogs ran onto the grass.
How many dogs are on the grass?
7 + 5 = 12
12 dogs

2. Doug used 5 apples and 8 bananas in a fruit salad.
~~He put the fruit in 2 bowls.~~
How many pieces of fruit did he use?
5 + 8 = 13
13 pieces of fruit

3. Lauren ate 9 crackers.
Chris ate 7 crackers.
~~Pedro ate 6 hamburgers.~~
How many crackers did they eat?
9 + 7 = 16
16 crackers

4. ~~Doyle counted 6 green cars.~~
He counted 4 blue trucks and 8 red trucks.
How many trucks did Doyle count?
4 + 8 = 12
12 trucks

5. Chen built 8 sandcastles.
~~Mary dug 3 holes in the sand.~~
Leo built 8 sandcastles.
How many sandcastles did they build?
8 + 8 = 16
16 sandcastles

6. Larry has 9 keys.
~~He has 4 books.~~
He gets 8 more keys.
How many keys does Larry have?
9 + 8 = 17
17 keys

- Have students find the extraneous information in Exercise 1 and cross it out. (They put the shells in 2 buckets.) Then, have students complete the exercises independently.

Using page 50 Have students look at Exercise 1. Read the problem aloud while students read along. Ask students to find the extra information. (There are 3 orange cats.) Have them cross out the second sentence. Review the steps that students will use to solve the problem. Have students complete the exercises independently.

4 Assess

Have students write story problems that contain too much information. Then, have them exchange their problems with each other to solve.

For Mixed Abilities

Common Errors • Intervention

If students are having a hard time deciding which piece of information is extra, try writing each sentence of the problem on a separate index card. Then, you can group together the information cards and question card that refer to the same topic. See which card gets removed.

Enrichment • Number Sense

1. Tell students to write an addition word problem of two or three addends and present the problem to other students.
2. Have students find the total number of pets owned by 5 classmates.

More to Explore • Number Sense

Draw a large circle on the board with smaller circles around it to look like a Ferris wheel. Randomly place numbers 1 through 9 in the smaller circles and one number in the center of the wheel. Ask students to see how quickly they can go around the Ferris wheel by adding the middle number to each number around the edge. Students may take turns and time themselves. Repeat and change the number in the center. This activity could also be used for practicing subtraction.

page 51

Items	Objectives
1–2	To review addition through sums of 18 (see pages 35–44)
3	To review money sums through 18¢ (see pages 47–48)
4	To add three 1-digit numbers for sums through 18 (see pages 45–46)
5–6	To solve problems with sums through 18 (see pages 49–50)

Alternate Chapter Test

You may wish to use the Alternate Chapter Test on page 317 of this book for further review and assessment.

Name ______________________

Add.

1

9	6	7	6	8	6	9
+ 6	+ 6	+ 4	+ 7	+ 6	+ 5	+ 9
15	12	11	13	14	11	18

2

8	2	3	8	7	8	3
+ 3	+ 8	+ 9	+ 8	+ 5	+ 4	+ 7
11	10	12	16	12	12	10

3

8¢	4¢	5¢	7¢	5¢	7¢	9¢
+ 7¢	+ 9¢	+ 8¢	+ 9¢	+ 9¢	+ 7¢	+ 8¢
15¢	13¢	13¢	16¢	14¢	14¢	17¢

Add.

4

2	5	8	9	7	6	3
3	4	2	5	3	4	4
+ 4	+ 7	+ 6	+ 1	+ 7	+ 8	+ 7
9	16	16	15	17	18	14

Solve.

5 Casey bought one flower for 9¢ and another flower for 7¢. How much did both cost?

16¢

9 ¢
+ 7 ¢
16 ¢

6 There were 7 girls and 8 boys at Sandy's party. How many children were at the party?

15 children

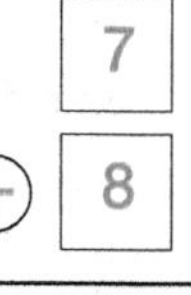

7
+ 8
15

Add or subtract.

1. $12 - 3 =$ 9 $12 - 8 =$ 4 $11 - 2 =$ 9
2. $11 - 5 =$ 6 $11 - 4 =$ 7 $8 + 4 =$ 12
3. $5 + 5 =$ 10 $12 - 5 =$ 7 $3 + 8 =$ 11

Add.

4.

7	8	9	6	7	8	7
+ 7	+ 8	+ 9	+ 7	+ 8	+ 9	+ 6
14	16	18	13	15	17	13

5.

8	9	9	6	8	9	7
+ 7	+ 8	+ 7	+ 8	+ 5	+ 6	+ 9
15	17	16	14	13	15	16

6.

				5	3	6
9	5	6	5	3	2	4
+ 5	+ 8	+ 9	+ 7	+ 5	+ 7	+ 7
14	13	15	12	13	12	17

Solve.

7. There were 12 frogs. 7 hopped away. How many frogs were left?

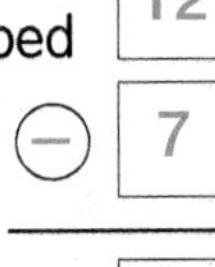

12 − 7 = 5

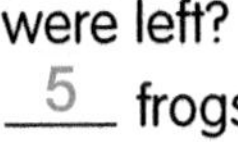

5 frogs

8. Bruce saved 9¢ on Monday and 5¢ on Friday. How much money did he save?

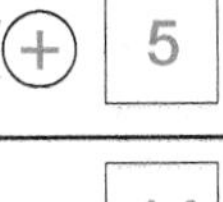

9¢ + 5¢ = 14¢

14¢

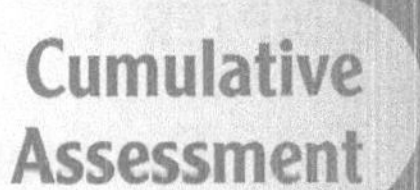

Cumulative Assessment

page 52

Items	Objectives
1–7	To review addition and subtraction facts with sums and minuends through 18 (see pages 3–12, 17–20, 23–26, 35–38, 41–46)
8	To review money sums through 14¢ (see pages 39–40)

4-1 Review Subtracting From 12 and Less

pages 53–54

1 Getting Started

Objective
- To subtract minuends through 12

Materials
12 counters

Warm Up • Mental Math
Ask students which is less.

1. 1 ten 1 one or 9 (9)
2. 26 or 21 (21)
3. 11 or 13 (11)
4. 2 + 9 or 3 + 5 (3 + 5)
5. 9 − 2 or 8 (9 − 2)
6. 17 − 9 or 4 + 3 (4 + 3)

Warm Up • Pencil and Paper
Have students lay out 10 counters and take away 9. Ask how many are left. (1) Have students write the number sentence. (10 − 9 = 1) Repeat to find other facts for the minuend 10. Have students write each number sentence. Repeat for the minuends 6 and 8.

Name ______________________

Chapter 4

Subtraction Facts Through 18

Lesson 4-1

How many are there in all? 12
How many are crossed out? 4
How many are left? 8
12 − 4 = 8

Subtract.

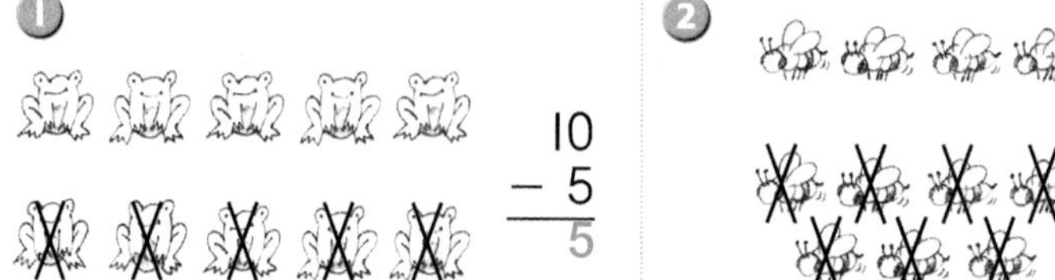

1	10 − 5	5
2	11 − 7	4

3	12 − 3 = 9	11 − 5 = 6	10 − 1 = 9	12 − 6 = 6	11 − 2 = 9	10 − 5 = 5	11 − 9 = 2
4	10 − 2 = 8	12 − 7 = 5	9 − 4 = 5	10 − 6 = 4	11 − 3 = 8	10 − 8 = 2	12 − 9 = 3
5	11 − 4 = 7	9 − 1 = 8	10 − 4 = 6	12 − 8 = 4	11 − 8 = 3	12 − 5 = 7	10 − 3 = 7

---

2 Teach

Develop Skills and Concepts To show that subtraction is the inverse of addition, tell students that we want to find all the numbers that are addends for the sum of 11 and then write the related subtraction facts. Have students lay out 11 counters, remove 9, and tell how many are left. (2) Have a student write the problem on the board. (11 − 9 = 2) Have a student write the two addends of 11. (9, 2) Follow this procedure for all other addends of 11. Repeat for addends of 12.

3 Practice

Using page 53 Have a student read the first question in the example on the top of the page and tell the number of objects there are in all. (12) Have students write the answer. Continue for the next two questions and then have students trace the 12 and 4 and write the answer to the problem. (8) Remind students that we use the minus sign to mean take-away subtraction. Have students complete the page independently.

Using page 54 Work through the first exercise in the first two tables with students. Remind students to subtract in each problem on this page. Have students complete the tables and rows of problems independently.

Complete each table.

1

Subtract 3.	
9	6
7	4
12	9
10	7
8	5
11	8

2

Subtract 4.	
11	7
8	4
4	0
10	6
12	8
9	5

3

Subtract 5.	
12	7
7	2
9	4
11	6
8	3
10	5

4

Subtract 6.	
7	1
9	3
6	0
10	4
8	2
11	5

Subtract.

5

8	9	10	11	9	12	11
− 7	− 2	− 9	− 7	− 9	− 9	− 2
1	7	1	4	0	3	9

6

10	12	8	9	10	12	11
− 1	− 8	− 0	− 7	− 2	− 6	− 9
9	4	8	2	8	6	2

7

9	10	12	11	9	10	7
− 8	− 7	− 7	− 8	− 1	− 8	− 4
1	3	5	3	8	2	3

4 Assess

Draw the following table on the board:

Subtract 7.	
12	
9	
7	
11	
8	
10	

Have students copy the table and complete it with the correct answers. (5, 2, 0, 4, 1, 3)

For Mixed Abilities

Common Errors • Intervention

Some students may need practice with subtraction. Have them work with partners and subtraction fact cards. Have students group the cards into those facts related to doubles, such as $6 - 3 = 3$, $8 - 4 = 4$, and so on, and facts related to sums of 9, 10, 11, or 12 like $9 - 4 = 5$.

Enrichment • Number Sense

1. Tell students to fold a sheet of paper in half and draw a picture on one half to show an addition fact. Using the same numbers, they should illustrate a related subtraction fact on the other half of the paper. Then, have them write each fact under its picture.
2. Tell students to work in pairs using addition and subtraction fact cards for sums of 9 through 12. They should pick two cards and tell if the facts are related.
3. Tell students to write a story to tell about a dozen eggs and how some were broken.

More to Explore • Classification

Give students a sheet of paper with 12 circles on it. Ask them to design sets that have three members each, and that have these properties:

3 sets of the same color

3 sets of the same shapes

2 sets of the same color, different shapes

2 sets of the same shapes, different colors

2 sets of different shapes and different colors

Then, ask students questions such as the following: Do you need to use all 12 circles to complete the list of properties? Can you make a set that is not identical to one of the sets but has size, shape, and color in common? Can you make a set that has an element in common with all the other sets?

4-2 Subtracting From 14 and Less

pages 55–56

1 Getting Started

Objective

- To subtract from minuends through 14

Materials

14 counters; *subtraction fact cards for minuends through 12

Warm Up • Mental Math

Tell students to name three addends whose sum is

1. 14
2. 15
3. 17
4. 11
5. 18
6. 12
7. 9
8. 13

Warm Up • Number Sense

Have students give answers for subtraction facts for the minuend 11 and then place the cards in order along the chalk tray from the greatest answer to the least. Repeat for the minuend 12.

Name ______________________ **Lesson 4-2**

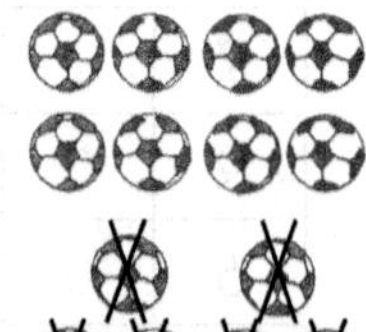

How many are there in all? 14
How many are crossed out? 6
How many are left? 8

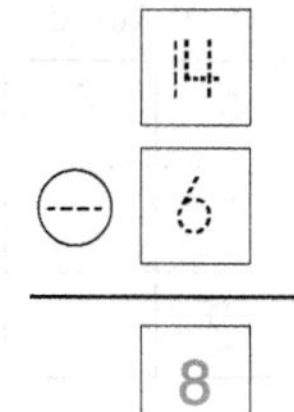

Subtract.

1. 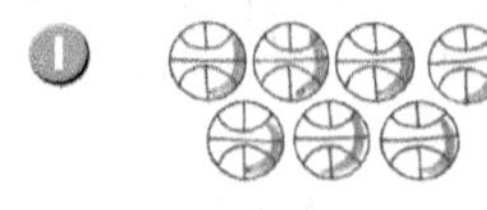 

$$\begin{array}{r} 12 \\ -\ 5 \\ \hline 7 \end{array}$$

2. 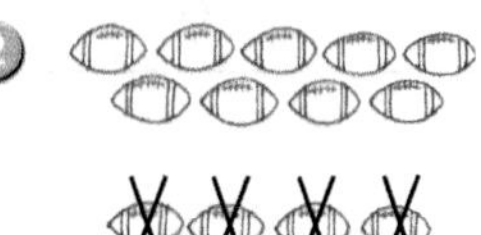

$$\begin{array}{r} 13 \\ -\ 4 \\ \hline 9 \end{array}$$

3. $\begin{array}{r} 13 \\ -\ 4 \\ \hline 9 \end{array}$ $\begin{array}{r} 13 \\ -\ 9 \\ \hline 4 \end{array}$ $\begin{array}{r} 14 \\ -\ 6 \\ \hline 8 \end{array}$ $\begin{array}{r} 14 \\ -\ 8 \\ \hline 6 \end{array}$ $\begin{array}{r} 11 \\ -\ 5 \\ \hline 6 \end{array}$ $\begin{array}{r} 13 \\ -\ 8 \\ \hline 5 \end{array}$ $\begin{array}{r} 14 \\ -\ 7 \\ \hline 7 \end{array}$

4. $\begin{array}{r} 13 \\ -\ 6 \\ \hline 7 \end{array}$ $\begin{array}{r} 13 \\ -\ 7 \\ \hline 6 \end{array}$ $\begin{array}{r} 12 \\ -\ 5 \\ \hline 7 \end{array}$ $\begin{array}{r} 12 \\ -\ 7 \\ \hline 5 \end{array}$ $\begin{array}{r} 13 \\ -\ 5 \\ \hline 8 \end{array}$ $\begin{array}{r} 14 \\ -\ 5 \\ \hline 9 \end{array}$ $\begin{array}{r} 14 \\ -\ 9 \\ \hline 5 \end{array}$

Solve.

5. There are 14 bears asleep. 6 wake up. How many are still asleep?
8 bears

6. There were 13 deer grazing. 5 went to drink water. How many were still grazing?
8 deer

2 Teach

Develop Skills and Concepts Tell students that we want to find all the numbers that are addends for the sum of 13, and then write the related subtraction facts. Allow students to use counters to develop each fact. Have students write two subtraction sentences for each pair of addends for the sum of 13. (13 – 9 = 4, 13 – 4 = 9, and so on) Repeat for addends of 14.

3 Practice

Using page 55 Have a student read the first question in the example at the top of the page and tell the answer. (14) Tell students to write the answer after the question. Repeat for the next two questions. Ask students what operation is necessary in this problem. (subtraction) Have students trace the minus sign in the exercise and then trace 14 and 6 and write the answer. Have students complete the next two exercises independently.

- Have students read the story problems at the bottom of the page and tell what operation is needed in each. (subtraction) Remind students to write out and solve the problem for each and then record the answer in the solution statement. Have students complete the page independently.

Using page 56 Ask students how many would be left from 13 if 4 were taken away. (9) Have students trace the 9 in the first wheel. Go through another example with students if necessary. In the next section, have students subtract 3 from 10 in the first table and trace the 7. Remind students to subtract the number at the top. Tell students to decide which operation to do in each of the story problems before beginning to solve the problem. Have students complete the page independently.

Complete each wheel.

1

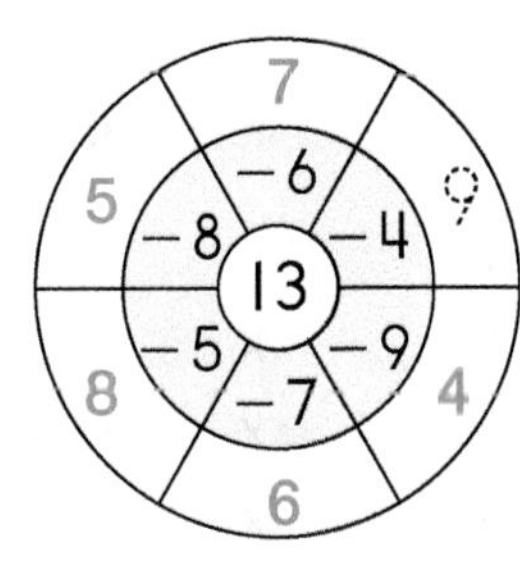

2

Complete each table.

3

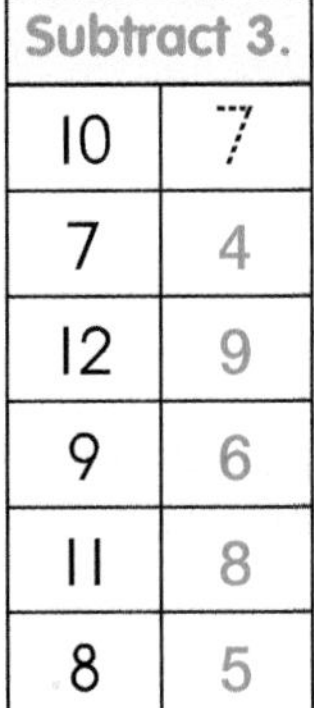

Subtract 3.	
10	7
7	4
12	9
9	6
11	8
8	5

4

Subtract 4.	
11	7
13	9
9	5
8	4
12	8
10	6

5

Subtract 5.	
10	5
12	7
11	6
14	9
13	8
9	4

6

Subtract 6.	
10	4
13	7
11	5
12	6
14	8
9	3

Solve.

7 Bev puts 13 balls on a shelf. 7 roll off. How many are left on the shelf?

__6__ balls

8 Janet picks 14 flowers. She gives 7 of them to Beth. How many does Janet have left?

__7__ flowers

4 Assess

Tell students to write all subtraction facts for minuends through 14 that have an answer of 9.
(14 − 5, 13 − 4, 12 − 3, 11 − 2, 10 − 1)

For Mixed Abilities

Common Errors • Intervention

To practice subtraction from minuends through 14, have students work with partners and subtraction fact cards. For each card, have them take turns writing the entire fact with the difference and then writing the related addition fact.

Enrichment • Number Sense

1. Have students write and solve a problem that tells how they would find the number of strawberry plants they have already planted if they started with 14 and have 6 left.
2. Tell students to draw a picture that shows that at 4:00, there were 13 children at a party. At 6:00, there were 7 children, and at 7:00, there were only 2 children left. They should then write two subtraction problems to explain their work.

More to Explore • Geometry

Make a master set of different-colored geometric shapes in two different sizes. You could use construction paper or posterboard in blue, red, and yellow. Make patterns of large and small circles, triangles, squares, rectangles, and hexagons. Have students trace the large and small patterns onto colored paper, cutting out a large and small set in each color. Start the activities by first having students sort the pieces by size, shape, and then color. Then, have students find a set of pieces that are the same size and color but different shapes. Ask them what other sets they can find and describe, and share them with the class.

ESL/ELL STRATEGIES

Ask volunteers to explain the meaning of the terms *crossed out*, *woke up*, and *grazing* or explain them yourself. *Crossed out* means "put an X through it," *woke up* means "stopped sleeping," and *grazing* means "eating grass."

4-3 Problem Solving: Make and Use a Line Plot

pages 57–58

1 Getting Started

Objectives
- To make and use a line plot to answer questions
- To add and subtract with sums and minuends through 19

Vocabulary
line plot

Warm Up • Mental Math
Have students find the sum or difference.

1. 9 + 5 (14)
2. 8 + 7 (15)
3. 6 + 6 (12)
4. 17 − 8 (9)
5. 14 − 7 (7)
6. 13 − 5 (8)

Warm Up • Pencil and Paper
Write the following exercises on the board:

7 + 6 = (13)	12 − 7 = (5)
4 + 6 = (10)	15 − 8 = (7)
10 − 3 = (7)	6 + 5 = (11)
9 − 4 = (5)	5 + 7 = (12)
9 + 8 = (17)	14 − 5 = (9)

Have students copy and complete each exercise.

Name ______

A line plot is used to organize information. Each X is equal to 1.

This line plot shows how many pets the children in Mr. Jones's class have. How many children have 3 pets?

Number of Pets Children Have

Number of Pets	0	1	2	3
Number of Children	X X X X	X X X X X	X X X X	X X X

Count the number of Xs to find how many children have 3 pets.

There are 3 children who have 3 pets.

Use the line plot above to answer each question.

1. How many children do not have pets?

   4 children

2. How many pets do the most children have?

   1 pet

3. Make a tally from the line plot.

Number of Pets	Tally of Students	Number of Students
0	IIII	4
1	𝍸	5
2	IIII	4
3	III	3

2 Teach

Develop Skills and Concepts On the board, create a line plot with the categories Vanilla, Chocolate, and Strawberry. Tell students that they are going to vote on their favorite flavor of ice cream. Have students place an X in the graph above their favorite flavor. Then, explain that a line plot, like a tally table, is a way to organize information.

3 Practice

Using page 57 Have students look at the line plot. Ask students what represents one item. (X)

- Now, apply the four-step plan to the example. For SEE, ask, *What are you being asked to do?* (find how many children have 3 pets) Then, *What information is given?* (a line plot with the numbers of children that have 0 to 3 pets) For PLAN, ask students which column should they read. (3 pets) For DO, have students answer the question. For CHECK, have them count the Xs above 3. (3) Ask, *Does this match the number that you wrote?* (yes) Have students complete the page independently.
- For Exercise 3, ask, *How do you represent 1 by using a tally?* (|). Then, *What represents 5?* (𝍸) Have students complete the tally table.

Using page 58 Have students look at the tally table at the top of the page. Ask students for the title. (Number of Brothers We Have) Then, ask them, *What does each tally represent?* (1 student) Have students complete the line plot. Ask students to check that the number of Xs for each category that they drew is equal to the number listed in the tally table. Have students complete Exercise 1 independently.

- For Exercise 2, have students write the number sentence needed to answer what they are being asked. Ask, *How many children have 1 brother?* (8) *How many*

Miss Johnson asked her class how many brothers they each have. The results are shown in the tally table.

Number of Brothers We Have	
Brothers	**Tally**
0	IIII
1	~~IIII~~ III
2	~~IIII~~
3	II

Use the tally table to complete the line plot.

Number of Brothers We Have

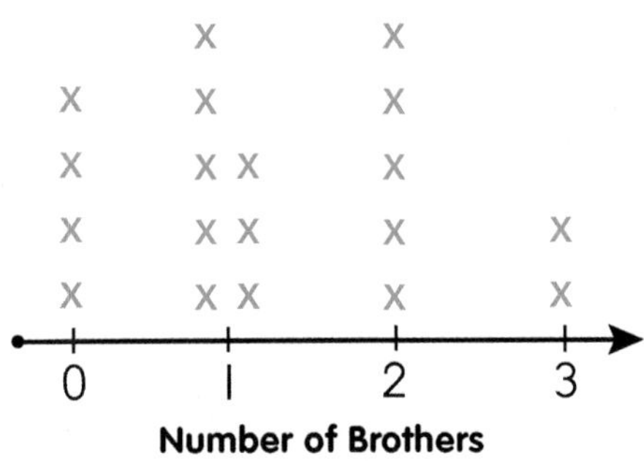

1. How many children have 2 brothers?

   5 children

2. How many more children have 1 brother than 3 brothers?

   6 more children

3. How many brothers do the least number of children have?

   3 brothers

4. How many children are in the class altogether?

   19 children

children have 3 brothers? (2) *What operation do you need to solve the problem?* (subtraction) Have students subtract 2 from 8 to find how many more children have 1 brother than 3 brothers.

- Have students complete Exercises 3 and 4 independently.

4 Assess

Have students work in groups of three. Give groups some red, blue, and green crayons, so that they have ten crayons in all. Have each group create a line plot labeled, "Our Crayons."

For Mixed Abilities

Common Errors • Intervention

If students are having difficulty interpreting the information from the line plot, have them count and record the number for each category beside each column of the line plot.

Enrichment • Statistics

Have students ask ten people what their favorite type of movie is: cartoon, action, comedy, or drama. Then, compile the data to create a class line plot to display the results.

More to Explore • Statistics

Divide the class into groups of three. Tell students to write a number between 1 and 6. Then, have group members share their numbers and create a line plot of the data. After the groups have made their line plots, explain to students that in statistics, the mode is the number that occurs most often in a set, and the range is the difference between the greatest and least numbers. Have students find the mode and the range of their line plots.

4-4 Subtracting From 16 and Less

pages 59–60

1 Getting Started

Objective

- To subtract from minuends through 16

Materials

16 counters

Warm Up • Mental Math

Tell students to name the number that

1. comes after 10, 20, 30 (40)
2. is 2 more than 20 (22)
3. comes before 40 (39)
4. tells today's date
5. comes after 8, 10, 12 (14)
6. is the double of 9 (18)

Warm Up • Number Sense

Have two students hold up ten fingers and match their hands palm to palm. Ask how many more fingers one student is showing than the other. (none) Write **10 − 10 = 0** on the board. Have one student fold down three fingers and match palms with the other student. Ask how many more fingers are extended on one student's hand. (3) Have a student write and solve the subtraction problem on the board. (10 − 3 = 7) Continue for other examples.

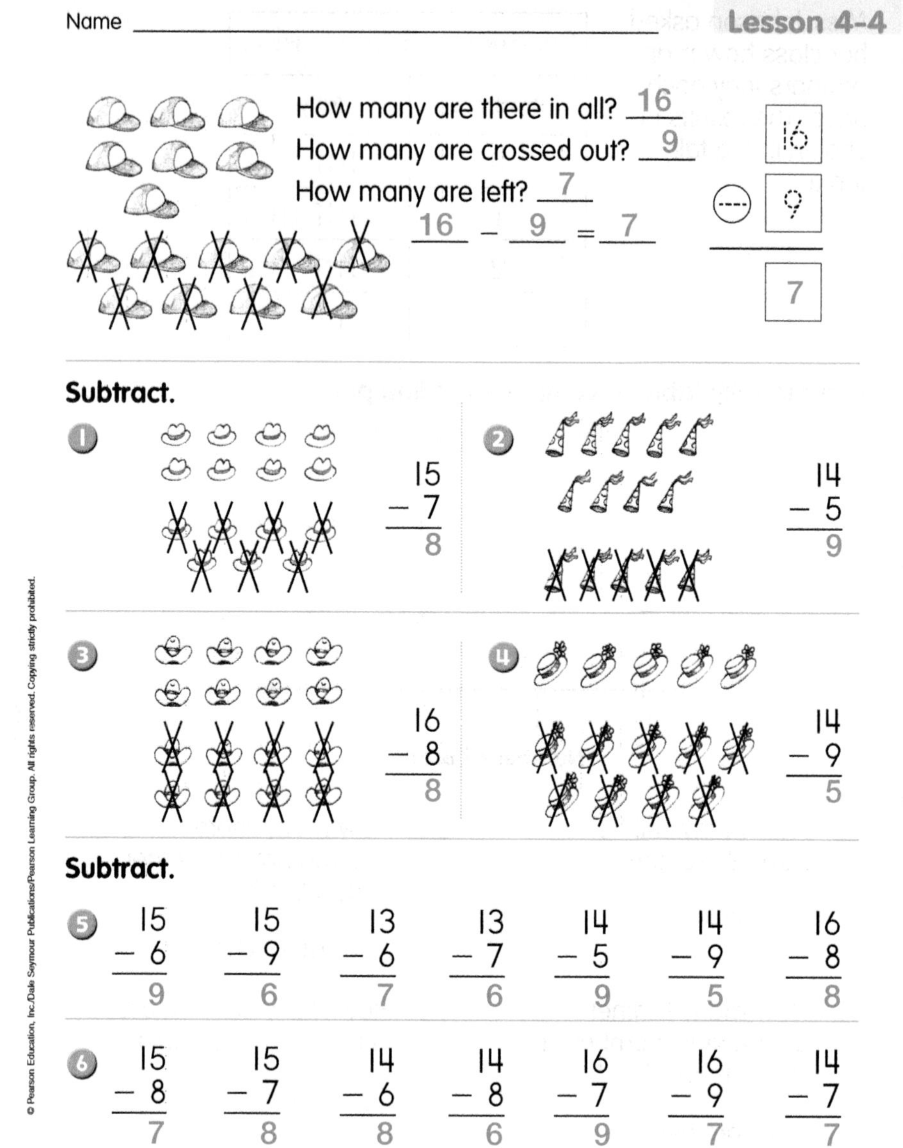

Name ______________________ **Lesson 4-4**

How many are there in all? 16
How many are crossed out? 9
How many are left? 7

16 − 9 = 7

16
− 9
7

Subtract.

1	15 − 7 = 8
2	14 − 5 = 9
3	16 − 8 = 8
4	14 − 9 = 5

Subtract.

5	15 − 6 = 9	15 − 9 = 6	13 − 6 = 7	13 − 7 = 6	14 − 5 = 9	14 − 9 = 5	16 − 8 = 8
6	15 − 8 = 7	15 − 7 = 8	14 − 6 = 8	14 − 8 = 6	16 − 7 = 9	16 − 9 = 7	14 − 7 = 7

Lesson 4-4 • Subtracting From 16 and Less fifty-nine 59

2 Teach

Develop Skills and Concepts Tell students that we want to find all the numbers that are addends for the sum of 15 and then write the related subtraction facts. Allow students to use counters to develop each fact. Have students write two subtraction sentences for each pair of addends for 15. (15 − 9 = 6, 15 − 6 = 9, and so on) Remind students that all addends should be 9 or less. Ask students how many subtraction facts there are for 15. (4) Repeat for addends of 16. Ask students how many subtraction facts there are for 16. (3) Ask students how many more subtraction facts there are for 15 than for 16. (1)

3 Practice

Using page 59 Help students work through the example, crossing out as they count. Have students complete the page independently. Allow use of counters if necessary.

Using page 60 Have students complete the four half-circles independently. Now, have students trace the ring around 12 − 7 in Exercise 5 to show it is a name for the number 5. Ask students if 14 − 5 is a name for 5. (no) Tell students that it is not to be circled. Continue through the next two facts as students see they are both names for 5 and should be circled. Continue for Exercise 6 and then have students complete the page independently.

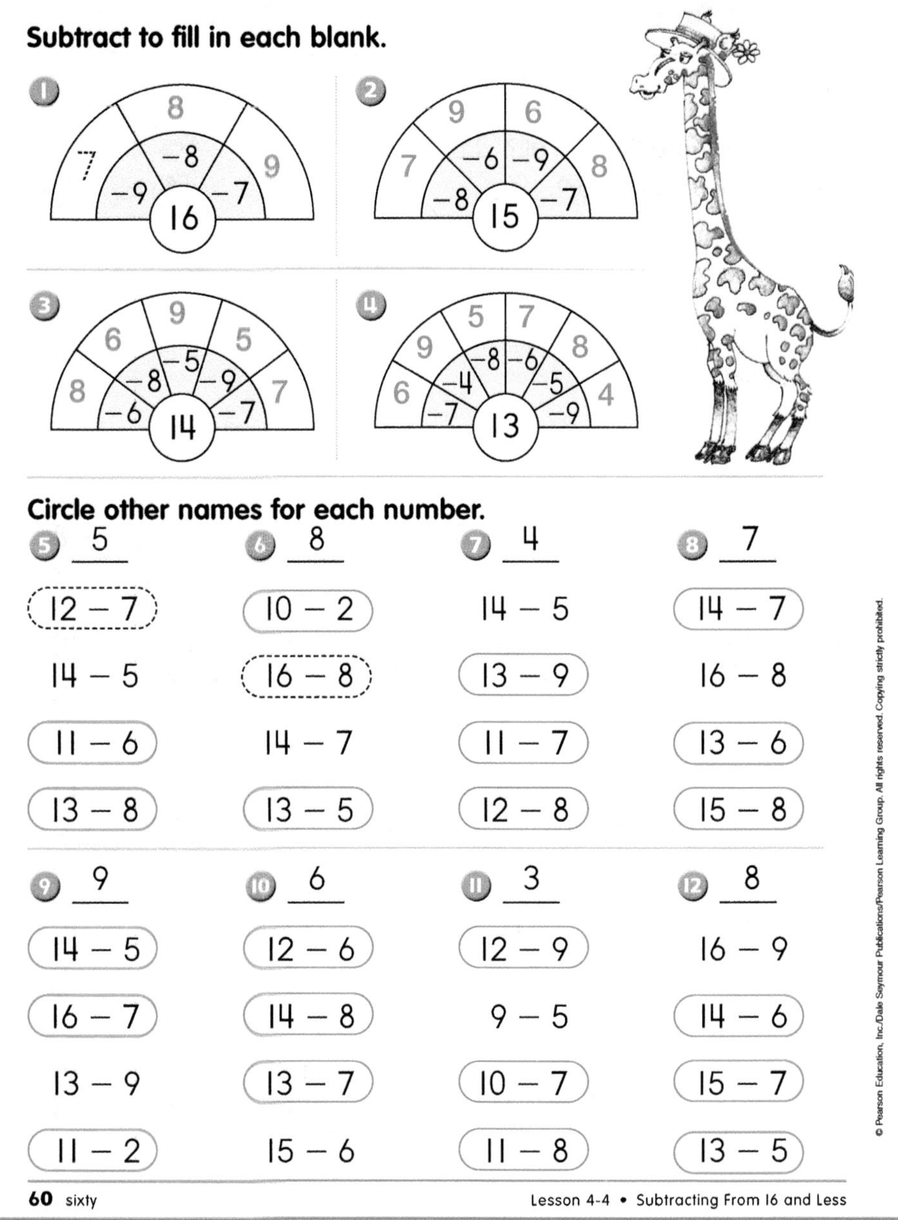

Subtract to fill in each blank.

1. 16: −8 → 8, −9 → 7, −7 → 9
2. 15: −6 → 9, −9 → 6, −8 → 7, −7 → 8
3. 14: −5 → 9, −8 → 6, −9 → 5, −6 → 8, −7 → 7
4. 13: −8 → 5, −6 → 7, −4 → 9, −5 → 8, −7 → 6, −9 → 4

Circle other names for each number.

5. 5	6. 8	7. 4	8. 7
12 − 7	10 − 2	14 − 5	14 − 7
14 − 5	16 − 8	13 − 9	16 − 8
11 − 6	14 − 7	11 − 7	13 − 6
13 − 8	13 − 5	12 − 8	15 − 8

9. 9	10. 6	11. 3	12. 8
14 − 5	12 − 6	12 − 9	16 − 9
16 − 7	14 − 8	9 − 5	14 − 6
13 − 9	13 − 7	10 − 7	15 − 7
11 − 2	15 − 6	11 − 8	13 − 5

4 Assess

Have students write a subtraction story problem. Then, have students switch papers to solve.

For Mixed Abilities

Common Errors • Intervention

Some students may need more practice subtracting from the minuends 15 and 16. Have students work with partners and subtraction fact cards for the minuends 15 and 16. One partner can draw objects to represent the minuend, and the other partner can cross out the number indicated by the subtrahend. Then, each partner should write the fact. Partners can then reverse roles and follow the same procedure for the other facts.

Enrichment • Number Sense

1. Have students use facts for sums and minuends through 16 to write all the names for 9. Tell students that there should be 18 facts.
2. Have students make a half-circle subtraction activity like those on page 60. They should write 11 in the circle and have a friend solve the problems. Tell them to check their friend's work.

More to Explore • Classification

Have students make two circles by cutting two lengths of string 2 feet long and tying the ends. Have students overlap the circles on their desks to form a Venn diagram. Have them practice with buttons or colored shapes, placing sets within the circles.

Demonstrate the property that some sets have elements in common. For example, put all of the yellow pieces in one circle and all of the triangles in another. Have students decide where the yellow triangle will be placed. Let students practice making sets that have elements in common and placing them within the circles.

4-5 Subtracting From 18 and Less

pages 61–62

1 Getting Started

Objective
- To subtract from minuends through 18

Materials
*addition fact cards for sums 12 through 18; 18 counters

Warm Up • Mental Math
Ask students what ordinal number comes after

1. third (fourth)
2. ninth (tenth)
3. first (second)
4. eighth (ninth)
5. seventh (eighth)
6. second (third)
7. fifth (sixth)
8. nineteenth (twentieth)

Warm Up • Number Sense
Show students addition fact cards for sums 12 through 18. Have students give the sums and then put the cards on the chalk tray under the headings of Sums 12 through 14 and Sums 15 through 18.

Name ______________________

How many are there in all? 17

How many flew away? 9

How many are left? 8

17 − 9 = 8

Subtract.

1. 18 − 9 = 9
2. 16 − 8 = 8

3	15 − 9 = 6	12 − 3 = 9	16 − 7 = 9	14 − 9 = 5	15 − 7 = 8	13 − 9 = 4	14 − 5 = 9
4	12 − 7 = 5	17 − 9 = 8	15 − 6 = 9	14 − 6 = 8	12 − 6 = 6	17 − 8 = 9	13 − 5 = 8
5	13 − 8 = 5	12 − 4 = 8	16 − 8 = 8	13 − 4 = 9	17 − 9 = 8	14 − 7 = 7	12 − 8 = 4
6	13 − 6 = 7	14 − 8 = 6	12 − 5 = 7	18 − 9 = 9	13 − 7 = 6	12 − 9 = 3	15 − 8 = 7

2 Teach

Develop Skills and Concepts Have students lay out 18 counters in two groups of 9 or less. Ask students what the addends are. (9, 9) Have a student write the related subtraction fact on the board. (18 − 9 = 9) Students should note that there is only one subtraction fact for 18. Repeat for addends of 17 to show 17 − 9 = 8 and 17 − 8 = 9. Help students to see that basic facts have only 1-digit numbers, so there are only two subtraction facts for 17.

3 Practice

Using page 61 Have students read each question in Exercise 1 and write the answers. Have students decide the operation to be used and trace the sign in the circle. Have students trace and solve the problem. Have students complete the page independently.

Using page 62 Have students complete the page independently.

Subtract.

1.
15	12	14	9	15	12	13
− 9	− 5	− 6	− 9	− 6	− 9	− 5
6	7	8	0	9	3	8

2.
12	17	14	15	12	16	12
− 4	− 8	− 9	− 8	− 6	− 9	− 8
8	9	5	7	6	7	4

3.
10	13	17	12	14	12	16
− 6	− 8	− 9	− 3	− 7	− 7	− 7
4	5	8	9	7	5	9

4.
16	14	15	18	13	14	13
− 8	− 5	− 7	− 9	− 7	− 8	− 6
8	9	8	9	6	6	7

Now Try This!

It's Algebra!

Answer each riddle.

1. When you add me to 5, the sum is 11. Who am I? 6

2. When you double me, the sum is 16. Who am I? 8

3. When you add me to 8, the sum is 17. Who am I? 9

4. When you double me and add 1, you get 13. Who am I? 6

Now Try This! Read the first exercise and have students discuss what is being asked. Ask students what operation is suggested. (addition) Ask students to think of an addition fact that has a 5 and another number for a sum of 11. (5 + 6 = 11) Have students complete the next three exercises independently. Then, discuss the solutions and how they were found.

4 Assess

Tell students that there are 7 days in a week. Then, ask students to write and solve a problem to find out how many more days are in 2 weeks than in 1 week.

For Mixed Abilities

Common Errors • Intervention

Some students may have difficulty with certain subtraction facts. Have them work with partners to practice the subtraction facts. Give each pair of students fact-family cards similar to the one shown below.

17	9
	8

For each such card, the partners should write two addition and two subtraction facts.

9	8	17	17
+ 8	+ 9	− 9	− 8
17	17	8	9

Enrichment • Number Sense

Have students write addition and subtraction problems for sums and minuends through 18 to show all the ways to name 9. Tell students that should be 20 facts.

More to Explore • Application

Bring a stopwatch to school. Discuss with students its use for timing a race. Take students outside and help them measure a distance of 50 yards. Have them line up behind the starting point and tell them they will run a 50-yard dash. Have one student give the "ready, set, go" and time each runner. Have other students take turns writing down the times. When all students have had a chance to run, post the times on a board so the class can compare them. Have students identify the time most frequently run.

ESL/ELL STRATEGIES

Explain that the word *double* means "to add the same number twice." Write this sentence frame on the board: **When you double _____ you get _____.** Ask several students to complete the sentence using different numbers.

4-6 Practice Subtracting From 18 and Less

pages 63–64

1 Getting Started

Objective
- To practice subtraction from minuends through 18

Materials
18 counters

Warm Up • Mental Math
Tell students that Monday is the second day of the week. Then, ask which day is

1. Wednesday (fourth)
2. first (Sunday)
3. third (Tuesday)
4. Saturday (seventh)
5. Thursday (fifth)
6. sixth (Friday)

Warm Up • Number Sense
Organize students into pairs and give each student in the pair counters. Students should use a divider so that they cannot see each other's counters. Tell each student to lay out a subtraction fact for the minuend 12 or more. Have students remove their divider and tell their fact with the answer.

Name ______________________

Subtract.

1

14	13	15	12	11	12	13
− 5	− 8	− 6	− 3	− 5	− 7	− 9
9	5	9	9	6	5	4

2

12	11	16	11	10	12	14
− 4	− 6	− 8	− 2	− 7	− 5	− 7
8	5	8	9	3	7	7

3

13	10	11	13	10	11	16
− 4	− 1	− 7	− 5	− 8	− 3	− 7
9	9	4	8	2	8	9

4

17	12	11	15	10	13	14
− 8	− 6	− 4	− 9	− 2	− 6	− 8
9	6	7	6	8	7	6

Complete each table.

5

Subtract 9.	
11	2
15	6
18	9
13	4
17	8
14	5
16	7

6

Subtract 8.	
11	3
15	7
17	9
14	6
12	4
16	8
13	5

7

Subtract 7.	
13	6
10	3
15	8
12	5
16	9
14	7
11	4

8

Subtract 6.	
9	3
14	8
11	5
12	6
13	7
10	4
15	9

2 Teach

Develop Skills and Concepts Write the following on the board:

Subtract 4.	
8	(4)
12	(8)
(10)	6
13	(9)
(7)	3

Subtract 5.	
11	(6)
14	(9)
(13)	8
10	(5)
(12)	7

Have students complete the tables, using addition or subtraction facts.

3 Practice

Using page 63 Have students complete the page independently.

Using page 64 Ask students what operation they will use in the first two parts of the page. (subtraction) Have students complete the page independently.

Subtract.

1. 11 − 8 = 3   16 − 9 = 7   10 − 6 = 4
2. 10 − 3 = 7   10 − 5 = 5   15 − 8 = 7
3. 14 − 6 = 8   12 − 8 = 4   9 − 9 = 0
4. 18 − 9 = 9   10 − 9 = 1   8 − 5 = 3
5. 10 − 4 = 6   13 − 7 = 6   14 − 9 = 5
6. 12 − 9 = 3   9 − 3 = 6   9 − 0 = 9
7. 15 − 7 = 8   17 − 9 = 8   11 − 9 = 2

Complete each wheel.

8.

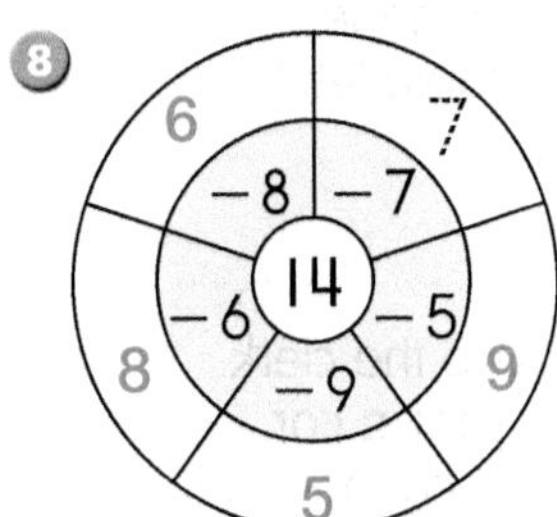

9.

Now Try This!

Write in the correct sign. It's Algebra!

1. 13 (−) 6 = 7   16 (−) 8 = 8   8 (+) 5 = 13
2. 9 (+) 9 = 18   13 (−) 7 = 6   11 (−) 5 = 6
3. 8 (+) 8 = 16   5 (+) 9 = 14   12 (−) 6 = 6
4. 17 (−) 9 = 8   7 (+) 2 = 9   14 (−) 5 = 9

Now Try This! Tell students to write a plus or minus sign in each number sentence to make it true. Have students trace the minus sign in the first exercise and read it to tell if it is true. (yes) Ask if a plus sign would make the exercise true. (no) Ask why. (13 + 6 would not be 7) Remind students to check each exercise to be sure it is true. Have students complete the activity independently.

It's Algebra! The concepts in this activity prepare students for algebra.

4 Assess

Have students write a subtraction story problem comparing two numbers. Have students switch problems with a classmate and solve that problem.

For Mixed Abilities

Common Errors • Intervention

Some students may need more practice with certain subtraction facts. Have them work in pairs. Give each pair two cards on which a number is written, such as shown below.

7	8

For each pair of cards, the pair of students writes four facts.

$$\begin{array}{r}7\\+8\\\hline 15\end{array}\quad\begin{array}{r}8\\+7\\\hline 15\end{array}\quad\begin{array}{r}15\\-8\\\hline 7\end{array}\quad\begin{array}{r}15\\-7\\\hline 8\end{array}$$

Enrichment • Number Sense

1. Tell students to make a table with **Subtract** at the top. Have them write minuends down the left side. On the right side, tell them to write numbers to show what would be left if the secret number were subtracted from each minuend. Have students trade with a classmate and figure out the secret number.
2. Tell students to find this mystery number: If it is doubled, has 7 subtracted from it, and then has 4 added to it, the number will equal 13. Hint: Start with 13 and work backward. (8)

More to Explore • Number Sense

Fill containers with small items such as counters, buttons, beads, dried peas, small toys, etc. Place the containers in various locations around the room. Give each pair of students a card with a numerical value printed on it; examples include: less than 8, more than 50, between 25 and 30. Have students look for the container having their set number, then count the items to check. Tell them to label each container with its identifying card. As a conclusion, students can arrange the containers in order from the least to greatest numbers.

4-7 Subtracting From 18¢ and Less

pages 65–66

1 Getting Started

Objective
- To solve subtraction word problems for minuends through 18¢

Materials
objects priced through 9¢; 3 real or play nickels; 18 real or play pennies

Warm Up • Mental Math
Have students tell the tens and ones in the following numbers:

1. 78 (7 tens 8 ones)
2. 46 (4 tens 6 ones)
3. 99 (9 tens 9 ones)
4. 65 (6 tens 5 ones)
5. 80 (8 tens 0 ones)
6. 29 (2 tens 9 ones)
7. 35 (3 tens 5 ones)

Warm Up • Number Sense
Have students lay out 2 nickels and tell the total amount. (10¢) Have students add another nickel and count by fives to find the sum. (15¢) Have students find other sums of money made with combinations of nickels and pennies through 18¢.

Name ______________________ Lesson 4-7

Solve.

7¢ 9¢ 8¢ 5¢ 6¢

1. Carlos had 15¢. He bought a bear. How much money is left? 9 ¢
2. A truck costs 9 ¢. A ring costs 7 ¢. How much more does the truck cost? 2 ¢
3. Joan had 17¢. She bought a truck. How much money is left? 8¢
4. Donna had 15¢. She bought a train. How much money does she have left? 7¢
5. Chuck gave the clerk 10¢ to pay for a ring. How much change did he get? 3¢
6. Marge gave the clerk 10¢ to pay for a car. How much change did she get? 5¢
7. Dorothy had 18¢. She bought a truck. How much does she have left? 9¢
8. Cal had 13¢. He bought a bear. How much does he have left? 7¢

2 Teach

Develop Skills and Concepts Have students lay out 18¢. Show students an object priced at 9¢ and ask how much money they would have left if they bought the item. (9¢) Have a student write and solve the subtraction problem on the board. (18¢ − 9¢ = 9¢) Repeat for other amounts and other priced objects. Show students two objects priced at 9¢ and 8¢. Ask students how to find how much more the 9¢ object costs than the 8¢ object. (subtract) Have a student write and solve the problem. (9¢ − 8¢ = 1¢) Repeat for more comparisons of costs.

- Ask students to write a problem to tell how much change they would receive if an item costs 6¢ and they gave the clerk 10¢. (10¢ − 6¢ = 4¢) Now, show students two objects priced at 8¢ and 6¢ and ask how to find their total cost. (add) Have a student write and solve the problem. (8¢ + 6¢ = 14¢) Repeat for more addition problems of two prices.

3 Practice

Using page 65 Have students tell the name and price of each item at the top of the page. Help students solve the first exercise. Remind students to first decide which operation to use. Remind them to use cent signs and operation signs and to write their answer in the solution statement. Have students complete the page independently. Then, discuss each exercise and talk through its solution.

Using page 66 Remind students that they have done this first activity before, but now the cent sign has been added. Help students complete Exercise 1 and then have students complete the rest of the page independently.

Circle other names for each amount.

1 7¢	2 5¢	3 4¢	4 6¢
16¢ − 9¢	12¢ − 7¢	11¢ − 7¢	11¢ − 6¢
12¢ − 5¢	13¢ − 6¢	13¢ − 9¢	14¢ − 8¢
13¢ − 8¢	14¢ − 9¢	10¢ − 6¢	13¢ − 7¢
10¢ − 3¢	10¢ − 5¢	12¢ − 7¢	12¢ − 6¢

Subtract.

5	16¢ − 8¢ = 8¢	15¢ − 6¢ = 9¢	14¢ − 7¢ = 7¢	13¢ − 4¢ = 9¢	15¢ − 7¢ = 8¢	17¢ − 9¢ = 8¢
6	14¢ − 5¢ = 9¢	17¢ − 8¢ = 9¢	13¢ − 5¢ = 8¢	15¢ − 8¢ = 7¢	12¢ − 3¢ = 9¢	14¢ − 6¢ = 8¢
7	16¢ − 7¢ = 9¢	12¢ − 4¢ = 8¢	11¢ − 5¢ = 6¢	18¢ − 9¢ = 9¢	12¢ − 8¢ = 4¢	15¢ − 9¢ = 6¢

Now Try This!

1 

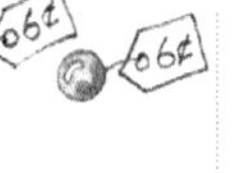

How much more do two marbles cost than one ball?

5¢

2 Linda wants to buy a fish for 15¢. She has 8¢. How much more money does she need?

7¢

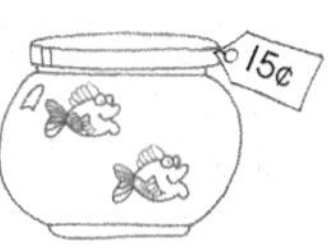

Now Try This! Draw two kites on the board and write 8¢ under each to show their costs. Draw a piece of candy priced at 7¢. Ask a student to write and solve a problem on the board to show the total cost of two kites. (8¢ + 8¢ = 16¢) Ask students how they could find out how much more two kites would cost than the one piece of candy. (subtract) Have a student write and solve the problem on the board. (16¢ − 7¢ = 9¢) Discuss with the students how to solve each of the exercises and then have students complete them independently.

4 Assess

Give each student 12 pennies and an object with a price tag between 3¢ and 9¢. Ask students how many pennies they would have left over if they bought the object.

For Mixed Abilities

Common Errors • Intervention

For students who need practice adding and subtracting with money, have them work with partners and pennies to model each problem. One partner should read the problem aloud and use the pennies to model it. The other partner should write and solve the addition or subtraction fact that matches the first partner's action.

Enrichment • Number Sense

1. Tell students to draw the change that they would receive from 18¢ if they bought gum for 5¢ and a toy for 8¢.
2. Ask students how much change they would get from 50¢ if they bought items costing 2¢, 11¢, 5¢, 9¢, and 3¢. (20¢)

More to Explore • Logic

Play the game Guess Who's Missing. Write the names of all the students and the teacher on small pieces of paper and put them in a bag. One student is picked to be the Witness, and another is called Detective. The Witness draws a name out of the bag and keeps the name secret from everyone. The Witness then gives the Detective clues that will point to the Missing Person. For example, the person is not an adult, the person was last seen wearing tennis shoes, the person is female. As each clue is given, the Detective sorts out the groups of possible missing persons. As the subsets get smaller and sets are eliminated, the clues will be more specific: the person has brown hair and blue eyes. Eventually, the Detective will be able to find the Missing Person, and reveal the name that the Witness has drawn.

Chapter 4 Test

page 67

Items Objectives

1–6, 8 To review subtraction facts with minuends through 18 (see pages 53–56, 59–64)

7 To subtract from minuends through 18¢ (see pages 65–66)

Alternate Chapter Test

You may wish to use the Alternate Chapter Test on page 318 of this book for further review and assessment.

Name ______________________

Chapter 4 Test

Subtract.

1.

10 − 7 = 3	13 − 5 = 8	12 − 3 = 9	15 − 6 = 9	8 − 0 = 8	13 − 4 = 9	14 − 7 = 7

2.

14 − 6 = 8	11 − 5 = 6	13 − 7 = 6	16 − 8 = 8	15 − 9 = 6	13 − 8 = 5	15 − 7 = 8

3.

17 − 8 = 9	13 − 9 = 4	9 − 9 = 0	16 − 7 = 9	14 − 8 = 6	11 − 4 = 7	12 − 7 = 5

4.

18 − 9 = 9	14 − 5 = 9	16 − 9 = 7	15 − 8 = 7	13 − 6 = 7	14 − 9 = 5	17 − 9 = 8

Solve.

5. Brenda saw 14 lightning bugs. Elmer saw 9. How many more lightning bugs did Brenda see?

   5 lightning bugs

6. Matt has 17 marbles. Paul has 9 marbles. How many more marbles does Matt have?

   8 marbles

7. Sonja had 15¢. She bought a balloon for 8¢. How much money does she have left?

   7¢

8. Roy counted 16 crows. 8 of them flew away. How many are left?

   8 crows

Add or subtract.

1

7	9	6	7	4	8	9
+ 0	+ 1	− 5	− 5	− 0	+ 2	+ 7
7	10	1	2	4	10	16

2

9	10	8	10	7	9	7
− 3	− 5	− 7	− 9	+ 3	+ 5	+ 6
6	5	1	1	10	14	13

3

11	12	8	9	8	13	14
− 4	− 7	+ 4	+ 3	+ 8	− 5	− 7
7	5	12	12	16	8	7

4

15	7	8	9	16	17	15
− 6	+ 9	+ 6	+ 9	− 7	− 9	− 8
9	16	14	18	9	8	7

Solve.

5 Nancy counted 9 deer and 5 wild turkeys. How many animals did she count?

14 animals

6 Bert picked 11 tulips. Fay picked 8 tulips. How many more tulips did Bert pick?

3 tulips

7 Bill ran 7 blocks. Then he ran 6 blocks more. How many blocks did Bill run?

13 blocks

8 There are 12 dogs in the park. 7 dogs run home. How many dogs are left in the park?

5 dogs

Cumulative Assessment

page 68

Items	Objectives
1–8	To review adding and subtracting with sums and minuends through 18 (see pages 3–12, 17–20, 23–28, 35–44, 53–56, 59–64)

5-1 Numbers Through 100

pages 69–70

1 Getting Started

Objective

- To read and write numbers through 100

Materials

counting sticks; rubber bands; base-ten blocks

Warm Up • Mental Math

Ask students how many tens and ones are in the number that comes

1. before 20 (1, 9)
2. after 82 (8, 3)
3. after 89 (9, 0)
4. before 50 (4, 9)
5. next in the sequence: 45, 50, 55 (6, 0)
6. before 11 (1, 0)
7. next in the sequence: 77, 78, 79 (8, 0)

Warm Up • Number Sense

Write **12 = 10 + 2** on the board and ask students how many tens are in the number. (1) Ask how many ones. (2) Have students tell a basic addition fact that has a sum of 12. (8 + 4, 9 + 3, and so on) Continue for numbers 11 through 18.

Name ____________________

Chapter 5

Numbers Through Hundreds

Lesson 5-I

Write each number.

1 tens — ten 10
2 tens — twenty 20
3 tens — thirty 30
4 tens — forty 40
5 tens — fifty 50

6 tens — sixty 60
7 tens — seventy 70
8 tens — eighty 80
9 tens — ninety 90

10 tens — one hundred 100

Write each number.

1. 33
2. 49
3. 56
4. 72

Write the missing numbers before and after.

5. 15, 16, 17
6. 53, 54, 55
7. 30, 31, 32
8. 98, 99, 100

2 Teach

Develop Skills and Concepts Have students work in pairs to count out 26 sticks and use rubber bands to make bundles of ten. Ask how many ones are left. (6) Write **2 tens 6 ones = 26** on the board. Point to the 2 and the 6 in 26 as the students read the number as 2 tens 6 ones. Write **twenty-six** on the board and have students read the number name. Repeat for the number of tens and ones in other numbers through 99. Have students lay out 100 sticks, bundle them into tens, and tell how many tens and ones there are. (10, 0) Remind students that 10 tens 0 ones is 100 as you write **one hundred** and **100** on the board. Write a 2-digit number on the board and have students tell information about the number, such as the number of tens and ones, the number that comes before and after, the number that is 10 more or 10 less, and so on.

3 Practice

Using page 69 Have students trace the 1, 10, 2, and 20 at the top of the page. Tell students to write how many tens are shown and then write the number. Tell students that in the following exercises they are to write the number shown. Tell students that in the exercises in the last section, they are to fill in the missing numbers before and after each number in the middle column. Have students complete the page independently.

Using page 70 Have students read the first three numbers, trace the dotted numbers, and write in the missing numbers to complete the sequence in Exercise 1. Have students complete the next sequences in Exercises 2 to 4. In the next group of exercises, help students read the number names if necessary as they write the numbers.

Write the missing numbers.

1. 24, 25, 26, 27, 28, 29, 30, 31, 32
2. 37, 38, 39, 40, 41, 42, 43, 44
3. 56, 57, 58, 59, 60, 61, 62, 63
4. 41, 42, 43, 44, 45, 46, 47, 48

Write each number.

5. seventeen 17
6. fifty-two 52
7. fifteen 15
8. sixty-three 63
9. twelve 12
10. seventy-seven 77
11. fourteen 14
12. eighty-one 81
13. sixteen 16
14. ninety-four 94
15. eighteen 18
16. thirty-five 35
17. twenty-nine 29
18. forty-eight 48

Now Try This!

Use these digits to write 2-digit numbers.

1. | 2 | 7 | 6 | 27, 26, 72, 76, 62, 67
2. | 9 | 1 | 5 | 15, 19, 51, 59, 91, 95

Now Try This! Write **8** and **4** on the board. Ask students what 2-digit numbers can be made using an 8 and a 4. (84 and 48) Now, write **1**, **2**, and **3** on the board and have students make 2-digit numbers. Tell students to use each digit only one time in each 2-digit number. (12, 13, 21, 23, 31, 32) Repeat for the numbers 3, 4, and 5. (34, 35, 43, 45, 53, 54) Have students trace the four numbers and then write two more in the first exercise. (62, 67) Have students complete the second exercise independently.

4 Assess

Have students choose a number between 20 and 99. Have them write this number at the top of a sheet of paper. Then, have students model the number using both counting sticks and base-ten blocks.

For Mixed Abilities

Common Errors • Intervention

Some students may have difficulty writing missing numbers in a sequence. Have them work with partners on number charts from 0 to 100. Have one partner point to a number on the chart and the other partner say the numbers before and after it. Partners should repeat this procedure taking turns. Then, have a partner point to a number, such as 24, and the other partner read it two ways, for example, 2 tens 4 ones and twenty-four.

Enrichment • Number Sense

1. Tell students to write all the 2-digit numbers that have the same number of tens in them as ones.
2. Have students write all the number words they would say if they counted by tens from 10 to 100.
3. Tell students to write all the 2-digit numbers that are 1 less than each number they would say if they were counting by 5s from 0 to 100.

More to Explore • Application

Have students draw a large clock on the floor with chalk, omitting the hands. Take two pieces of rope or yarn to use for the hands. Have a student sit in the center of the clock to hold one end of each rope. Make one rope the minute hand, extending to the rim of the clock. Make the other rope the hour hand, noticeably shorter than the first rope. Choose two students to be the hour and minute hands. Tell students different times to the quarter-hour they must act out by walking around the circle holding the rope and stopping at the correct number. Repeat so that all students get a chance to participate.

5-2 Counting Hundreds, Tens, and Ones

pages 71–72

1 Getting Started

Objective

- To understand and write 3-digit numbers

Materials

hundred flats, tens rods, and ones cubes; base-ten blocks

Warm Up • Mental Math

Have students count by

1. 1s from 40 to 60
2. 10s from 10 to 100
3. 5s from 25 to 50
4. 2s from 4 to 18
5. 5s from 70 to 100
6. 1s from 76 to 92
7. 2s from 18 to 30
8. 5s from 35 to 70

Warm Up • Number Sense

Have students use tens rods and ones cubes to show various 2-digit numbers. Have students write the numbers and their number names on the board.

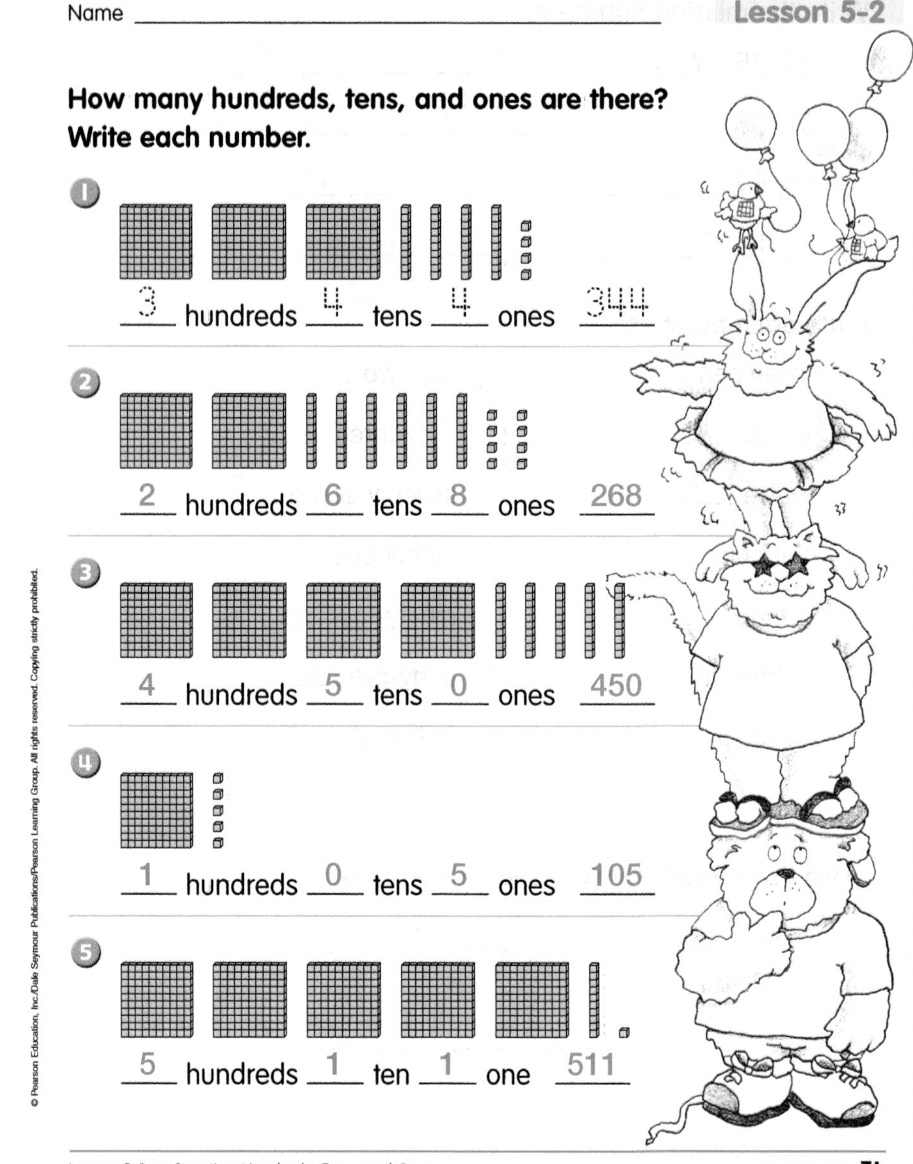

Name ______________________ **Lesson 5-2**

How many hundreds, tens, and ones are there? Write each number.

1. 3 hundreds 4 tens 4 ones 344
2. 2 hundreds 6 tens 8 ones 268
3. 4 hundreds 5 tens 0 ones 450
4. 1 hundreds 0 tens 5 ones 105
5. 5 hundreds 1 ten 1 one 511

2 Teach

Develop Skills and Concepts Have students put out 10 tens rods and tell how many tens and ones there are. (10, 0) Remind students that the number represented is **100** or **one hundred** as you write both on the board. Show students a hundred flat. Have students place 10 tens rods on the flat to see that 10 tens rods equal 1 hundred flat. Tell students that 100 is 1 hundred 0 tens 0 ones because the 10 tens can be traded for 1 hundred. Help students see that the 1 hundred flat is easier to use than the 10 tens rods to represent 100. Now, display 1 hundred flat, 2 tens rods, and 6 ones cubes, and ask students to tell how many of each there are. (1 hundred 2 tens 6 ones) Have a student write the number on the board. (126) Continue for other 3-digit numbers through 999. Lay out 1 hundred flat and 1 tens rod and have students write the number. (110) Continue to add 1 tens rod at a time to have students count by 10s. Show students the trading of 10 tens for another hundred flat and continue through 300 or 400.

3 Practice

Using page 71 Tell students to trace the numbers in Exercise 1 to tell how many hundreds, tens, and ones there are and then trace the 344. Have students complete the page independently.

Using page 72 Have students complete the page independently. Remind them to write the correct 3-digit number in the last answer blank.

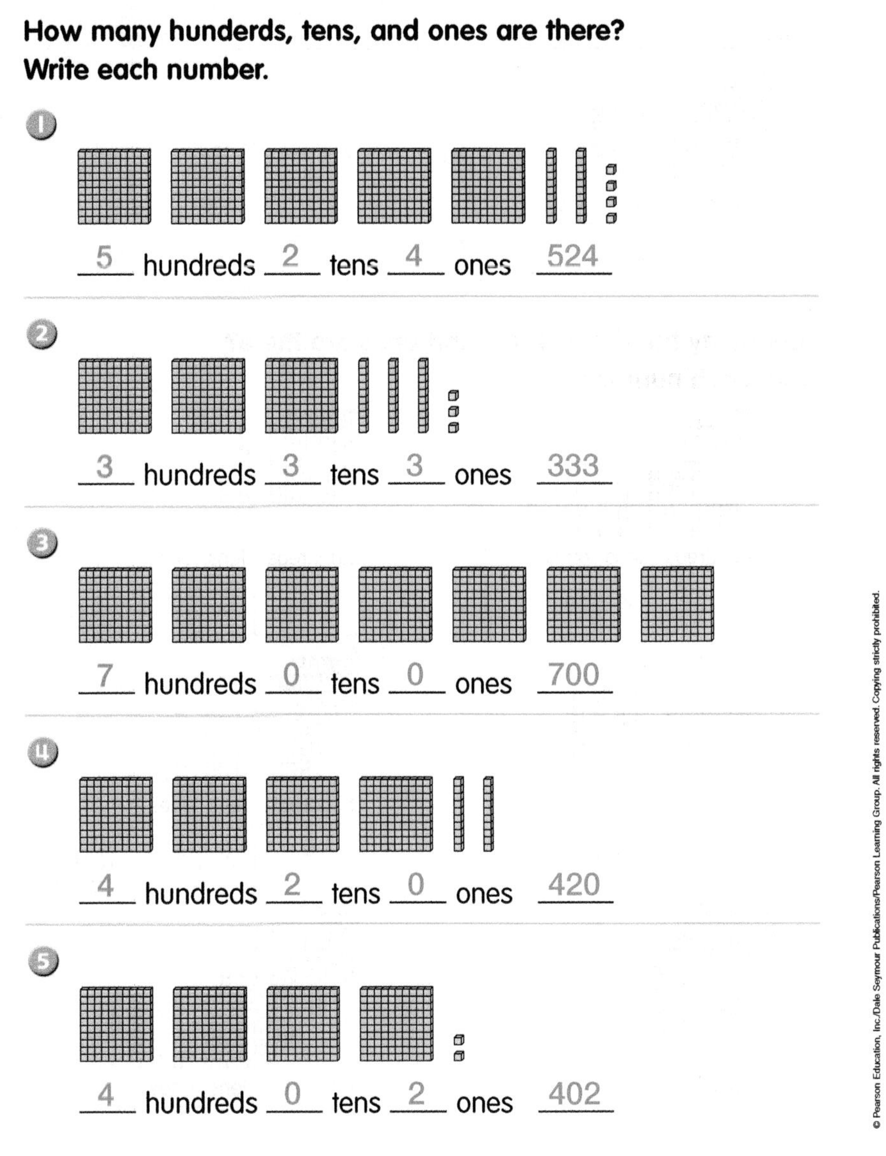

How many hunderds, tens, and ones are there? Write each number.

1. 5 hundreds 2 tens 4 ones 524

2. 3 hundreds 3 tens 3 ones 333

3. 7 hundreds 0 tens 0 ones 700

4. 4 hundreds 2 tens 0 ones 420

5. 4 hundreds 0 tens 2 ones 402

4 Assess

Write **592** on the board. Have students use base-ten blocks to model the number of hundreds, tens, and ones in the number. Repeat with the numbers 362 and 40.

For Mixed Abilities

Common Errors • Intervention

Some students may write a number like four hundred twenty-eight as 4028. Use a place-value chart to show that numbers in the hundreds (those less than 1,000) have only three digits. Have students write the numbers on a place-value chart before they write the standard numeral.

Enrichment • Number Sense

1. Have students write the largest 3-digit number in hundreds, tens, and ones. Then, have them write the smallest 3-digit number. (999, 100)
2. Tell students to write all the 3-digit numbers that have no ones beginning with 800. What sequence have they written? (800, 810, 820, 830, 840, 850, 860, 870, 880, 890, 900, 910, 920, 930, 940, 950, 960, 970, 980, 990)
3. Have students write all the 3-digit numbers that have no tens. How many numbers did they write? (101, 102, 103, 104, 105, 106, 107, 108, 109, repeat for 200 to 909; they will have written 81 numbers.)

More to Explore • Application

Bring several decks of cards to class and teach students how to play Go Fish. Go through a deck with them, pointing out that there are four kinds of cards (hearts, diamonds, clubs, and spades) and that there are 13 of each kind (from the ace to the king). Divide the class into groups of three or four. Show them how to deal the cards, giving each player the same number. Explain that the game begins with one player asking one of the others for a card, by number and kind, or suit. In order to request a card, the player must have at least one of this kind already in his or her hand. If players get the requested card, they take another turn. Explain that they are trying to get all four kinds of a given number and that as soon as they reach their goal, they put the four matching cards down in front of them.

5-3 Place Value Through Hundreds

pages 73–74

1 Getting Started

Objective
- To understand and write 3-digit numbers

Materials
hundred flats, tens rods, and ones cubes; *blank cards

Warm Up • Mental Math
Ask students what operation is used to go from

1. 62 to 72 (addition)
2. 42 to 40 (subtraction)
3. 20 to 25 (addition)
4. 16 to 15 (subtraction)
5. 80 to 70 (subtraction)
6. 52 to 49 (subtraction)
7. 30 to 36 (addition)
8. 0 to 20 (addition)

Warm Up • Number Sense
Write **176** on the board and have students tell how many ones, hundreds, and tens there are. (6, 1, 7) Having students tell the values out of order helps to put emphasis on the place value of each number. Repeat for more 3-digit numbers.

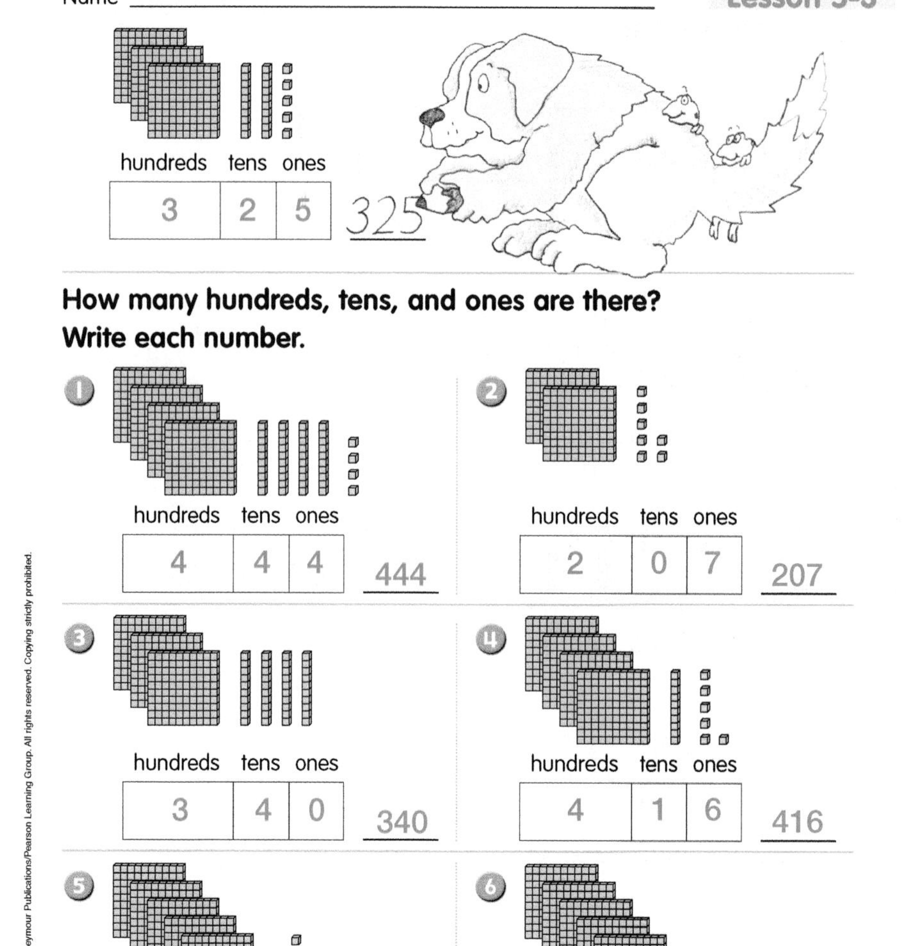

2 Teach

Develop Skills and Concepts Lay out 3 hundred flats, 8 tens rods, and 4 ones cubes. Write (3) **hundreds** (8) **tens** (4) **ones** = (384) on the board and have a student complete the sentence. Repeat for more 3-digit numbers and then have students lay out the manipulatives for any 3-digit numbers they write on the board. Now, have students write the number that comes before and after 200. (199, 201) Repeat to have students tell the numbers before and after more 3-digit numbers. Write **998** on the board and help students write the numbers before and after it. Tell students to write the number of hundreds, tens, and ones in each number and then write the number.

3 Practice

Using page 73 Have students look at the example at the top of the page, then count the 325. Have students complete the page independently.

Using page 74 Ask students what they will do in Exercises 1 to 4. (write the number of hundreds, tens, and ones in each number and then write the number) Tell students that they are to write the number that comes before and after the number in the next set of exercises. Have students complete the page independently.

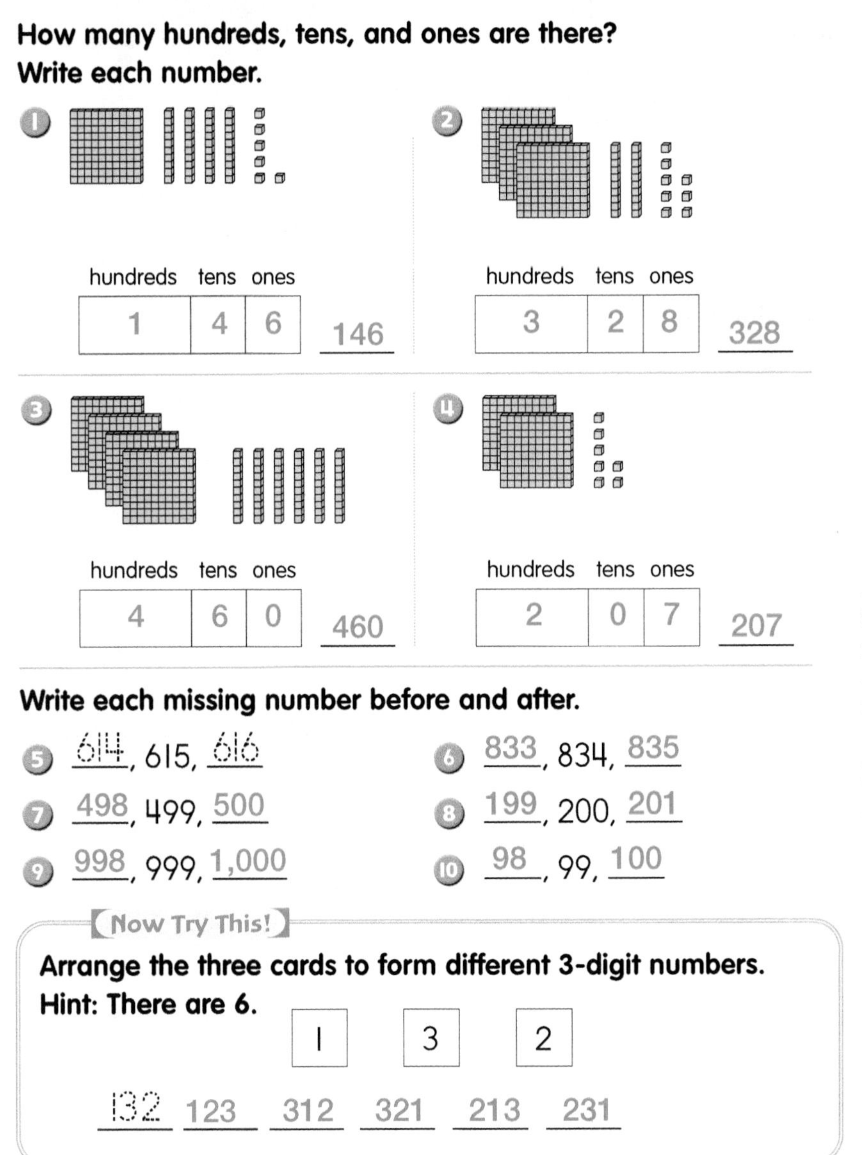

How many hundreds, tens, and ones are there? Write each number.

1

hundreds	tens	ones
1	4	6

146

2

hundreds	tens	ones
3	2	8

328

3

hundreds	tens	ones
4	6	0

460

4

hundreds	tens	ones
2	0	7

207

Write each missing number before and after.

5. 614, 615, 616
6. 833, 834, 835
7. 498, 499, 500
8. 199, 200, 201
9. 998, 999, 1,000
10. 98, 99, 100

Now Try This!

Arrange the three cards to form different 3-digit numbers. Hint: There are 6.

1 3 2

132 123 312 321 213 231

Now Try This! Write **5**, **2**, and **3** on each of three cards. Help students arrange the cards to form six different 3-digit numbers. (523, 253, 352, 235, 325, 532) Then, have students complete the activity independently.

4 Assess

Write **576** on the board. Ask students to write the five numbers that come before 576 and the five numbers that come after 576. (571, 572, 573, 574, 575; 577, 578, 579, 580, 581)

For Mixed Abilities

Common Errors • Intervention

Some students may have difficulty understanding place value. Have them work with partners. Give each pair the hundred flats, tens rods, and ones cubes, in mixed up order, for a number such as 375. Have them group the hundred flats, tens rods, and ones cubes and then say and write the numeral.

Enrichment • Number Sense

1. Tell students to write five 3-digit numbers and place them in order from the least to the greatest.
2. Have students use the numbers 4, 6, 9, and 8 to write as many 3-digit numbers as they can.
3. Tell students to use the numbers 2, 3, 6, 8, and 9 to write as many 2-digit numbers as they can. Then, have them write all the 3-digit numbers they can.

More to Explore • Application

Invite the class to plan a party. Explain that students will have to decide on a day and a time, a place, and the list of people to be invited. This can be an opportunity to invite parents or school administrators to visit the class. Help students plan a simple menu and point out that they will need cups, plates, napkins, and spoons or forks. Ask them to list the number of each item they will need. Ask when they will have to make the food to be served, and help them organize themselves into groups responsible for different items. Afterward, have students list the math skills used in the planning and preparation of the party.

5-4 Counting Dollars, Dimes, and Pennies

pages 75–76

1 Getting Started

Objective
- To count dollars, dimes, and pennies through $5

Vocabulary
dollar

Materials
hundred flats, tens rods, and ones cubes; real or play dollars, dimes, and pennies

Warm Up • Mental Math
Have students find the answer.

1. 4 + 9 + 2 + 1 (16)
2. 16 − 4 + 2 (14)
3. 7 + 17 + 4 (28)
4. 9 − 9 + 9 (9)
5. 0 + 7 + 10 (17)
6. 12 − 4 + 10 (18)

Warm Up • Number Sense
Dictate a 2- or 3-digit number and have a student show the number using the hundred flats, tens rods, and ones cubes. Then, have a student rename the number in hundreds, tens, and ones and write the number on the board. Have another student write the number before and the number after the dictated number. Repeat for more 2- or 3-digit numbers.

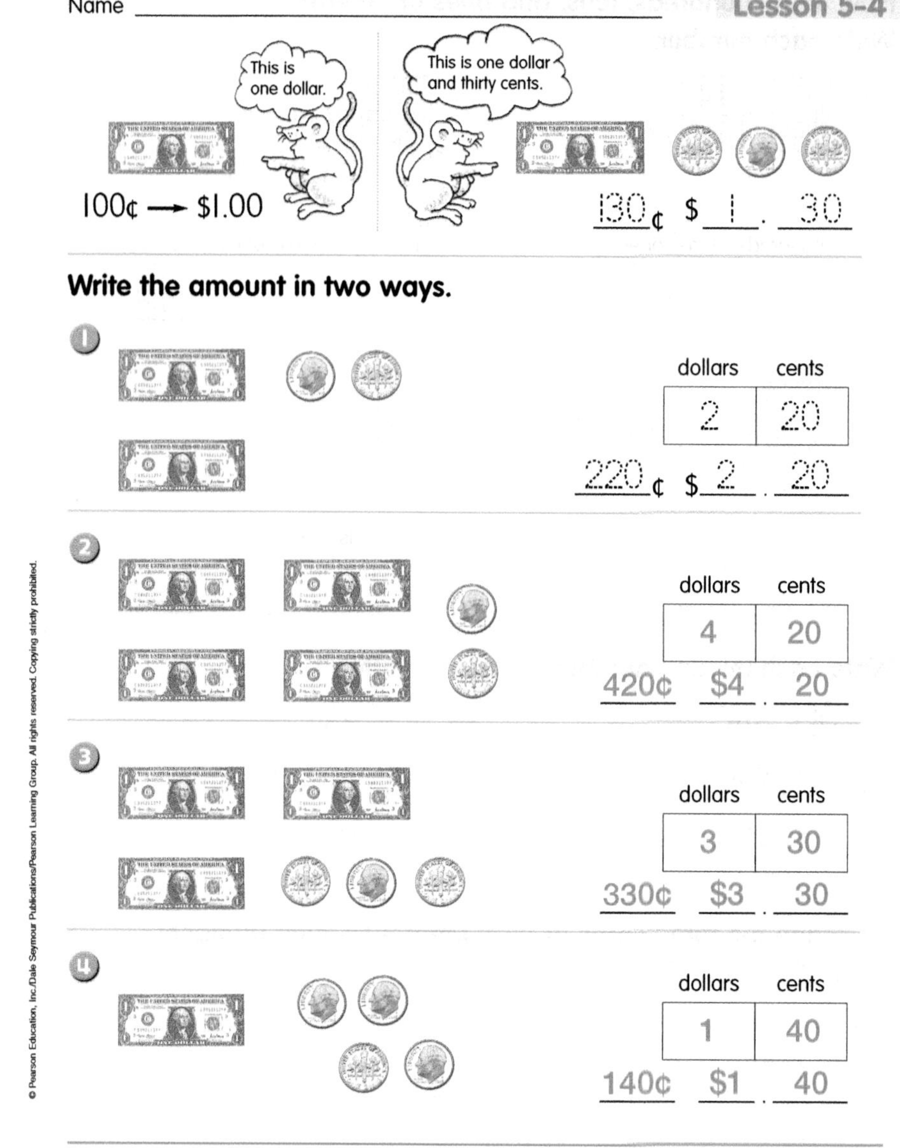

Name ______________________ **Lesson 5-4**

100¢ → $1.00

130¢ $1.30

Write the amount in two ways.

1. dollars 2, cents 20 — 220¢ $2.20
2. dollars 4, cents 20 — 420¢ $4.20
3. dollars 3, cents 30 — 330¢ $3.30
4. dollars 1, cents 40 — 140¢ $1.40

2 Teach

Develop Skills and Concepts Show a dime and remind students that it is worth 10¢ or 10 pennies. Have students count by 10s as you lay out 10 dimes. Tell students that 10 dimes can be traded for $1 because $1 is equal to 100 pennies, just as 1 hundred is equal to 10 tens. Write the following on the board: **10 dimes = 100 cents = 1 dollar.** Write **$1.00** on the board and tell students that the decimal point separates the dollars from the cents. Remind students that we say the word *and* at the decimal point. Now, write **$1.25 = 125¢** on the board and have a student read the number sentence. Lay out 2 dollars, 4 dimes, and 6 pennies, and have a student write and read the amount. ($2.46, two dollars and forty-six cents) Lay out 4 dimes and 2 pennies, and have a student write and read the amount. ($0.42, forty-two cents) Remind students that we can also write this as 42¢ as you write **42¢** on the board. Repeat for more amounts through $5.

3 Practice

Using page 75 Go through the example at the top of the page with students as they count the money and trace it in two ways. Help students complete Exercise 1 and then have students complete the page independently.

Using page 76 Help students complete the first exercise and ask them what difference there is between the two answer lines. (One shows the decimal point.) Have them complete the page independently.

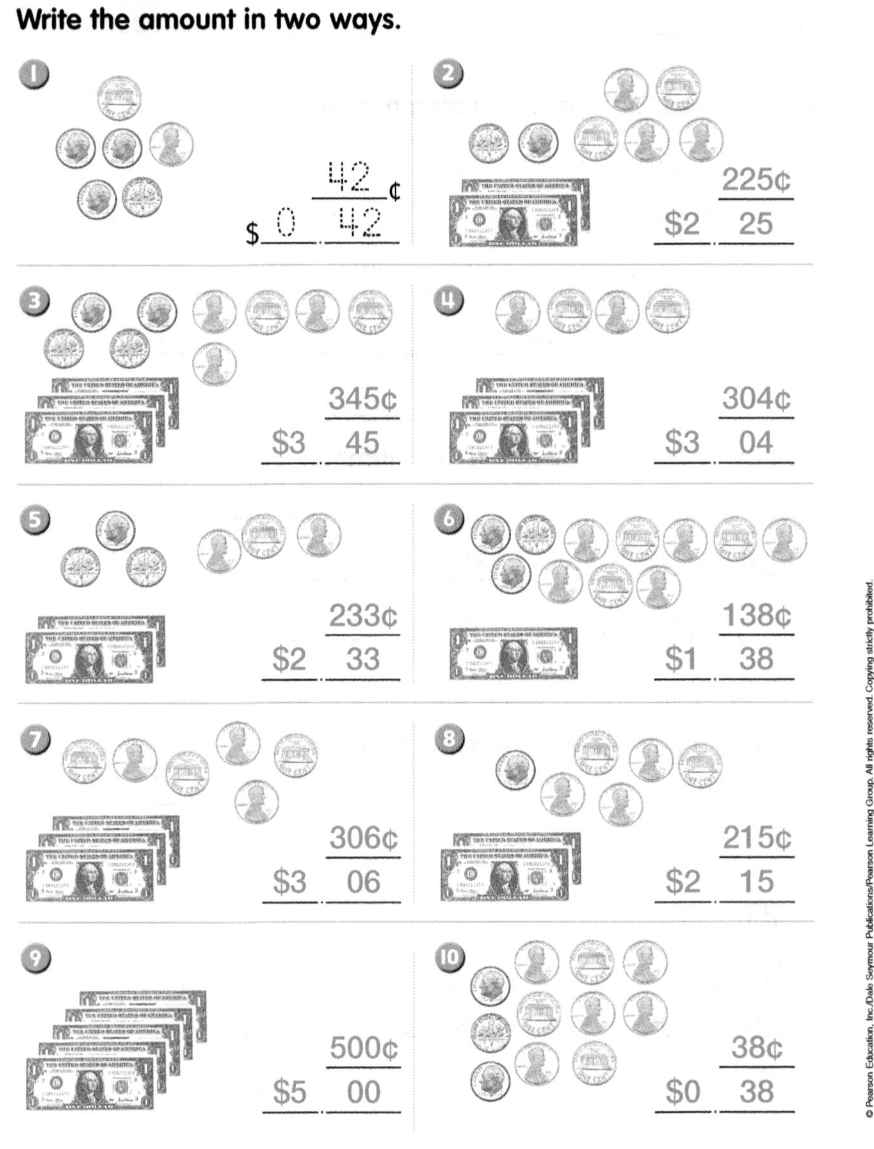

Write the amount in two ways.

1. 42¢ — $0.42
2. 225¢ — $2.25
3. 345¢ — $3.45
4. 304¢ — $3.04
5. 233¢ — $2.33
6. 138¢ — $1.38
7. 306¢ — $3.06
8. 215¢ — $2.15
9. 500¢ — $5.00
10. 38¢ — $0.38

4 Assess

Show students four 1-dollar bills, 8 dimes, and 9 pennies. Have students write the amount two different ways. (489¢, $4.89) Repeat the activity with different amounts.

For Mixed Abilities

Common Errors • Intervention

Some students may forget to write the dollar sign and decimal point when writing amounts of money such as $3.20. Stress that the decimal point separates the dollars from the dimes, that is, the dollars from the cents, and that without it, the amount of money has a different value.

Enrichment • Number Sense

1. Tell students to write the number of dimes they would have if they had each of these amounts all in dimes: 320¢, 460¢, $5.20, 150¢, $7.90, 60¢.
2. Have students see how many ways they can make $2.26 with dimes, pennies, and a dollar.
3. Tell students to use grid paper, crayons, and money to show why 1 hundred 2 tens 9 ones is equal to 1 dollar, 2 dimes, and 9 pennies.

More to Explore • Application

Read aloud the story of *Goldilocks and the Three Bears.* This tale is easily remembered by children because each bear has its own bowl, chair, and bed. This one-to-one correspondence is very important in graphing. To reinforce students' understanding of this idea, ask them to draw the three bowls of porridge, the three chairs, the three beds, and the three bears. Now, have students connect each bear with its own bowl, chair, and bed. Post these illustrations so that students can see each other's work.

5-5 Counting Through 1,000

pages 77–78

1 Getting Started

Objectives

- To count by 1s, 5s, 10s, and 100s through 1,000
- To recognize place value through hundreds

Materials

hundred flats, tens rods, and ones cubes

Warm Up • Mental Math

Have students tell the time when the long hand is on

1. 12 and the short hand is on 11 (11:00)
2. 12 and the short hand is on 2 (2:00)
3. 6 and the short hand is between 12 and 1 (12:30)
4. 6 and the short hand is between 5 and 6 (5:30)

Warm Up • Number Sense

Have students write the numbers for counting by 10s through 100 on the board, leaving spaces between. (10, 20, 30, . . . , 100) Have students fill in the numbers to change the sequence to counting by 5s. (5, 15, . . . , 95) Help students write the numbers for counting by 2s through 100.

Name ______________________

Count by ones. Write each missing number.

1. 185, 186, 187, 188, 189, 190, 191, 192
2. 96, 97, 98, 99, 100, 101, 102, 103, 104
3. 396, 397, 398, 399, 400, 401, 402, 403
4. 105, 106, 107, 108, 109, 110, 111, 112
5. 215, 216, 217, 218, 219, 220, 221, 222

Count by fives. Write each missing number.

6. 5, 10, 15, 20, 25, 30, 35, 40, 45
7. 105, 110, 115, 120, 125, 130, 135, 140
8. 535, 540, 545, 550, 555, 560, 565, 570
9. 380, 385, 390, 395, 400, 405, 410, 415

Count by tens. Write each missing number.

10. 10, 20, 30, 40, 50, 60, 70, 80, 90
11. 110, 120, 130, 140, 150, 160, 170, 180
12. 450, 460, 470, 480, 490, 500, 510, 520
13. 580, 590, 600, 610, 620, 630, 640, 650

Count by hundreds. Write each missing number.

14. 100, 200, 300, 400, 500, 600, 700, 800, 900, 1,000

2 Teach

Develop Skills and Concepts Display 1 hundred flat and add ones cubes as students count by 1s through 120. Write each number on the board in sequence. Now, have students use the manipulatives to count from 100 to 120 by 2s, 5s, and 10s as you write the sequences on the board. Repeat for counting from 570 to 590 and from 790 to 810. Now, have students put out hundred flats and count by hundreds through 1,000. Have students tell the number before and after 999, and write these on the board. Note: Place value is not extended beyond 1,000 in second grade.

3 Practice

Using page 77 Have a student read the directions aloud for each section. Have them complete the page independently.

Using page 78 Have students tell the value of each of the digits in 275. (2 hundreds 7 tens 5 ones) Have them tell again what the 7 means (tens) and trace the circle around the word. Tell students to circle the word that tells the value of the blue digit in the first section. Students will write the correct value in the second section. Have students complete all exercises independently.

What does the blue digit mean? Circle the correct word.

1. 275 — tens / ones / hundreds (circled: tens)
2. 341 — hundreds / tens / ones (circled: ones)
3. 204 — ones / tens / hundreds (circled: hundreds)
4. 526 — tens / hundreds / ones (circled: ones)
5. 973 — hundreds / ones / tens (circled: hundreds)
6. 858 — tens / ones / hundreds (circled: tens)

Write the number of hundreds, tens, and ones.

7. 732 — 2 ones, 3 tens, 7 hundreds
8. 467 — 7 ones, 6 tens, 4 hundreds
9. 618 — 8 ones, 1 ten, 6 hundreds
10. 279 — 9 ones, 7 tens, 2 hundreds
11. 312 — 2 ones, 1 ten, 3 hundreds
12. 103 — 3 ones, 0 tens, 1 hundred

Now Try This!

Solve.

1. I am thinking of a number. It has 2 tens, 3 hundreds, and 5 ones. What is my number? 325
2. My number has no ones, two hundreds, and no tens. What is my number? 200

Now Try This! Tell students to think of a number that has 2 tens and 0 ones. Have a student write the number. (20) Continue for more 2- and 3-digit numbers. Then, have students complete the two exercises independently.

4 Assess

Have students count by 10s from 360 to 500. (360, 370, 380, 390, 400, 410, 420, 430, 440, 450, 460, 470, 480, 490, 500)

For Mixed Abilities

Common Errors • Intervention

Some students may name the place value of a digit incorrectly. Have them place each 3-digit number, such as 356, on a place-value chart and give the place-value names for all 3 digits.

Hundreds	Tens	Ones
3	5	6

Enrichment • Number Sense

1. Have students draw a street with six houses on each side and number the first house on one side 464 and the last house 474. Tell them to number the first two houses on the other side 463 and 465 and to have a friend write in the missing house numbers.
2. Tell students to count backward from 1,000, counting by 100s.
3. Have students draw an office building with ten floors. Then, tell them to draw a sign on each floor that tells the office numbers if the third floor sign reads "300–330."

More to Explore • Number Sense

Tell students that they are going to play a game called Fox and Goose. Have them form a circle of Geese with the Fox in the center. The Fox calls a student by name and gives a single-digit addition or subtraction problem for the named student to solve. If the sum or difference is not given correctly, the Goose is caught and joins the Fox in the center of the circle. Another Goose is named and play continues. A caught Goose may escape by giving a correct answer when the Fox accepts a wrong answer or by giving the answer before the named Goose can give it. Periodically, choose a new Fox and allow the caught Geese to go back to the ring. Extend the activity to include 2-digit problems.

5-6 10 More, 10 Less; 100 More, 100 Less

pages 79–80

1 Getting Started

Objectives
- To write numbers that are 10 more and 10 less than a number
- To write numbers that are 100 more and 100 less than a number

Materials
hundred flats, tens rods, and ones cubes

Warm Up • Mental Math
Have students tell the number that comes
1. between 49 and 51 (50)
2. before 210 (209)
3. after 400 (401)
4. before 1,000 (999)
5. between 376 and 378 (377)
6. after 750 (751)
7. between 126 and 124 (125)
8. between 206 and 204 (205)

Warm Up • Number Sense
Review counting by 10s by having a student write a decade number such as 110 on the board. Have the next three or four students count on by 10s and write the numbers on the board. Repeat until all students have contributed. Leave the sequences on the board for later use in this lesson.

Name ______________________ Lesson 5-6

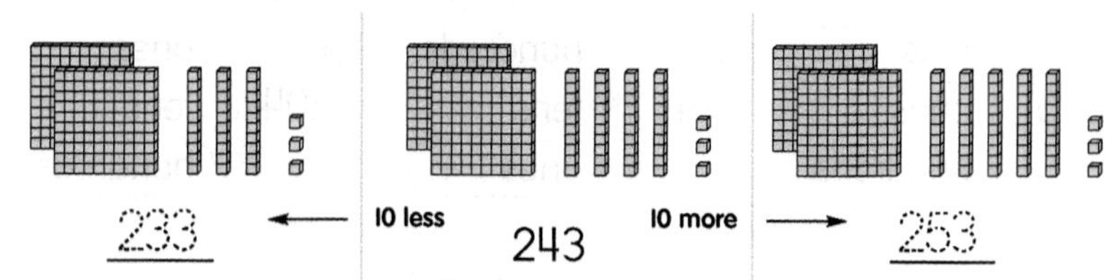

233 ← 10 less 243 10 more → 253

Write each missing number.

	10 less		10 more		10 less		10 more
1	324	334,	344	9	761	771,	781
2	70	80,	90	10	95	105,	115
3	252	262,	272	11	583	593,	603
4	418	428,	438	12	312	322,	332
5	100	110,	120	13	597	607,	617
6	539	549,	559	14	979	989,	999
7	842	852,	862	15	390	400,	410
8	891	901,	911	16	980	990,	1,000

Solve.

17 Diane saves baseball cards. She has 210 cards. Her brother has 10 more cards than Diane. How many cards does Diane's brother have?

220 cards

18 Cynthia has 102 shells in her collection. Dino has 10 fewer shells than Cynthia. How many shells does Dino have?

92 shells

2 Teach

Develop Skills and Concepts Lay out 3 hundred flats, 4 tens rods, and 2 ones cubes. Have a student write the number on the board. (342) Remove a tens strip and have a student write the number in front of the 342. (332) Tell students that 332 is 10 less than 342. Replace the tens rod to show 342 and ask students what the number would be if we added a tens rod. (352) Have a student write **352** after 342. Now, write **332, 342,** and **352** vertically for students to easily see the change in the tens digits. Repeat for more examples as needed. Repeat the activity for 232, 332, and 432 to have students see the change in the hundreds digit.

3 Practice

Using page 79 Ask students what number is 10 less than 243 (233) and 10 more than 243 (253). Have students trace the numbers 233 and 235 and tell how each number shown differs from the next one. (10 less or 10 more) Read the story problems with students and have them complete the page independently.

Using page 80 Go through the example with the students as they trace the numbers. Tell students that they are to find the number that is 100 more or 100 less than another number. Read the story problems at the bottom of the page with students and have them complete the page independently.

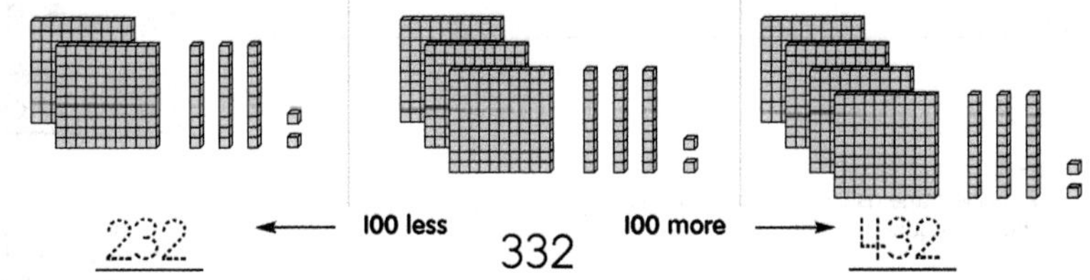

232 ← 100 less 332 100 more → 432

Write the missing numbers.

100 less		100 more
1. 235	335	435
2. 162	262	362
3. 328	428	528
4. 10	110	210
5. 449	549	649
6. 550	650	750
7. 701	801	901

100 less		100 more
8. 671	771	871
9. 5	105	205
10. 493	593	693
11. 222	322	422
12. 507	607	707
13. 300	400	500
14. 790	890	990

Solve.

15. The Perez family took a trip. They drove 183 miles on Thursday. On Friday, they drove 100 miles farther than they did on Thursday. How many miles did they drive on Friday?

283 miles

16. In a contest, the champion jumped rope 315 times without missing. Marcie jumped 100 times less than the champion. How many times did Marcie jump?

215 times

4 Assess

Have students tell the number that is 10 more than 476. (486) Have them tell the number that is 10 more than 486 and so on until they reach 556. (496, 506, 516, 526, 536, 546, 556) Have students tell the number that is 100 less than 732. (632) Have them tell the number that is 100 less than 632, and so on until they reach 32. (532, 432, 332, 232, 132, 32)

For Mixed Abilities

Common Errors • Intervention

When students are asked to write the number that is 10 more or 10 less, or 100 more or 100 less, they may change the digit in the wrong place. Have them first draw an arrow above the place with which they are working, for example, above the tens place for 10 more or 10 less and above the hundreds place for 100 more or 100 less. Then, have them add 1 to or subtract 1 from that digit.

Enrichment • Number Sense

1. Tell students to write the numbers of the runners who finished 10 ahead and 10 behind runner 267.
2. Have students tell how much money each of three friends would have if one has $472 and one friend is $100 poorer while the other friend is $100 richer than the first.

More to Explore • Statistics

Introduce the idea of a many-to-one correspondence. Ask students to draw any collection of special things they have. This activity could well be combined with a show-and-tell day when students bring in their collections. Have them draw themselves in the picture as well. Explain that unlike the story of *Goldilocks and the Three Bears*, where there was one bed, one bowl, and one chair for each bear, there are times when there are many items all corresponding to the same person. Ask one student to hold up the drawing of his or her collection. Point out that the objects in the picture all belong to the same person. Ask students to draw lines from the objects to themselves in the pictures. See if students can think of other examples of a many-to-one correspondence. Examples are: a tree with many leaves, a wagon with four wheels, and a book with many pages.

5-7 Comparing 2-Digit Numbers

pages 81–82

1 Getting Started

Objectives

- To find the greater or lesser of 2-digit numbers
- To use the >, <, and = signs to compare 2-digit numbers

Vocabulary

= (equals sign), < (less than sign), > (greater than sign)

Materials

tens rods and ones cubes

Warm Up • Mental Math

Have students tell the number.

1. 2 hundreds 2 tens (220)
2. 4 tens 9 ones (49)
3. 9 ones 3 hundreds (309)
4. 6 tens 6 hundreds 2 ones (662)
5. 7 ones 9 tens (97)
6. 2 ones 1 ten (12)

Warm Up • Number Sense

Write **756** on the board. Have a student write the number that is 100 less than 756 above the number. (656) Have a student write the number that is 100 more below 756. (856) Write **756** again on the board and have a student write the number that is 10 less. (746) Have a student write the number that is 10 more. Repeat for more numbers.

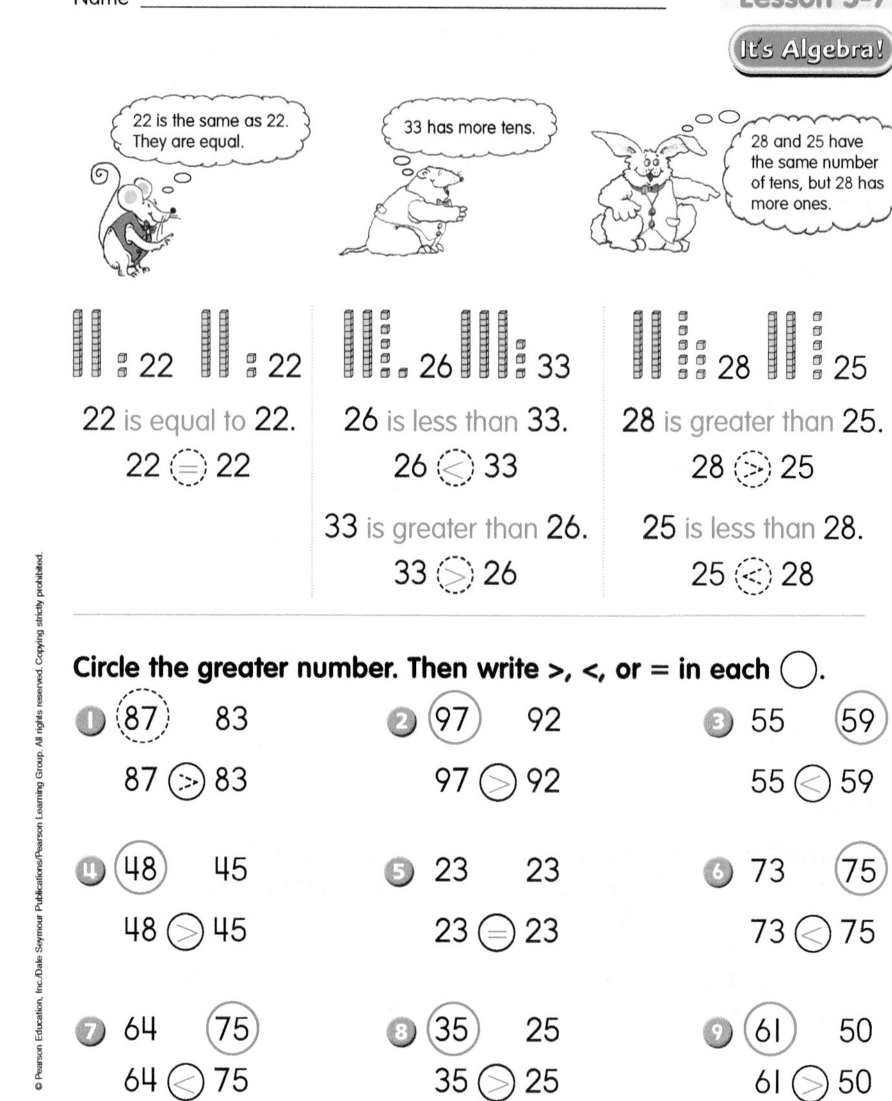

Name ____________________

Lesson 5-7

It's Algebra!

22 22 | 26 33 | 28 25

22 is equal to 22.
22 (=) 22

26 is less than 33.
26 (<) 33

33 is greater than 26.
33 (>) 26

28 is greater than 25.
28 (>) 25

25 is less than 28.
25 (<) 28

Circle the greater number. Then write >, <, or = in each ◯.

1. (87) 83 — 87 (>) 83
2. (97) 92 — 97 (>) 92
3. 55 (59) — 55 (<) 59
4. (48) 45 — 48 (>) 45
5. 23 23 — 23 (=) 23
6. 73 (75) — 73 (<) 75
7. 64 (75) — 64 (<) 75
8. (35) 25 — 35 (>) 25
9. (61) 50 — 61 (>) 50

Lesson 5-7 • Comparing 2-Digit Numbers — eighty-one 81

2 Teach

Develop Skills and Concepts Have a student lay out 32 in tens rods and ones cubes. Have another student lay out 36 in tens rods and ones cubes. Ask how many tens each number has. (3, 3) Ask how many ones each number has. (2, 6) Ask which number is greater. (36) Ask why. (36 has more ones.)

- Write **32 is less than 36** on the board and tell students that this can be written a shorter way as you write **32** < **36** on the board. Write **36 is greater than 32** on the board and tell students that this can also be written a shorter way as you write **36** > **32** on the board. Tell students that the point of the sign always points to the smaller number.
- Write **92** ◯ **87** on the board and have a student write the sign to compare the numbers. (>) Now, write **87** ◯ **92** and have a student write the sign. (<) Have students tell why 92 is greater than 87. (9 tens is more than 8 tens.) Repeat for more comparisons as you emphasize comparing the tens digits first.

It's Algebra! The concepts in this lesson prepare students for algebra.

3 Practice

Using page 81 Help students read the three examples at the top of the page, reading the words aloud for each sign. Then, help students work Exercises 1 and 2. Have students complete the page independently.

Using page 82 Tell students to write the =, >, or < sign in each circle to show how the numbers compare in the first section. Tell them to arrange the numbers in the next

Write >, <, or = in each ◯.

1. 39 (<) 93	2. 91 (<) 97	3. 70 (>) 60
4. 27 (<) 38	5. 57 (<) 67	6. 82 (>) 72
7. 41 (=) 41	8. 32 (<) 52	9. 63 (=) 63
10. 54 (<) 65	11. 96 (>) 89	12. 75 (>) 57
13. 70 (>) 50	14. 71 (=) 71	15. 88 (<) 98

Write the numbers in order from least to greatest.

Item	Numbers	least		greatest
16.	39 29 61	29	39	61
17.	60 80 40	40	60	80
18.	85 55 75	55	75	85
19.	51 34 19	19	34	51
20.	67 50 76	50	67	76
21.	39 45 72	39	45	72

Solve.

22. Frank has 38 flower seeds. René has 42 flower seeds. Who has more seeds?

René

23. Mei Ling scored 51 points. Richard scored 49 points. Who lost the game?

Richard

section so that the smallest number is first and the greatest number is last. Read through the two story problems with the students and then assign the page to be completed independently.

4 Assess

Tell students to use > and < signs to compare 46 to each of the following numbers: 29, 45, 82, 56, and 39.

For Mixed Abilities

Common Errors • Intervention

Some students may have difficulty comparing two numbers. Have them work with partners to compare two numbers such as 29 and 35. Have them use tens rods and ones cubes to model each number and decide, after discussing why, which number is greater. Repeat the activity with other numbers, including those where the digits in the tens place are identical.

Enrichment • Number Sense

1. Have students use > and < signs to compare their age with that of each member of their family.
2. Tell students to illustrate the > and < signs in a way that may help someone remember them. (A sign could be an alligator's mouth or an arrow.)

More to Explore • Number Sense

Tell students to write as many correct addition and subtraction problems as they can in 5 minutes, using the numbers 0 to 50. Have students work in pairs, one computing and the other timing. Have them repeat the activity after each has had a turn, in order to better their time. Extend the activity by having students create the same problems but use each number, 0 to 50, only once.

ESL/ELL STRATEGIES

To clarify the meaning of *less than, greater than, the least,* and *the greatest,* ask students to paraphrase some of the statements in this lesson. For example, *36 is less than 43* means "36 is smaller than 43."

5-8 Comparing 3-Digit Numbers

pages 83–84

1 Getting Started

Objectives

- To find the greater or lesser of two 2- or 3-digit numbers
- To use the $>$ and $<$ signs to compare 2 numbers

Materials

hundred flats, tens rods, and ones cubes; number cards

Warm Up • Mental Math

Have students find the sum or difference.

1. 16 + 2 (18)
2. 9 + 8 + 3 (20)
3. 18 − 2 − 4 (12)
4. 10 + 20 (30)
5. 8 + 8 + 2 (18)
6. 14 − 9 + 13 (18)
7. 2 tens + 6 tens (8 tens or 80)

Warm Up • Algebra

Have each of four students select a number card. Ask students to hold the cards to form two 2-digit numbers for the rest of the students to compare. Have a student write the numbers on the board with the $>$ or $<$ sign. Continue for more students to form numbers to be compared.

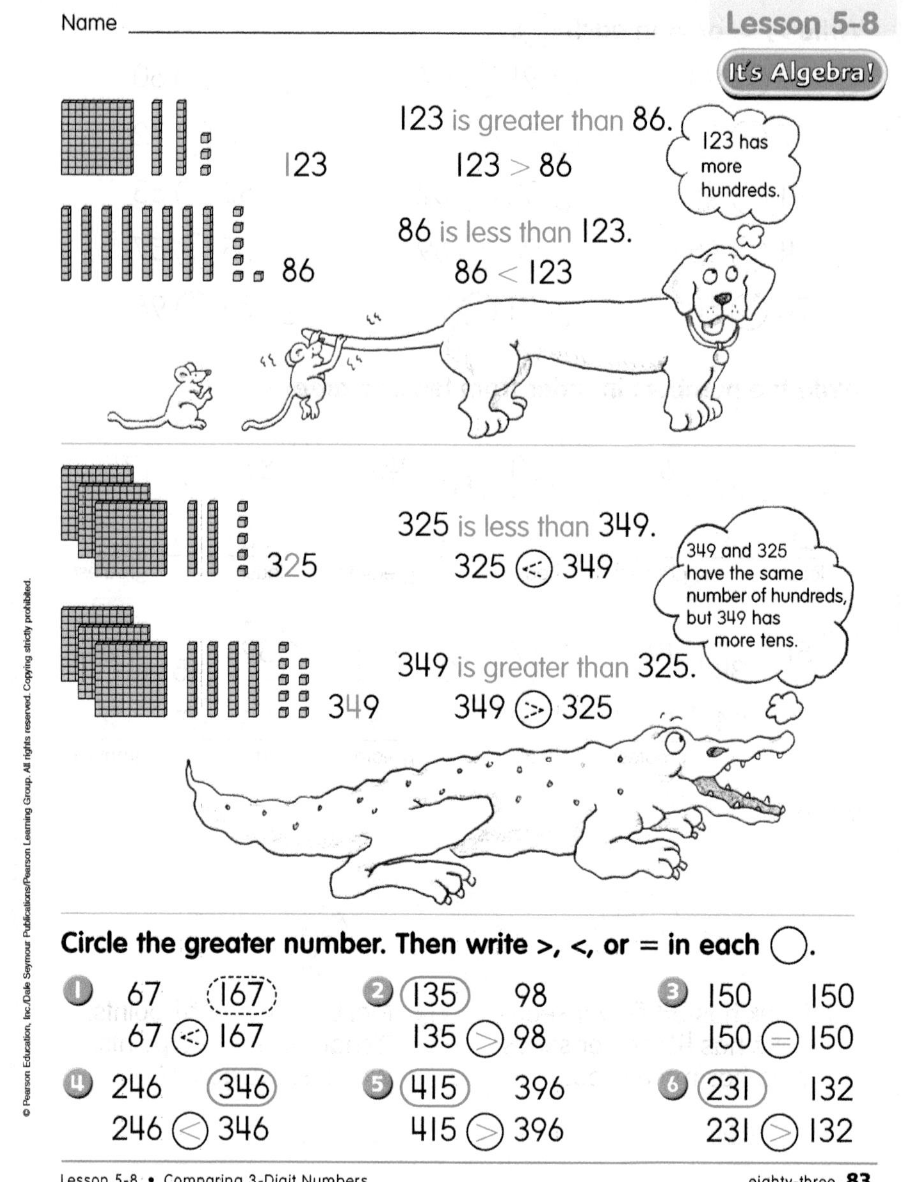

Name ____________________

Lesson 5-8

It's Algebra!

123

86

123 is greater than 86.

$123 > 86$

86 is less than 123.

$86 < 123$

325

349

325 is less than 349.

325 (<) 349

349 is greater than 325.

349 (>) 325

Circle the greater number. Then write >, <, or = in each ◯.

1. 67 (167)	2. (135) 98	3. 150 150
67 (<) 167	135 (>) 98	150 (=) 150
4. 246 (346)	5. (415) 396	6. (231) 132
246 (<) 346	415 (>) 396	231 (>) 132

2 Teach

Develop Skills and Concepts Write **512 ◯ 826** on the board and have students lay out manipulatives to show the numbers. Ask students which number has more hundreds. (826) Ask which number is larger. (826) Have a student write $<$ in the circle. Repeat for more comparisons of two 3-digit numbers having a different number of hundreds.

- Then, write **423 ◯ 416** on the board as you remind students to compare the digits in the largest place first. Ask how many hundreds each number has. (4, the same) Tell students to then compare the next digits and tell which number has more tens. (423) Ask students if the ones need to be compared. (no) Have a student write $>$ in the circle. Continue for students to compare two 3-digit numbers having the same number of hundreds but different digits in the ones place.
- Write **172 ◯ 98** on the board and help students see that 172 is larger because there are no hundreds in 98. Repeat for more examples.

It's Algebra! The concepts of this lesson prepare students for algebra.

3 Practice

Using page 83 Remind students to compare the highest digits first as you work through the two examples at the top of the page with them. Then, tell students that in the following exercises they are to circle the greater number and write the sign in the circle to compare the numbers. If the numbers are equal, they are to write = in the circle. Have students complete the page independently.

Using page 84 Have students complete the exercises in the first section. Read aloud the instruction sentence in the next section. Help students complete Exercise 22 and then complete the rest of the page independently.

Write >, <, or = in each ○.

1. 458 (>) 302	2. 86 (<) 129	3. 265 (=) 265
4. 912 (>) 832	5. 901 (>) 109	6. 302 (>) 298
7. 600 (<) 706	8. 97 (>) 79	9. 989 (<) 999
10. 350 (<) 450	11. 120 (=) 120	12. 325 (<) 523
13. 367 (=) 367	14. 554 (>) 455	15. 717 (>) 698
16. 302 (>) 285	17. 998 (=) 998	18. 502 (>) 499
19. 230 (>) 99	20. 707 (>) 706	21. 445 (>) 435

Write the numbers in order from least to greatest.

22. 301 | 95 | 102

95 (least) 102 301 (greatest)

23. 249 | 234 | 251

234 (least) 249 251 (greatest)

24. 9 | 999 | 99

9 (least) 99 999 (greatest)

25. 275 | 546 | 489

275 (least) 489 546 (greatest)

Now Try This!

Make the greatest possible number and the least possible number. Use all three number cards each time.

1. 6 | 3 | 9

greatest 963

least 369

2. 2 | 1 | 7

greatest 721

least 127

Now Try This! Write **3**, **1**, and **2** on the board. Tell students to use each digit once to make all the 3-digit numbers possible. Help students discover and write on the board the following numbers: 312, 321, 132, 123, 231, and 213. Tell students to find the smallest and largest of the six numbers. Ask how this should be done. (arrange the numbers in order from least to greatest) Remind students to compare the hundreds digits first, then the tens, and then the ones. Have students complete this activity independently. Tell students to write each possible number combination on a slip of paper if needed.

4 Assess

Tell students, *Mary has 325 stamps in her collection. Luis has 327. Who has more stamps?* (Luis) Then, have students write their own greater than or less than story problems.

For Mixed Abilities

Common Errors • Intervention
Some students may confuse the "is less than" and "is greater than" symbols. Have them think of each symbol as the mouth of an alligator, like the alligator shown on page 83. When choosing, the alligator will always open its mouth to eat the greater amount. So, the wide part of the symbol always opens toward the greater number.

Enrichment • Number Sense

1. Tell students to draw a picture to show which floors Rooms 526 and 283 are on. Room 826 is on the eighth floor and Room 403 is on the fourth floor.
2. Have students draw money to show if $4.67 is less than or greater than $4.57. Tell them to circle the money that shows the greater amount.
3. Tell students to draw a number line to show how 599, 601, and 593 compare in size.

More to Explore • Application
Set up a small store in the classroom as a continuing project. Have students decide what kind of store it will be. Students can price the items and use buttons or bottle caps to represent coins. Muffin tins make good cash registers. Appoint a cashier and a bagger. Allow small groups to make purchases. Give students a different number of "coins" and challenge them to make purchases so they will have a specific number of coins left. Encourage students to count their change carefully.

5-9 Ordinal Numbers

pages 85–86

1 Getting Started

Objectives
- To read ordinal numbers through thirty-second
- To use ordinal numbers to tell about days on a calendar

Vocabulary
ordinal numbers

Materials
*ordinal cards first through thirty-second; *calendar of present month

Warm Up • Mental Math
Have students tell the number.

1. 2 more than 41 (43)
2. 1 quarter and 1 dime (35¢)
3. 7 hundreds 4 ones (704)
4. between 140 and 142 (141)
5. 10 more than 470 (480)

Warm Up • Algebra
Have students write a 2- or 3-digit number on paper. Have two students show their numbers and tell which is greater or lesser and why. Continue with more numbers. Help students order all the numbers by asking for those less than 100, those with 9 tens, those with 8 tens, and so on. Continue until all numbers have been placed in order.

Name ______________________ **Lesson 5-9**

First	Second	Third	Fourth	Fifth

The walrus is first. The mouse is fourth.

Look at Mrs. Jones's class roll.
Tell where each person is in order.

1 Adam	17 Leah	first Adam	seventeenth Leah
2 Beverly	18 Linda	fourth Chan	nineteenth Mary
3 Bill	19 Mary	eighth Dorothy	twenty-second Noah
4 Chan	20 Me Lin	twelfth Isaac	twenty-sixth Rosa
5 Cheryl	21 Mike	sixteenth Ken	thirty-first Vera
6 Diane	22 Noah	fourteenth Jean	twenty-fourth Paul
7 Dick	23 Opal	tenth George	eighteenth Linda
8 Dorothy	24 Paul	sixth Diane	thirtieth Tom
9 Emma	25 Raul	second Beverly	thirty-second Wade
10 George	26 Rosa	seventh Dick	twenty-fifth Raul
11 Harry	27 Sarah	third Bill	twenty-seventh Sarah
12 Isaac	28 Stacey	fifteenth Juan	twenty-ninth Terry
13 Jack	29 Terry	fifth Cheryl	twentieth Me Lin
14 Jean	30 Tom	thirteenth Jack	twenty-third Opal
15 Juan	31 Vera	eleventh Harry	twenty-first Mike
16 Ken	32 Wade	ninth Emma	twenty-eighth Stacey

2 Teach

Develop Skills and Concepts Review first through tenth with students by placing the ordinal number cards first through tenth along the chalk tray. Help students write the corresponding number above each ordinal number.

- Now, place the ordinal numbers eleventh through twentieth on the chalk tray and repeat the activity. Have students count by ordinal numbers from first through twentieth. Repeat the activity for the ordinal numbers twenty-first through thirty-second.

3 Practice

Using page 85 Have a student read about Mrs. Jones. Ask what is to be done. (write the students' names in order) Have a student read the first five names and the numbers beside each. Have students find the word *first* and trace *Adam* beside it. Help students see that Adam is number 1, so his name goes beside the word *first*. Help students locate several more numbered names and then have them complete the page independently.

Using page 86 Have students read the numbers on the calendar in ordinal numbers from first through thirty-first. Help students name the ordinal numbers for all the Sundays, Mondays, and so on in January. Have students find the first Wednesday, the fourth Tuesday, and so on. Have students complete the first exercises. Then, tell them to find the day of the week for January first. Help students complete two or three more exercises in the second section before assigning the page to be completed

January						
Sunday	Monday	Tuesday	Wednesday	Thursday	Friday	Saturday
		1	2	3	4	5
6	7	8	9	10	11	12
13	14	15	16	17	18	19
20	21	22	23	24	25	26
27	28	29	30	31		

Use the calendar to write the day of the month.

1. first Monday 7
2. fourth Saturday 26
3. second Sunday 13
4. fifth Tuesday 29
5. third Wednesday 16
6. second Friday 11

Use the calendar to write the day of the week.

7. January first Tuesday
8. January sixteenth Wednesday
9. January tenth Thursday
10. January twelfth Saturday
11. January eleventh Friday
12. January fifteenth Tuesday
13. January thirteenth Sunday
14. January twenty-first Monday
15. January eighteenth Friday
16. January seventh Monday
17. January thirty-first Thursday
18. January twenty-sixth Saturday
19. January thirtieth Wednesday
20. January twentieth Sunday
21. January seventeenth Thursday
22. January twenty-eighth Monday

independently. Students may notice that the current year's calendar shows January first on a different day. Explain that the calendar changes each year.

4 Assess

Show students the calendar for the current month and have them locate the twenty-fifth day, the seventeenth day, and so on.

For Mixed Abilities

Common Errors • Intervention

Some students may have difficulty with ordinal numbers. Distribute cards with the numerals 1 to 30 on them and cards with ordinal names from first to thirtieth on them. Have students place the sets of cards in order but separately on the chalk tray. Then, call for ordinal numbers randomly and have students remove both cards, saying, for example, "This is the eighth card," as they pick up the ordinal name, and "This is card number eight," as they pick up its mate.

Enrichment • Number Sense

1. Have students write a paragraph telling about themselves that includes ordinal numbers to tell the date of their birth and the position of their birth in the family (first child, second child, and so on).
2. Tell students to write today's, tomorrow's, and yesterday's dates in ordinal numbers.

More to Explore • Number Sense

Begin a class collection to count large numbers. Have students bring bottle caps or buttons to school. Group them into tens at a work station. As students bring more, group the tens into hundreds. As needed, group hundreds into thousands. Another sorting method would be to count the objects and store a specified number, such as 25, in empty baby food jars. Then, students can stack four jars to show 100 buttons.

ESL/ELL STRATEGIES

As you teach the ordinal numbers in this lesson, ask, *Which ordinal numbers have* -th *added to the regular number?* (all except *first, second, and third*) Say a variety of ordinal numbers and have different students spell each one aloud.

5-10 Number Names

pages 87–88

1 Getting Started

Objectives

- To read 3-digit number names
- To write 2- and 3-digit numbers to solve problems

Warm Up • Mental Math

Tell students to name two numbers that are between the following numbers:

1. 726 and 729 (727, 728)
2. 106 and 103
3. 48 and 51
4. 98 and 104
5. 78 and 90
6. 450 and 472
7. 106 and 92

Warm Up • Number Sense

Have students form a line and name their place in line using ordinal numbers. Have students change places and tell their new ordinal number. Now, assign the number 32 to the last person and ask students to tell their place in ordinal numbers.

Name ______________________

Lesson 5-10

Match the number name to the number.

1	two hundred	400
2	six hundred	900
3	nine hundred	200
4	four hundred	700
5	seven hundred	600
6	three hundred seventy	130
7	one hundred thirty	490
8	five hundred ten	860
9	eight hundred sixty	370
10	four hundred ninety	510
11	two hundred fifty-three	255
12	five hundred sixty-six	998
13	nine hundred ninety-eight	566
14	five hundred sixteen	516
15	two hundred fifty-five	253
16	eight hundred seventy-two	344
17	three hundred forty-four	872
18	eight hundred twenty-seven	418
19	three hundred four	827
20	four hundred eighteen	304

2 Teach

Develop Skills and Concepts Write **two hundred forty-six** on the board for a student to read and then write the number. (246) Continue for more 3-digit numbers. Now, tell students to guess the 3-digit number you are thinking of if all its digits are 9s. Have a student write the number. (999) Have a student write the number that is less than 9 tens 4 ones but greater than 9 tens 2 ones. (93) Ask a student to write the 3-digit number that is greater than 476, less than 500, and has 8 tens and 4 ones. (484) Continue for other puzzles to have students write 2- and 3-digit numbers.

3 Practice

Using page 87 Tell students to draw a line from each number name to its number. Help students complete two matches and then assign the page to be completed independently.

Using page 88 Tell students to read each number name and write the number. Have students complete the first section independently. Work through the first story problem with the students, pointing out that each story problem is a puzzle. Have them complete the page independently.

Write each number.

1. forty-five 45
2. nine hundred ninety 990
3. one hundred forty-five 145
4. four hundred five 405
5. two hundred nineteen 219
6. seven hundred eighteen 718
7. five hundred 500
8. ninety-nine 99
9. three hundred ten 310
10. eight hundred eight 808
11. six hundred fifty 650
12. five hundred twenty 520

Solve.

13. I am a number greater than 8 tens and 5 ones. I am less than 8 tens and 7 ones.

    Who am I? 86

14. We are two numbers. We are both less than 8 tens. We are both greater than 77.

    Who are we? 78 79

15. We are two numbers. We are both less than 2 hundreds and 5 tens, and 6 ones. We are both greater than 2 hundreds 5 tens, 3 ones.

    Who are we? 254, 255

16. I am a 3-digit number. All my digits are the number 3.

    Who am I? 333

17. I am a number 1 less than 1,000.

    Who am I? 999

18. I am a number 100 more than 900.

    Who am I? 1,000

4 Assess

Write the following numbers on the board: **300, 470, 290, 598,** and **999.** Have students write the number names for each number. (three hundred, four hundred seventy, two hundred ninety, five hundred ninety-eight, nine hundred ninety-nine)

For Mixed Abilities

Common Errors • Intervention

Students may need practice with identifying numbers from number names. Give a different number-name card to each student. Place a number card on the chalk tray and ask the student who has that number-name card to place it next to the number card on the tray.

Enrichment • Number Sense

1. Tell students to write the number that is 200 more and the number that is 200 less than two hundred fifty-six.
2. Have students write all 3-digit numbers that are more than 900 and have 9 ones. Ask them to tell the sequence. (909, 919, 929, 939, 949, 959, 969, 979, 989, 999)
3. Have students write the number name to tell the total number of students in your school.

More to Explore • Statistics

Introduce many-to-many correspondence in this lesson. Ask for three volunteers. Write their names in a circle on the board. In another circle, write these words: **cookies, milk, pizza, hamburgers,** and **apples.** Now, ask volunteers to go to the board and draw an arrow from their name to each of the items they like to eat. Explain that they will draw from one to five arrows, depending on the number of different kinds of food they like. After all three volunteers have shown their preferences, ask another student to point to foods liked by more than one person. Have students construct their own many-to-many correspondence by listing three forms of transportation in one circle on a sheet of paper. Now, have them list at least three destinations in another circle. Have students draw lines between modes of transportation and destinations.

5-11 Problem Solving: Look for a Pattern

pages 89–90

1 Getting Started

Objective
- To identify and extend patterns

Materials
index cards

Warm Up • Mental Math
Have students find the sum or difference.

1. 7 + 3 (10)
2. 4 + 9 (13)
3. 8 + 2 (10)
4. 15 − 9 (6)
5. 12 − 7 (5)
6. 16 − 7 (9)

Warm Up • Number Sense
Write the following on the board:

5 + 10 = (15)
16 − 5 = (11)
8 + 10 = (18)
13 − 9 = (4)
14 − 2 = (12)
9 + 9 = (18)
12 − 7 = (5)
11 + 8 = (19)
13 + 3 = (16)
15 − 6 = (9)

Name ______________________

Problem Solving
Lesson 5-11

You can use a hundred chart to count forward by 10.
You can also use it to count backward by 10.

1	2	3	4	5	6	7	8	9	10
11	12	13	14	15	16	17	18	19	20
21	22	23	24	25	26	27	28	29	30
31	32	33	34	35	36	37	38	39	40
41	42	43	44	45	46	47	48	49	50
51	52	53	54	55	56	57	58	59	60
61	62	63	64	65	66	67	68	69	70
71	72	73	74	75	76	77	78	79	80
81	82	83	84	85	86	87	88	89	90
91	92	93	94	95	96	97	98	99	100

Count forward by tens.

1. 10, 20, 30, 40, 50, 60, 70, 80, 90, 100
2. 5, 15, 25, 35, 45, 55, 65, 75, 85, 95

Count backward by tens.

3. 100, 90, 80, 70, 60, 50, 40, 30, 20, 10
4. 98, 88, 78, 68, 58, 48, 38, 28, 18, 8

2 Teach

Develop Skills and Concepts Give each student an index card. Then, have each student skip-count by 2s starting with 2 and have each student write the number that a particular student says. When the class has finished skip-counting, call out the number 22. Have that student stand up. Ask the student that has the number that is 10 more than 22 to stand up. Then, ask the student that has the number that is 10 less than 22 to stand up. Ask students what number is 10 less than 12 (2) and 10 more than 32 (42). Have the students with those cards order themselves from least number to greatest number at the front of the room.

3 Practice

Using page 89 Have students look at the hundred chart at the top of the page.

- Now, apply the four-step plan to Exercise 1. For SEE, ask, *What are you being asked to do?* (count forward by tens to find the missing numbers) Then, *What information is given?* (a chart with numbers from 1 to 100) For PLAN, ask students how they can count by 10s to find the missing numbers. (read the 0s column) For DO, have students complete the exercise. For CHECK, have students skip-count from 0 to 100 by 10s. Ask, *Did all of your numbers have a 0 in the ones place?* (yes) *Were the numbers in the tens place in order?* (yes) Have students complete the page independently.

Using page 90 Have students look at the hundred chart at the top of the page. Work through the first exercise with students. Remind them to use the four-step plan.

Use the hundred chart. Write each number.

1	2	3	4	5	6	7	8	9	10
11	12	13	14	15	16	17	18	19	20
21	22	23	24	25	26	27	28	29	30
31	32	33	34	35	36	37	38	39	40
41	42	43	44	45	46	47	48	49	50
51	52	53	54	55	56	57	58	59	60
61	62	63	64	65	66	67	68	69	70
71	72	73	74	75	76	77	78	79	80
81	82	83	84	85	86	87	88	89	90
91	92	93	94	95	96	97	98	99	100

1. What number is between 74 and 76? 75
2. What number is 10 less than 63? 53
3. What number comes after 47? 48
4. What number is 20 more than 32? 52
5. What number is 30 less than 88? 58
6. What number comes before 40? 39
7. What number is 60 more than 13? 73
8. Name the numbers between 15 and 24. 16, 17, 18, 19, 20, 21, 22, 23

Assess

Point to two numbers on the hundred chart on page 89 and ask students to describe a pattern. (Possible answer: 50 is 10 less than 60.)

For Mixed Abilities

Common Errors • Intervention

Some students may have trouble skip-counting by 10s. Have those students read and write the numbers from the hundred chart by columns.

Enrichment • Number Sense

1. Start with 0. Skip-count by 5s to 100. What numbers did you skip-count? (5, 10, 15, 20, 25, 30, 35, 40, 45, 50, 55, 60, 65, 70, 75, 80, 85, 90, 95, 100)
2. Start with 0. Skip-count by 4s to 100. What numbers did you skip-count? (4, 8, 12, 16, 20, 24, 28, 32, 36, 40, 44, 48, 52, 56, 60, 64, 68, 72, 76, 80, 84, 88, 92, 96, 100)
3. Have students work in pairs. One partner should pick a number between 1 and 10 and then the other partner should skip-count by 10s to 100 using that number in the ones place. Then, the partner that did the skip counting should pick a number between 91 and 100 and the other partner skip-counts by 10s back to a 1-digit number.

More to Explore • Number Sense

On the board, write five numbers from 11 to 89. Using addition and subtraction, students can write number sentences for 10 more and 10 less than the five numbers you chose. For example, for the number 72, students can write $72 + 10 = 82$ and $72 - 10 = 62$.

Chapter 5 Test

page 91

Items	Objectives
1	To understand and write 3-digit numbers (see pages 71–74)
2	To count dollars, dimes, and pennies through $5 (see pages 75–76)
3–4, 7–8	To count by 1s through 1,000 (see pages 77–78)
5–6	To recognize place value through 1,000 (see pages 77–78)
9–12	To use the =, <, and > signs to compare 3-digit numbers (see pages 91–92)

Name ______________________

How many hundreds, tens, and ones are there? Write the number.

1 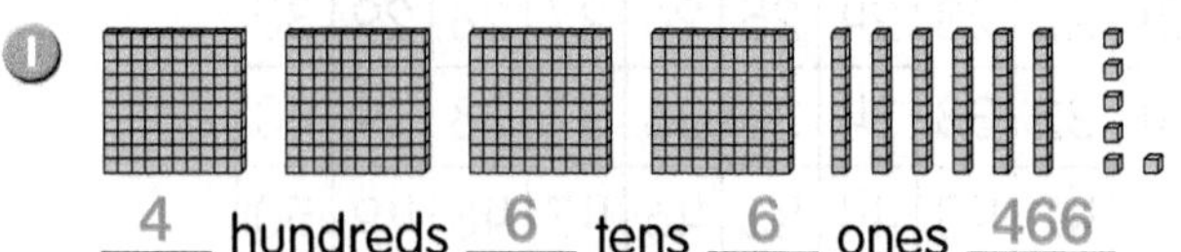

4 hundreds 6 tens 6 ones 466

Write the amount in two ways.

2 

325¢

$3 . 25

Write each missing number.

3 125, 126, 127, 128, 129, 130, 131

4 70, 80, 90, 100, 110, 120, 130

Write the number of hundreds, tens, and ones.

5 971
9 hundreds 7 tens
1 one

6 804
8 hundreds 0 tens
4 ones

Write each missing number before and after.

7 997, 998, 999

8 399, 400, 401

Write >, <, or = in each ◯.

9 342 (<) 415

10 625 (=) 625

11 773 (>) 737

12 899 (<) 900

Alternate Chapter Test

You may wish to use the Alternate Chapter Test on page 319 of this book for further review and assessment.

Add or subtract.

1	2 + 7 9	5 + 5 10	8 + 3 11	3 + 6 9	11 − 7 4	14 − 6 8	15 − 8 7
2	12 − 5 7	17 − 8 9	2 + 9 11	9 + 7 16	8 + 8 16	11 − 5 6	15 − 6 9
3	11 − 8 3	13 − 7 6	10 − 6 4	7 + 7 14	9 + 3 12	8 + 5 13	16 − 7 9
4	18 − 9 9	14 − 8 6	16 − 9 7	2 + 8 10	7 + 7 14	9 + 9 18	5 + 7 12

Solve.

5

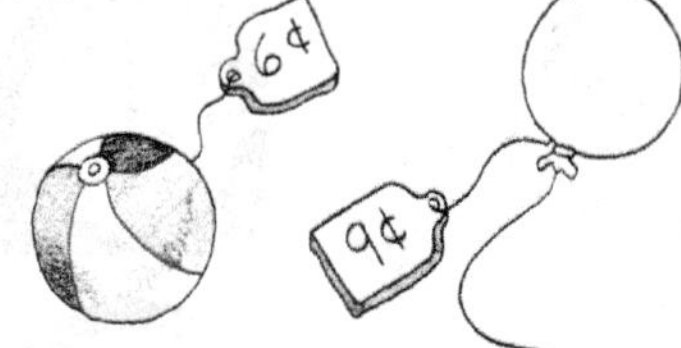

How much do both toys cost altogether?

15¢

6

How much more does the truck cost?

9¢

Cumulative Assessment

page 92

Items	Objectives
1–4	To review addition and subtraction facts with sums and minuends through 18 (see pages 3–12, 17–20, 23–28, 35–44, 53–56, 59–64)
5	To review money sums through 18¢ (see pages 47–48)
6	To review subtracting money from 18¢ and less (see pages 65–66)

6-1 Telling Time to the Hour and Half-Hour

pages 93–94

1 Getting Started

Objective
- To tell time to the hour and half-hour

Vocabulary
clock, minute, hour

Materials
*demonstration clock

Warm Up • Mental Math
Have students tell the next number.

1. 47, 48, 49 (50)
2. 800, 700, 600 (500)
3. 92, 91, 90 (89)
4. 14, 16, 18 (20)
5. 1, 3, 5, 7 (9)
6. 262, 362, 462 (562)
7. 90, 95, 100 (105)
8. 120, 110, 100 (90)

Warm Up • Number Sense
Write the following on the board:

nineteenth
thirtieth
twenty-first
tenth
twenty-ninth
thirty-second
fifth

Have students write the cardinal number beside its ordinal number and then place the numbers in order from least to greatest.

Name ______________________

Chapter 6

Time and Money

Lesson 6-1

There are 12 hour marks on a clock. Write the hour numbers on the clock.

The minute hand is on 12.

The hour hand is on 3.

It is 3 o'clock. We can also write 3:00.

Color the minute hand blue.

Color the hour hand red.

Match the clocks that show the same time.

1 2 3 4 5 6

12:30
9:30
1:00
11:30
5:00
8:00

2 Teach

Develop Skills and Concepts Have students identify the hour and minute hands on the demonstration clock. Place the minute hand on 12 and the hour hand on 4. Have a student tell the time. (4:00) Write **four o'clock**, **4 o'clock**, and **4:00** on the board and tell students the three ways of writing this time are all read the same.

- Ask students to tell what happens to the hour, or short, hand as you move the minute, or long, hand around the clock once and back to 12. (It moves slowly to 5.) Ask the time now. (5:00) Have a student write **5 o'clock**, **five o'clock**, and **5:00** on the board.
- Continue to move the minute hand one revolution and have students write the three ways to tell the time on the board. Remind students that digital clocks show the time as 3:00 and so on.

3 Practice

Using page 93 Have students read the sentence about the hour marks aloud and then write the hour numbers on the clock face. Have students color the hands according to the directions. Have a student read the remaining information about the hour and minute hands and ways to write time. Tell students they are to draw a line from each clock face to the digital clock that tells the same time. Have students complete the page independently.

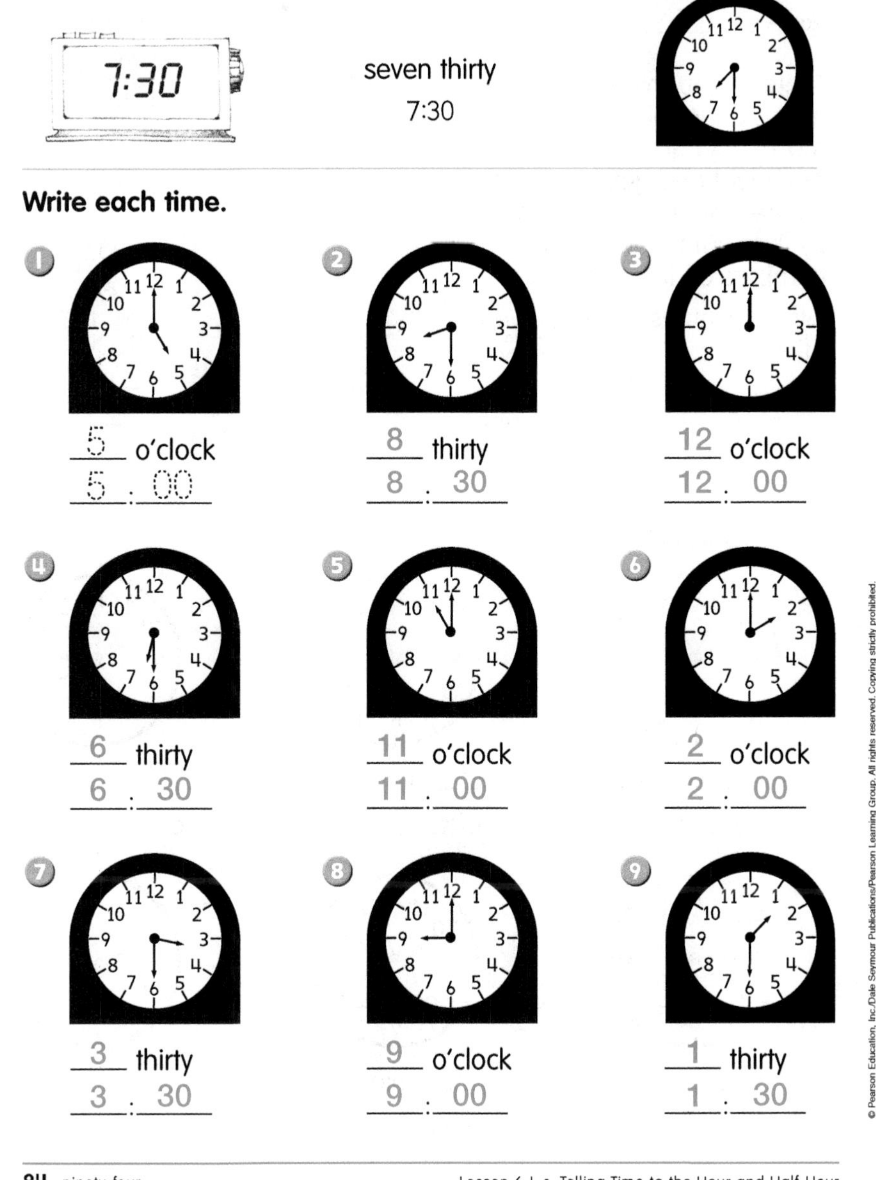
7:30

seven thirty

7:30

Write each time.

1. 5 o'clock
5 : 00

2. 8 thirty
8 : 30

3. 12 o'clock
12 : 00

4. 6 thirty
6 : 30

5. 11 o'clock
11 : 00

6. 2 o'clock
2 : 00

7. 3 thirty
3 : 30

8. 9 o'clock
9 : 00

9. 1 thirty
1 : 30

Using page 94 Have students read the time on the digital clock and the clock face and then read the two ways to write time. Tell students that they are to write the number under each clock to tell the time and then write the time as it would look on a digital clock. Have students complete the page independently.

4 Assess

Set up a demonstration clock to show 3:00. Have children write the time three ways. Repeat for 8:00 and 12:00.

For Mixed Abilities

Common Errors • Intervention

Some students may confuse the hour hand and the minute hand. Have them work with partners to draw hands on a clock face for times such as 2:00, 7:00, and 11:00. Discuss how the short hand shows the hour; hence, it is the hour hand. Some may be helped by thinking that, in an hour, the shorter hand goes the shorter distance from one hour to the next, and the longer hand goes the longer distance, completely around the clock face.

Enrichment • Number Sense

1. Have students list activities that take a half-hour to complete. Then, have students list activities that take an hour to complete.
2. Have students show any o'clock on a clock face. Then, have a friend tell the time and show the next o'clock.
3. Ask students to draw a clock face and a digital clock to show the time, to the nearest hour, when they eat lunch, go to school, and arrive home from school. Have them label each clock with the activity they are doing at that time.

More to Explore • Application

Showing a correspondence between things is often called mapping. Give students a paper arranged in the following way:

sponge		bath towel
peanut butter		soap
dish cloth	kitchen	knife
toilet		milk
frying pan		plate
sugar	bathroom	glass

Ask students to draw lines of correspondence connecting the item with the room in which it is found. See if students recognize that while many of the items belong in one room or the other, some could be found in either.

6-2 Telling Time to 5 Minutes

pages 95–96

1 Getting Started

Objective

- To tell time in 5-minute intervals

Materials

*demonstration clock

Warm Up • Mental Math

Have students name two addition facts for the following sums.

1. 17 (8 + 9 = 17, 9 + 8 = 17)
2. 13 (6 + 7 = 13, 9 + 4 = 13, etc.)
3. 15 (8 + 7 = 15, 9 + 6 = 15, etc.)
4. 16 (8 + 8 = 16, 9 + 7 = 16, etc.)

Have them name two subtraction facts for the following minuends.

5. 15 (15 − 8 = 7, 15 − 9 = 6, etc.)
6. 17 (17 − 9 = 8, 17 − 8 = 9)
7. 11 (11 − 9 = 2, 11 − 8 = 3, etc.)
8. 12 (12 − 9 = 3, 12 − 4 = 8, etc.)

Warm Up • Number Sense

Have students count by 5s through 100 in unison. Now, have one student begin with 5 and count on by 5s for three or four numbers. Have the next student continue from there to say the next three or four numbers by 5s. Continue until students reach 100. Have students repeat the activity by writing the three or four numbers on the board as they count by 5s.

There are 60 minutes in each hour. As the minute hand moves around the clock face, the hour hand gets closer to the next hour number. Count by fives. Write the minute numbers on the clock.

It is 25 minutes after 3.

We can also write 3:25.

The hour hand is between the 3 and the 4.

The minute hand is on the 5.

00, 05, 10, 15, 20, 25, 30, 35, 40, 45, 50, 55

Write each time.

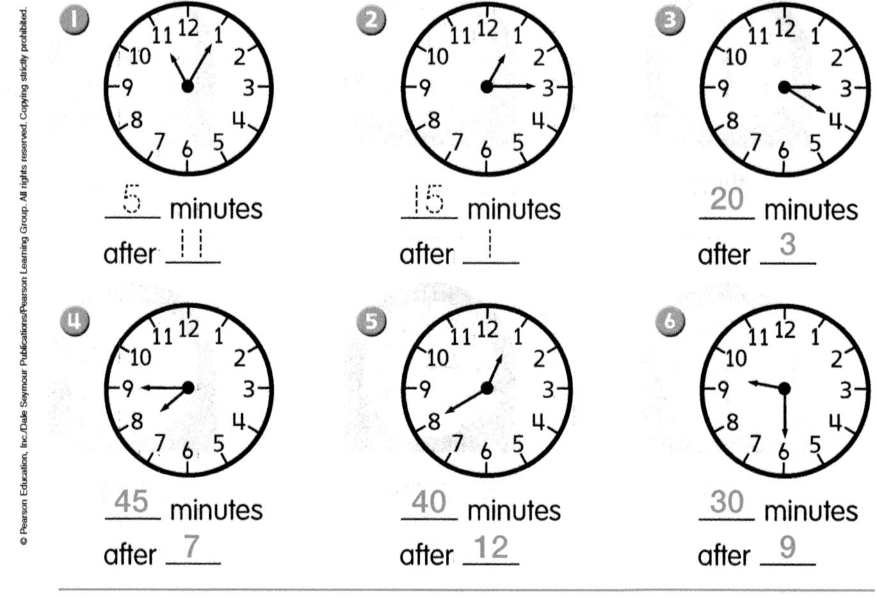

2 Teach

Develop Skills and Concepts Set the demonstration clock to 5:00. Have students notice the 1-minute marks on the demonstration clock face. Tell students that there are 60 of these marks on a clock face because there are 60 minutes in 1 hour. Tell students to count by 5s as you move the minute hand around the clock from one number to the next. Help students see that the hour hand moved slowly from the 5 to the 6 as 60 minutes went by.

- Now, place the minute hand on the 1 and tell students it is 5 minutes after 6:00. Write **6:05** on the board and tell students that we write five minutes after 6 this way. Continue to move the minute hand around the clock as you tell students it is 10 minutes after 6:00, 15 minutes after 6:00, and so on through 55 minutes after 6:00. Then, show 7:00 because 60 minutes, or 1 whole hour, has passed.
- Place the hour hand on 7 and the minute hand on the 5 and ask a student to count by 5s to see how many minutes after 7:00 it is. (25 minutes) It is important to refer to all times as after the hour in this lesson because reading time after and before the hour in the same lesson is confusing to students.

3 Practice

Using page 95 Have students read the sentences aloud with you. Help students write in the numbers for counting by 5s in their texts. Help students work each of the exercises, if necessary, or assign the page to be completed independently.

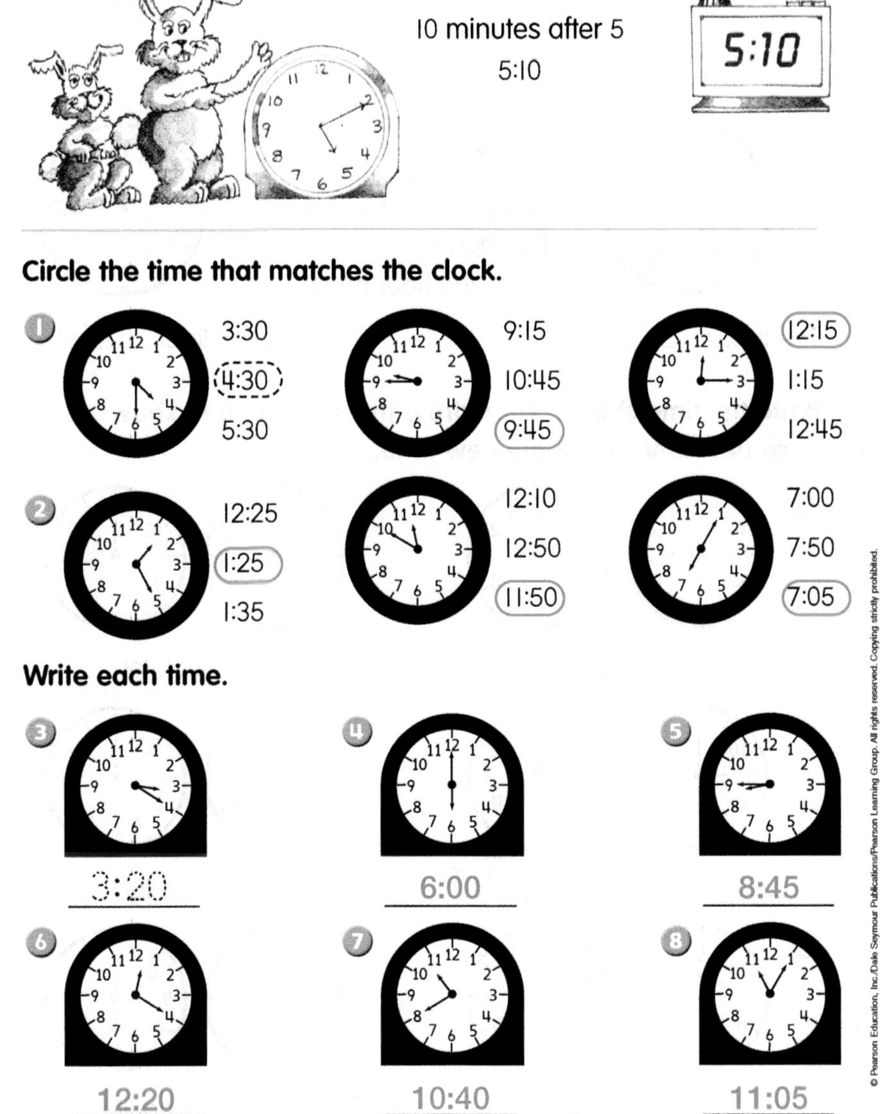

10 minutes after 5

5:10

5:10

Circle the time that matches the clock.

1. 3:30 / (4:30) / 5:30 — 9:15 / 10:45 / (9:45) — (12:15) / 1:15 / 12:45

2. 12:25 / (1:25) / 1:35 — 12:10 / 12:50 / (11:50) — 7:00 / 7:50 / (7:05)

Write each time.

3. 3:20
4. 6:00
5. 8:45
6. 12:20
7. 10:40
8. 11:05

96 ninety-six — Lesson 6-2 • Telling Time to 5 Minutes

Using page 96 Have students read the times on the two clocks. Tell students that in the first section they are to circle one of the three times to show the correct time on the clock. Then, tell them that they are to write the time for each of the clocks in Exercises 3 to 8. Have students complete the problems. Now, have students show on the demonstration clock all times in each of the first problems to check their answers.

4 Assess

Have students draw four clocks on a sheet of paper. Then, ask them to draw the clock hands to represent the following times: 5:25, 6:35, 3:20, and 11:45.

For Mixed Abilities

Common Errors • Intervention

Some students may confuse the numbers for the hours on the clock with the number of minutes after the hour and write 3 minutes after 1 instead of 15 minutes after 1. Encourage them to write the 5-minute intervals around the outside of the clock until they become familiar with counting by 5s to get the number of minutes.

Enrichment • Number Sense

1. Have students draw pictures to show some things that they can do in 5 minutes of time, 30 minutes of time, and 60 minutes of time.
2. If students have mastered telling time to the 5 minutes, introduce them to different ways to say 5:45, 5:30, and 5:15. (quarter to, half past, quarter after) Then, write **4:15, 3:30,** and **2:45** on the board and have them say the different ways to tell the time.

More to Explore • Probability

Give each student a penny and a sheet of paper. Have them fold the paper in half, the long way. Next, write the words **heads** and **tails** on the board. Ask a student to explain what the head and tail of a penny mean. Have students predict how many heads and tails they will get if they flip the penny 20 times. (Answers will vary, but many students will say ten of each.) Now, have each student flip the penny 20 times. Explain that each time students toss the coin, they are to mark the result on one side of the paper or the other. Some may illustrate each head or tail, others will just make an X or a slash mark. At the end of the activity ask students how many actually got exactly ten heads and ten tails. Explain that on the average, they will expect equal numbers of heads and tails, but that for any single trial of 20 coin tosses, they may expect any answer.

6-3 Telling Time, Before and After

pages 97–98

1 Getting Started

Objective
- To solve problems by telling time before and after

Materials
*demonstration clock

Warm Up • Mental Math
Have students say the numbers in order from least to greatest.

1. 6, 4, 8, 9 (4, 6, 8, 9)
2. 212, 201, 215 (201, 212, 215)
3. 50, 10, 100 (10, 50, 100)
4. 900, 400, 800 (400, 800, 900)
5. 20, 0, 200 (0, 20, 200)
6. 18, 24, 14 (14, 18, 24)
7. 151, 51, 91 (51, 91, 151)
8. 3, 7, 11, 9, 5 (3, 5, 7, 9, 11)

Warm Up • Application
Have a student move the hands of the demonstration clock to read any hour, half-hour, or 5-minute interval. Have a student read the times and write it one way on the board. Have students write the time another way. Repeat for students to practice positioning the hands and then saying and writing the times.

Name ______________________

Ellen wants to meet a friend 1 hour from now. What time will she meet her friend?

Draw the hour hand.

The time is 7:00.   1 hour later 8:00

Write the time shown. Then draw the hour hand to show each new time. Write the new time.

1. 3:00 1 hour later 4:00
2. 5:00 2 hours later 7:00
3. 9:00 1 hour earlier 8:00
4. 9:00 3 hours later 12:00
5. 10:00 6 hours later 4:00
6. 8:00 2 hours earlier 6:00

2 Teach

Develop Skills and Concepts Remind students that there are 60 minutes in 1 hour as you move the minute hand on a demonstration clock one full revolution to go from 12:00 to 1:00. Tell students that each time the minute hand goes around the clock, 1 hour has passed. Ask students what time is shown now. (1:00) Ask students to tell how much later 1:00 is than 12:00. (1 hour) Ask students to tell how many hours later than 12:00 it is now as you show 4:00. (4 hours) Repeat for more on-the-hour times. Give students some times where they must count beyond the 12, such as 4 hours later than 9:00 and so on. Now, show 9:00 on the clock and ask students how many hours are between 9:00 and 10:00. (1 hour) Tell students that 9:00 is 1 hour earlier than 10:00. Show 12:00 and ask students how many hours ago the clock showed 4:00. (8 hours)

3 Practice

Using page 97 Help students read the example. Ask what is to be solved. (the time Ellen will meet her friend) Ask what time it is now. (7:00) Have students trace 7:00. Ask how many hours from now the friends will meet. (1 hour) Ask what time it will be 1 hour later than 7:00. (8:00) Have students trace the hour hand and 8:00.

- Have a student read the directions for Exercises 1 to 6. Ask what is to be done. (draw the hour hand in the second clock and write both times) Have students complete the page independently.

Using page 98 Tell students to read each problem, draw the hour hand, and write the times in the first section.

Solve.

1
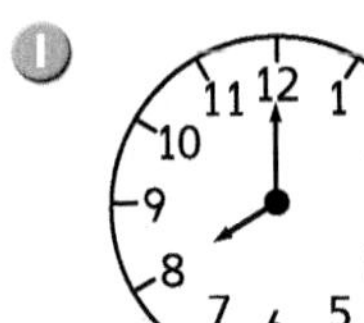

Andy fished for 2 hours. What time did he stop? Draw the hour hand.

The time is 8:00.

He stopped at 10:00.

2

Laura played ball for 3 hours. What time did she stop? Draw the hour hand.

The time is 11:00.

She stopped at 2:00.

Now Try This!

Roman Numerals are very old. They are still used on some clocks.

1	2	3	4	5	6
I	II	III	IV	V	VI

7	8	9	10	11	12
VII	VIII	IX	X	XI	XII

Write the Roman Numerals on the clock face.

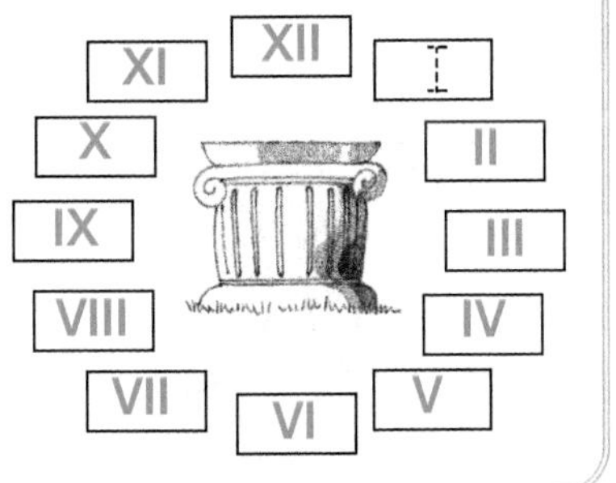

Now Try This! Show students a clock or picture of a clock with Roman numerals. Have students compare the Roman numerals to the numbers on a clock with Arabic numerals. Tell students that the Roman numeral I means 1, V means 5, and X means 10. Write **IV** and **VI** on the board and tell students the IV means 5 − 1 or 4 and VI means 5 + 1 or 6. Repeat for **IX** and **XI**. Have students write the numbers from 1 to 12 with their corresponding Roman numerals. Have students write the Roman numerals on the clock face independently.

4 Assess

Tell students that it is 1:00. Ask what time it will be in 3 hours (4:00), 5 hours (6:00), and 11 hours (12:00).

For Mixed Abilities

Common Errors • Intervention

Some students may have difficulty determining previous and elapsed time. Have them practice with partners by completing a chart like the following. When they have finished, ask them to choose one line on the chart and draw clocks to show the times.

1 hour earlier	TIME	1 hour later
(3:00)	4:00	(5:00)
(10:00)	11:00	(12:00)
(12:00)	1:00	(2:00)
(11:00)	12:00	(1:00)

Enrichment • Number Sense

Tell students to draw clocks to show the time they get up in the morning and when they have dinner in the evening. Then, have them tell how many hours earlier than dinner they rise and how many hours it is after they rise until they eat dinner.

More to Explore • Application

Set up a shop in class where students can trade tokens for actual items. Invent your own token system. Students can earn tokens by doing their homework, keeping their desk tidy, or being a good citizen for a week. The items for sale in the shop might include pencils, small notebooks, or packs of paper or stickers. Have students help set the prices for the various items in the shop and rotate the job of shopkeeper. Have other students act as the bookkeepers, recording the items sold each day and the number of tokens taken in.

ESL/ELL STRATEGIES

Review the use of the prepositions *in* and *for* when telling time. *In* describes a point of time in the future as it relates to the present moment. For example, in 30 minutes means "30 minutes from now." *For* describes a continuous period of time.

6-4 Elapsed Time

pages 99–100

1 Getting Started

Objectives
- To tell the time that is 5 minutes later
- To solve problems by telling time in 5-minute intervals

Materials
*2 demonstration clocks

Warm Up • Mental Math
Ask students how are they counting the following numbers.

1. 193, 194, 195, 196 (by 1s)
2. 4th, 6th, 8th, 10th (by 2s)
3. 215, 220, 225, 230 (by 5s)
4. 680, 780, 880, 980 (by 100s)
5. 25, 35, 45, 55 (by 10s)
6. 35, 40, 45, 50 (by 5s)
7. 82, 92, 102, 112 (by 10s)

Warm Up • Time Activity
Have students begin at the 1 on the clock and count the minutes by 5s around the clock through 60 minutes. Now, point to the 4 and have students begin at 20 and count on by 5s through 60. Repeat for counting on by 5s through 60 from any number on the clock.

Name ______________________________ Lesson 6-4

Ryan must meet his mother in 30 minutes. What time will it be then?
Draw the minute hand.

The time is 1:15. 30 minutes later 1:45.

Write the time shown. Then draw the minute hand to show each new time. Write the new time.

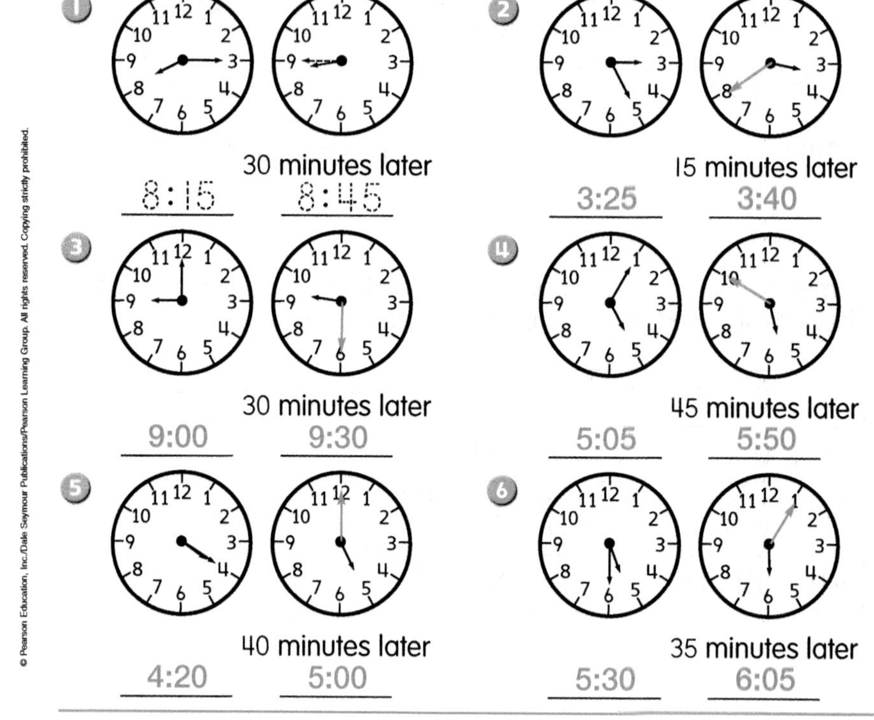

1. 8:15 — 30 minutes later — 8:45
2. 3:25 — 15 minutes later — 3:40
3. 9:00 — 30 minutes later — 9:30
4. 5:05 — 45 minutes later — 5:50
5. 4:20 — 40 minutes later — 5:00
6. 5:30 — 35 minutes later — 6:05

2 Teach

Develop Skills and Concepts Review the time for 2 hours later or earlier than 10:00 by having students tell the number of hours later or earlier and the new time. Now, show the present time on a demonstration clock and tell students that in 20 minutes, they will go out to play or go to lunch. Have a student set the second demonstration clock at the present time and then move the minute hand 20 minutes ahead. Ask students the new time. Set the first clock at other times and tell stories that ask the students to add on minutes in increments of 5s through 55 minutes. Have students show the new times on the second clock and tell the time. Now, set the clock to show 10 minutes later than the first and have students tell how many minutes later. Repeat for more examples of less than 60 minutes later.

3 Practice

Using page 99 Have students read aloud the example and tell what is to be solved. (the time when Ryan will meet his mother) Ask the time on the first clock and have students trace the 1:15. Ask students how many minutes will pass before Ryan is to meet his mother. (30) Have students trace the minute hand, tell the time that is 30 minutes later, and trace the 1:45. Help students complete the first exercise and then assign the page to be completed independently.

Using page 100 Help students complete the first exercise and then have students complete the page independently. Remind students to answer the question for each exercise.

Solve.

1 

Alan started at 3:15. He stopped at 3:30. How long did Alan jump rope? 15 minutes

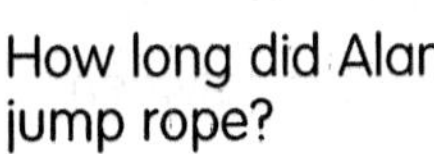

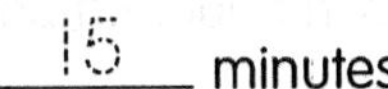

2 

Amanda started at 5:05. She stopped at 5:45. How long did Amanda jog? 40 minutes

3 

Becky started at 12:10. She stopped at 12:45. How long did Becky play tennis? 35 minutes

4 

Royce started at 2:45. He stopped at 3:15. How long did Royce ride? 30 minutes

4 Assess

Set a demonstration clock to 8:25. Ask students what time it will be in 10 minutes (8:35), in 25 minutes (8:50), and in 50 minutes (9:15).

For Mixed Abilities

Common Errors • Intervention

For students who need more practice, have them work with partners and the clock flashcards. Have them take turns selecting two cards, telling the two times on the cards, and giving the interval of time between them.

Enrichment • Application

1. Tell students to draw five clocks in a row with each clock showing a time that is 20 minutes later than the one before it.
2. Have students list an activity they do each morning, such as eat breakfast, and draw a clock that shows what time they do that activity. Then, have students list an activity they do each afternoon or evening, such as do homework, and draw a clock that shows what time they do that activity.
3. Have students draw a clock that shows the present time and then draw a second clock that shows 90 minutes later.

More to Explore • Number Sense

Have each student draw a playing grid with 15 squares, 3 across and 5 down. Call out a sum less than 50. Each student fills in each horizontal row by writing numbers that equal the sum given when added across. For example, if the sum is 18, students may write 8, 1, 9 in the first row.

Each student receives one point for each different combination of numbers that correctly equals the sum. Repeat for other sums.

A variation could be to have 16 squares (4 across and 4 down) with four addends for each sum.

6-5 Telling Time to the Minute

pages 101–102

1 Getting Started

Objective
- To tell time to the minute

Materials
*demonstration clock

Warm Up • Mental Math
Ask students where the minute hand is when it is

1. 1:15 (on the 3)
2. 5:05 (on the 1)
3. 20 minutes after 4 (on the 4)
4. 55 minutes after 10 (on the 11)
5. 12:40 (on the 8)
6. 7:25 (on the 5)
7. 9:00 (on the 12)

Warm Up • Time Activity
Have a student write **4:45** on the board and show the time on the demonstration clock. Have another student show the time that is 20 minutes later and write the new time on the board. Have a third student show the time that is 40 minutes later than the first time and write the new time on the board. Continue until all students have participated.

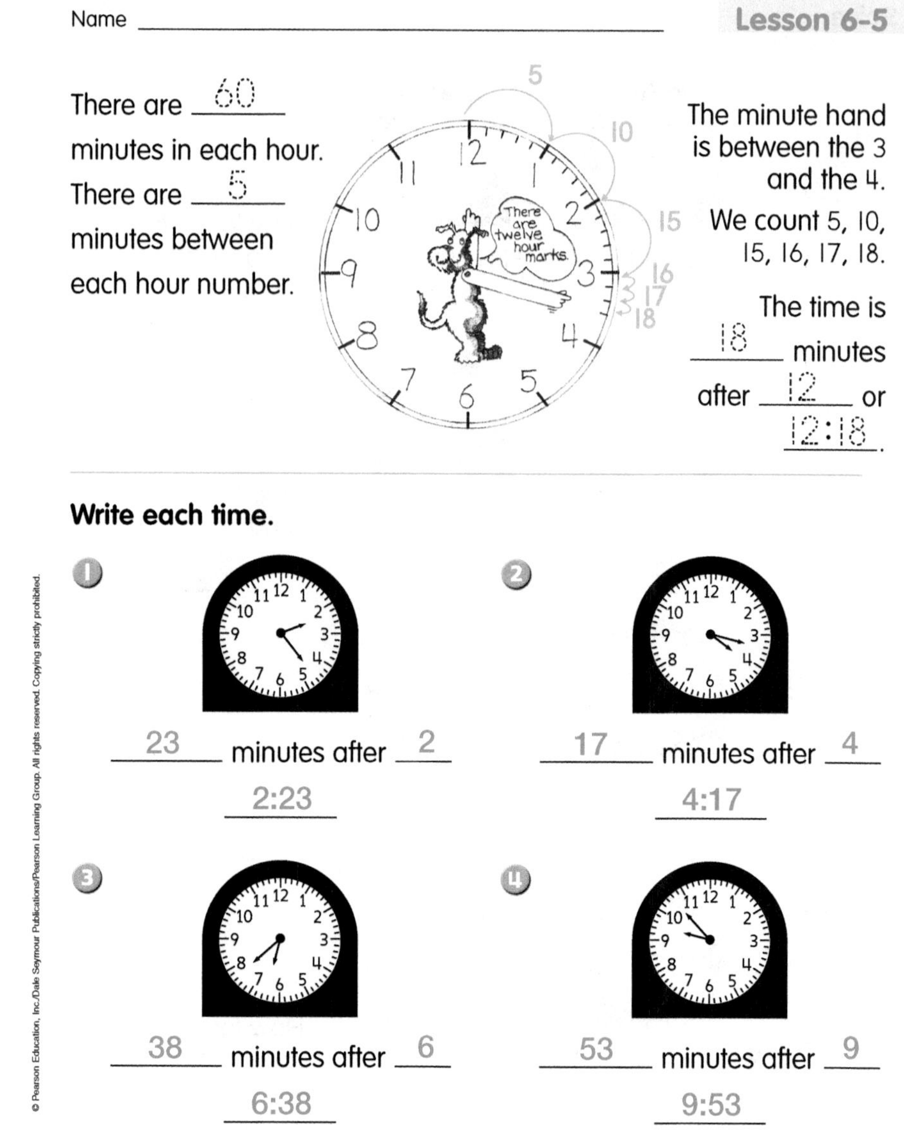

Name ______________________ Lesson 6-5

There are 60 minutes in each hour. There are 5 minutes between each hour number.

The minute hand is between the 3 and the 4. We count 5, 10, 15, 16, 17, 18.

The time is 18 minutes after 12 or 12:18.

Write each time.

1. 23 minutes after 2
2:23

2. 17 minutes after 4
4:17

3. 38 minutes after 6
6:38

4. 53 minutes after 9
9:53

2 Teach

Ask students the number of minutes in 1 hour. (60) Have students count by 5s from 5 to 60 as one student moves the minute hand accordingly around the clock. Now, show students the minute marks between each number on the clock as you remind students that there are 5 minutes between each number. Have a student begin at the 12 and point to each minute mark as students count by 1s through 8. Have other students point to the minute marks as students continue to count by 1s through 60.

- Move the hour hand to the 10 and the minute hand to the 3 and ask students how many minutes after 10:00 it is. (15) Have a student write **10:15** on the board. Move the minute hand to 22 minutes after 10 and have students count 5, 10, 15, 20, 21, 22 to tell the number of minutes after 10:00. (22) Have a student write **10:22** on the board. Continue for more times after the hour.

Now, write **3:06** on the board and have a student show the time on the clock and say the time. (6 minutes after 3) Repeat for more practice.

3 Practice

Using page 101 Have students read the information at the top of the page as they trace the answers to find 12:18. Remind students to count by 5s as far as possible and then count by 1s. Help students count the minutes on each clock and have students complete the page independently.

Using page 102 Tell students that in the first section they are to draw a line from each clock face to the digital clock reading the same time. Tell students to write the time under each clock in the second section. Have students complete the page independently.

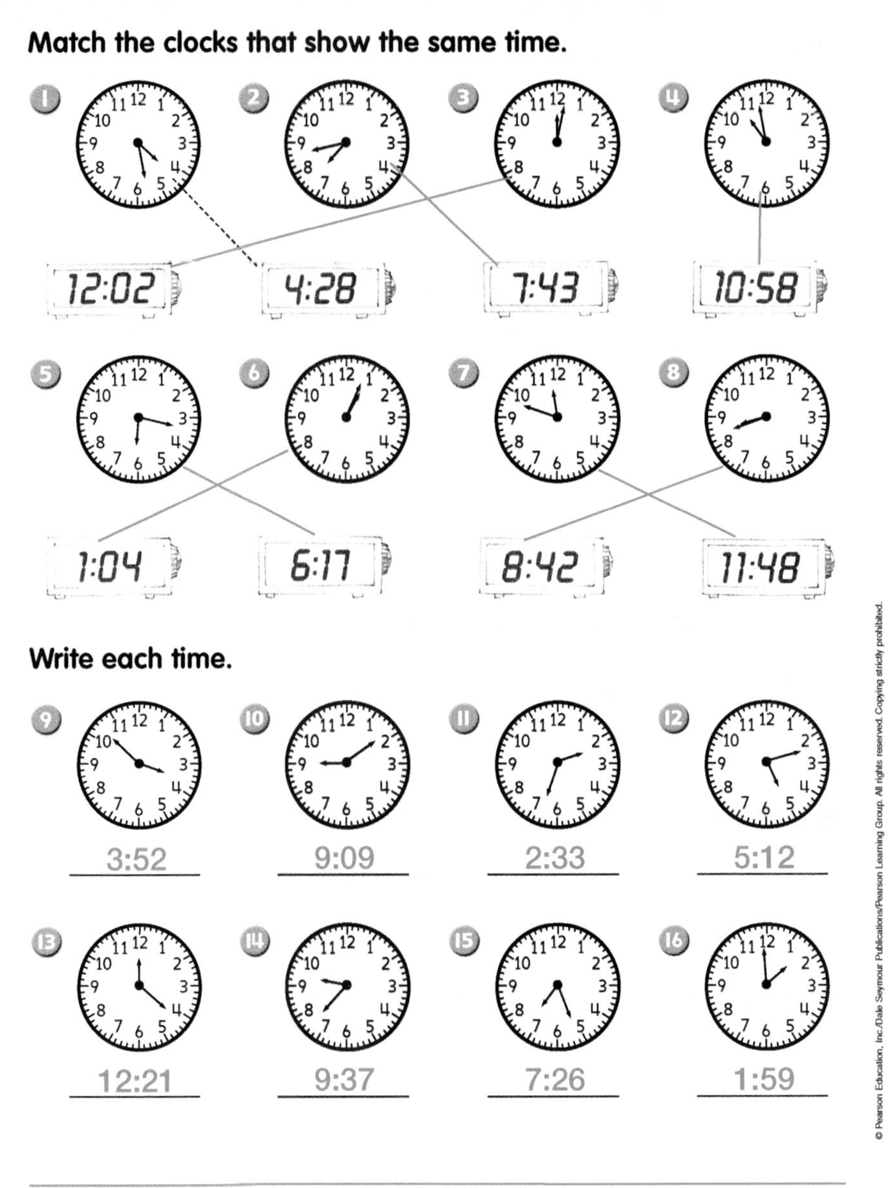

Match the clocks that show the same time.

1 2 3 4

12:02 4:28 7:43 10:58

5 6 7 8

1:04 6:17 8:42 11:48

Write each time.

9	10	11	12
3:52	9:09	2:33	5:12

13	14	15	16
12:21	9:37	7:26	1:59

4 Assess

Write **4:13, 8:32**, and **12:08** on the board. Have students draw clocks showing each of these times.

For Mixed Abilities

Common Errors • Intervention

If students have difficulty telling time to the minute, have them work with partners and a clock face. One partner can write a time for the other partner to show on the clock. They can then reverse roles and continue showing other times.

Enrichment • Number Sense

1. Have students write five different times as they would look on a digital clock and have a friend show the times on a clock face.
2. Tell students to draw clocks to show 4:22 and 9:49. Ask them how the hands are positioned on each.
3. Tell students to draw clocks to show five different times when the minute and hour hands point to the same place on the clock.

More to Explore • Logic

Bring a lunch bag and five small objects to class. Examples might be a crayon, paper clip, rubber band, rock, and bandage. Show students the objects and then put them in the bag. Now, take out four of the things and ask students to name the fifth. Replace the objects and have a student come up and take four out. Ask another student to name the fifth. Make the game harder by pulling three objects out. Ask them to name the two that remain in the bag. This can be repeated with different objects. Each time you play, have a student withdraw a different number of things from the bag.

An alternate activity with the bag is to describe a hidden object with two words. If you said that the object you were thinking of was straight and colorful, they should guess you are thinking of the crayon. Have one student describe and another guess the mystery object.

6-6 Days, Weeks, and Months

pages 103–104

1 Getting Started

Objectives
- To write the days of the week
- To write the months of the year

Vocabulary
day, week, month, year, calendar

Materials
*calendar; *flashcards of days of the week; *flashcards of months of the year

Warm Up • Mental Math
Have students name the number.

1. 10 less than 902 (892)
2. 100 more than 216 (316)
3. 10 more than 4 tens 2 ones (52)
4. 376 plus 100 more (476)
5. 777 minus 10 (767)
6. 1 ten more than 5 hundreds (510)
7. 1 ten less than 400 (390)
8. 8 hundreds 9 tens 8 ones and 1 ten more (908)

Warm Up • Application
Show students a calendar of the present month. Have them tell the day of the month for the second Tuesday, the first Wednesday, the third Saturday, and so on. Then, have students name the day of the week for the thirtieth, the sixteenth, the seventh, and so on.

Name ______________________ **Lesson 6-6**

Sunday	Monday	Tuesday	Wednesday	Thursday	Friday	Saturday

There are 7 days in a week.

Write the days of the week in order.

1. Sunday, Monday, Tuesday, Wednesday, Thursday, Friday, Saturday

Write the day that follows:

2. Thursday, Friday
3. Wednesday, Thursday
4. Monday, Tuesday
5. Sunday, Monday

Write the day that comes before:

6. Thursday, Friday
7. Sunday, Monday
8. Tuesday, Wednesday
9. Friday, Saturday

2 Teach

Develop Skills and Concepts Show the present month on the calendar and have students read the days of the week in order. Name a day of the week and have students begin with that day and write the days in order through the named day again. Repeat for more practice.

- Place the day of the week flashcards in order on the chalk tray and have students say the days in order. Scramble the cards and have students place them in order again. Ask the day that comes third, sixth, before Tuesday, after Saturday, between Monday and Wednesday, and so on. Now, have students name the months of the year in order as you flip the calendar pages from January to December.
- Place the month flashcards in order on the chalk tray and have students say them in order. Scramble the cards and have students use the calendar if necessary to place the months in order again. Now, have students tell the month that comes before September, after December, between April and June, and so on. Have students write the third month, twelfth month, and so on, on the board.

3 Practice

Using page 103 Have students read the days of the week in order and then complete the page independently.

Using page 104 Have students read the months in order and then complete the page independently.

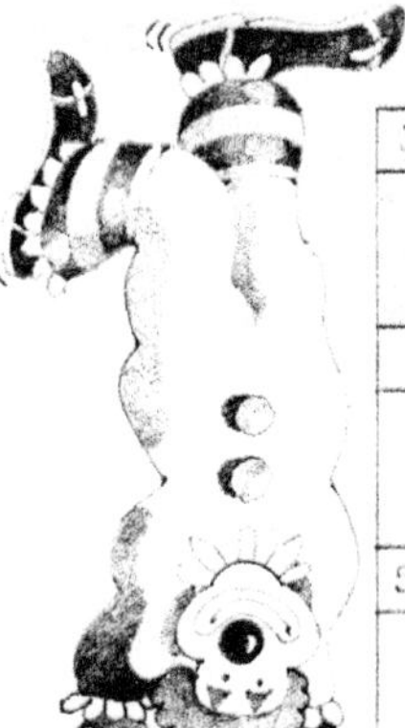

January	February	March	April
May	June	July	August
September	October	November	December

Write the correct month or number on the line.

1. There are 12 months in one year.
2. The first month of the year is January.
3. The last month of the year is December.
4. The fourth month of the year is April.
5. Which month comes before June? May
6. Which month comes before November? October
7. Which month comes before March? February
8. Which month comes after April? May
9. Which month comes after February? March
10. Which month comes after December? January

4 Assess

Ask, *Which days are between Wednesday and Sunday?* (Thursday, Friday, and Saturday) *Which months are between May and August?* (June, July)

For Mixed Abilities

Common Errors • Intervention

Some students may have difficulty remembering the months of the year in order. Have them work in cooperative-learning groups of five. Each member should write the month of his or her birthday on a card and then the group can cooperatively arrange the cards in order from earliest month in the year to the latest.

Enrichment • Application

1. Tell students to begin with August and write the months in order.
2. Have students use the calendar for the present year to write each month in order and the number of days in each month.

More to Explore • Geometry

Give students a brief description of the meaning of *symmetry*. Take a square sheet of paper and fold it in half. Open the paper and hold it up for students to see. Explain that one side is the same as the other. They can prove it by superimposing one on the other as they fold it. Point out that the line through the square is a line of symmetry and that we say that the figure is symmetrical. Have a student stand before the class and ask if people are symmetrical. (yes) Draw an imaginary line down the middle of the student and point out that the student is the same on either side of the line. Illustrate a spoon on the board and sketch a line through the drawing to show the spoon's symmetry. Have students bring an object from home that is symmetrical and explain their choice to the class.

6-7 Using a Calendar

pages 105–106

1 Getting Started

Objective
- To make and read a calendar

Materials
*calendar; flashcards of months of the year; flashcards of days of the week

Warm Up • Mental Math
Have students answer the following.

1. 7 + 6 + 3 (16)
2. 14 − 7 + 6 (13)
3. 100 less than 100 (0)
4. 15 + 1 − 8 (8)
5. 9 + 9 + 9 + 9 (36)
6. 18 − 1 − 9 (8)
7. number of minutes in 1 hour (60)
8. number of days in 1 week (7)

Warm Up • Application
Distribute the month flashcards to students and have them place the cards in order on the chalk tray. Repeat for more students to participate. Repeat the activity for the days of the week flashcards. Now, distribute the month cards and call for September to be placed on the chalk tray. Have students place the cards in order from September through August. Repeat for a different beginning month and then repeat the activity using the day cards.

Name ______________________

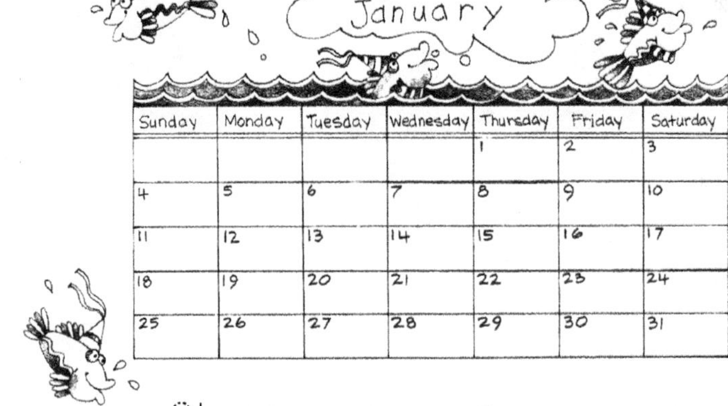

January

Sunday	Monday	Tuesday	Wednesday	Thursday	Friday	Saturday
				1	2	3
4	5	6	7	8	9	10
11	12	13	14	15	16	17
18	19	20	21	22	23	24
25	26	27	28	29	30	31

January has 31 days.

Write the dates for each day of the week.

1. Monday: 5, 12, 19, 26
2. Friday: 2, 9, 16, 23, 30
3. Saturday: 3, 10, 17, 24, 31
4. Which day of the week does this month begin on? Thursday

Write the day of the week for each of the following.

5. January fourth: Sunday
6. January twelfth: Monday
7. January nineteenth: Monday
8. January thirtieth: Friday
9. January twenty-third: Friday
10. January fifteenth: Thursday

2 Teach

Develop Skills and Concepts Show the present month on the classroom calendar and ask students the name of the month. Ask a student to find the year and the present day. Ask students to find the first and last days of the month and tell the day of the week for each. Ask how many Saturdays, Tuesdays, and so on there are in the month. Ask how many days there are in the month. Have students tell the date and the day of the week of any holidays or students' birthdays in the month. Ask students to tell the day of the week of the twenty-nineth day, the fourteenth day, and so on. Make sure students understand that while the number of days in the year do not change, each year the calendar changes.

3 Practice

Using page 105 Tell students to use the calendar at the top of the page to complete the exercises. Have students complete the page independently.

Using page 106 Help students complete the calendar. Tell students to use their calendar month to complete the page independently.

Complete the calendar for this month.

Answers will vary.

______ Month					______ Year	
Sunday	Monday	Tuesday	Wednesday	Thursday	Friday	Saturday

1. How many days are in this month? ______
2. ______ is the first day of the month.
3. ______ is the last day of the month.
4. There are ______ holidays in this month.

How many of each of the following days are there in this month?

5. Sundays ______
6. Mondays ______
7. Tuesdays ______
8. Wednesdays ______
9. Thursdays ______
10. Fridays ______
11. Saturdays ______

4 Assess

Show students a calendar for the present year. Ask them when their birthdays are. Then, have them find the month and day of their birthday in the calendar and tell you what day of the week their birthday falls on this year.

For Mixed Abilities

Common Errors • Intervention

Some students may have difficulty working with a calendar. Have them work in pairs, choosing a calendar page for a month of the year. They should take turns asking each other to give the day for a particular date. Encourage students to place their finger on the number for the date that is given and slide it up the column to find the day.

Enrichment • Application

1. Have students make a calendar for their favorite month. Tell them to write in all special activities that make that month their favorite.
2. Ask students which numbers in the present month fall on a Sunday, Monday, Thursday, and Saturday.

More to Explore • Geometry

Ask each student to bring three different leaves to class. Remind the class of the meaning of symmetry. Then, trace a large leaf on the board and, if the leaf is symmetrical, draw the line of symmetry through the center of the tracing.

Have students trace their three leaves and draw in the line of symmetry if they can. Some may bring in leaves that are not symmetrical. The begonia has asymmetric leaves, for example. If they have time, let students trade leaves and trace several more. If students have trouble tracing leaves, you can have them make crayon rubbings that will give them the same outline.

6-8 Counting Money Through Dimes

pages 107–108

1 Getting Started

Objective
- To count dimes, nickels, and pennies through 99¢

Vocabulary
dime

Materials
*items priced through 99¢; real or play pennies, nickels, and dimes

Warm Up • Mental Math
Have students name the day or month.

1. third month of the year (March)
2. second day of the week (Monday)
3. sixth day of the week (Friday)
4. months beginning with the letter *m* (March, May)
5. days beginning with the letter *t* (Tuesday, Thursday)

Warm Up • Number Sense
Have students count by 10s aloud through 200. Have a student start at 10 and say the first three numbers for counting by 10s. Have a second student say the next three numbers and continue for all students to say three numbers. Repeat for counting by 5s and by 1s.

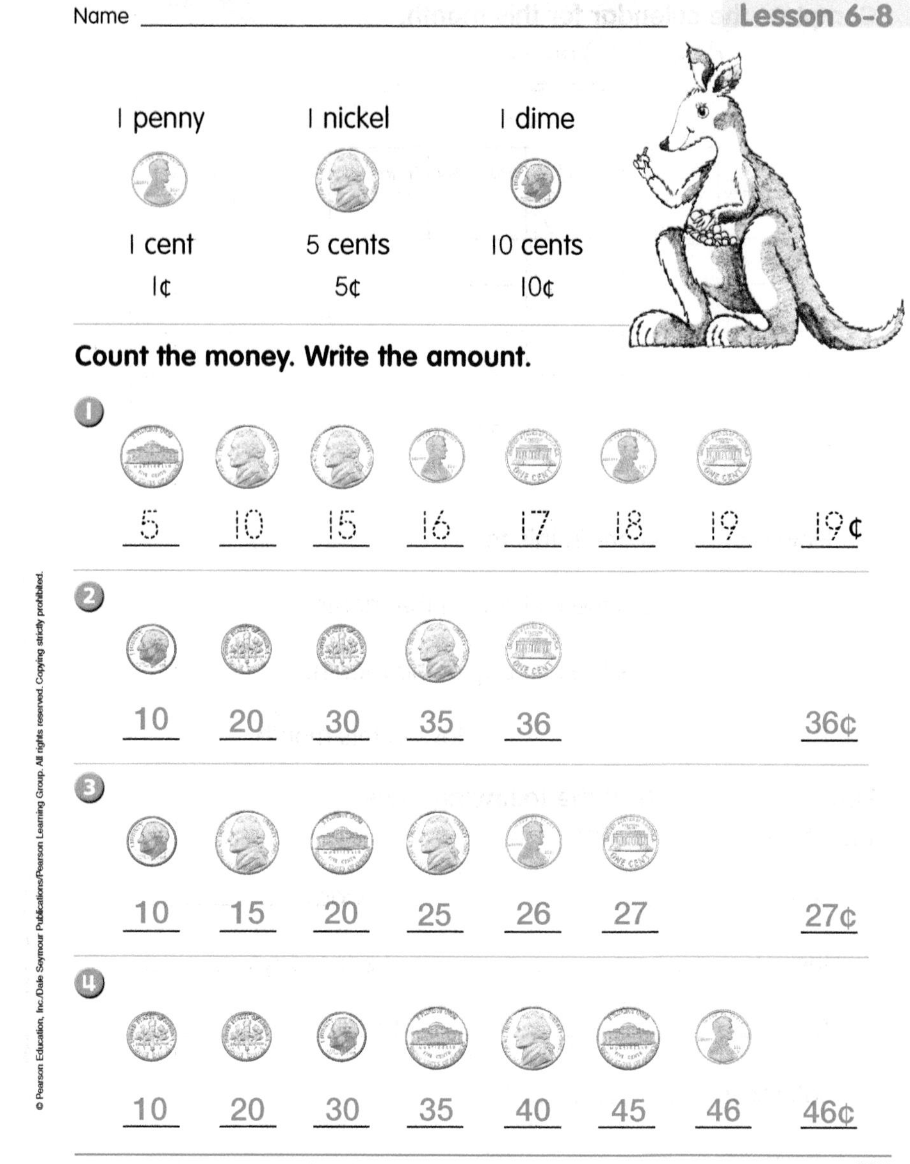

Name ______________________ Lesson 6-8

I penny	I nickel	I dime
I cent	5 cents	10 cents
I¢	5¢	10¢

Count the money. Write the amount.

1. 5, 10, 15, 16, 17, 18, 19 — 19¢
2. 10, 20, 30, 35, 36 — 36¢
3. 10, 15, 20, 25, 26, 27 — 27¢
4. 10, 20, 30, 35, 40, 45, 46 — 46¢

2 Teach

Develop Skills and Concepts Have students put out 2 dimes, 1 nickel, and 1 penny. Tell students that we count the dimes by 10s, nickels by 5s, and pennies by 1s as you count out 10, 20, 25, 26¢. Have students repeat the counting through 26¢. Have a student write **26¢** on the board. Have students lay out other amounts of coins and practice counting on by 10s, then by 5s, and then by 1s. Encourage students to sort coins for easier counting, with dimes first, then nickels, and then pennies. Have a student write each amount on the board with the cent sign.

- Hold up a priced item and draw coins on the board as you count by 10s, then 5s, and then 1s to show the coins needed to buy the item. Continue to show priced items and have students display coins to show the costs. Remind students that the cent sign must be used to denote money.

3 Practice

Using page 107 Help students complete the first exercise by tracing the numbers. Then, assign the page to be completed independently.

Using page 108 Help students complete the first exercise before assigning the page to be completed independently. Remind students that there will be coins not used in each exercise.

Circle the coins needed to buy each item.

1 27¢

2 17¢

3 25¢

4 21¢

5 33¢

4 Assess

Give each student 2 dimes, 3 nickels, and 2 pennies. Ask students if they have enough to buy a 35¢ ball. (yes) Ask them if they have enough to buy a 50¢ pencil. (no)

For Mixed Abilities

Common Errors • Intervention

Some students may have difficulty switching from counting one kind of coin to counting another kind when a group of coins are given. Have them work with partners, giving each pair a handful of coins. Have students count aloud, pausing when they finish counting one type of coin and before they count another.

Enrichment • Number Sense

1. Have students draw coins in order to show this counting sequence: 10, 20, 30, 35, 36, 46, 47, 57¢.
2. Give students an item that is priced 99¢ or less and have them draw the coins they would need to buy it.
3. Ask students to draw the coins they would have left if they bought an item priced at 47¢ and had 8 dimes, 3 nickels, and 4 pennies to spend.

More to Explore • Technology

Show students examples of prices found in decimal notation. Tell them that 25¢ can be written as $0.25. The numbers written to the left of the decimal are dollars and the numbers written to the right are cents. The first place to the right tells the number of dimes that could be used to express the change and the number in the second place on the right tells the number of pennies in the change. Have students select five coins from a collection of pennies, nickels, dimes, and quarters. Have students use a calculator to find the total value of the collection. Money must be entered into the calculator in decimal form. For example, if a student picks 1 quarter, 2 dimes, and 2 nickels, the student enters 0.25 + 0.10 + 0.10 + 0.05 + 0.05 =. The display will read 0.55. Note: If the display ends in a zero after a decimal point, such as 0.60, the calculator will not display the last zero. It will read 0.6. Explain to students that they must record the zero when they write down their answer.

6-9 Counting Money Through Quarters

pages 109–110

1 Getting Started

Objective
- To count quarters, dimes, nickels, and pennies through 99¢

Materials
*items priced through 99¢; real or play quarters, dimes, nickels, and pennies

Warm Up • Mental Math
Have students tell how they are counting from

1. 4 to 14 to 24 to 34 (by 10s)
2. 20 to 25 (by 5s)
3. 85 to 86 (by 1s)
4. 400 to 500 (by 100s)
5. 70 to 75 (by 5s)
6. 60 to 70 (by 10s)
7. 26 to 36 (by 10s)

Warm Up • Money Activity
Have students tell the total amount of money they would have if they had 4 dimes, 2 nickels, and 6 pennies. (56¢) Repeat for more amounts of dimes, nickels, and pennies. Have students lay out 70¢ in dimes, nickels, and pennies and tell what coins make the amount. (Coins will vary.) Repeat for more amounts through 99¢.

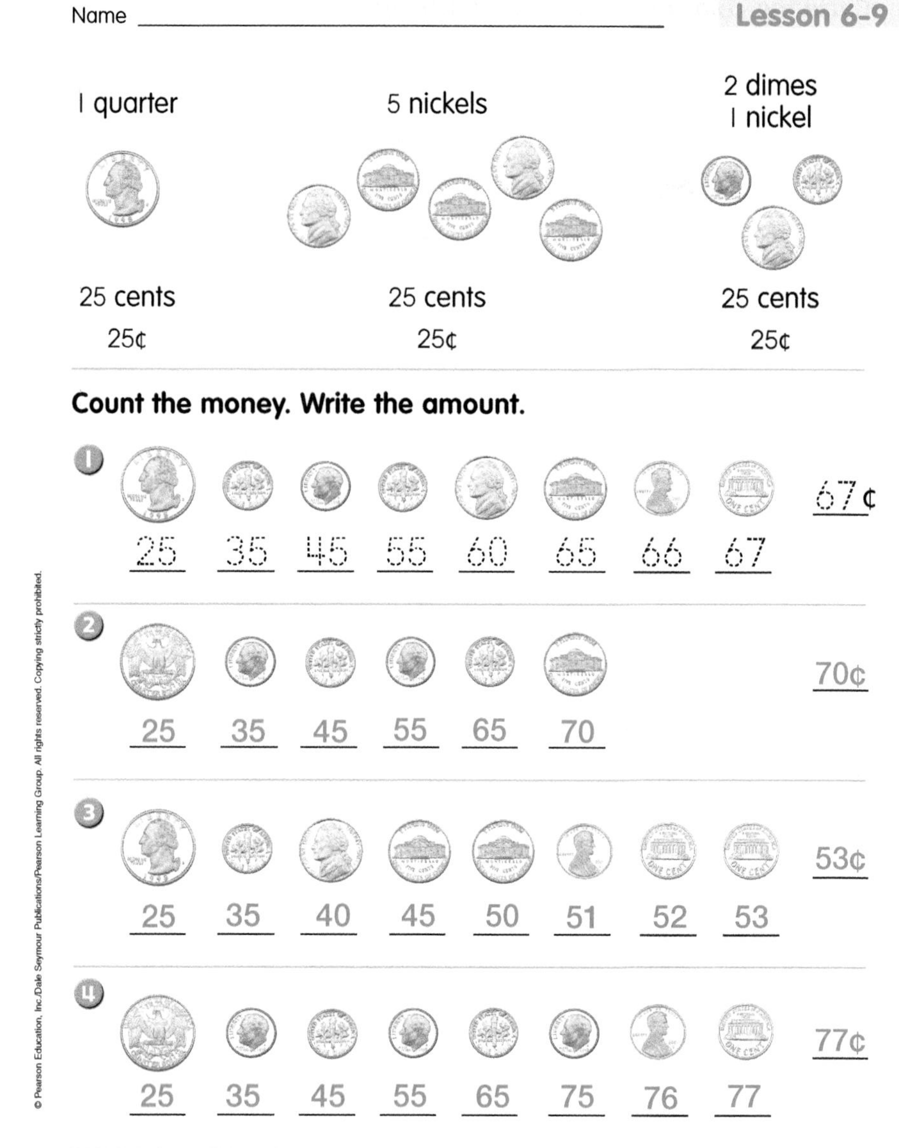

Name ______________________ Lesson 6-9

1 quarter	5 nickels	2 dimes 1 nickel
25 cents	25 cents	25 cents
25¢	25¢	25¢

Count the money. Write the amount.

1. 25 35 45 55 60 65 66 67 — 67¢
2. 25 35 45 55 65 70 — 70¢
3. 25 35 40 45 50 51 52 53 — 53¢
4. 25 35 45 55 65 75 76 77 — 77¢

2 Teach

Develop Skills and Concepts Draw a circle on the board and write **25¢** in it. Tell students that a quarter has a value of 25¢. Discuss the head and tail sides of the quarter and other coins. Draw a dime on the board and write **10¢** in it. Tell students that we want to know the total amount of money in a quarter and dime. Write **25¢** and **35¢** under the coins as you tell students to begin at 25 and count by 10s to 35¢ to find the total.

- Draw another 2 dimes and write **45¢** and **55¢** under them. Have students begin at 25 and count by 10s to tell the total money. (55¢) Now, add 2 nickels and 2 pennies to the row of coins and write **60¢, 65¢, 66¢,** and **67¢** under them. Have students begin at 25 and count the coins with you. (25, 35, 45, 55, 60, 65, 66, 67¢)
- Repeat for more amounts using 1 quarter and any number of other coins for amounts through 99¢. Have students lay out an amount of coins using 1 quarter.

Hold up a priced item and ask students if they have enough money to buy the item. Continue for more items priced less and more than their coins.

3 Practice

Using page 109 Have students read the values of the coins at the top of the page and help them complete the first exercise. Then, have students work the next problems independently. When they have completed the page, have them count the amounts of money out loud.

Using page 110 Ask students how much the item in Exercise 1 costs. (55¢) Tell students to count the money in the first exercise. (55¢) Ask if there is enough to buy the item. (yes) Have students trace the circle to answer the question. Tell students to complete the next exercises independently.

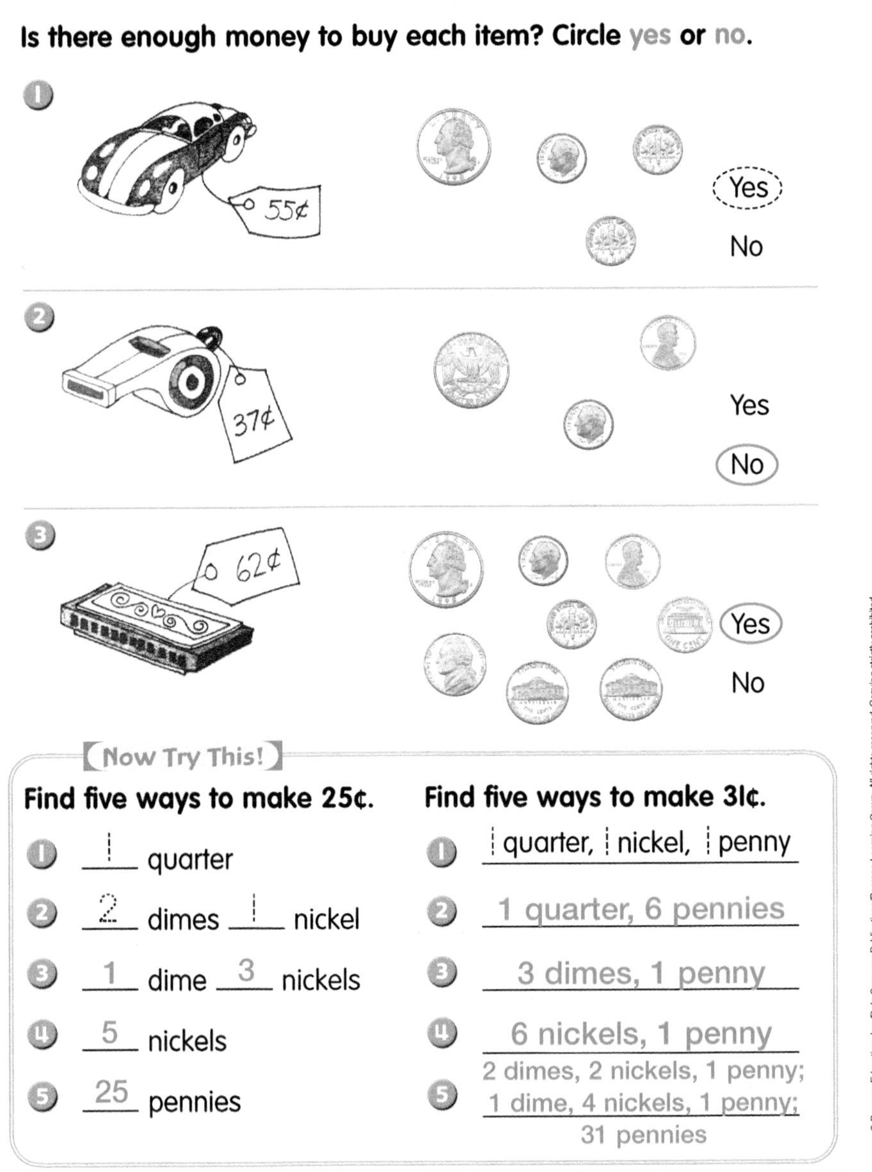

Is there enough money to buy each item? Circle yes or no.

1. 55¢ — Yes (circled) / No
2. 37¢ — Yes / No (circled)
3. 62¢ — Yes (circled) / No

Now Try This!

Find five ways to make 25¢.	Find five ways to make 31¢.
1. 1 quarter	1. 1 quarter, 1 nickel, 1 penny
2. 2 dimes 1 nickel	2. 1 quarter, 6 pennies
3. 1 dime 3 nickels	3. 3 dimes, 1 penny
4. 5 nickels	4. 6 nickels, 1 penny
5. 25 pennies	5. 2 dimes, 2 nickels, 1 penny; 1 dime, 4 nickels, 1 penny; 31 pennies

Now Try This! Have students use coins to find and record all five ways to make 25¢. Tell students to now find and record five ways to make 31¢. Help students see that a systematic way to find coins to equal 31¢ is to start with 31 pennies and then trade 5 pennies for a nickel, 10 pennies for 2 nickels, 2 nickels for 1 dime, and so on. Accept any reasonable answers for this activity.

4 Assess

Tell students to draw 92¢ in coins. Tell students they must use at least 1 quarter in their drawing.

For Mixed Abilities

Common Errors • Intervention

Some students will need more practice counting with money. Place a number of priced items around the room. Give each student a different amount of real or play money with which to shop. Ask students to count the amount of money that they have and then make a list of all the purchases that they could make.

Enrichment • Application

1. Tell students to draw coins to show four ways to pay for an item costing 46¢.
2. Ask students to draw the change they would have left if they had 1 quarter, 4 dimes, 2 nickels, and 8 pennies and bought an item for 53¢.

More to Explore • Application

Write these sentences on the board:

A truck is longer than a car.
A house is smaller than a school.
A baby is shorter than a second-grader.

Ask students to think of their own sentence that compares the size of two objects. Tell students to write and illustrate their comparison. Help them with words they do not know how to spell. This can be assigned as homework. When students bring their sentences and drawings in, post them in a place where they can look at the comparisons other students have made.

6-10 Counting Money Through Half-Dollars

pages 111–112

1 Getting Started

Objective

- To count a half-dollar, quarters, dimes, nickels, and pennies through 99¢

Vocabulary

half-dollar

Materials

real or play half-dollars, quarters, dimes, nickels, and pennies

Warm Up • Mental Math

Have students name a related fact for the following equations:

1. 15 − 8 = 7 (8 + 7 = 15, etc.)
2. 6 + 7 = 13 (7 + 6 = 13, etc.)
3. 17 − 8 = 9 (9 + 8 = 17, etc.)
4. 18 − 9 = 9 (9 + 9 = 18)
5. 9 − 0 = 9 (9 + 0 = 9, etc.)
6. 10 − 1 = 9 (9 + 1 = 10, etc.)
7. 12 − 3 = 9 (12 − 9 = 3, etc.)
8. 11 − 6 = 5 (11 − 5 = 6 , etc.)

Warm Up • Pencil and Paper

Have students lay out 76¢ using a quarter, dimes, nickels, and pennies and then draw the coins. Repeat for other amounts through 99¢. Discuss with students why it is easier to use larger denomination coins rather than all nickels and pennies, and so on.

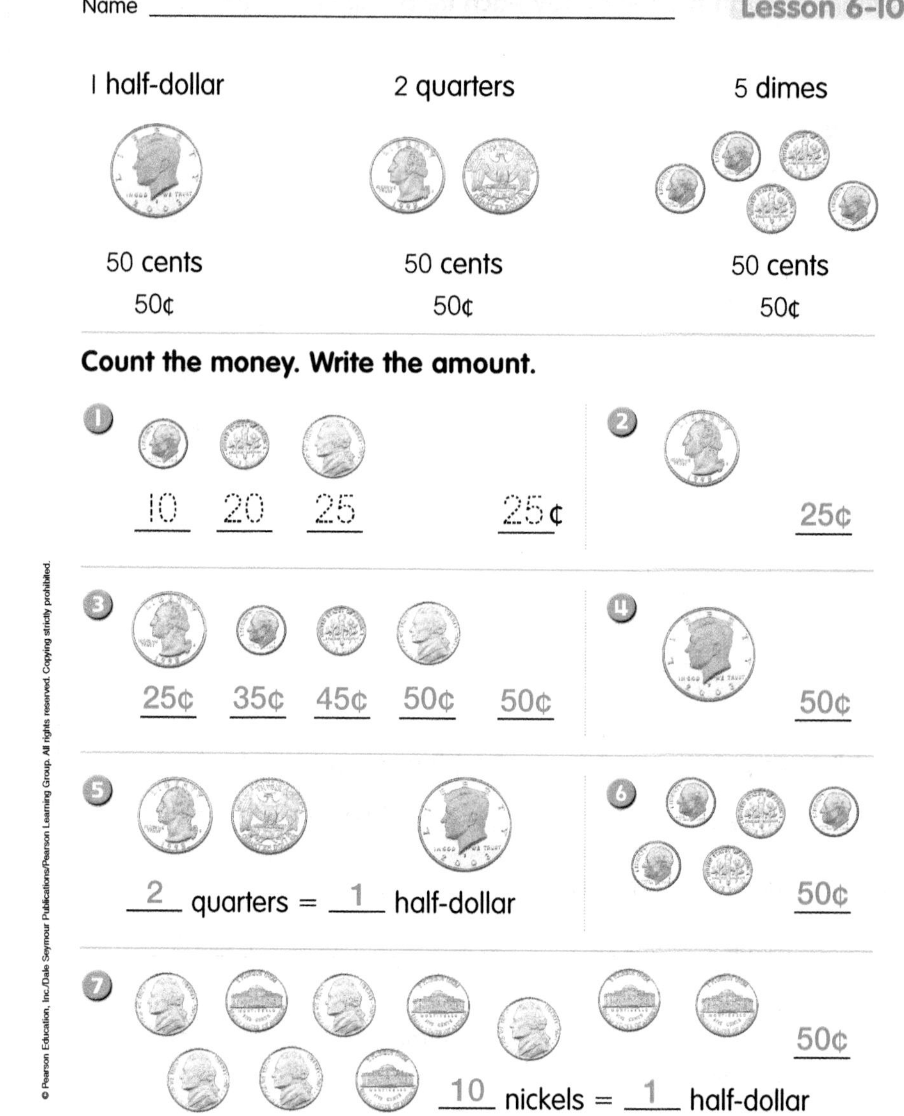

2 Teach

Develop Skills and Concepts Have students lay out 5 dimes and write the amount on the board. (50¢) Tell students that they could use 2 quarters to show 50¢ also. Have students lay out 2 quarters and write the amount on the board. (50¢) Show students a half-dollar or 50-cent piece as you tell the two names for the coin. Tell students the half-dollar is our largest coin whose value is less than 1 dollar and it can be used in place of 5 dimes or 2 quarters.

- Remind students there are 2 nickels in 1 dime as you ask students to lay out nickels to make 50¢. Ask how many nickels there are. (10) Now, ask students to draw coins on the board to show all the ways to use one kind of coin to make 50¢. (1 half-dollar, 2 quarters, 5 dimes, 10 nickels, 50 pennies) Discuss the convenience of having one or two coins versus 5, 10, or 50.
- Have students note the heads and tails sides of the half-dollar. Have students lay out a half-dollar and 2 dimes. Tell students to begin at 50 and count by 10s to tell the total. (70¢) Repeat for other amounts using a half-dollar or 2 quarters.

3 Practice

Using page 111 Read through the coin values at the top of the page with the students before having them complete the page independently.

Using page 112 Tell students that they are to count the money, write the amount, and then decide if there is enough money to purchase the priced item. Tell students to circle the word that answers the question. Have students complete the page independently.

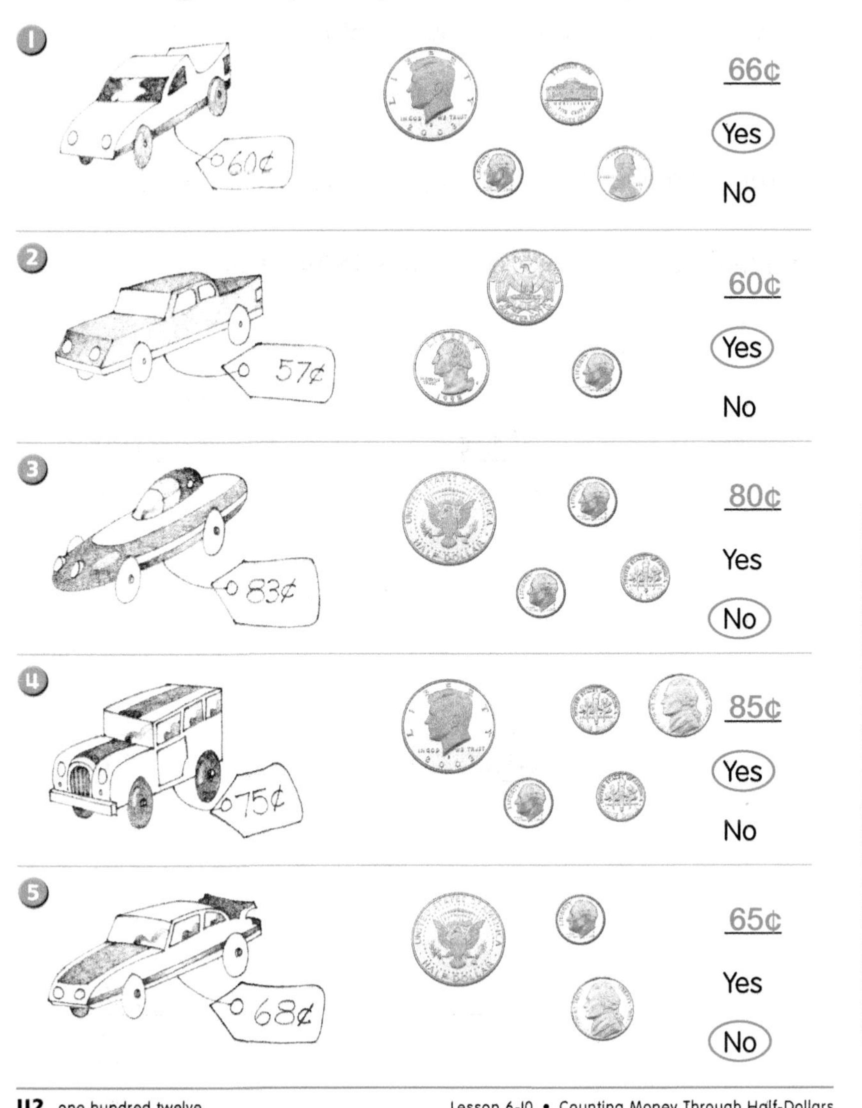

Count the money. Write the amount.
Is there enough money to buy each item? Circle yes or no.

1. 60¢ — 66¢ — (Yes) No
2. 57¢ — 60¢ — (Yes) No
3. 83¢ — 80¢ — Yes (No)
4. 75¢ — 85¢ — (Yes) No
5. 68¢ — 65¢ — Yes (No)

4 Assess

Give each student 1 half-dollar, 2 quarters, 1 dime, 2 nickels, and 5 pennies. Have them lay out 83¢. (1 half-dollar, 1 quarter, 1 nickel, and 3 pennies) Repeat for 93¢. (1 half-dollar, 1 quarter, 1 dime, 1 nickel, and 3 pennies)

For Mixed Abilities

Common Errors • Intervention

Some students will have difficulty counting with a half-dollar. Have students work with partners and coins. Give them three different cards with an item and its price pictured on each. Ask them to use their coins, beginning with a half-dollar, to show the amount of money they would need to buy the item pictured on each card. Remind students that this means they start counting at 50¢.

Enrichment • Application

1. Tell students to draw coins to show as many ways to make 50¢ as they can.
2. Tell students to draw coins to show 91¢ without using any coin twice.

More to Explore • Probability

Give each pair of students a coin and two sheets of graph paper. Ask each pair to flip the coin ten times and make a simple bar graph of the results. Remind students to use one square to represent one toss on their graphs. Then, ask pairs to tell how many heads and how many tails they got in ten flips. List these results on the board:

Heads	Tails	Pairs With This Result
5	5	
4	6	(numbers will vary)
6	4	

and so on . . .

Then, ask each pair to graph the class results on another sheet of graph paper and compare it to the first.

ESL/ELL STRATEGIES

Some students may never have seen a half-dollar coin. Pass one around the room so that everyone can examine it. Explain that it is sometimes called a fifty-cent piece. The reason it is called a *half*-dollar is because two of them equal a whole dollar.

6-11 Counting Money Through Dollars

pages 113–114

1 Getting Started

Objective

- To count 1 dollar, half-dollars, quarters, dimes, nickels, and pennies through $5

Materials

real or play dollars, half-dollars, quarters, dimes, nickels, and pennies

Warm Up • Mental Math

Have students tell the amount of money.

1. 50¢ more than 2 dimes (70¢)
2. 25¢ more than 4 nickels (45¢)
3. 10¢ less than 50¢ (40¢)
4. 3 dimes more than 20¢ (50¢)
5. 1 quarter plus 1 quarter (50¢)
6. 1 quarter less than 85¢ (60¢)
7. 5 dimes and 1 quarter (75¢)
8. 1 of each kind of coin (91¢)

Warm Up • Pencil and Paper

Have students work in pairs. Give each pair an amount of money through 99¢. Have students see how many different ways they can draw their amount of money. Have one pair check another pair's work.

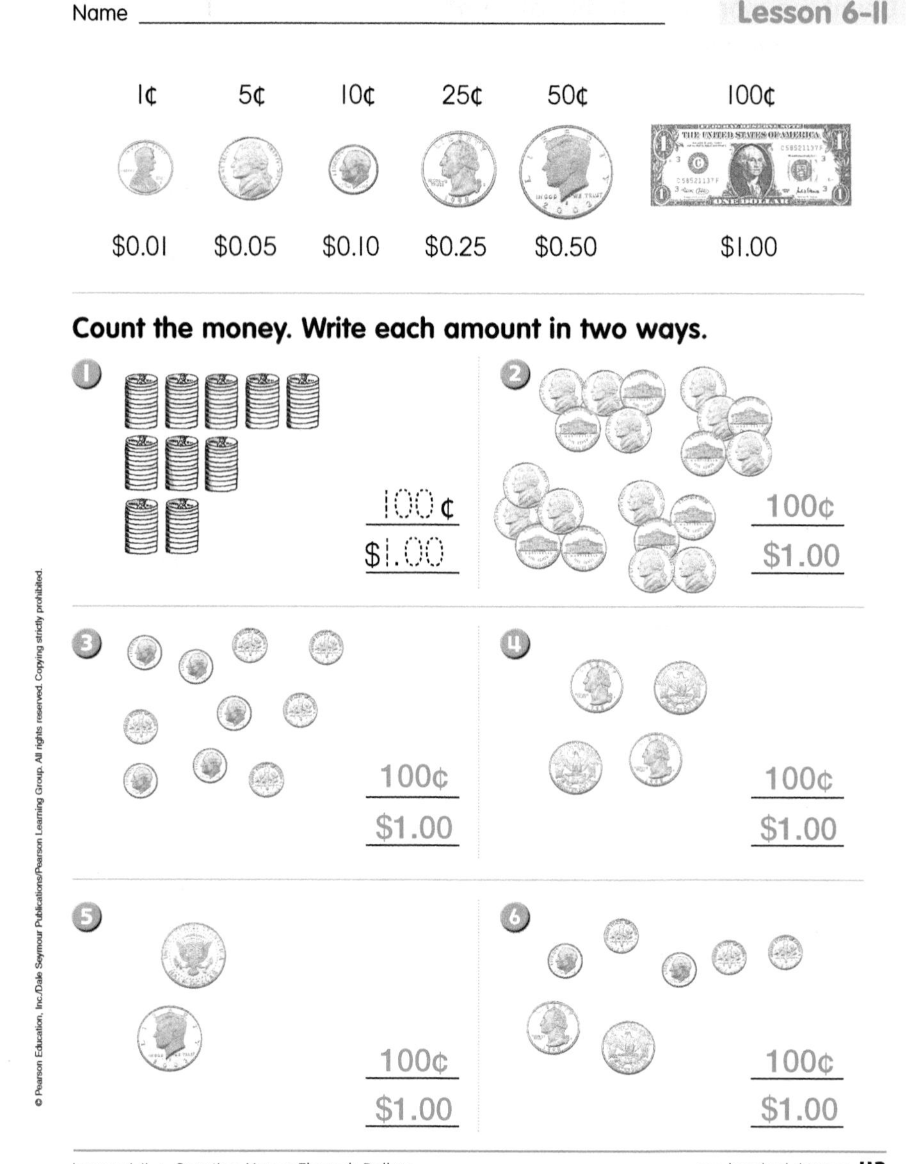

Name ______________________ Lesson 6-11

1¢	5¢	10¢	25¢	50¢	100¢
$0.01	$0.05	$0.10	$0.25	$0.50	$1.00

Count the money. Write each amount in two ways.

1. 100¢ $1.00
2. 100¢ $1.00
3. 100¢ $1.00
4. 100¢ $1.00
5. 100¢ $1.00
6. 100¢ $1.00

2 Teach

Develop Skills and Concepts Have students display coins to show 99¢. Have students lay out 1 more penny to make 100¢. Write **100¢** on the board. Remind students to use the cent sign to show money amounts. Tell students that 100¢ or more can be written another way as you write **$1.00** on the board. Tell students that the dollar sign and decimal point are used together instead of the cent sign. Tell students that less than 100¢ can also be written using the dollar sign and decimal point.

- Write **92¢** and **$0.92** on the board and have students read each as 92 cents. Have students notice that a zero is written to show there are no dollars. Repeat for other amounts less than $1.
- Show students a dollar and discuss the convenience of holding one piece of money rather than many coins. Write **$1.00** on the board. Now, have students draw on the board some ways to make $1.00 using coins. Have students lay out 1 dollar and 2 quarters. Tell students we can write this amount of money as **150¢** or **$1.50** as you write each on the board. Have students lay out another dollar and 2 dimes and tell the total cents as you write **270¢** on the board. Have a student write **$2.70** on the board. Continue for amounts of money less than $1.00 through $4.99.

3 Practice

Using page 113 Read through the money amounts across the top of the page with students and then have them complete the page independently.

Using page 114 Tell students to count the money and use the cent sign to write the amount in total cents. Tell students to write the amount of money using the dollar sign and decimal point. Help students write the amount in the first exercise before assigning the page to be completed independently.

Count the money. Write each amount in two ways.

1. 175¢ $1.75
2. 178¢ $1.78
3. 347¢ $3.47
4. 191¢ $1.91
5. 77¢ $0.77
6. 245¢ $2.45
7. 103¢ $1.03
8. 432¢ $4.32

4 Assess

Give students coins. Have them lay out the coins to show $1.00.

For Mixed Abilities

Common Errors • Intervention

Students may have trouble writing amounts of money with a dollar sign and decimal point. Dictate amounts of money from $1.00 through $4.99 for students to write two ways, using the cents sign and then using the dollar sign and decimal point. Then, have them draw pictures or use play money of the dollars and coins to show the amount of money. Be sure they understand that an amount like $2.45 is always written with the dollar sign and decimal point and that only amounts less than a dollar are written with the cent sign.

Enrichment • Application

1. Have students use dollars and coins to draw as many ways as they can to show $2.50. Then, tell them to write the total for each amount in two ways.
2. Have students work with a friend as each of them lays out an amount of money through $4.99 behind a cover. Tell them to remove the covers and read each other's amounts.
3. Tell students to work with a friend to lay out coins and dollars for the least number of coins possible to show an amount of money through $4.99.

More to Explore • Application

Invite a student who has a paper route to come to your classroom. Ask the paper carrier to demonstrate and discuss the math skills needed to run a successful route. Some of these might include counting, record keeping, scheduling, and making change. Ask the carrier to discuss the hardest and easiest parts of his or her job, and allow students to ask questions.

6-12 Problem Solving: Act It Out

pages 115–116

1 Getting Started

Objective

- To count money to solve problems

Materials

*items priced through $4.99; real or play dollars, half-dollars, quarters, dimes, and pennies

Warm Up • Mental Math

Tell students to name the coins if

1. 3 coins equal 75¢ (25, 25, 25)
2. 5 coins equal 25¢ (5, 5, 5, 5, 5)
3. 5 coins equal 91¢ (50, 25, 10, 5, 1)
4. 5 coins equal 50¢ (10, 10, 10, 10, 10)
5. 3 coins equal 25¢ (10, 10, 5)
6. 3 coins equal 45¢ (25, 10, 10)
7. 2 coins equal 50¢ (25, 25)
8. 2 coins equal 75¢ (50, 25)

Warm Up • Application

Show a priced item and have students lay out the amount of money shown on the price tag. Have students count their money to check the amount. Repeat for more practice.

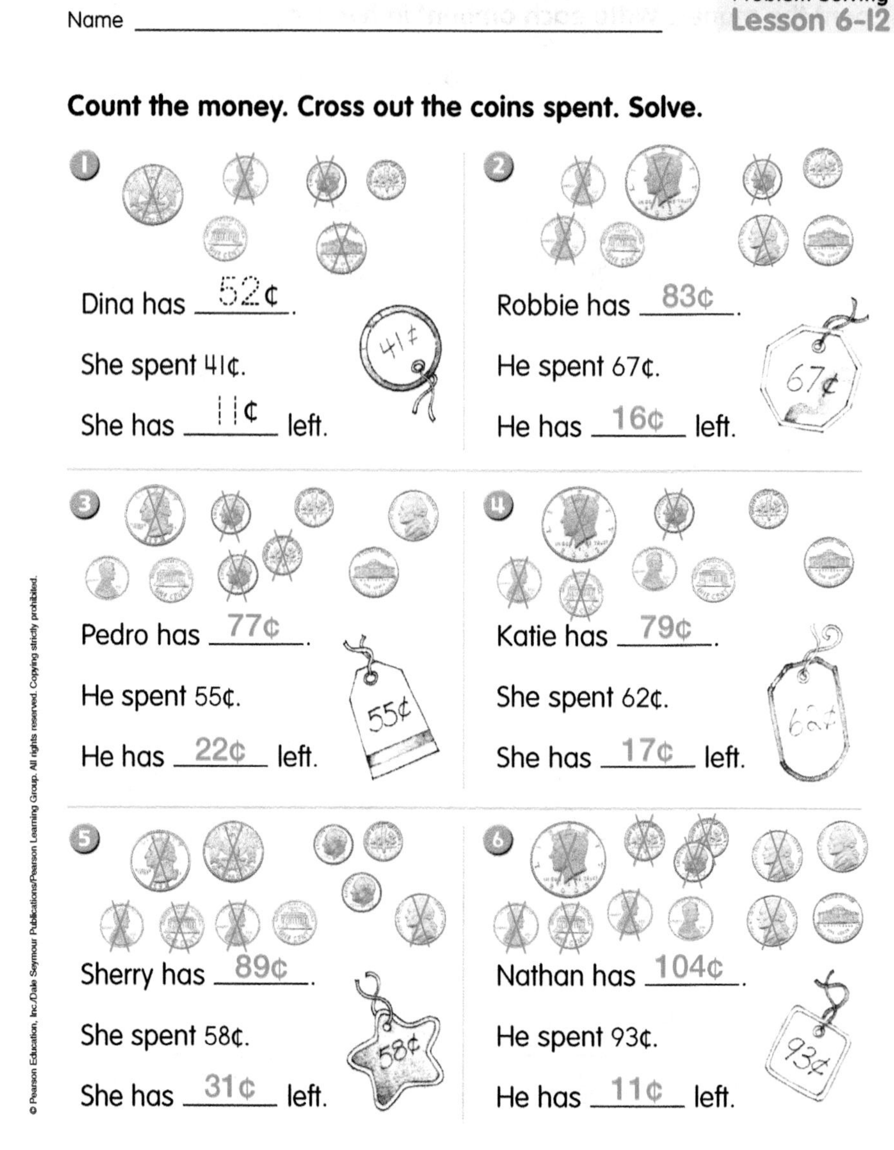

2 Teach

Develop Skills and Concepts Have students lay out 1 half-dollar, 2 quarters, 2 dimes, and 4 nickels. Ask students the amount. ($1.40) Have a student write the amount on the board in dollar notation. Show students an item priced less than $1.40 and ask students to move aside the coins they would need to purchase the item. Ask a student to write the cost of the item on the board. Have another student write the amount of money that would be left after purchasing the item. Repeat for more amounts of money and priced items for students to practice selecting the money needed to buy an item and counting the money left.

3 Practice

Using page 115 Have students look at Exercise 1.

- Now, apply the four-step plan. For SEE, ask, *What are you asked to do?* (find out how much money Dina has left) Then, *What information is given?* (1 quarter, 2 dimes, 1 nickel, 2 pennies, and a price tag for 41¢) For PLAN, ask students how they will find out how much money Dina has left. (count the coins and subtract the price of the item from the amount of money Dina has) For DO, have students subtract to find how much money is left. (11¢) For CHECK, ask students to check their subtraction by adding the amount of money left and the price of the item.
- Have students complete the remaining exercises independently.

Using page 116 Ask students to read the directions and tell what they are to do. (count the money and cross out the money spent and solve for how much is left) Remind students to write the amount of money left and then tell them to complete the exercises independently.

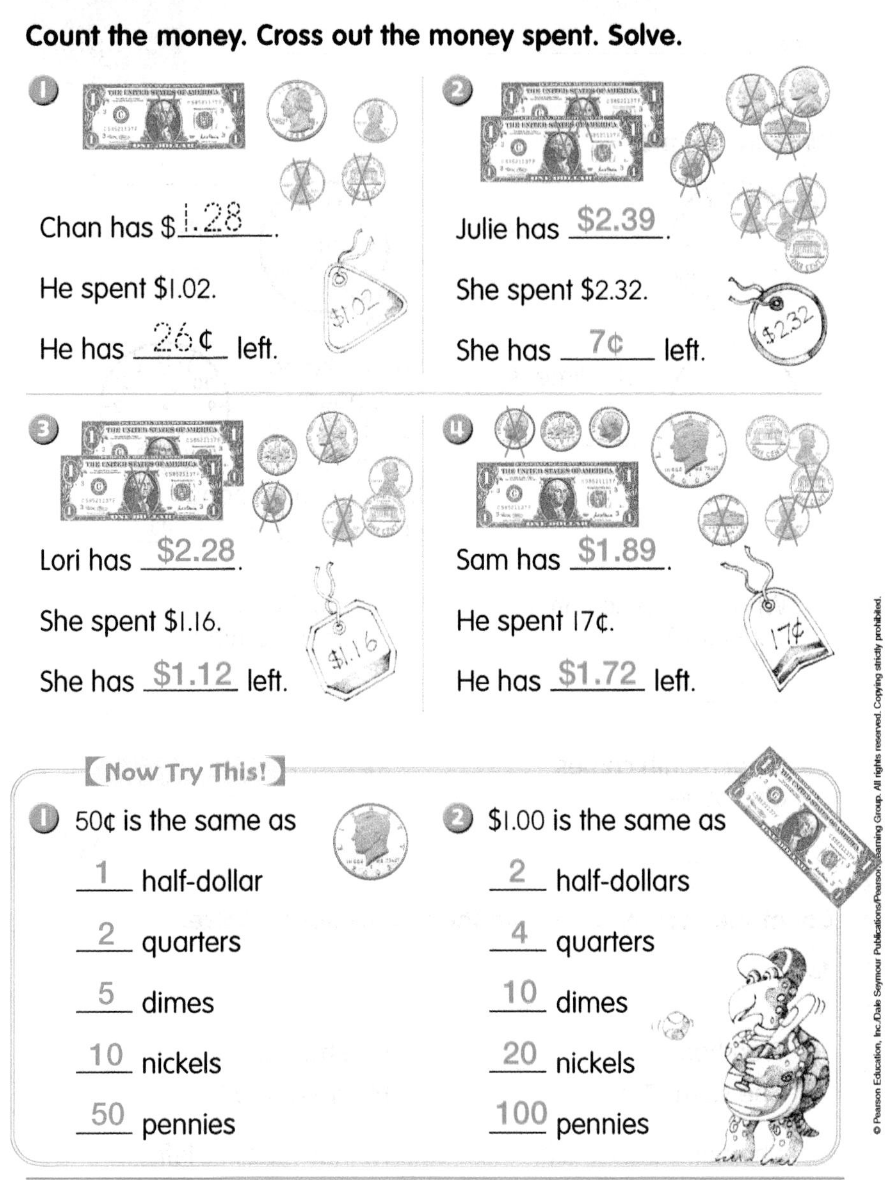
Count the money. Cross out the money spent. Solve.

1. Chan has $1.28.
He spent $1.02.
He has 26¢ left.

2. Julie has $2.39.
She spent $2.32.
She has 7¢ left.

3. Lori has $2.28.
She spent $1.16.
She has $1.12 left.

4. Sam has $1.89.
He spent 17¢.
He has $1.72 left.

Now Try This!

1. 50¢ is the same as
1 half-dollar
2 quarters
5 dimes
10 nickels
50 pennies

2. $1.00 is the same as
2 half-dollars
4 quarters
10 dimes
20 nickels
100 pennies

Now Try This! It is helpful to have students work in pairs and begin with 50 pennies, trade pennies for nickels, then nickels for dimes, and so on. Help students complete Exercise 1 and then work the second exercise independently.

4 Assess

Give students coins. Have them lay out the coins to show how much they have. Have students work in pairs. The first student lays out any number and combination of money with a value less than $4.99. The second student then tells how much money is there and how much of this money he wants to spend. The first student then chooses the appropriate amount from the group and tells how much money is left.

For Mixed Abilities

Common Errors • Intervention

Students may have difficulty figuring out how much they have left after they make a purchase. Have them work with partners with 3 quarters, 1 dime, 1 nickel, and 5 pennies. Give them index cards showing items that cost 32¢, 51¢, and 84¢. Have them count their money aloud (95¢) and tell how much they would have left if they bought the first item (63¢), the second item (44¢), and the third item (11¢). Encourage students to show the price of the item and the change with extra coins. Then, they can show that the amounts are correct by counting the money in both groups together.

Enrichment • Application

1. Tell students to draw $4.83 in dollars and coins. Have them cut ads from newspapers for items costing less than $4.83. Tell students to circle the money they would have left.
2. Have students draw money to show four different ways to make $4.25 and circle the way that uses the least number of coins.

More to Explore • Number Sense

This activity is an addition ring-toss. Prepare a target by turning a chair upside down and taping a card with any number from 2 to 9 to each leg. Draw a chalk line on the floor about 6 feet away. Tell students that they are to stand behind the line and toss jar rings, or similar circular items, over the legs. Tell them to add the numbers on any legs they successfully ring and to write their names and totals on the board. Any student adding incorrectly must record a zero. This activity can be repeated, with each student's totals added together at the end.

Encourage students to try to ring the chair legs with the largest numbers because the student with the largest cumulative total wins.

Chapter 6 Test

page 117

Items	Objectives
1–2	To tell time to the hour and in 5-minute intervals (see pages 93–96)
3	To solve problems by telling time before and after (see pages 97–98)
4–5	To write the days of the week and the months of the year (see pages 103–104)
6	To count quarters, dimes, nickels, and pennies through 99¢ (see page 109–110)
7–8	To count money to solve problems (see page 115–116)

Name ______________________

Chapter 6 Test

Write each time.

1. 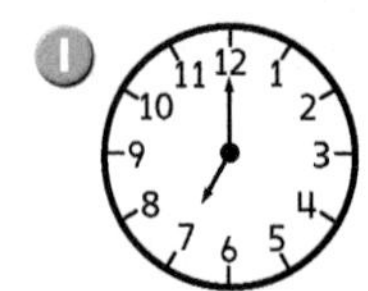
7 o'clock
7 : 00

2. 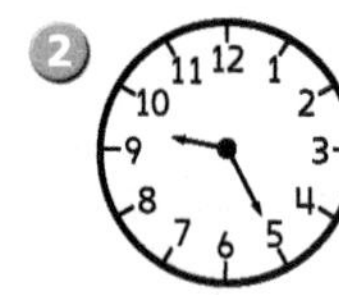
25 minutes after 9
9:25

3. The time is 9:00.

Sheila skated for 2 hours. What time did she stop? Draw the hour hand.
She stopped at 11:00.

4. What day comes after Thursday?
Friday

5. What month comes after June?
July

6. Count the money. Write the amount.

25 35 45 50 51
51¢

Count the money. Cross out the money spent. Solve.

7. 
Fran has 97¢.
She spent 75¢.
She has 22¢ left.

8. 
Emil has $1.42.
He spent $1.05.
He has 37¢ left.

Alternate Chapter Test

You may wish to use the Alternate Chapter Test on page 320 of this book for further review and assessment.

Add or subtract.

1	7 + 4 = 11	8 + 7 = 15	5 + 5 = 10	14 − 6 = 8	10 − 9 = 1	15 − 6 = 9	12 − 5 = 7
2	11 − 6 = 5	13 − 6 = 7	6 + 6 = 12	8 + 5 = 13	16 − 8 = 8	8 + 6 = 14	9 + 9 = 18

Write the number.

3 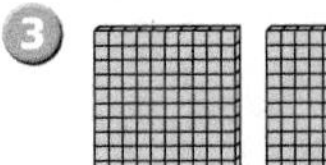 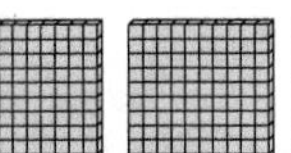 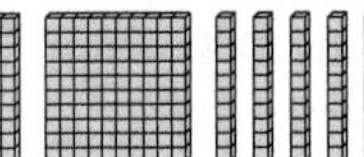 364

Count by ones. Write the numbers.

4 96, 97, 98, 99, 100, 101, 102, 103

5 308, 309, 310, 311, 312, 313, 314

6 896, 897, 898, 899, 900, 901, 902

Write the time.

7 

3:25

Count the money. Cross out the coins spent. Solve.

8   

Carl has 87¢.

He spent 66¢. He has 21¢ left.

Cumulative Assessment

page 118

Items	Objectives
1–2	To review addition and subtraction facts with sums and minuends through 18 (see pages 3–12, 17–20, 23–28, 35–44, 53–56, 59–64)
3	To understand and write 3-digit numbers (see pages 71–74)
4–6	To count by 1s through 1,000 (see pages 77–78)
7	To tell time in 5-minute intervals (see pages 95–96)
8	To count money to solve problems (see pages 115–116)

Math Transition Award

pages 119–120

The Math Award on page 119 signals the students' completion of the first portion of Level B. As students reach this point, fill in their Certificates of Completion and sign your name at the bottom. Emphasize to students that this is a significant accomplishment and that now they are ready for a new lesson approach. Have them color the page if desired. Encourage students to take the certificates home so that parents are also aware of changes in the lesson approach.

Page 120 will familiarize students with the new lesson format they will be using in the remainder of Level B.

The **model problem** that will introduce most lessons is designed to be worked by you and the students together. This model is representative of the kind of problem the student will be working on in that particular lesson.

The **Getting Started** section gives students sample problems to work on in order to practice the new skill being introduced. At this point, you can immediately see if students have an understanding of the problems.

The **Practice** page gives students ample practice to reinforce the skill they have learned.

Students also learn to solve word problems in the **Problem Solving** section, using both new and previously learned math skills.

Finally, the **Now Try This!** activities continue to offer students a chance to have fun with mathematics while being challenged to extend mastered skills.

Have a student read each item description, as you explain it. Remind students that they must watch for each new item and read directions carefully.

7-1 Adding 2-Digit and 1-Digit Numbers

pages 121–122

1 Getting Started

Objective
- To add 2- and 1-digit numbers with no regrouping

Materials
tens rods and ones cubes

Warm Up • Mental Math
Tell students to name another fact with the same sum or difference as

1. 7 + 6 (9 + 4, 8 + 5, etc.)
2. 12 − 9 (11 − 8, 10 − 7, etc.)
3. 8 + 5 (9 + 4, 7 + 6, etc.)
4. 9 + 6 (7 + 8)
5. 13 − 9 (2 + 2, 6 − 2, etc.)
6. 17 − 9 (4 + 4, 12 − 4, etc.)
7. 8 + 6 (7 + 7)
8. 14 − 9 (2 + 3, 11 − 6, etc.)

Warm Up • Number Sense
Write **46** on the board and have students show the number in tens rods and ones cubes. (4 tens 6 ones) Have students lay out tens rods and ones cubes for other 1- and 2-digit numbers. Now, tell students to lay out tens rods and ones cubes for 5 tens 3 ones. Have students write the number on the board. Dictate more numbers for students to arrange on their desks. Have each number written on the board.

Name ____________________

Addition With 2-Digit Numbers

Chapter 7

Lesson 7-1

Adding 2-Digit and 1-Digit Numbers

Anita took 32 pictures on Monday.
She took 4 pictures on Tuesday.
How many pictures did Anita take?

We are looking for the total number of pictures that Anita took.

Anita took 32 pictures on Monday.

She took 4 pictures on Tuesday.

To find the total, we add 32 and 4.

Add the ones first.

tens	ones
3	2
+	4
	6

Add the tens.

tens	ones
3	2
+	4
3	6

Anita took 36 pictures.

Getting Started

Add.

1.

tens	ones
4	4
+	3
4	7

2.

tens	ones
7	3
+	5
7	8

3.

tens	ones
2	1
+	6
2	7

4. 83 + 1 = 84
5. 13 + 2 = 15
6. 57 + 2 = 59
7. 95 + 1 = 96
8. 64 + 4 = 68
9. 33 + 2 = 35

---

2 Teach

Develop Skills and Concepts Tell students that Jack fed an elephant 15 peanuts. Have them lay out tens rods and ones cubes to show 15. Ask how many tens and ones there are. (1, 5) Make a tens and ones grid on the board and put 15 in the proper columns.

- Tell students that Jack then fed the elephant 4 more peanuts. Ask students how to find the total number of peanuts. (add) Tell students to add 4 ones to their counters. Write 4 under the 5 in the ones column. Tell students to add the ones first. Have a student write the sum on the board. (9) Have another student write the total number of tens in the tens column. (1) Ask how many peanuts there are in all. (19) Ask how many tens and ones in 19. (1, 9)
- Repeat for more problems of 1-digit numbers added to 2-digit numbers where no regrouping is needed.

3 Practice

Using page 121 Have students tell about the picture at the top of the page. Read the problem aloud with students and ask what is to be solved. (the number of pictures Anita took) Ask what information is given in the problem. (Anita took 32 pictures on Monday and 4 pictures on Tuesday.)

- Continue reading aloud with students as they complete the information sentences. Work through the addition model with students and then have them complete the solution sentence. Have students count the tens rods and ones cubes to check their addition work.
- Help students complete the Getting Started exercises if necessary.

Practice

Add.

1. 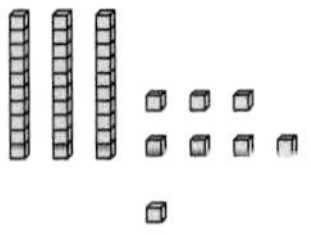

	tens	ones
	3	7
+		1
	3	8

2. 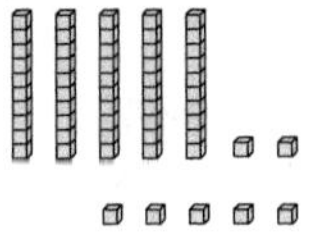

	tens	ones
	5	2
+		5
	5	7

3.

	tens	ones
	4	2
+		5
	4	7

4.

	tens	ones
	6	5
+		3
	6	8

5.

	tens	ones
	5	2
+		7
	5	9

6.

	tens	ones
	2	2
+		1
	2	3

7. 70 + 9 = 79
8. 43 + 6 = 49
9. 55 + 1 = 56
10. 23 + 2 = 25
11. 18 + 1 = 19
12. 86 + 3 = 89
13. 31 + 7 = 38
14. 14 + 3 = 17
15. 93 + 6 = 99
16. 84 + 1 = 85
17. 44 + 4 = 48
18. 63 + 4 = 67

Problem Solving

Solve.

19. Hector had 35 pennies. Alan gave him 3 more. How many pennies does Hector have now?

 38 pennies

20. Joyce ran for 21 minutes. Then she ran laps for 8 minutes. How many minutes did Joyce run?

 29 minutes

For Mixed Abilities

Common Errors • **Intervention**

Some students may have difficulty understanding the concept of addition when a 1-digit number is added to a 2-digit number. Have them work with partners and tens rods and ones cubes, taking turns modeling the problems. One partner can use the manipulatives to model each addend, and the other partner can join the tens and ones for both addends and show any regrouping. Then, both partners should discuss what number is shown by the finished model and write it as the answer to the problem.

Enrichment • Number Sense

Tell students to write and solve a problem to tell what day of the year February 4 is if January 31 is the thirty-first day of the year.

More to Explore • Logic

Write the following on the board or duplicate for students:

Some months have 30 days, some have 31. How many months have 28 days? (all of them)

Using page 122 Remind students to add the ones first and then the tens. Students may wish to circle the ones for help in adding them. Help students read each word problem if necessary. Remind students to add the ones first. Tell students to write each answer on the line. Have students complete the page independently.

4 Assess

Have students solve the following exercise. Have them draw base-ten blocks to help them.

Ashley had 24 customers on her paper route. She just added 5 new customers. How many customers does Ashley now have? (29)

5 Mixed Review

1. 6 − 2 (4)
2. 3 + 2 (5)
3. 4 + 5 (9)
4. 5 − 1 (4)
5. 8 − 2 (6)
6. 6 + 4 (10)
7. 0 + 5 (5)
8. 2 + 8 (10)
9. 9 − 5 (4)
10. 6 + 7 (13)

7-2 Adding With Regrouping

pages 123–124

1 Getting Started

Objective

- To add 1-digit numbers to 2-digit numbers with regrouping

Materials

counting sticks; rubber bands; tens rods and ones cubes

Warm Up • Mental Math

Ask students how many tens are in

1. 264 (6)
2. 59 (5)
3. 40 (4)
4. 6 (0)

Ask students how many ones are in

5. 97 (7)
6. 189 (9)
7. 64 (4)
8. 490 (0)

Warm Up • Number Sense

Have students work the following problems vertically on the board as other students work with tens rods and ones cubes: 43 + 6 (49), 72 + 7 (79), 54 + 3 (57), 61 + 8 (69), 82 + 6 (88).

Name ______________________

Adding With Regrouping

Andrew hopped 26 times on his left foot and 8 times on his right foot. How many times did Andrew hop?

We want to find out how many times Andrew hopped.

Andrew hopped 26 times on his left foot.

He hopped 8 times on his right foot.

To find the total number of hops, we add 26 and 8.

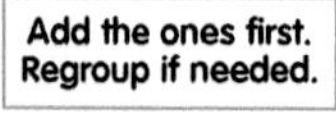

Add the ones first. Regroup if needed.

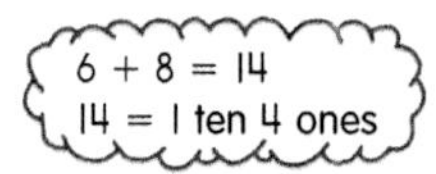

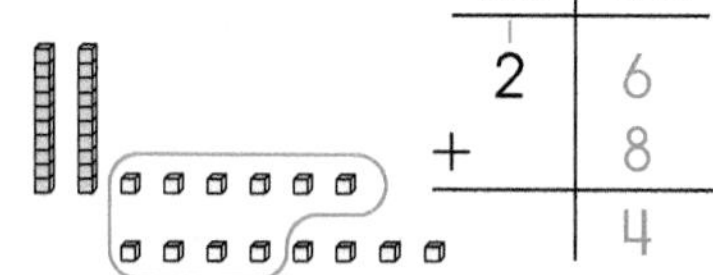

	tens	ones
	2	6
+		8
		4

Add the tens.

1 + 2 tens = 3 tens

	tens	ones
	2	6
+		8
	3	4

Andrew hopped 34 times.

Getting Started

Add. Regroup if needed.

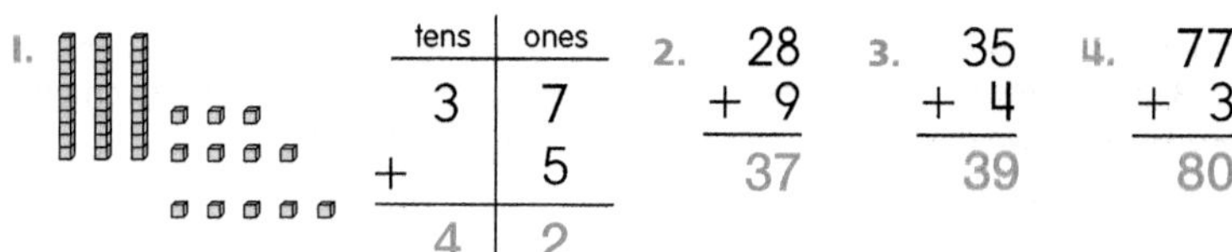

1.

	tens	ones
	3	7
+		5
	4	2

2. 28 + 9 = 37

3. 35 + 4 = 39

4. 77 + 3 = 80

2 Teach

Develop Skills and Concepts Have students lay out 23 counting sticks and bundle the groups of 10. Ask how many tens and ones there are. (2, 3) Ask students how many ones there are in all if we add 8 more ones. (11) Ask if another ten can be bundled now. (yes) Have students bundle the ten and tell how many tens and ones there are. (3, 1) Repeat for more numbers.

- Now, write **26 + 8** vertically on the board and have students lay out 26 sticks, bundle them into tens, add 8, and bundle another ten. Talk through the work as you write **4** in the ones place and regroup the 10 ones for 1 ten. Have a student write **3** in the tens place and read the sum in tens and ones. (3, 4) Help students work more problems using the tens rods and ones cubes in place of counting sticks.

3 Practice

Using page 123 Have students tell about the picture at the top of the page. Have a student read the problem aloud. Ask students what is to be found. (number of times Andrew hopped) Ask what information is known. (He hopped 26 times on his left foot and 8 times on his right foot.) Ask students how to find the total number of hops. (add) Have students read aloud with you as they complete the information sentences. Work through the model and then have students complete the solution sentence. Have students count the tens and ones pictured to check their work.

- Help students complete the Getting Started exercises if necessary.

Using page 124 Remind students to add the ones first and regroup if necessary before adding the tens. Have students complete the exercises at the top of the page independently.

Practice

Add. Regroup if needed.

1\.

tens	ones
3	7
+	6
4	3

2\.

tens	ones
5	3
+	9
6	2

3\. 34 + 5 = 39 4. 65 + 6 = 71 5. 83 + 9 = 92 6. 62 + 7 = 69 7. 29 + 5 = 34 8. 56 + 8 = 64

9\. 23 + 6 = 29 10. 39 + 3 = 42 11. 28 + 6 = 34 12. 61 + 8 = 69 13. 75 + 9 = 84 14. 57 + 4 = 61

Now Try This!

It's Algebra!

Write the missing number.

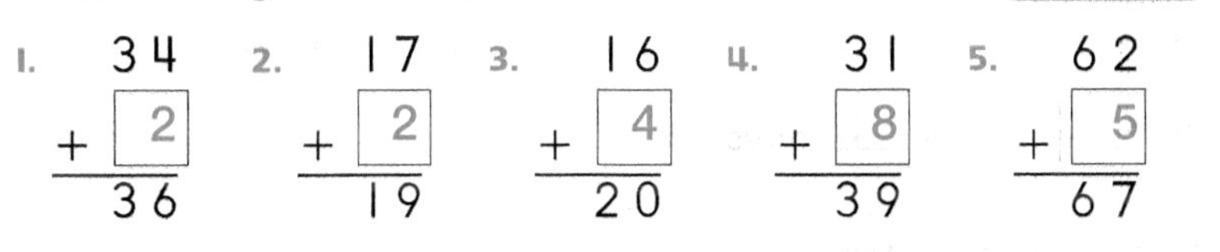

1\. 34 + [2] = 36 2. 17 + [2] = 19 3. 16 + [4] = 20 4. 31 + [8] = 39 5. 62 + [5] = 67

6\. 23 + [7] = 30 7. 35 + [6] = 41 8. 63 + [9] = 72 9. 46 + [7] = 53 10. 57 + [8] = 65

Now Try This! Write **18 +** _____ **= 21** vertically on the board. Ask students what number needs to be added to 8 to get 1 one and 1 ten. (3) Have students experiment with other numbers, if necessary, to see that 3 is the only number that satisfies the problem. Repeat for **34 +** _____ **= 43** (9), **56 +** _____ **= 63** (7) and **29 +** _____ **= 33** (4).

Tell students to complete each exercise by finding the number that makes the exercise true.

It's Algebra! The concepts of this activity prepare students for algebra.

4 Assess

Have students write and solve a problem to find how many desks would be in their classroom if 9 new students joined the class.

For Mixed Abilities

Common Errors • Intervention

Some students may have difficulty regrouping. Have them work with partners to rewrite problems such as the following with ten less ones and one more ten.

3 tens 16 ones (4 tens 6 ones)
4 tens 19 ones (5 tens 9 ones)
2 tens 11 ones (3 tens 1 one)
8 tens 15 ones (9 tens 5 ones)
5 tens 10 ones (6 tens 0 ones)

Encourage students to use tens rods and ones cubes to show each regrouping.

Enrichment • Number Sense

Have students write their own word problems that include addition with regrouping. Have students exchange papers and answer each other's word problems.

More to Explore • Geometry

Have students experiment with mosaics. Provide many squares of construction paper in a variety of colors. Squares that are 1 inch on a side are easy to make with a paper cutter. Give students plain paper and glue. Explain that they can arrange the squares any way they like to make a picture or a pattern. Encourage them to cover the entire paper.

This activity can be enhanced by bringing in pictures of real tile mosaics. The mosaics will be a good introduction to the idea of tessellations, the repetition of a simple shape forming a pattern. Display the finished creations.

ESL/ELL STRATEGIES

Review the meaning of *regrouping* by having volunteers explain the process in their own words. For example, *When you regroup, you take ten from the ones column and count it as one in the tens column.* Discuss the example on page 123.

7-3 Adding 2-Digit Numbers

pages 125–126

1 Getting Started

Objective

- To add two 2-digit numbers with some regrouping for sums through 99

Materials

tens rods and ones cubes

Warm Up • Mental Math

Tell students to name the number.

1. 2 tens + 3 tens + 4 tens (90)
2. 6 ones + 4 ones + 9 ones (19)
3. 7 hundreds + 2 hundreds (900)
4. 2 tens + 5 tens + 1 ten (80)
5. 0 hundreds 0 tens 0 ones (0)
6. 14 ones + 2 ones (16)
7. 1 one + 1 hundred (101)
8. 5 tens 6 ones 4 hundreds (456)

Warm Up • Pencil and Paper

Dictate the following problems: 46 + 6 (52), 35 + 4 (39), 3 tens 8 ones + 9 (47), 75 + 5 (80), 8 tens 9 ones + 4 (93), 62 + 7 (69). Have students work with manipulatives and write and solve the problems on paper. Remind students to add the ones first and then the tens.

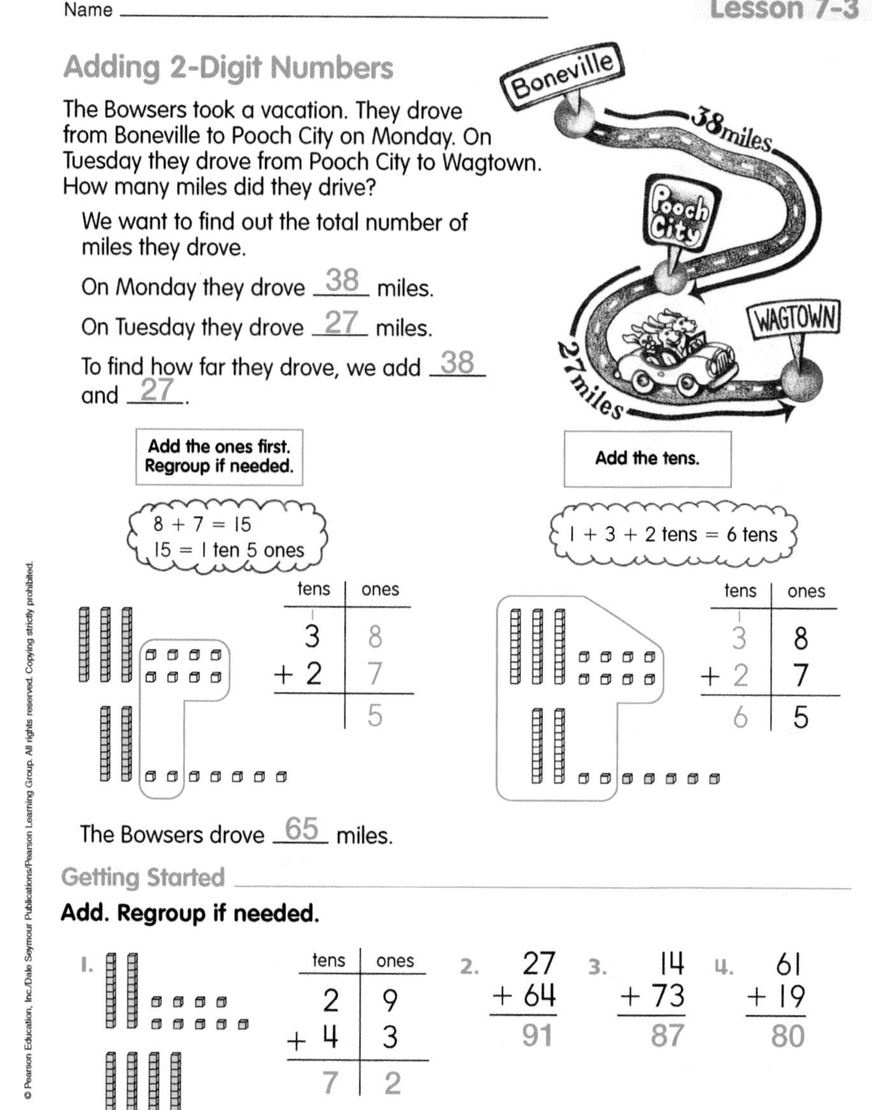

Getting Started

Add. Regroup if needed.

1.
tens	ones
2	9
+ 4	3
7	2

2. 27 + 64 = 91

3. 14 + 73 = 87

4. 61 + 19 = 80

2 Teach

Develop Skills and Concepts Write **46 + 28** vertically on the board and have students lay out the numbers in tens rods and ones cubes. Ask how many ones there are in all. (14) Ask students what they need to do. (regroup 10 ones for 1 ten) Have students regroup and tell how many ones are left. (4) Have a student write **4** in the ones place and show the regrouped ten on the board. Ask how to find the number of tens in all. (add 4 + 2 + 1) Have a student write **7** in the tens column. Ask students to read the sum of 46 and 28 aloud. (74) Have students check by counting their tens rods and ones cubes.

- Repeat the procedure for 52 + 28 (80), 76 + 19 (95), 42 + 53 (95), and 73 + 18 (91).

3 Practice

Using page 125 Have students tell about the picture at the top of the page. Have a student read the problem aloud. Ask students what is to be solved. (the total number of miles the Bowsers drove) Ask what information is given in the picture. (38 miles from Boneville to Pooch City and 27 miles from Pooch City to Wagtown) Have students read and complete the information sentences. Remind students that the ones are always added first as you work through the model together. Have students complete the solution statement.

- Have students complete the Getting Started exercises independently. Have them check their work with manipulatives.

Using page 126 Tell students to complete Exercises 1 to 20 independently. Then, go through each word problem to be sure students know what operation they will use. Have students complete the word problems independently.

Practice

Add. Regroup if needed.

1.

tens	ones
4	6
+ 1	6
6	2

2.

tens	ones
3	5
+ 4	9
8	4

3. 36 + 47 = 83
4. 52 + 45 = 97
5. 35 + 16 = 51
6. 53 + 46 = 99
7. 37 + 48 = 85
8. 52 + 18 = 70
9. 60 + 25 = 85
10. 16 + 17 = 33
11. 29 + 44 = 73
12. 48 + 23 = 71
13. 56 + 39 = 95
14. 19 + 31 = 50
15. 28 + 37 = 65
16. 46 + 45 = 91
17. 18 + 68 = 86
18. 25 + 14 = 39
19. 73 + 17 = 90
20. 49 + 38 = 87

Problem Solving

Solve.

21. The cafeteria sold 35 ham sandwiches and 25 cheese sandwiches. How many sandwiches were sold?

60 sandwiches

22. The cafeteria sold 45 cartons of milk and 29 cartons of orange juice. How many cartons were sold?

74 cartons

4 Assess

Have students tell if regrouping is necessary for the following problems:

41 + 52 (no)

35 + 39 (yes)

29 + 10 (no)

83 + 7 (yes)

5 Mixed Review

1. 3¢ + 5¢ (8¢)
2. 1¢ + 3¢ (4¢)
3. 9¢ − 6¢ (3¢)
4. 8¢ − 4¢ (4¢)
5. 3 + 3 (6)
6. 10 − 4 (6)
7. 5¢ + 5¢ (10¢)
8. 2 + 4 (6)
9. 1 + 9 (10)
10. 9 − 3 (6)

For Mixed Abilities

Common Errors • Intervention

Some students may add incorrectly because they add each column separately, failing to regroup.

Incorrect	Correct
	1
26	26
+ 18	+ 18
314	44

Correct students by having them use place-value materials to model the problem.

Enrichment • Number Sense

Tell students to write and solve a problem that finds the number of people in two classes at their school. Tell them to include the teachers. Now, have them write out and solve a problem that finds out how many pencils are needed if each person needs two pencils.

More to Explore • Application

Introduce the application of mathematics to growing things. Bring to class a package of seeds, enough foam cups so that each student will have one, and a bag of potting soil. Plants that will grow reliably and quickly include radishes, marigolds, beans, and grasses. Read the directions for planting to the class. Explain that the germination time is the number of days it takes the plant to sprout from a seed. Have each student plant several different seeds in foam cups filled with potting soil. Put the labeled cups in a sunny place and have students keep them watered until they germinate. Now, have students measure their own plants, using inches or centimeters, every other day. Help them keep track of the height of their seedlings on a chart that lists Day 1 as the day the seed was planted. Remind them that until the seed actually sprouts, the height will be zero.

7-4 Adding Multiples of 10

pages 127–128

1 Getting Started

Objective

- To add any two 2-digit multiples of 10

Materials

hundred flat and tens rods

Warm Up • Mental Math

Tell students to name a related subtraction fact for the following:

1. 7 + 9 (16 − 7, 16 − 9)
2. 6 + 8 (14 − 8, 14 − 6)
3. 9 + 9 (18 − 9)
4. 8 + 9 (17 − 9, 17 − 8)
5. 6 + 4, (10 − 4, 10 − 6)
6. 9 + 4 (13 − 4, 13 − 9)
7. 8 + 8 (16 − 8)

Warm Up • Number Sense

Have students count by 10s through 200. Write **80 + 10** vertically on the board for a student to find the sum. (90) Repeat for **60 + 30** (90), **20 + 40** (60), **30 + 40** (70), and so on for sums of 90 or less. Ask students how many ones are in each sum. (none)

Name ________________________

Adding Multiples of 10

Manuel and Christy wanted to see how many times they could bounce a basketball without missing. What is the total number of times they bounced the ball?

We want to know the total number of times they bounced the ball.

Manuel bounced the ball __60__ times.

Christy bounced the ball __50__ times.

To find how many times they bounced the ball, we add __60__ and __50__.

Add the ones first.

tens	ones
6	0
+ 5	0
	0

Add the tens. Regroup if needed.

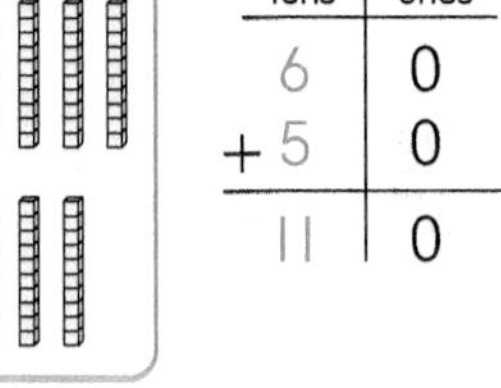

tens	ones
6	0
+ 5	0
11	0

11 tens = 1 hundred 1 ten

They bounced the ball __110__ times.

Getting Started

Add. Regroup if needed.

1. 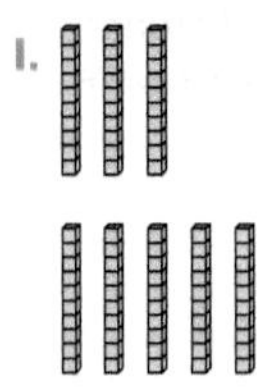

tens	ones
3	0
+ 5	0
8	0

2. 20 + 90 = 110

3. 50 + 50 = 100

4. 90 + 90 = 180

2 Teach

Develop Skills and Concepts Have students lay out 6 tens and 3 tens and tell the number. (90) Tell students to lay out another ten and tell the total number of tens. (10) Ask how many ones there are. (0) Write **100 = 10 tens 0 ones** on the board.

- Have students lay out another ten and tell the number of tens. (11) Ask how many ones there are. (0) Write **110 = 11 tens 0 ones = 1 hundred 1 ten 0 ones** on the board. Continue to develop 120, 130, and so on.
- Write **60 + 40** vertically on the board and have a student add the ones column. (0) Have a student add the tens column. (10) Ask students to read the number. (one hundred) Ask students to tell the number of hundreds, tens, and ones in 100. (1, 0, 0) Repeat for 90 + 20 (110) and other sums through 180 that are multiples of 10.

3 Practice

Using page 127 Have students tell about the picture. Ask a student to read the problem aloud and tell what is being asked. (the total number of times the ball bounces) Ask students what information is known. (Manuel bounced the ball 60 times and Christy bounced the ball 50 times.) Have students read aloud with you as they complete the sentences. Work through the model with students and then have them complete the solution sentence. Have students lay out tens rods to check their answer.

- Help students complete the Getting Started exercises if necessary.

Using page 128 Remind students to add the ones column first and then find the sum of the tens column. Have students read through the two word problems and tell what they will do in each. (add) Assign the page to be completed independently.

Practice

Add. Regroup if needed.

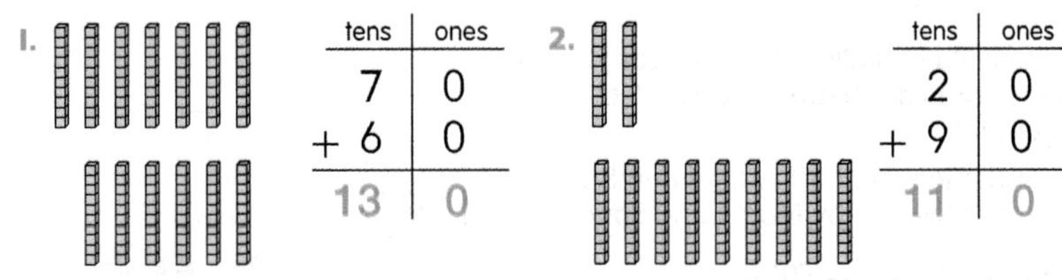

1.

tens	ones
7	0
+ 6	0
13	0

2.

tens	ones
2	0
+ 9	0
11	0

3. 40 + 30 = 70
4. 60 + 60 = 120
5. 80 + 80 = 160
6. 30 + 50 = 80
7. 90 + 90 = 180
8. 50 + 50 = 100
9. 50 + 40 = 90
10. 90 + 50 = 140
11. 70 + 80 = 150
12. 10 + 90 = 100
13. 80 + 40 = 120
14. 70 + 50 = 120
15. 80 + 90 = 170
16. 90 + 70 = 160
17. 20 + 30 = 50
18. 70 + 60 = 130
19. 20 + 80 = 100
20. 60 + 50 = 110

Problem Solving

Solve.

21. Phil took 30 steps to the door and 30 steps back. How many steps did Phil take?
60 steps

22. Myra rode her bike for 40 minutes. She played ball for 70 minutes. How many minutes did Myra play?
110 minutes

4 Assess

Give students 10 tens rods. Tell them to write five addition problems that add multiples of 10 and have a sum of 100. (10 + 90, 20 + 80, 30 + 70, 40 + 60, 50 + 50, 60 + 40, 70 + 30, 80 + 20, 90 + 10)

5 Mixed Review

1. 8 + 3 (11)
2. 7¢ + 2¢ (9¢)
3. 5 − 5 (0)
4. 4 + 8 (12)
5. 7¢ − 1¢ (6¢)
6. 7 − 5 (2)
7. 12¢ − 9¢ (3¢)
8. 3¢ + 9¢ (12¢)
9. 11 − 9 (2)
10. 6 + 5 (11)

For Mixed Abilities

Common Errors • Intervention

When adding multiples of 10, some students will omit the zero in the ones place. One way to impress on them the importance of the placeholder is for them to model a simple problem like 10 + 10, using first ones and then trading ones for tens rods. Encourage them to verbalize how 2 is different from 20.

Enrichment • Number Sense

Tell students to write and solve problems to show ten ways to add three multiples of 10 to have a sum of 120.

More to Explore • Application

Have students display the charts they made for measuring their growing seeds from the More to Explore activity in Lesson 7-3. Hold up one of the charts and ask the class if it is easy to read at a distance. (probably not) Help them make a bar graph on graph paper, using their data. Put a sample graph on the board in this form:

Date				
Day 5				
Day 4				
Day 3				
Day 2				
Day 1				
	1	2	3	4

Height in Inches

Help them see that before the seed has sprouted, they will not color in any squares. When the seed has sprouted, they will begin to color in one square for each inch or centimeter. Tell students to show that the sprout has grown more or less than an inch by coloring in a part of a square.

ESL/ELL STRATEGIES

Review the meaning of *missing* in the phrase *missing number*. Then, ask students to explain what the word *missing* means in the phrase *bounce a basketball without missing*. (bounce the ball without stopping)

7-5 Finding 3-Digit Sums

pages 129–130

1 Getting Started

Objective

- To add two 2-digit numbers with regrouping for 2- or 3-digit sums

Materials

hundred-flat, tens rods, and ones cubes

Warm Up • Mental Math

Ask students to tell the total amount of money for the following:

1. 5 dimes and 2 nickels (60¢)
2. 4 pennies and 1 quarter (29¢)
3. 1 dollar and 4 nickels ($1.20)
4. 1 half-dollar and 3 dimes (80¢)
5. 8 nickels and 1 dime (50¢)
6. 2 quarters and 1 nickel (55¢)
7. 1 dollar and 1 half-dollar ($1.50)
8. 3 quarters and 1 half-dollar ($1.25)

Warm Up • Number Sense

Have students work the following problems vertically on the board: 78 + 4 (82), 80 + 5 (85), 47 + 9 (56), 29 + 8 (37), 30 + 80 (110), 72 + 8 (80), 60 + 90 (150), 15 + 6 (21).

Name ______________________

Finding 3-Digit Sums

Some children collect baseball cards. How many cards did Morris and Sandi collect together?

We are looking for the total number of cards collected by Morris and Sandi.

Morris has 58 cards.

Sandi has 67 cards.

To find how many cards Morris and Sandi have, we add 58 and 67.

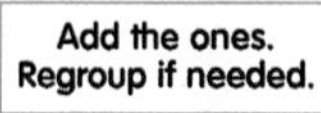

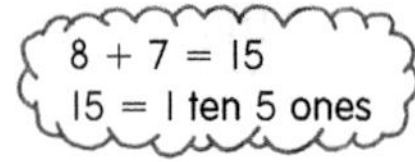

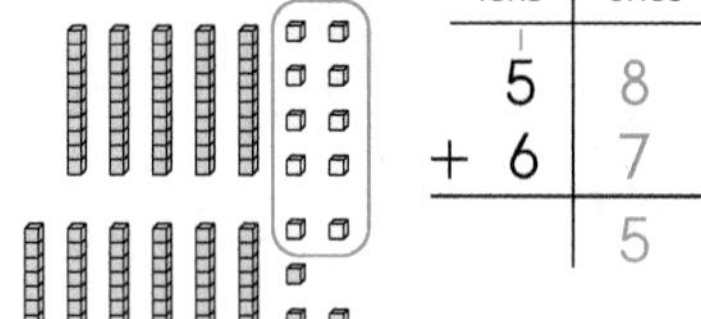

	tens	ones
	5	8
+	6	7
		5

Add the tens.
Regroup if needed.

12 tens = 1 hundred 2 tens

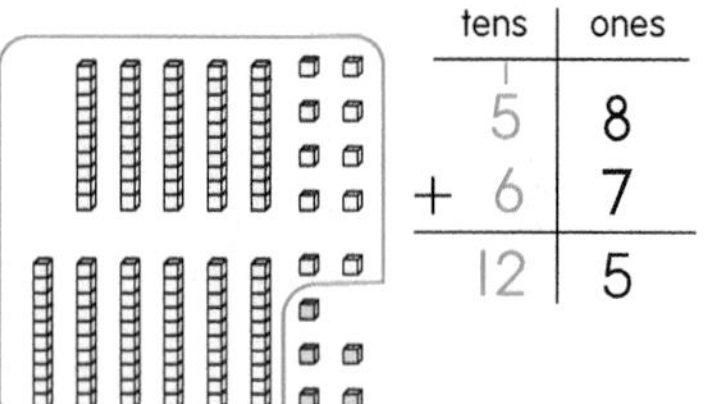

	tens	ones
	5	8
+	6	7
	12	5

Morris and Sandi have 125 cards.

Getting Started

Add. Regroup if needed.

1.

	tens	ones
	5	7
+	8	5
	14	2

2. 38 + 85 = 123
3. 27 + 58 = 85
4. 79 + 65 = 144

2 Teach

Develop Skills and Concepts Write **48 + 96** vertically on the board. Have students lay out tens rods and ones cubes to show each number. Ask how many ones there are in all. (14) Ask if regrouping is needed. (yes) Have students regroup 10 ones for 1 ten as you write **4** in the ones column. Tell students to add 4 tens and 9 tens plus the 1 regrouped ten for the total number of tens. (14) Ask if there are enough tens to regroup for 1 hundred. (yes) Tell students to regroup 10 tens for 1 hundred as you write **4** in the tens column. Ask students how many hundreds there are. (1) Write **1** in the hundreds column. Have students read the sum. (one hundred forty-four) Repeat for 79 + 85 (164), 37 + 48 (85), 56 + 99 (155), and 72 + 96 (168).

3 Practice

Using page 129 Have students tell about the picture and read the chart at the top of the page. Have a student read the problem. Ask what is to be found. (the number of cards Morris and Sandi collected) Ask students where information can be gained to solve the problem. (from the chart) Ask what information is needed from the chart. (Morris collected 58 and Sandi collected 67.) Ask if they will use the information about Del's cards to solve this problem. (no) Have students read aloud with you as they complete the information sentences. Work through the model with students and then have them complete the solution statement. Have students lay out tens rods and ones cubes to check their answer.

- Help students complete the Getting Started exercises if necessary.

Practice

Add. Regroup if needed.

1.

tens	ones
2	9
+ 7	4
10	3

2.

tens	ones
8	8
+ 7	7
16	5

3.	4.	5.	6.	7.	8.
34	85	29	16	43	91
+ 23	+ 57	+ 76	+ 37	+ 44	+ 26
57	142	105	53	87	117

9.	10.	11.	12.	13.	14.
35	67	38	75	41	27
+ 45	+ 78	+ 38	+ 75	+ 99	+ 98
80	145	76	150	140	125

15.	16.	17.	18.	19.	20.
57	56	99	65	36	43
+ 23	+ 65	+ 99	+ 85	+ 55	+ 75
80	121	198	150	91	118

21.	22.	23.	24.	25.	26.
25	69	47	38	67	83
+ 63	+ 32	+ 77	+ 95	+ 27	+ 79
88	101	124	133	94	162

Using page 130 Remind students to add the ones column first. Help students complete the first few problems if necessary before assigning the page to be completed independently.

4 Assess

Use the information on page 129 to find out how many cards Sandi and Del collected. (118)

5 Mixed Review

1. 3 + 4 (7)
2. 7¢ − 2¢ (5¢)
3. 12 − 5 (7)
4. 10 + 3 (13)
5. 12¢ − 6¢ (6¢)
6. 11 − 6 (5)
7. 0 + 7 (7)
8. 10 − 3 (7)
9. ____ + 3 = 12 (9)
10. 4 + ____ = 5 (1)

For Mixed Abilities

Common Errors • Intervention

Watch for students who rename incorrectly because they reverse the tens and ones.

Incorrect	Correct
6	1
17	17
+ 29	+29
91	46

Correct students by having them use place-value materials to model the problem and show the regrouping.

Enrichment • Number Sense

Tell students that there are 48 hours in 2 days. Then, ask them to find how many hours are in 3 days. (72 hours) In 4 days? (96 hours) In 5 days? (120 hours)

More to Explore • Geometry

Provide a worksheet having several geometric shapes with many smaller geometric shapes within such as the following:

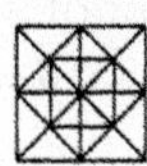

Have students count how many squares and how many triangles are in the shape.

Have students color the geometric shapes after they count them. Encourage them to use a ruler and design their own geometric patterns and write related questions. Display the geometric designs and have students count the total number of squares, circles, and triangles.

7-6 Adding Money

pages 131–132

1 Getting Started

Objective
- To add money for sums through $1.99

Materials
real or play dollar bills and coins

Warm Up • Mental Math
Ask students if regrouping is needed for the following:

1. 7 tens + 2 tens (no)
2. 4 ones + 9 ones (yes)
3. 6 ones + 0 ones (no)
4. 8 tens + 2 tens (yes)
5. 5 tens + 9 tens (yes)
6. 2 ones + 9 ones (yes)
7. 6 tens + 6 tens (yes)
8. 1 one + 8 ones (no)

Warm Up • Number Sense
Show a dollar and ask students to write the amount of money on the board using the cent sign and then using the dollar sign and a decimal point. (100¢, $1.00) Repeat for a half-dollar, quarter, dime, nickel, and penny. Now, show two or three coins or a dollar and some coins and have students write the amount two ways. Repeat for more amounts of money.

Name ______________________

Lesson 7-6

Adding Money

Gene went shopping for gifts. He bought a bag of marbles and a yo-yo. How much did he pay?

We want to find out how much Gene paid for the gifts.

The bag of marbles cost 48¢.

The yo-yo cost 75¢.

To find the total cost, we add 48¢ and 75¢.

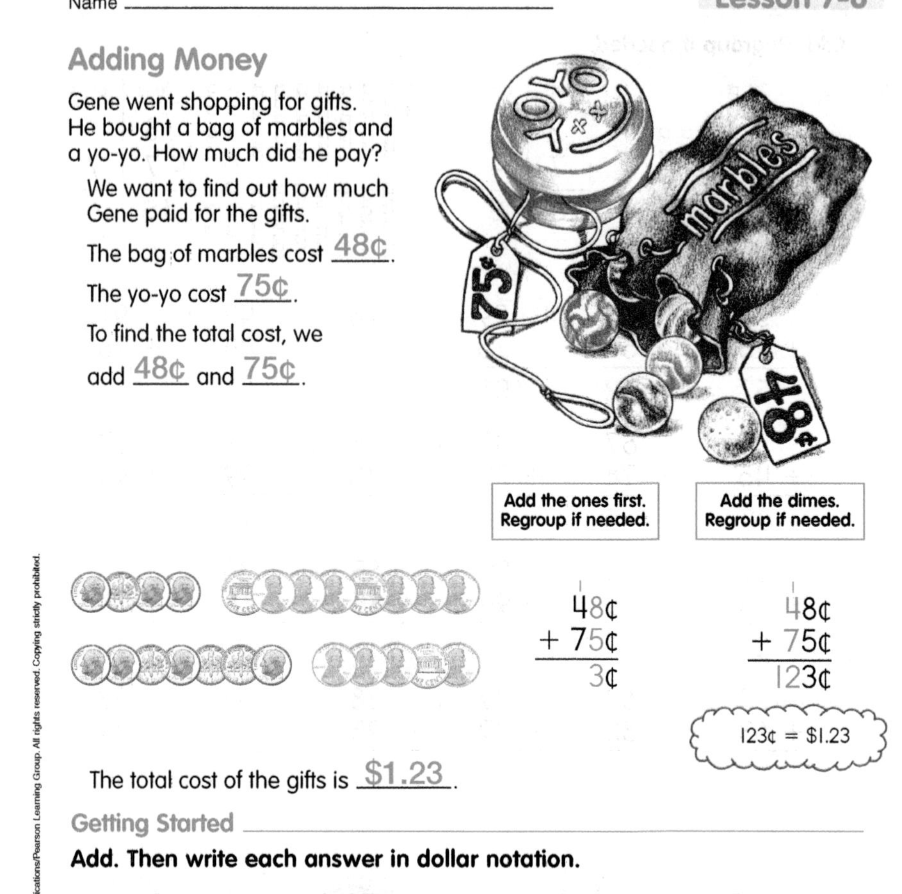

Add the ones first. Regroup if needed.	Add the dimes. Regroup if needed.
48¢ + 75¢ = 3¢	48¢ + 75¢ = 123¢

123¢ = $1.23

The total cost of the gifts is $1.23.

Getting Started

Add. Then write each answer in dollar notation.

1. 96¢ + 25¢ = 121¢ → $1.21
2. 37¢ + 88¢ = 125¢ → $1.25
3. 56¢ + 38¢ = 94¢ → $0.94
4. 75¢ + 25¢ = 100¢ → $1.00

2 Teach

Develop Skills and Concepts Write **47¢ + 85¢** vertically on the board. Cover the cent signs and remind students that this problem is familiar to them. Have students use coins to show 47¢ and 85¢. Ask how many pennies or ones there are in all. (12) Ask if 10 pennies can be regrouped for 1 dime. (yes) Have students regroup as you record it. Ask how many pennies are left as you record the 2. Have students add the dimes or tens (13) and tell if regrouping is needed. (yes) Have students regroup as you record it. Ask how many dimes are left as you record the 3. Ask how many dollars or hundreds there are. (1) Record the 1 and write the cent sign. Have a student tell the amount. (132¢) Tell students this amount can also be written another way as you write **$1.32** on the board.

- Repeat for other sums with 2, 1, or no regroupings. Note: Have students record a zero in the dollar place when there are no dollars.

3 Practice

Using page 131 Have a student read the problem aloud and tell what is to be found. (how much Gene paid for a bag of marbles and a yo-yo) Ask what information is needed. (the cost of each) Ask students where the cost is given. (in the picture) Have students read and complete the information sentences. Work through the model and then have students complete the solution sentence. Have students lay out coins and regroup for 1 dollar to check their solution.

- Help students complete the Getting Started exercises if necessary. Remind them to write zero in the dollar place if there are no dollars.

Using page 132 Tell students to find each sum in cents and then write the sum using the dollar sign and decimal point. Remind students to show their work for each word problem. Assign the page to be completed independently.

Practice

Add. Then write each answer in dollar notation.

1.	2.	3.	4.	5.
30¢ + 30¢	45¢ + 56¢	62¢ + 76¢	79¢ + 75¢	99¢ + 8¢
60¢	101¢	138¢	154¢	107¢
$0.60	$1.01	$1.38	$1.54	$1.07

6.	7.	8.	9.	10.
81¢ + 93¢	84¢ + 68¢	91¢ + 65¢	87¢ + 26¢	58¢ + 82¢
174¢	152¢	156¢	113¢	140¢
$1.74	$1.52	$1.56	$1.13	$1.40

11.	12.	13.	14.	15.
40¢ + 87¢	55¢ + 98¢	90¢ + 71¢	73¢ + 68¢	64¢ + 63¢
127¢	153¢	161¢	141¢	127¢
$1.27	$1.53	$1.61	$1.41	$1.27

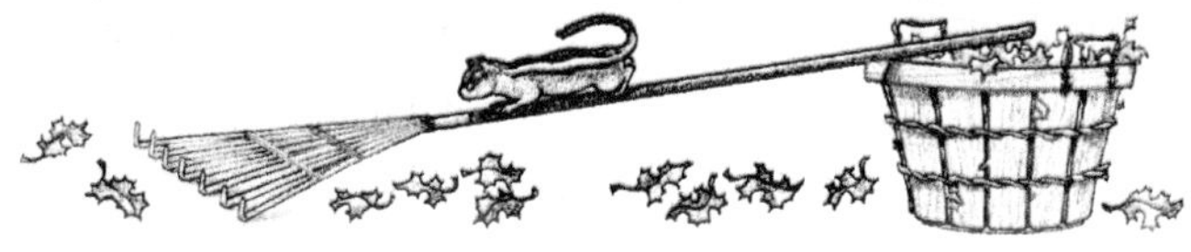

Problem Solving

Solve. Then write each answer in dollar notation.

16. Lu had 50¢. She earned 75¢ raking leaves. How much money does she have now?
$1.25

17. Walt bought one book for 89¢ and another book for 95¢. How much money did he spend?
$1.84

4 Assess

Set up a classroom store by attaching price tags to items such as erasers, pencils, and pads of paper. Then, ask students how much different combinations of the items will cost.

5 Mixed Review

1. 4 + 5 (9)
2. 8 − 5 (3)
3. _____ + 2 = 2 (0)
4. 14 − 8 (6)
5. _____ + 5 = 11 (6)
6. 6¢ − 3¢ (3¢)
7. 7 + 1 (8)
8. 7¢ + 3¢ (10¢)
9. 5 + 8 (13)
10. 8¢ + 4¢ (12¢)

For Mixed Abilities

Common Errors • Intervention

Some students may place the decimal point incorrectly when changing from cents to dollars and cents. Review how 100¢ is equal to 1 dollar, or $1.00, and that the decimal point separates the dollars from the cents. Tell them that this means that money written with the decimal point will always have two digits and no more after the point.

Enrichment • Application

Tell students to cut ads from newspapers for three items priced less than $1.00. Have them write and solve three problems to find the cost of any two of the items. Tell them to find out which combination of two items would cost the most.

More to Explore • Mental Math

Have students play baseball with mental math problems suitable to students' ability. Place four bases such as chairs, erasers, beanbags, and so on, on the floor so that they form a baseball diamond. Divide the class into two teams. Have one of the students be the pitcher. The pitcher will give the batter a mental math problem. If the problem is answered in 5 seconds, the batter goes to first base. Players advance one base for each consecutive correct answer. If the batter fails to answer, or answers incorrectly, he makes an out. Rotate the teams being "up" according to regular baseball rules, such as each team being allowed three outs, and so on. Stop the game at a point where each team has had an equal number of innings at bat. Extend the activity over a week so students can play a series of games.

7-7 Problem Solving: Make an Organized List

pages 133–134

1 Getting Started

Objectives

- To make an organized list to solve problems
- To identify the value of coins and make change

Warm Up • Mental Math

Add or subtract.

1. 10 plus 6 (16)
2. 7 plus 7 (14)
3. 5 plus 6 (11)
4. 12 minus 9 (3)
5. 11 minus 4 (7)
6. 15 minus 7 (8)

Warm Up • Number Sense

Write the following on the board:

10 + 10 = (20)
18 − 9 = (9)
7 + 6 = (13)
15 − 8 = (7)
17 − 3 = (14)
12 + 4 = (16)
11 − 8 = (3)
6 + 12 = (18)
7 + 9 = (16)
10 − 3 = (7)

Name ______________________________

It's Algebra!

Problem Solving: Make an Organized List

Joe has $1.00. He buys a pencil that costs 75¢. He gets 25¢ back as change. How many different ways can Joe get 25¢?

The chart below shows three ways.

 = 25¢ = 10¢ = 5¢ = 1¢

				Amount
1				25¢
		5		25¢
			25	25¢

Getting Started

Make a chart to answer the questions.

1. Using only dimes and nickels, how can you make 25¢?
   2 dimes, 1 nickel; 1 dime, 3 nickels; 5 nickels
2. Using only dimes and pennies, how can you make 25¢?
   2 dimes, 5 pennies; 1 dime, 15 pennies; 25 pennies
3. Using only nickels and pennies, how can you make 25¢?
   4 nickels, 5 pennies; 3 nickels, 10 pennies; 2 nickels, 15 pennies; 1 nickel, 20 pennies; 5 nickels, 25 pennies
4. Using dimes, nickels, and pennies, how can you make 25¢?
   1 dime, 2 nickels, 5 pennies; 1 dime, 1 nickel, 10 pennies; 5 nickels; 25 pennies

2 Teach

Develop Skills and Concepts Read the following word problem to students: *John has 15 cents. How many coins can John have?* Now, allow time for students to solve it. Ask students to read their solutions. Some students may say two coins, a dime and a nickel, whereas others may have used a different combination. On the board, make a table with columns for dimes, nickels, and pennies to show the different ways that 15 cents can be made. Allow students to generate the six ways that 15 cents can be made. (15 pennies; 1 dime, 5 pennies; 1 dime, 1 nickel; 3 nickels; 2 nickels, 5 pennies; 1 nickel, 10 pennies) Discuss with students the benefits to making an organized list to solve problems. (Possible answer: It lets you keep track of the possible answers that you have figured out.)

It's Algebra! The concepts presented in this lesson prepare students for algebra.

3 Practice

Using page 133 Have students look at the example at the top of the page. Have students look at the table as you read the problem to see how they can use the table to solve the problem.

- Now, apply the four-step plan to the example at the top of the page. For SEE, ask, *What are you being asked to do?* (find how many ways 25 cents can be made) Then, *What information is given?* (the value of each coin) For PLAN, ask students how they can find the different amounts. (add 1s, 5s, and 10s to make 25) For DO, have students make their lists. For CHECK, Ask, *Do all of your answers have a value of 25¢?* (yes)
- Have students repeat this process and complete the Getting Started exercises.

Practice

Complete the chart to answer the questions.

 = 25¢ = 10¢ = 5¢ = 1¢

1. Roberta has one of each coin above. If she picks 2 coins, what amounts can she make?

				Amount
1	1	0	0	35¢
		1	1	6¢
	1		1	11¢
	1	1		15¢
1			1	26¢
1		1		30¢

2. If Roberta picks 3 coins, what amounts can she make?
See notes on page T134 of the Teacher's manual.

3. How many different amounts can Roberta make in all?
15 different amounts

Solve.

4. Ling has $1.00. She buys a ruler for 60¢. How much change does she receive? 40¢

5. Ling did not receive any pennies in the change. List the combinations of change she could have received.

			Amount
1	1	1	40¢
1	0	3	40¢
0	4	0	40¢
0	3	2	40¢
0	2	4	40¢
0	1	6	40¢
0	0	8	40¢

Using page 134 Have students look at Exercise 1. Ask students for the given information. (There is a penny, nickel, dime, and quarter; two different coins will be used for each amount.) Ask students how they can go about finding the different amounts. (make every combination with a penny and then a nickel) Have students make their lists.

- For Exercises 2 and 3, have students extend their tables to solve. Review the correct combinations with the class. For Exercise 4, students can subtract to find Ling's change. For Exercise 5, tell students to use the table.

4 Assess

Have students work in pairs. One partner should write a money amount from **65¢** to **80¢**. The other partner is the cashier, who has to make change from $1.00. Partners can determine how much change is needed and then make a table of the different ways that the change can be made.

For Mixed Abilities

Common Errors • Intervention

If students are having difficulty coming up with a list of coins, allow them to use real or play coins to count out different combinations. If students are having difficulty counting combinations, have them work with a partner and practice counting. One partner can choose a group of coins and the other partner can count aloud to find the value. The first partner should listen carefully for any mistakes in counting. Have students switch roles.

Enrichment • Number Sense

Tell students, *You have one of each coin. What amounts can you make using two of the coins?* (6¢, 11¢, 15¢, 26¢, 30¢, 35¢, 51¢, 55¢, 60¢, 75¢)

More to Explore • Logic

Have students work in groups of three. Have one partner write a number from 1 to 50. The other two partners take turns asking yes-or-no questions about the number. They should make a list of their questions and the answers to help them determine the mystery number. Groups should be able to find the mystery number in seven questions or less. The activity can be repeated with another student choosing the mystery number.

Chapter 7 Test

page 135

Items	Objectives
1–3, 17	To add 2- and 1-digit numbers with no regrouping (see pages 121–122)
4–6, 15	To add any two 2-digit multiples of 10 (see pages 127–128)
7–8, 12, 16, 18–19, 21	To add two 2-digit numbers with some regrouping for sums through 99 (see pages 125–126)
9–11, 14, 20, 24, 30	To add two 2-digit numbers with regrouping for 3-digit sums (see pages 129–130)
13, 22–23	To add 1-digit numbers to 2-digit numbers with regrouping (see pages 123–124)
25–29, 31	To add money for sums through $1.99 (see pages 131–132)

Alternate Chapter Test

You may wish to use the Alternate Chapter Test on page 321 of this book for further review and assessment.

Name ____________________

Chapter 7 Test

Add. Regroup if needed.

1. 83 + 5 = 88
2. 35 + 9 = 44
3. 86 + 7 = 93
4. 80 + 50 = 130
5. 30 + 70 = 100
6. 90 + 40 = 130
7. 57 + 31 = 88
8. 65 + 29 = 94
9. 34 + 82 = 116
10. 76 + 77 = 153
11. 99 + 99 = 198
12. 42 + 38 = 80
13. 16 + 7 = 23
14. 56 + 68 = 124
15. 30 + 80 = 110
16. 76 + 21 = 97
17. 64 + 4 = 68
18. 43 + 17 = 60
19. 45 + 45 = 90
20. 59 + 84 = 143
21. 38 + 37 = 75
22. 27 + 9 = 36
23. 98 + 3 = 101
24. 75 + 83 = 158

Add. Then write each answer in dollar notation.

25. 68¢ + 7¢ = 75¢ — $0.75
26. 70¢ + 50¢ = 120¢ — $1.20
27. 64¢ + 24¢ = 88¢ — $0.88
28. 75¢ + 18¢ = 93¢ — $0.93
29. 96¢ + 89¢ = 185¢ — $1.85

Solve.

30. There were 65 girls and 77 boys on the skating rink. How many children were skating?
142 children

31. Cleve has 85¢.
Lu Ann has 98¢.
How much money do they have in all?
$1.83

Circle the letter of the correct answer.

1.
8
+ 7

a. 16
(b.) 15
c. 14
d. NG

2. 9 + 3

a. 10
b. 16
(c.) 12
d. NG

3.
15
− 6

(a.) 9
b. 7
c. 6
d. NG

4.
13
− 7

a. 5
b. 7
(c.) 6
d. NG

5.

a. 3:10
(b.) 2:15
c. 2:03
d. NG

6.

a. $3.45
b. $3.35
(c.) $3.40
d. NG

7. What is the value of the 6 in 267?

a. hundreds
(b.) tens
c. ones
d. NG

8. What is the value of the 7 in 750?

(a.) hundreds
b. tens
c. ones
d. NG

9. 364 ◯ 446

a. >
(b.) <

10.
37
+ 58

a. 94
b. 85
(c.) 95
d. NG

11.
60
+ 60

a. 12
b. 102
c. 130
(d.) NG

12.
35
+ 7

(a.) 42
b. 32
c. 47
d. NG

13.
75
+ 88

a. 153
b. 165
(c.) 163
d. NG

score

STOP

Cumulative Assessment

page 136

Items	Objectives
1–4	To review addition and subtraction facts with sums and minuends through 18 (see pages 3–12, 17–20, 23–28, 35–44, 53–56, 59–64)
5	To tell time in 5-minute intervals (see pages 95–96)
6	To count money through $5 (see pages 75–76)
7–8	To understand 3-digit numbers (see pages 71–74)
9	To find the greater or lesser of 3-digit numbers (see pages 83–84)
10	To add two 2-digit numbers with some regrouping for sums through 99 (see pages 125–126)
11	To add any two multiples of 10 (see pages 127–128)
12	To add 1-digit numbers to 2-digit numbers with regrouping (see pages 123–124)
13	To add two 2-digit numbers with regrouping for 3-digit sums (see pages 129–130)

Alternate Cumulative Assessment

Circle the letter of the correct answer.

1.
9
+ 6

a 14
(b) 15
c 16
d NG

2. 4 + 6

a 9
(b) 10
c 11
d NG

3.
18
− 9

(a) 9
b 8
c 7
d NG

4.
12
− 9

a 2
(b) 3
c 4
d NG

5.

a 5:15
b 4:20
(c) 3:25
d NG

6.

a $2.06
b $2.29
(c) $2.54
d NG

7. What is the value of 5 in 875?

(a) ones
b tens
c hundreds
d NG

8. What is the value of 9 in 591?

a ones
(b) tens
c hundreds
d NG

9. 258 ◯ 268

a >
(b) <
c =

10.
56
+ 24

a 70
b 90
c 710
(d) NG

11.
80
+ 40

a 40
b 102
(c) 120
d NG

12.
34
+ 7

(a) 41
b 411
c 51
d NG

13.
85
+ 36

a 111
b 129
(c) 121
d NG

8-1 Subtracting 2-Digit Numbers

pages 137–138

1 Getting Started

Objective
- To subtract any two 2-digit numbers with no regrouping

Materials
subtraction fact cards

Warm Up • Mental Math
Ask if the following amounts are greater or less than $1.00.

1. 60¢ + 30¢ (less)
2. 75¢ + 50¢ (greater)
3. 4 dimes and 1 half-dollar (less)
4. 2 half-dollars and 1 dime (greater)
5. 6 quarters (greater)
6. 90¢ + 20¢ (greater)

Warm Up • Number Sense
Write the numbers **0** to **9** across the board. Give a subtraction fact card to a student to place on the chalk tray under the number that tells its answer. Have other students tell if the fact is correctly placed. Repeat until all facts have been placed on the chalk tray.

Name ____________________

Subtraction with 2-Digit Numbers

Subtracting 2-Digit Numbers

Gary had 47 fish in his aquarium.
He gave 15 fish to Sun Li.
How many fish does he have left?

We want to know how many fish Gary has left.

Gary had 47 fish.

He gave 15 fish to Sun Li.

To find the number of fish he has left, we subtract 15 from 47.

Subtract the ones first.

tens	ones
4	7
− 1	5
	2

Subtract the tens.

tens	ones
4	7
− 1	5
3	2

Gary has 32 fish left.

Getting Started

Subtract.

1.

tens	ones
6	7
− 2	5
4	2

2.

tens	ones
9	6
− 4	3
5	3

3.

tens	ones
5	5
− 3	1
2	4

4.

tens	ones
7	8
−	5
7	3

5. 97 − 22 = 75
6. 42 − 11 = 31
7. 28 − 3 = 25
8. 79 − 46 = 33
9. 48 − 28 = 20
10. 37 − 10 = 27

---

2 Teach

Develop Skills and Concepts Write the following on the board:

tens	ones
8	9
− 4	5
(4)	(4)

Have a student subtract 5 ones from 9 ones and write the number left. (4) Have a student subtract 4 tens from 8 tens and write the number left. (4) Have students read the number. (forty-four)

- Repeat for 76 − 46 (30), 99 − 66 (33), 87 − 12 (75), 42 − 30 (12), and 79 − 25 (54), using a tens and ones grid. Then, erase all work from the board and work similar problems using no grid. Have students tell the number of tens and ones in each answer.

3 Practice

Using page 137 Have a student read the example at the top of the page aloud and tell what is to be solved. (how many fish Gary has left) Ask students what information is given. (He had 47 fish and gave 15 fish away.) Ask what operation needs to be used to solve the problem. (subtraction) Have students read and complete the information sentences. Work through the model with students and then have them complete the solution sentence.

- Help students work through Getting Started Exercises 1 to 4. Then, have them complete Exercises 5 to 10 independently.

Using page 138 Remind students to subtract the ones first and then the tens. Have students complete the rows of problems independently. Help students plan how to solve each of the word problems if necessary and then have students work independently to find and record the answers.

Practice

Subtract.

1. tens	ones	2. tens	ones	3. tens	ones	4. tens	ones
8	3	5	7	6	8	2	9
− 2	1	− 4	1	− 6	4	−	9
6	2	1	6		4	2	0

5.	6.	7.	8.	9.	10.
78 − 52 = 26	35 − 2 = 33	46 − 22 = 24	99 − 4 = 95	76 − 6 = 70	87 − 83 = 4

11.	12.	13.	14.	15.	16.
47 − 31 = 16	75 − 55 = 20	18 − 7 = 11	88 − 46 = 42	36 − 26 = 10	50 − 20 = 30

17.	18.	19.	20.	21.	22.
56 − 54 = 2	22 − 1 = 21	77 − 50 = 27	96 − 36 = 60	49 − 2 = 47	58 − 30 = 28

Problem Solving

Solve.

23. At the bake sale, they sold 48 blueberry muffins and 36 bran muffins. How many more blueberry muffins were sold?

    12 blueberry muffins

24. The sale started with 28 loaves of bread. They had 5 left. How many loaves of bread were sold?

    23 loaves

4 Assess

Have students write word problems in which they subtract two 2-digit numbers. Have students exchange papers to answer each other's word problem.

5 Mixed Review

1. 10 + 4 (14)
2. ____ + 4 = 6 (2)
3. 11 − 7 (4)
4. 5 + 6 (11)
5. 6 − 1 (5)
6. 9 + 4 (13)
7. 13¢ − 6¢ (7¢)
8. 5¢ + 9¢ (14¢)
9. 8 + ____ = 10 (2)
10. 2 + 3 (5)

For Mixed Abilities

Common Errors • Intervention

Some students may subtract from left to right. Although it gives the correct answer when there is no regrouping required, it is not a desired habit for them to develop because it will affect their answer when there is regrouping. Direct them, as in addition, to operate with the ones first and then the tens. Remind them to work toward the minus sign rather than away from it.

Enrichment • Number Sense

Tell students to subtract 12 from each number they would say if they counted by 10s from 16 to 96. (16 − 12 = 4, 26 − 12 = 14, 36 − 12 = 24, 46 − 12 = 34, and so on)

More to Explore • Measurement

Have a volunteer set up a pattern of five or six chairs. Challenge teams of students to

1. Walk the longest path passing each chair once
2. Walk the shortest path passing each chair once

Then, have the teams use a trundle wheel to measure and compare the distances walked on each of the two routes. Then, ask another student to rearrange the chairs and repeat the activity.

8-2 Regrouping a Ten to Subtract

pages 139–140

1 Getting Started

Objective

- To subtract a 1-digit number from a 2-digit number with regrouping

Materials

*subtraction fact cards; tens rods and ones cubes

Warm Up • Mental Math

Tell students to skip two numbers and say the next number.

1. 48 (51)
2. 761 (764)
3. 115 (118)
4. 0 (3)
5. 398 (401)
6. 969 (972)
7. 83 (86)
8. 500 (503)

Warm Up • Pencil and Paper

Show students a subtraction fact card such as 15 − 8 and have students give the difference. (7) Ask students to write three related facts for 15 − 8. (8 + 7, 7 + 8, and 15 − 7) Repeat for 17 − 9, 16 − 8, and so on.

Name ______________________

Regrouping a Ten to Subtract

The pet store had 34 puppies for sale. The store sold 8 puppies. How many puppies are left?

There were 34 puppies for sale.

The store sold 8 puppies.

To find out how many are left, we subtract 8 from 34.

REMEMBER Subtract the ones first.

Do you need more ones?	Regroup 1 ten to get 10 ones.	Subtract the ones.	Subtract the tens.

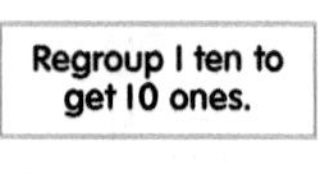

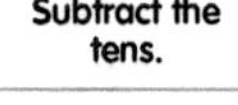

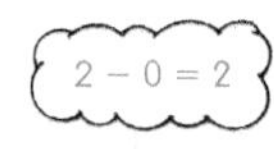

tens	ones
3	4
−	8
	?

tens	ones
2	14
~~3~~	~~4~~
−	8
	6

tens	ones
2	14
~~3~~	~~4~~
−	8
2	6

The pet store has 26 puppies left.

Getting Started

Do you need more ones? Circle yes or no. Then subtract and regroup if needed.

1.

tens	ones
5	6
−	9
4	7

(Yes) No

2.

tens	ones
2	2
−	8
1	4

(Yes) No

3.

tens	ones
6	8
−	7
6	1

Yes (No)

2 Teach

Develop Skills and Concepts Write the following on the board:

tens	ones
(8)	(17)
9	7
−	8
(8)	(9)

Ask students if 8 ones can be taken from 7 ones. (no) Tell students that to get more ones we can regroup a ten for 10 ones. Show the regrouping and ask students if 8 ones can be taken from 17 ones. (yes) Have a student write the number of ones left. (9) Ask students how many tens are left. (8) Have students read the number that is left when 8 is subtracted from 97. (eighty-nine)

- Repeat for 46 − 8 (38), 72 − 6 (66), 34 − 7 (27), 96 − 8 (88), and 55 − 9 (46).

3 Practice

Using page 139 Have a student read the example aloud and tell what is to be solved. (how many puppies are left in the store) Ask students what facts are known. (There were 34 and 8 were sold.) Ask students what operation needs to be used to find the number left. (subtraction) Have students read and complete the information sentences. Work through the model with students and then have them complete the solution sentence.

- Help students complete the Getting Started exercises if necessary. Have students use manipulatives to check their answers.

Using page 140 Tell students to circle the word *yes* or *no* to tell if more ones are needed. Tell students to then solve each exercise independently. Remind students to decide what operation to use when solving the word problems.

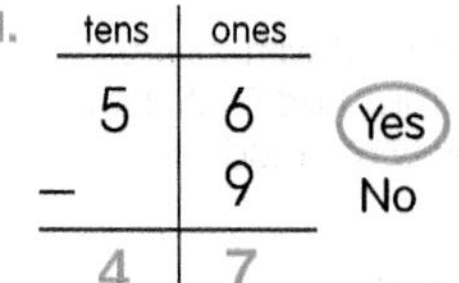

Practice

Do you need more ones? Circle yes or no. Then subtract and regroup if needed.

1.
tens	ones
6	8
−	5
6	3

Yes (No)

2.
tens	ones
5	2
−	8
4	4

(Yes) No

3.
tens	ones
7	7
−	7
7	0

Yes (No)

4.
tens	ones
8	0
−	3
7	7

(Yes) No

5.
tens	ones
7	9
−	6
7	3

Yes (No)

6.
tens	ones
3	3
−	4
2	9

(Yes) No

7.
tens	ones
5	7
−	8
4	9

(Yes) No

8.
tens	ones
4	6
−	9
3	7

(Yes) No

9.
tens	ones
7	3
−	1
7	2

Yes (No)

Problem Solving

Solve.

10. Charlie collects eggs on his farm. One day he gathered 87 white eggs and 9 brown eggs. How many more white eggs did he collect?
78 white eggs

11. Debra picked 24 ears of corn. Father cooked 9 ears for dinner. How many ears of corn were not cooked?
15 ears of corn

4 Assess

Have students write five subtraction problems with regrouping. Have students exchange papers to answer each other's problems.

5 Mixed Review

1. 9 + 5 (14)
2. 12¢ − 7¢ (5¢)
3. 6 − 0 (6)
4. 2 − 1 (1)
5. 6 + ____ = 12 (6)
6. 2 + ____ = 9 (7)
7. 10 + 3 (13)
8. 6¢ + 2¢ (8¢)
9. 10 + 7 (17)
10. 6 + 9 (15)

For Mixed Abilities

Common Errors • Intervention

Some students may forget to decrease the tens by one when they are regrouping. Have them work with partners to rewrite problems such as the following with one less ten and ten more ones.

6 tens 4 ones (5 tens 14 ones)
3 tens 7 ones (2 tens 17 ones)
2 tens 2 ones (1 ten 12 ones)
5 tens 4 ones (4 tens 14 ones)
8 tens 1 one (7 tens 11 ones)
4 tens 0 ones (3 tens 10 ones)

They can model these problems with tens rods and ones cubes to demonstrate why the tens are reduced by one.

Enrichment • Application

Tell students to write and solve a problem to find how many hours are left in the day when 8 hours have passed since midnight. Have them work another problem that tells how many hours are left when 6 hours have passed since midnight.

More to Explore • Logic

Duplicate the following math riddle or write it on the board:

How can a cat go into a basement with 4 feet and come out with 8 feet?
(by catching a mouse)

ESL/ELL STRATEGIES

Write on the board the words *collect*, *gather*, and *pick*. Read the problems at the bottom of page 140 and ask students to guess the meaning of these words. (In this context, all three words mean "to harvest.")

8-3 Subtracting With Regrouping

pages 141–142

1 Getting Started

Objective

- To subtract a 2-digit number from a 2-digit number with regrouping

Materials

tens rods and ones cubes; real or play coins

Warm Up • Mental Math

Tell students to name the following numbers:

1. 72 + 6 (78)
2. 90 − 10 − 10 (70)
3. 25¢ + 25¢ + 25¢ (75¢)
4. $1.40 + 1 nickel ($1.45)
5. $1.00 + 25¢ − 10¢ ($1.15)
6. 40 + 50 + 20 (110)
7. 91 − 2 (89)
8. 2 nickels + 6 dimes + 2 quarters ($1.20)

Warm Up • Number Sense

Write various problems of 2-digit numbers minus 1-digit numbers on the board and have students tell if regrouping is needed in each. Then, have students write similar problems on the board for classmates to tell if regrouping is needed.

Name ______________________

Subtracting With Regrouping

Annie collects stuffed animals. She must take 17 of them to school for a display. How many are left at home?

We want to know how many stuffed animals she left at home.

Annie has 36 stuffed animals.

She is taking 17 stuffed animals to school.

To find how many stuffed animals she left at home, we subtract 17 from 36.

REMEMBER Subtract the ones first.

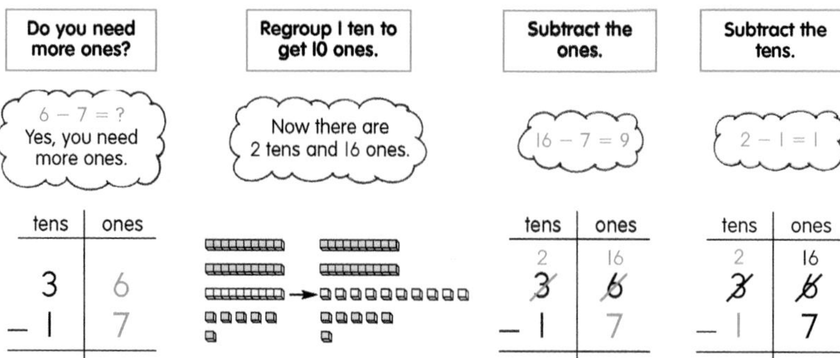

tens	ones
3	6
− 1	7
	?

tens	ones
2	16
~~3~~	~~6~~
− 1	7
	9

tens	ones
2	16
~~3~~	~~6~~
− 1	7
1	9

Annie left 19 stuffed animals at home.

Getting Started

Subtract. Regroup if needed.

1.

tens	ones
9	3
− 5	9
3	4

2.

tens	ones
6	2
− 3	6
2	6

3.

tens	ones
8	4
− 2	9
5	5

4.

tens	ones
8	8
− 1	8
7	0

2 Teach

Develop Skills and Concepts Have students lay out tens rods and ones cubes to show 45. Write the following on the board:

tens	ones
(3)	(15)
4	5
− 2	8
(1)	(7)

Ask if more ones are needed to subtract the 8 ones. (yes) Work through the regrouping with students and record it on the board. Have students read the answer (17) and then tell the answer in tens and ones. (1, 7)

- Repeat the procedure for 92 − 26 (66), 78 − 46 (32), 43 − 19 (24), and 61 − 39. (22)

3 Practice

Using page 141 Have a student read the example aloud and tell what is to be solved. (how many stuffed animals were left at home) Ask students what facts are given in the problem. (Annie took 17 to school.) Ask what information is not given in the problem. (number of animals in all) Have students study the picture and count to find how many stuffed animals Annie had in all. (36) Have students read and complete the information sentences. Work through the model with students and then have them complete the solution sentence. Now, have students cross out 17 of the stuffed animals and count the remaining ones to check their solution.

- Help students complete the Getting Started exercises if necessary.

Using page 142 Remind students to first see if regrouping is needed to subtract the ones. Tell students that some problems on this page do not need regrouping. Have students complete the problems independently.

Practice

Subtract. Regroup if needed.

1.

tens	ones
5	7
− 2	3
3	4

2.

tens	ones
8	0
− 3	0
5	0

3.

tens	ones
8	1
− 1	2
6	9

4.

tens	ones
4	2
− 1	7
2	5

5.

tens	ones
8	3
− 5	5
2	8

6.

tens	ones
5	0
− 2	9
2	1

7.

tens	ones
9	0
− 2	0
7	0

8.

tens	ones
7	5
− 4	5
3	0

9.

tens	ones
5	5
−	6
4	9

10.

tens	ones
7	9
− 3	0
4	9

11.

tens	ones
9	6
− 3	8
5	8

12.

tens	ones
6	7
− 4	9
1	8

Now Try This!

Stacey has 15¢. How many pennies, nickels, and dimes would make 15¢ if she had the following:

1. 2 coins 1 dime, 1 nickel
2. 3 coins 3 nickels
3. 6 coins 1 dime, 5 pennies
4. 7 coins 2 nickels, 5 pennies

Now Try This! Ask students to lay out two coins to equal 2¢. (2 pennies) Tell students to now lay out two coins to equal 10¢. (2 nickels) Continue for two coins to equal 50¢ (2 quarters), three coins to equal 60¢ (2 quarters 1 dime), and four coins to equal 20¢. (4 nickels)

Have a student read the problem and tell what is to be done. (find ways to make 15¢ using pennies, nickels, and dimes) Help students complete the first exercise, and assign the remaining exercises.

4 Assess

Have students decide if regrouping is needed in the following problems:

90 − 23 (yes), 87 − 33 (no), 56 − 47 (yes), 77 − 39 (yes), 66 − 61 (no)

For Mixed Abilities

Common Errors • Intervention

Some students may not regroup when necessary but subtract the lesser digit from the greater digit.

Incorrect	Correct
23	$\overset{1\,13}{\not{2}\not{3}}$
− 8	− 8
25	15

Correct students by having them work with partners and place-value materials to model each problem.

Enrichment • Application

Tell students to write and solve a problem to find the number of minutes before 3:00 if it is 15 minutes after 2 o'clock.

More to Explore • Geometry

Duplicate or write on the board the following puzzle:

1. (_ _ _ _ _ _ _)

4. (_ 2. (_ _ _ _ _ _ _ _ _)

3. (_ _ _ _ _ _ _ _ _ _)

_)

ACROSS

1. △ □ ○ ▭ are all called (shapes).
2. What figure can you make with three toothpicks? (triangle)
3. The door is shaped like a (rectangle).

DOWN

1. A saltine cracker is usually in the shape of a (square).
4. A shape without any straight sides is the (circle).

8-4 Review Subtracting With Regrouping

pages 143–144

1 Getting Started

Objective

- To subtract 2-digit numbers with some regrouping

Materials

2 tens and 2 ones jars; large and small paper clips; tens rods and ones cubes

Warm Up • Mental Math

Have students name the number that comes

1. next after 14, 16, 18 (20)
2. before 10 tens (99)
3. after 299 (300)
4. between 462 and 464 (463)
5. before 1,000 (999)
6. after 7 hundreds (701)
7. before 8 hundreds 2 ones (801)

Warm Up • Number Sense

Have students turn to page 67 in any book that has at least 100 pages. Ask students how many pages there are from page 67 to page 90. Have a student write **90 − 67** on the board and solve the problem. (23) Continue the activity to find the number of pages from 26 to 82 (56), 16 to 41 (25), 48 to 99 (51) and 53 to 82 (29).

Name ______________________

Lesson 8-4

Review Subtracting With Regrouping

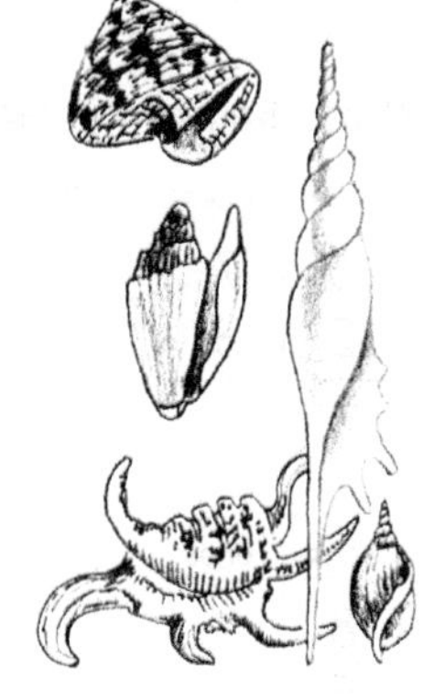

Rhoda collected 55 shells.
Diana collected 39 shells.
How many more shells did Rhoda collect?

We want to know how many more shells Rhoda has.

Rhoda has 55 shells.

Diana has 39 shells.

To find how many more shells Rhoda has, we subtract 39 from 55.

REMEMBER Subtract the ones first.

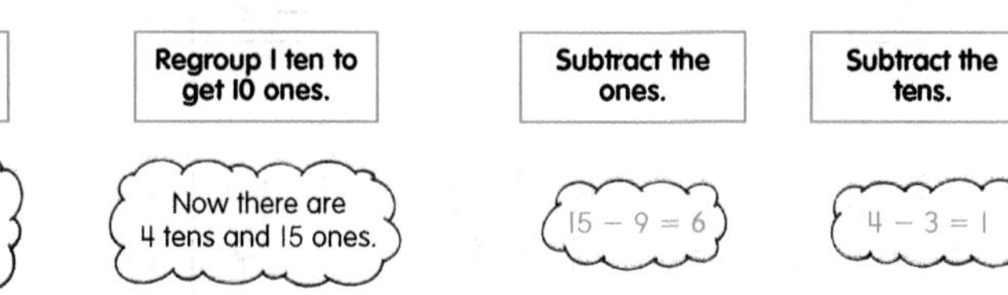

Do you need more ones?	Regroup 1 ten to get 10 ones.	Subtract the ones.	Subtract the tens.
5 − 9 = ? Yes, you need more ones.	Now there are 4 tens and 15 ones.	15 − 9 = 6	4 − 3 = 1

tens	ones
5	5
− 3	9
	?

tens	ones
4	15
~~5~~	~~5~~
− 3	9
	6

tens	ones
4	15
~~5~~	~~5~~
− 3	9
1	6

Rhoda has 16 more shells than Diana.

Getting Started

Subtract. Regroup if needed.

1.

tens	ones
6	3
− 2	8
3	5

2.

tens	ones
8	7
− 3	4
5	3

3. $75 - 12 = 63$

4. $52 - 25 = 27$

5. $90 - 52 = 38$

2 Teach

Develop Skills and Concepts Tell students that large paper clips represent tens and small paper clips represent ones. Have a student place large and small paper clips in the tens and ones jars to show 46. (4 large, 6 small) Have a student place clips in another set of jars to show 29. (2 large, 9 small)

- Tell students to find how many more are in the first student's jars than in the second student's jars. Write **46 − 29** on the board. Tell students to remove clips from the first student's jars until there are 29 left and then see how many were removed. Tell students that we know there are going to be 9 small clips left and since we only have 6 ones, a ten must be regrouped. Help students regroup 1 large clip for 10 small clips and complete the problem. Ask how many more clips were in the first student's jars. (17) Show the regrouping on the board and talk through the subtraction to show 17 as the difference.
- Repeat the activity for 77 − 48 (29), 52 − 28 (24), 39 − 16 (23), 82 − 57 (25), and 41 − 12 (29).

3 Practice

Using page 143 Have a student read the example aloud and tell what is to be found. (how many more shells Rhoda collected) Ask students what information is given. (Rhoda collected 55 shells and Diana collected 39.) Have students read and complete the information sentences. Work through the model with students and then have them complete the solution statement. Have students lay out tens rods and ones cubes to check their solution.

- Help students complete the Getting Started exercises if necessary.

Practice

Subtract.

1.

tens	ones
6	8
− 2	3
4	5

2.

tens	ones
7	1
− 3	9
3	2

3.

tens	ones
5	2
− 2	6
2	6

4.

tens	ones
8	5
− 2	5
6	0

5. $57 - 23 = 34$
6. $75 - 29 = 46$
7. $53 - 46 = 7$
8. $79 - 30 = 49$
9. $50 - 8 = 42$
10. $32 - 18 = 14$
11. $73 - 50 = 23$
12. $57 - 45 = 12$
13. $81 - 15 = 66$
14. $77 - 39 = 38$
15. $31 - 17 = 14$
16. $64 - 9 = 55$
17. $83 - 33 = 50$
18. $61 - 34 = 27$
19. $60 - 20 = 40$
20. $77 - 18 = 59$
21. $82 - 55 = 27$
22. $53 - 47 = 6$

Problem Solving

Solve.

23. Martha had 80¢.
She lost 35¢.
How much was left?
45¢

24. Allan earned 68¢ on Friday. He earned 25¢ on Saturday. How much more did he earn on Friday?
43¢

Using page 144 Remind students that in the subtraction problems, they must first decide if regrouping for more ones is needed. Tell students they will need to decide which operation to use in each of the word problems. Have students complete the page independently.

4 Assess

Tell students, *Louisa has 55 marbles. Pedro has 26 marbles. How many more marbles does Louisa have?* (29)

5 Mixed Review

1. 14 − 8 (6)
2. 8¢ + 1¢ (9¢)
3. 13 − 7 (6)
4. 14 − 7 (7)
5. 11 − 8 (3)
6. 10¢ − 6¢ (4¢)
7. 6 + ____ = 7 (1)
8. 9¢ + 6¢ (15¢)
9. 8 + 5 (13)
10. 9¢ − 4¢ (5¢)

For Mixed Abilities

Common Errors • Intervention

Watch for students who reduce the tens digit by one even though they do not need to regroup.

Incorrect	Correct
~~5~~⁴9 − 32 = 17	59 − 32 = 27

Correct students by having them use place-value materials to model the problem.

Enrichment • Number Sense

Tell students to write and solve a problem to find out how many dimes they would have left from 8 dimes and 4 pennies if they gave 26¢ to a friend. (5 dimes)

More to Explore • Application

Have students make a list of some common math skills such as counting, measuring, adding, subtracting, telling time, and so on. Tell students to make a second list of occupations that would use some of these skills. From that list, choose the occupation students are most interested in. Have the class write an invitation to someone in your community having that occupation, to speak to your class about the math skills he or she uses in that job. Discuss the importance of developing our individual math skills for use now and in the future.

8-5 Practice Subtracting With Regrouping

pages 145–146

1 Getting Started

Objective

- To subtract 2-digit numbers with some regrouping

Materials

colored chalk; tens rods and ones cubes

Warm Up • Mental Math

Ask students if regrouping is needed.

1. 62 − 46 (yes)
2. 50 − 41 (yes)
3. 29 − 2 (no)
4. 68 − 59 (yes)
5. 21 − 6 (yes)
6. 82 − 30 (no)
7. 53 − 12 (no)
8. 91 − 46 (yes)

Warm Up • Number Sense

Write **2 tens 8 ones** on the board and have students tell all the numbers of ones that can be subtracted from 8 ones without requiring regrouping. (0 through 8) Repeat for 6 ones, 2 ones, 7 ones, 5 ones, and 9 ones.

Name ______________________

Practice Subtracting With Regrouping

Anna had fun riding her bike. How many more blocks did she ride the first week than the second week?

Anna
1st week 61 blocks
2nd week 43 blocks
3rd week 63 blocks

We want to know how many more blocks she rode her bike the first week than the second week.

Anna rode her bike __61__ blocks the first week.

She rode her bike __43__ blocks the second week.

To find how many more blocks she rode her bike the first week than the second week, we subtract __43__ from __61__.

REMEMBER Subtract the ones first.

Subtract the ones. Regroup if needed.	Subtract the tens.
$\begin{array}{r} \overset{5}{\cancel{6}}\overset{11}{\cancel{1}} \\ -\ 4\ 3 \\ \hline 8 \end{array}$	$\begin{array}{r} \overset{5}{\cancel{6}}\overset{11}{\cancel{1}} \\ -\ 4\ 3 \\ \hline 1\ 8 \end{array}$

Anna rode her bike __18__ more blocks the first week than the second week.

Getting Started

Subtract. Regroup if needed.

1. $\begin{array}{r} 90 \\ -\ 49 \\ \hline 41 \end{array}$
2. $\begin{array}{r} 87 \\ -\ 23 \\ \hline 64 \end{array}$
3. $\begin{array}{r} 45 \\ -\ 18 \\ \hline 27 \end{array}$
4. $\begin{array}{r} 67 \\ -\ 47 \\ \hline 20 \end{array}$
5. $\begin{array}{r} 54 \\ -\ 39 \\ \hline 15 \end{array}$
6. $\begin{array}{r} 90 \\ -\ 40 \\ \hline 50 \end{array}$

2 Teach

Develop Skills and Concepts Tell students that there were 45 guests at one party and 16 guests at another. We want to know how many more guests were at the first party. Ask students if we need to add or subtract. (subtract)

- Write **45 − 16** on the board. Use colored chalk to show the regrouping of 1 ten for 10 ones. Show that 4 tens 5 ones is renamed as 3 tens 15 ones. Have a student use regular chalk to solve the problem. (29)
- Have students use colored chalk to show any regroupings before other students use regular chalk to solve the following problems on the board: 73 − 46 (27), 69 − 45 (24), 71 − 28 (43), 67 − 39 (28), 92 − 45 (47), and 55 − 18 (37).

3 Practice

Using page 145 Have a student read the example aloud and tell what is to be found. (how many more blocks Anna rode the first week than she rode the second week) Ask students what information is needed. (the number of blocks Anna rode each week) Ask students if any unnecessary information is given. (yes) Have students tell which information is needed. (61 blocks the first week and 43 blocks the second week) Have students read and complete the information sentences. Work through the model with students and then have them complete the solution sentence. Have students use tens rods and ones cubes to check their solution.

- Have students complete the Getting Started exercises independently.

Using page 146 Remind students that regrouping is not needed in some of the problems on this page. Have students complete the page independently.

Practice

Subtract. Regroup if needed.

1. $\begin{array}{r}90\\-\ 50\\\hline 40\end{array}$	2. $\begin{array}{r}65\\-\ 35\\\hline 30\end{array}$	3. $\begin{array}{r}73\\-\ 40\\\hline 33\end{array}$	4. $\begin{array}{r}65\\-\ 9\\\hline 56\end{array}$	5. $\begin{array}{r}51\\-\ 27\\\hline 24\end{array}$	6. $\begin{array}{r}86\\-\ 28\\\hline 58\end{array}$
7. $\begin{array}{r}75\\-\ 41\\\hline 34\end{array}$	8. $\begin{array}{r}48\\-\ 24\\\hline 24\end{array}$	9. $\begin{array}{r}34\\-\ 17\\\hline 17\end{array}$	10. $\begin{array}{r}56\\-\ 37\\\hline 19\end{array}$	11. $\begin{array}{r}83\\-\ 55\\\hline 28\end{array}$	12. $\begin{array}{r}51\\-\ 19\\\hline 32\end{array}$
13. $\begin{array}{r}62\\-\ 28\\\hline 34\end{array}$	14. $\begin{array}{r}97\\-\ 65\\\hline 32\end{array}$	15. $\begin{array}{r}80\\-\ 52\\\hline 28\end{array}$	16. $\begin{array}{r}45\\-\ 25\\\hline 20\end{array}$	17. $\begin{array}{r}37\\-\ 18\\\hline 19\end{array}$	18. $\begin{array}{r}64\\-\ 57\\\hline 7\end{array}$
19. $\begin{array}{r}83\\-\ 48\\\hline 35\end{array}$	20. $\begin{array}{r}77\\-\ 56\\\hline 21\end{array}$	21. $\begin{array}{r}44\\-\ 14\\\hline 30\end{array}$	22. $\begin{array}{r}32\\-\ 16\\\hline 16\end{array}$	23. $\begin{array}{r}58\\-\ 25\\\hline 33\end{array}$	24. $\begin{array}{r}33\\-\ 18\\\hline 15\end{array}$
25. $\begin{array}{r}92\\-\ 34\\\hline 58\end{array}$	26. $\begin{array}{r}83\\-\ 71\\\hline 12\end{array}$	27. $\begin{array}{r}41\\-\ 26\\\hline 15\end{array}$	28. $\begin{array}{r}94\\-\ 57\\\hline 37\end{array}$	29. $\begin{array}{r}88\\-\ 44\\\hline 44\end{array}$	30. $\begin{array}{r}71\\-\ 29\\\hline 42\end{array}$

Problem Solving

Solve.

31. There were 35 bikes in a race. 17 bikes got flat tires. How many bikes did not get flat tires?

    18 bikes

32. There were 25 prizes given. 19 children got bike lights. How many children got other prizes?

    6 children

4 Assess

Refer students to the table in the example on page 145. Ask, *How many more blocks did Anna ride her bike the third week than the second week?* (2) *Did you need to regroup to find the answers?* (no)

5 Mixed Review

1. 11 − 2 (9)
2. 10 − 7 (3)
3. 10 + 9 (19)
4. 7 − 4 (3)
5. 12 − 4 (8)
6. 5 + 10 (15)
7. 3¢ + 8¢ (11¢)
8. ____ + 1 = 4 (3)
9. 9¢ − 2¢ (7¢)
10. 8 + 9 (17)

For Mixed Abilities

Common Errors • Intervention

Watch for students who simply bring down the number that is being subtracted when there is a zero in the minuend.

Incorrect	Correct
$\begin{array}{r}80\\-\ 34\\\hline 54\end{array}$	$\begin{array}{r}{\scriptstyle 7\,10}\\\not{8}\not{0}\\-\ 34\\\hline 46\end{array}$

Have these students work with partners using place-value materials to model problems such as 30 − 12 and 40 − 28.

Enrichment • Number Sense

Ask students to find out how many more horses can be boarded on a farm that has barns with 16, 28, and 10 stalls than on a neighboring farm that has only 27 stalls in all. (27)

More to Explore • Probability

Give each student 2 pennies and a sheet of paper. Ask a student to explain all the possible ways the two coins could land if they are flipped at the same time. (heads, tails; heads, heads; and tails, tails) Tell the class to toss the two coins together a total of ten times, and mark each combination that turns up on a chart. Before they begin, ask them to guess how many of each combination they will get, writing their guess on paper.

	Guess	Actual
Heads/tails		
Heads/heads		
Tails/tails		

Give them time to try the experiment and to record their results.

ESL/ELL STRATEGIES

Use a simple line drawing of a bicycle on the board to clarify the meaning of a *flat tire* and a *bike light*. Explain that a *prize* is a gift or money given to the winner of a race.

8-6 Using Addition to Check Subtraction

pages 147–148

1 Getting Started

Objective
- To check subtraction by adding

Materials
tens rods and ones cubes

Warm Up • Mental Math
Have students name the number if they start at

1. 3, add 4, add 6 (13)
2. 8, add 7, subtract 7 (8)
3. 15, subtract 6, add 9 (18)
4. 12, add 2, subtract 7 (7)
5. 20, subtract 4, add 2 (18)
6. 32, subtract 12, add 4 (24)
7. 2, add 15, subtract 9 (8)
8. 26, subtract 14, add 0 (12)

Warm Up • Number Sense
Show the fact 15 − 6 and have students write the related facts on the board. (15 − 9, 9 + 6, 6 + 9) Repeat for other subtraction facts.

Name ______________________

Using Addition to Check Subtraction

The Pet Shoppe had 55 birds.
It sold 27 of them.
How many birds are left?

We want to know how many birds are left.

The store had 55 birds.

It sold 27 birds.

To find how many are left, we subtract 27 from 55.

Subtract the ones first. Regroup if needed.	Subtract the tens.	Check by adding.
4 15 ~~5~~ ~~5~~ − 2 7 8	4 15 ~~5~~ ~~5~~ − 2 7 2 8	2 8 + 2 7 5 5

These should be the same.

The Pet Shoppe has 28 birds left.

Getting Started

Subtract. Regroup if needed. Check your answers.

1. $37 - 15 = 22$; check: $22 + 15 = 37$
2. $81 - 43 = 38$; check: $38 + 43 = 81$
3. $75 - 39 = 36$; check: $36 + 39 = 75$
4. $43 - 17 = 26$; check: $26 + 17 = 43$
5. $64 - 41 = 23$; check: $23 + 41 = 64$
6. $57 - 28 = 29$; check: $29 + 28 = 57$

2 Teach

Develop Skills and Concepts Have students lay out 4 tens 3 ones. Tell students to take 2 tens 9 ones away as you write **43 − 29** on the board. Ask students what number is left. (14)

- Tell students that the solution can be checked by adding 14 and 29. Write **14 + 29** on the board. Have students add and tell the sum. (43) Ask students if the sum of the addition problem is the same as the minuend in the subtraction problem. (yes)
- Circle the 43 in each problem on the board and connect the circles with a line. Tell students that if the sum is the same as the minuend in the subtraction problem, then the answer is correct. Tell students that if the sum of the addition problem had not been 43, then we would know an error had been made. Explain that this is a good way to check their work in a subtraction problem.
- Repeat the procedure for 88 − 26 (62), 29 − 12 (17), 77 − 48 (29), and 90 − 66 (24). Ask students if an error has been made as each problem is checked by adding.

3 Practice

Using page 147 Have a student read the example aloud and tell what is to be solved. (how many birds are left) Ask students what information is given. (There were 55 birds and 27 were sold.) Have students read and complete the information sentences. Work through the model with students, emphasizing the checking procedure. Then, have students complete the solution sentence.

- Help students complete Getting Started Exercise 1. Then, have them complete the remaining exercises independently.

Using page 148 Remind students to show the work that checks each answer. Have students complete the problems independently.

Practice

Subtract. Regroup if needed. Check your answers.

1. $\begin{array}{r} 75 \\ -\ 25 \\ \hline 50 \end{array}$ $\begin{array}{r} 50 \\ +\ 25 \\ \hline 75 \end{array}$
2. $\begin{array}{r} 61 \\ -\ 27 \\ \hline 34 \end{array}$ $\begin{array}{r} 34 \\ +\ 27 \\ \hline 61 \end{array}$
3. $\begin{array}{r} 38 \\ -\ 13 \\ \hline 25 \end{array}$ $\begin{array}{r} 25 \\ +\ 13 \\ \hline 38 \end{array}$
4. $\begin{array}{r} 53 \\ -\ 36 \\ \hline 17 \end{array}$ $\begin{array}{r} 17 \\ +\ 36 \\ \hline 53 \end{array}$
5. $\begin{array}{r} 85 \\ -\ 59 \\ \hline 26 \end{array}$ $\begin{array}{r} 26 \\ +\ 59 \\ \hline 85 \end{array}$
6. $\begin{array}{r} 67 \\ -\ 39 \\ \hline 28 \end{array}$ $\begin{array}{r} 28 \\ +\ 39 \\ \hline 67 \end{array}$
7. $\begin{array}{r} 42 \\ -\ 15 \\ \hline 27 \end{array}$ $\begin{array}{r} 27 \\ +\ 15 \\ \hline 42 \end{array}$
8. $\begin{array}{r} 95 \\ -\ 58 \\ \hline 37 \end{array}$ $\begin{array}{r} 37 \\ +\ 58 \\ \hline 95 \end{array}$
9. $\begin{array}{r} 51 \\ -\ 43 \\ \hline 8 \end{array}$ $\begin{array}{r} 8 \\ +\ 43 \\ \hline 51 \end{array}$
10. $\begin{array}{r} 99 \\ -\ 69 \\ \hline 30 \end{array}$ $\begin{array}{r} 30 \\ +\ 69 \\ \hline 99 \end{array}$
11. $\begin{array}{r} 64 \\ -\ 25 \\ \hline 39 \end{array}$ $\begin{array}{r} 39 \\ +\ 25 \\ \hline 64 \end{array}$
12. $\begin{array}{r} 77 \\ -\ 48 \\ \hline 29 \end{array}$ $\begin{array}{r} 29 \\ +\ 48 \\ \hline 77 \end{array}$

Now Try This!

It's Algebra!

Solve.

1. Subtract two numbers. One number is 25. The answer is 50. What is the other number? 75
2. Subtract two numbers. The greater number is 60. The answer is 45. What is the other number? 15

Now Try This! Tell students that you are thinking of a number that, when added to 4, the sum will be 13. Write $4 +$ ____ $= 13$ and $13 - 4 =$ on the board. Have students complete the sentences. (9) Ask students to name a number if the difference of that number and 70 is 30. Help students write $70 -$ ____ $= 30$ on the board. Have students solve the problem. (40)

Have students work through each exercise to find its missing number.

It's Algebra! The concepts in this activity prepare students for algebra.

4 Assess

Write $55 - 12 = 37$ on the board. Have students use addition to check if the answer is correct. (no) Ask them to correct the problem and then use addition to check their answer. ($55 - 12 = 43$; $43 + 12 = 55$)

For Mixed A

Common Errors • In

Some students may add answer to the minuend w are checking subtraction. Correct students by havin them check using the form shown at the right, where there is no need to recopy any numbers.

Enrichment • Algebra

Have students write and solve problem that will show that an error was made when 29 was subtracted from 72 for a differen of 45. Tell them to correct the subtraction problem and then show their work to prove the solution is error free.

More to Explore • Number Sense

Tape 18-inch squares of heavy paper next to each other on the floor around the room to resemble a gameboard. Mark the first square start. Have students write two addition or subtraction math problems using 2-digit numbers less than 40 each on a separate card. Select a small group of students to play the first game. The first student selects a card and solves the problem. Starting at the marked square, the student walks the number of squares that are equivalent to the answer counting out loud. If a student answers incorrectly, he or she must sit down. Continue with each student in the group until one student passes the starting point. Each time a student passes the starting square, that student chooses another student to take his or her place. Continue playing until everyone has had a turn on the giant gameboard.

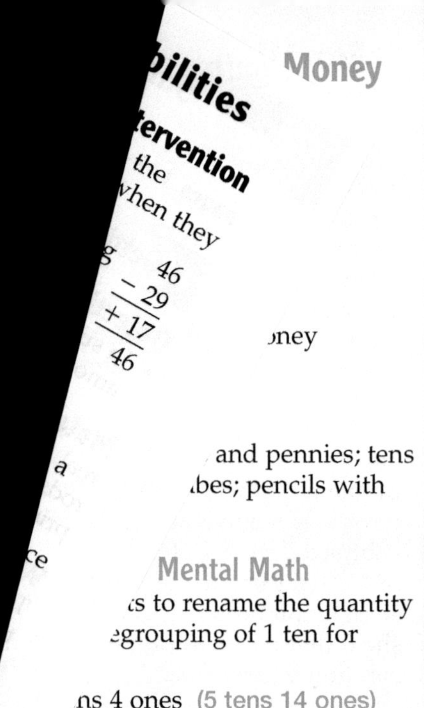

Money

…ney

…and pennies; tens …bes; pencils with

Mental Math

…s to rename the quantity …egrouping of 1 ten for

…ns 4 ones (5 tens 14 ones)
…ens 8 ones (8 tens 18 ones)
… tens 0 ones (6 tens 10 ones)
… 2 tens 4 ones (1 ten 14 ones)
… 1 ten 6 ones (0 tens 16 ones)
6. 9 tens 0 ones (8 tens 10 ones)
7. 2 tens 1 one (1 ten 11 ones)

Warm Up • Pencil and Paper

Write **46 − 12** on the board. Have a student solve the problem and check the solution on a sheet of paper. (34, 34 + 12 = 46) Repeat for 70 − 16 (54), 58 − 19 (39), 44 − 17 (27), 36 − 24 (12), and 85 − 67 (18).

Name ____________________

Subtracting Money

Alice saved 85¢ to buy a kite. After buying one kite, how much money does she have left?

We want to know how much money she has left.

Alice saved 85¢.

She spends 59¢.

To find how much money she has left, we subtract 59¢ from 85¢.

Subtract the pennies first. Regroup if needed.		Subtract the dimes.	
10¢	1¢	10¢	1¢
7	15	7	15
~~8~~	~~5~~¢	~~8~~	~~5~~¢
− 5	9¢	− 5	9¢
	6¢	2	6¢

Alice has 26¢ left.

Getting Started

Subtract. Regroup if needed.

1. 36¢ − 15¢ = 21¢
2. 47¢ − 19¢ = 28¢
3. 75¢ − 38¢ = 37¢
4. 78¢ − 56¢ = 22¢
5. 91¢ − 73¢ = 18¢
6. 83¢ − 42¢ = 41¢
7. 90¢ − 53¢ = 37¢
8. 84¢ − 58¢ = 26¢
9. 97¢ − 57¢ = 40¢
10. 46¢ − 28¢ = 18¢

2 Teach

Develop Skills and Concepts Have students lay out 75 in tens rods and ones cubes and 75¢ in dimes and pennies. Ask students the number of tens rods and dimes. (7) Ask how many ones cubes and pennies there are. (5)

- Tell students to take 4 tens and 8 ones and 4 dimes and 8 pennies away and tell how many are left. (2 tens and 7 ones, 2 dimes and 7 pennies) Remind students that the problems are the same, but money notation is used in one problem.
- Write **75 − 48** and **75¢ − 48¢** on the board. Have a student solve each problem on the board. (27, 27¢) Now, have a student check each problem by adding. (27 + 48 = 75, 27¢ + 48¢ = 75¢) Repeat for more subtraction problems using money.

3 Practice

Using page 149 Have a student read the example aloud and tell what is to be solved. (find the amount of money Alice has left after buying a kite) Ask students what information is given in the problem. (Alice had 85¢.) Ask what information is needed yet. (the cost of the kite) Ask students to use the picture to tell the cost of the kite. (59¢) Have students read and complete the information sentences. Work through the model with students and then have them complete the solution sentence. Ask students how the solution to this subtraction problem can be checked. (add the solution and the money spent) Have students check by adding.

- Have students complete the Getting Started exercises independently.

Using page 150 Remind students to subtract the pennies first. You may want them to check each solution by adding on another sheet of paper. Tell students to decide what operation to use in each word problem. Have students complete the page independently.

Practice

Subtract. Regroup if needed. Check your answers.

1. 70¢ − 30¢ = 40¢	2. 90¢ − 21¢ = 69¢	3. 84¢ − 27¢ = 57¢	4. 99¢ − 66¢ = 33¢	5. 51¢ − 23¢ = 28¢
6. 98¢ − 29¢ = 69¢	7. 45¢ − 22¢ = 23¢	8. 57¢ − 39¢ = 18¢	9. 75¢ − 50¢ = 25¢	10. 60¢ − 41¢ = 19¢
11. 27¢ − 9¢ = 18¢	12. 65¢ − 35¢ = 30¢	13. 80¢ − 50¢ = 30¢	14. 52¢ − 7¢ = 45¢	15. 45¢ − 36¢ = 9¢
16. 48¢ − 15¢ = 33¢	17. 73¢ − 55¢ = 18¢	18. 64¢ − 17¢ = 47¢	19. 35¢ − 15¢ = 20¢	20. 96¢ − 77¢ = 19¢

Problem Solving

Solve.

21. Li saved 95¢. She bought some crayons for 75¢. How much money does she have left? 20¢

22. Lonnie saved 45¢. He bought a truck for 35¢. How much money does he have now? 10¢

4 Assess

Give each student 63¢ in dimes and pennies and a pencil with a price tag of 14¢ on it. Ask students how much money they would have left after buying the pencil. (49¢)

5 Mixed Review

1. 18¢ − 9¢ (9¢)
2. 12 − 3 (9)
3. 4 + 7 (11)
4. 4¢ + 9¢ (13¢)
5. _____ + 5 = 13 (8)
6. 1 hundred 3 tens 2 ones (132)
7. 16 − 8 (8)
8. 10 + 6 (16)
9. 3 hundreds 0 tens 2 ones (302)
10. 11¢ − 5¢ (6¢)

For Mixed Abilities

Common Errors • **Intervention**

If students continue to have difficulty subtracting money, have them work with partners to use coins to model the problems. Have them pretend they go to a store with the amount of money shown in a minuend you give them and purchase an item that costs the amount shown in a subtrahend you give them. Be sure they understand that the answer to the problem tells them how much money they have left.

Enrichment • Number Sense

Ask students how much more money they would have left from 92¢ if they spent only 26¢ for a tablet than if they bought notebook paper for 22¢ and 3 pencils for 5¢ each. (11¢)

More to Explore • Number Sense

Give each pair of students a dozen counters to share equally. (Each should have six.) Now, take three counters away from each pair and ask them to share the counters again. (Each will have four with one left over.) Explain that 12 is called an even number and that even numbers can be divided into two equal groups. Ask if 9 is an even number. (no) Point out that 9 is called an odd number because it cannot be divided into two equal groups. Have students compose a tally like the following and have students use their counters to complete it.

Number of Counters	Odd Number	Even Number
5	x	
14		x
1	x	
20		x
6		x

and so on . . .

8-8 Problem Solving: Make and Use a Graph

pages 151–152

1 Getting Started

Objectives

- To use a bar graph to solve problems
- To add or subtract to solve problems

Materials

*large grid paper

Warm Up • Mental Math

Ask students to name an addition problem to check the following subtraction problems:

1. 26 − 14 (12 + 14)
2. 72 − 2 (2 + 70)
3. 46 − 31 (15 + 31)
4. 77 − 44 (33 + 44)
5. 15 − 6 (6 + 9)
6. 41 − 38 (3 + 38)
7. 50 − 35 (15 + 35)

Warm Up • Algebra

Write **84 − 46 = 32** vertically on the board. Have a student check the problem by adding. (32 + 46 = 78) Ask if the problem checks out to be correct. (no) Have the student correct the subtraction problem and check by adding. (84 − 46 = 38, 38 + 46 = 84) Continue for more subtraction problems that have correct or incorrect answers.

Name ______________________

Problem Solving: Make and Use a Graph

Mrs. Peach's class is taking a vote on its favorite kinds of fruits. The students are going to make a bar graph to show the results of their vote.

Apples	6 students
Oranges	7 students
Pears	3 students
Bananas	4 students

Use the information on the board to help Mrs. Peach and her class complete the bar graph. Then answer each question.

There are 4 kinds of fruit.
The graph needs 4 rows.

The most number of fruits is 7.
The least number of fruits is 3.

The graph can go from 0 to 10.
The title of the graph is Favorite Fruits.

Color in the boxes for each fruit.

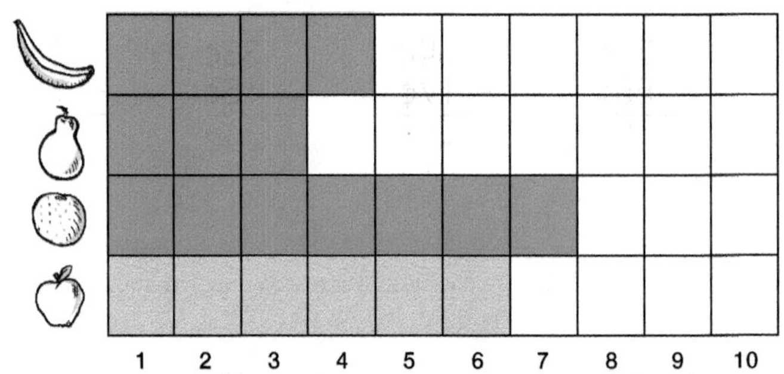

Use the graph to find the answers.

1. How many students picked bananas as their favorite fruit? 4
2. Which fruit got the most votes? oranges
3. Which fruit got the least votes? pears

2 Teach

Develop Skills and Concepts Have students survey at least 20 students in another class about what their favorite topping for ice cream is. As a class, compile the data into a tally chart. Then, use this data to construct a bar graph on large grid paper as a class. Help students label the horizontal axis with topping selections and place the number of students selecting that topping on the vertical axis. Have students come up with a title for the graph and tell them that all charts and graphs should have a title.

3 Practice

Using page 151 Have students look at the art in the example. Ask students what information is presented in the art. (The results of a class poll of favorite fruits.)

- Now, apply the four-step plan to the example. For SEE, ask, *What are you being asked to do?*(make a bar graph) Then, *What information is given?* (the favorite fruits and the number of students who like them) For PLAN, ask students how many rows they will need for their bar graph. (4) Then, ask to what number the graph can go to. (10) For DO, have students color the bar graph. For CHECK, have them compare the information in the chart to the information presented in the art to make sure they recorded data in the chart correctly.
- Have students use the graph to answer the questions independently.

Practice

Maria showed a list of four pets to her friends at school. She asked each friend to pick a favorite pet and then made a graph of their choices.

Use Maria's graph to find the answers.

1. 27 children chose a cat.
2. 35 children chose a dog.
3. 22 children chose a bird.
4. 9 children chose a rabbit.
5. How many children chose a cat or a dog?
   62
6. How many more children chose a dog than a cat?
   8
7. How many children chose a bird or a rabbit?
   31
8. How many children chose a dog or a rabbit?
   44
9. How many more children chose a cat than a rabbit?
   18

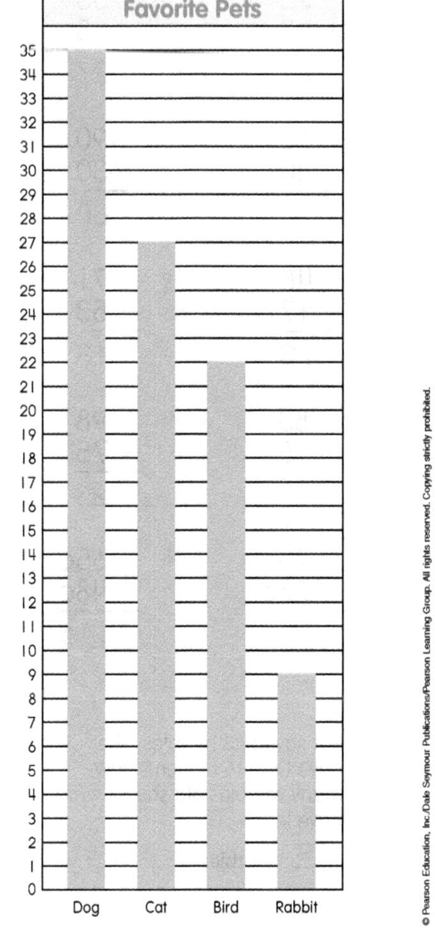

Using page 152 Have a student read the paragraph at the top of the page aloud. Help students read the graph to find and record how many of Maria's friends chose each pet. Have students fill in the first four statements. Have a student read Exercise 5 aloud. Help students recognize that this problem asks for the number of children who chose a cat and the number who chose a dog. Tell students to make a plan to solve each problem and then have them complete the exercises independently. Remind students to check each exercise to be sure their answers make sense.

4 Assess

Poll students on their favorite books. Then, have the class use the information to create a bar graph.

For Mixed Abilities

Common Errors • Intervention

Some students' bar graphs may not faithfully depict the situation in the problem. They may color above or below the number they are trying to represent. Have them use rulers to correctly measure and color their graphs.

Enrichment • Application

Have students make a bar graph showing the number of students in each of four classrooms in your school. Then, have students answer the following questions:

1. How many students are in each classroom?
2. Which class has the most students?
3. How many total students are in the four classrooms?
4. How many more students are in the class with the most students than in the class with the least students?

More to Explore • Measurement

Have students bring in various objects from home to be weighed. Weigh each object using an appropriate scale and make a chart showing each object's name and weight in pounds and ounces. Then, put each object in an unmarked paper bag. Have students choose a bag, estimate its weight in pounds, and guess its contents based on its weight. Then, have students weigh the bag to verify their guess. Repeat several times for students to estimate the weight of different bags and keep a chart of their responses.

Chapter 8 Test

page 153

Items	Objectives
1–4	To subtract a 1-digit number from a 2-digit number with some regrouping (see pages 139–140)
5–8	To subtract any two 2-digit numbers with no regrouping (see pages 137–138)
9–16	To subtract a 2-digit number from a 2-digit number with some regrouping (see pages 141–146)
17–20	To subtract 2-digit money amounts (see pages 149–150)
21–22	To subtract a 2-digit number from a 2-digit number with some regrouping (see pages 141–146)

Name ____________________

Chapter 8 Test

Subtract. Regroup if needed.

1. 25 − 3 = 22
2. 35 − 8 = 27
3. 71 − 5 = 66
4. 55 − 9 = 46
5. 80 − 30 = 50
6. 90 − 30 = 60
7. 60 − 20 = 40
8. 85 − 31 = 54
9. 45 − 17 = 28
10. 71 − 53 = 18
11. 64 − 19 = 45
12. 97 − 29 = 68
13. 83 − 15 = 68
14. 98 − 75 = 23
15. 81 − 67 = 14
16. 35 − 19 = 16
17. 75¢ − 25¢ = 50¢
18. 65¢ − 48¢ = 17¢
19. 92¢ − 55¢ = 37¢
20. 73¢ − 15¢ = 58¢

Solve.

21. Pat saved 35 marbles. She gave Dino 16 of them. How many marbles did she have left?
19 marbles

22. The pet store had 75 goldfish. It sold 39 of them. How many goldfish were left?
36 goldfish

Alternate Chapter Test

You may wish to use the Alternate Chapter Test on page 322 of this book for further review and assessment.

Circle the letter of the correct answer.

1. 15 − 9
   a. 24 b. 6 c. 14 d. NG

2. 7 + 4
   a. 11 b. 3 c. 4 d. NG

3. a. 81¢ b. 80¢ c. 76¢ d. NG

4. a. 4:25 b. 3:25 c. 5:15 d. NG

5. a. 135 b. 55 c. 145 d. NG

6. 51 + 37
   a. 14 b. 98 c. 89 d. NG

7. 29¢ + 34¢
   a. 63¢ b. 53¢ c. 513 d. NG

8. 80 + 70
   a. 160 b. 150 c. 10 d. NG

9. 76 + 97
   a. 163 b. 1,613 c. 173 d. NG

10. 80 − 30
   a. 50 b. 110 c. 40 d. NG

11. 59 − 15
   a. 44 b. 74 c. 54 d. NG

12. 98¢ − 35¢
   a. 133¢ b. 36¢ c. 63¢ d. NG

13. 71¢ − 23¢
   a. 52¢ b. 48¢ c. 94¢ d. NG

score

STOP

Cumulative Assessment

page 154

Items	Objectives
1–2	To review addition and subtraction facts with sums and minuends through 18 (see pages 3–12, 17–20, 23–28, 35–44, 53–56, 59–64)
3	To count money through $5 (see pages 75–76)
4	To tell time in 5-minute intervals (see pages 95–96)
5	To understand 3-digit numbers (see pages 71–74)
6–9	To add two 2-digit numbers with or without regrouping (see pages 125–130)
10–11	To subtract any two 2-digit numbers with no regrouping (see pages 137–138)
12–13	To subtract 2-digit money amounts (see pages 149–150)

Alternate Cumulative Assessment

Circle the letter of the correct answer.

1. 16 − 5
   a 11 b 10 c 9 d NG

2. 9 + 5
   a 14 b 15 c 16 d NG

3. 
   a $1.55 b $0.75 c $1.25 d NG

4. 

   a 5:15 b 4:20 c 3:25 d NG

5. 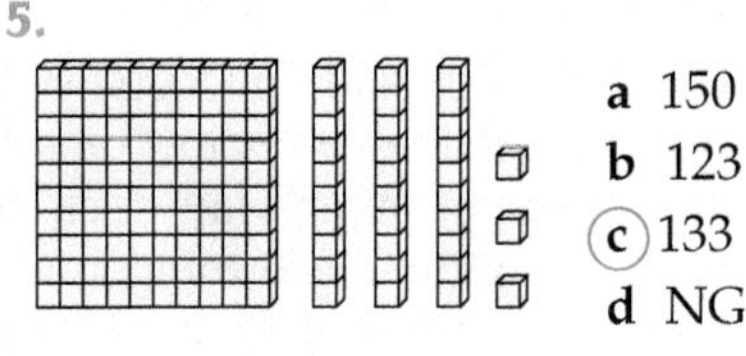
   a 150 b 123 c 133 d NG

6. 27 + 51
   a 88 b 78 c 76 d NG

7. 19¢ + 48¢
   a 67¢ b 57¢ c 71¢ d NG

8. 20 + 60
   a 120 b 80 c 90 d NG

9. 56 + 65
   a 101 b 111 c 119 d NG

10. 90 − 60
   a 140 b 50 c 30 d NG

11. 65 − 51
   a 14 b 16 c 19 d NG

12. 58¢ − 23¢
   a 81¢ b 35¢ c 29¢ d NG

13. 81¢ − 34¢
   a 47¢ b 57¢ c 67¢ d NG

9-1 Finding 2- or 3-Digit Sums

pages 155–156

1 Getting Started

Objective

- To add two 2-digit numbers for a 3-digit sum

Materials

hundred flat, tens rods, and ones cubes

Warm Up • Mental Math

Ask students which number is more and how many more it is.

1. 78, 64 (78, 14 more)
2. 52, 59 (59, 7 more)
3. 91, 89 (91, 2 more)
4. 50, 82 (82, 32 more)
5. 45, 76 (76, 31 more)
6. 90, 75 (90, 15 more)
7. 50, 20 (50, 30 more)
8. 66, 99 (99, 33 more)

Warm Up • Number Sense

Write **28 + 16** on the board and ask students if regrouping is needed. (yes) Ask what regrouping is needed. (10 ones for 1 ten) Write **47 − 26** on the board and ask if regrouping is needed. (no) Continue to write 2-digit addition or subtraction problems on the board and ask if regrouping is needed and, if so, what regrouping is needed.

Name ____________________

Adding and Subtracting 2-Digit Numbers

Chapter 9

Lesson 9-1

Finding 2- or 3-Digit Sums

The Walkers planted 75 tomato plants and 49 pepper plants in their garden. How many plants are there in all?

We are looking for the total number of plants.

There are __75__ tomato plants.

There are __49__ pepper plants.

To find the total, we add __75__ and __49__.

Add the ones first. Regroup if needed.	Add the tens.
5 + 9 = 14 14 = 1 ten and 4 ones	1 + 7 + 4 = 12 12 tens = 1 hundred and 2 tens
$\begin{array}{r} ^{1}\ \ \\ 75 \\ +\ 49 \\ \hline 4 \end{array}$	$\begin{array}{r} ^{1}\ \ \\ 75 \\ +\ 49 \\ \hline 124 \end{array}$

There are __124__ plants in all.

Getting Started

Add. Regroup if needed.

1. 68 + 79 = 147
2. 39 + 29 = 68
3. 65 + 25 = 90
4. 78 + 36 = 114
5. 47 + 41 = 88
6. 90 + 62 = 152
7. 57 + 37 = 94
8. 78 + 9 = 87
9. 87 + 78 = 165
10. 65 + 34 = 99
11. 46 + 27 = 73
12. 80 + 80 = 160

---

2 Teach

Develop Skills and Concepts Write **64 + 48** on the board and have students lay out tens rods and ones cubes to show each number. Have a student add 4 ones and 8 ones, show the regrouping, and record the number of ones left as other students regroup 10 ones for a tens rod and count the ones left. (2 ones) Ask students the number of tens rods in all as the student adds 6, 4, and 1. (11 tens) Tell students that 11 tens equals 1 hundred and 1 ten. Tell students to regroup 10 tens for 1 hundred and tell the number of tens left. (1) Have the student show the regrouping on the board and record the 1 ten left. Have students tell the total hundreds as 1 hundred is recorded in the problem on the board. Continue for the following problems where one, two, or no regrouping is needed: 26 + 93 (119), 64 + 21 (85), 45 + 66 (111), 87 + 87 (174), 36 + 90 (129), 76 + 85 (161), 40 + 60 (100), and 72 + 9 (81).

3 Practice

Using page 155 Have a student read the example aloud and tell what is to be solved. (the number of plants in all) Ask what information is given. (There are 75 tomato plants and 49 pepper plants.) Ask what operation is needed to find the total number of plants. (addition) Have students read and then complete the information sentences. Work through the model with students and then have them complete the solution sentence. Tell students to lay out tens rods and ones cubes to check their solution.

- Have students complete the Getting Started exercises independently. Allow students to use tens rods and ones cubes to check their answers.

Using page 156 Tell students that some of the addition problems on this page require no regrouping, but they may need to regroup in other problems. Tell students to make a plan to solve each of the word problems. Have students complete the page independently.

Practice

Add. Regroup if needed.

1.	2.	3.	4.	5.	6.
11 + 46 = 57	80 + 44 = 124	49 + 6 = 55	18 + 44 = 62	99 + 33 = 132	18 + 15 = 33

7.	8.	9.	10.	11.	12.
36 + 64 = 100	19 + 22 = 41	23 + 39 = 62	96 + 32 = 128	8 + 48 = 56	45 + 74 = 119

13.	14.	15.	16.	17.	18.
79 + 89 = 168	72 + 77 = 149	27 + 17 = 44	88 + 33 = 121	28 + 45 = 73	67 + 70 = 137

19.	20.	21.	22.	23.	24.
49 + 9 = 58	63 + 48 = 111	48 + 86 = 134	82 + 12 = 94	67 + 23 = 90	85 + 12 = 97

25.	26.	27.	28.	29.	30.
56 + 84 = 140	37 + 28 = 65	44 + 37 = 81	62 + 17 = 79	59 + 98 = 157	26 + 6 = 32

Problem Solving

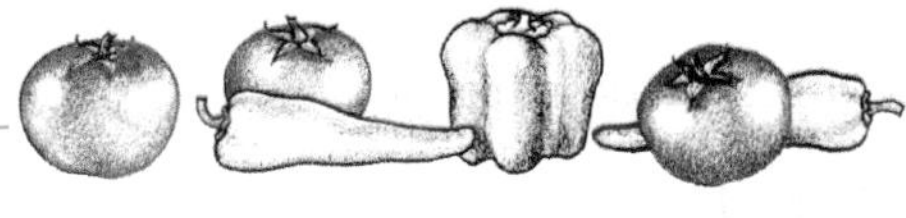

Solve.

31. Ellie picked 50 tomatoes in the morning and 80 in the afternoon. How many tomatoes did she pick?
130 tomatoes

32. Charley picked 75 green peppers and 65 yellow peppers. How many peppers did he pick?
140 peppers

4 Assess

Organize the class into pairs. Have each pair model addition problems with 2-digit numbers that make 3-digit sums using tens rods and ones cubes.

5 Mixed Review

1. 10 + 8 (18)
2. 7 + 8 (15)
3. 15, 20, 25, 30, ____ (35)
4. 0 + 4 (4)
5. 4 hundred 8 tens 6 ones (486)
6. 1¢ + 7¢ (8¢)
7. 30, 40, 50, ____ (60)
8. 17 − 9 (8)
9. 8¢ + 6¢ (14¢)
10. 10 − 5 (5)

For Mixed Abilities

Common Errors • Intervention

Some students may have difficulty adding when the sum is three digits. Have them work their problems on a place-value chart with columns for hundreds, tens, and ones. This will help them to see that an amount such as 14 tens is the same as and is written as 1 hundred 4 tens.

Enrichment • Logic

Tell students to find the sums of 99 + 1, 99 + 11, 99 + 21, 99 + 31, 99 + 41, 99 + 51, 99 + 61, 99 + 71, 99 + 81, and 99 + 91. Ask what pattern they see in the tens place.

More to Explore • Application

Write a fairly simple recipe on the board. Ask students to look at the recipe and tell how many people it will serve if each person has one item. How many if each person has two items? Ask students to list the abbreviations for measurements that they find in the recipe. Write the measurement words next to the abbreviations for students to copy. Discuss cup, teaspoon, and tablespoon measures. Explain how the temperature of the oven is set and how to use a timer. Finally, see if the students can list all the different ways they had to use math in order to make the recipe. Encourage them to try the recipe, with help, at home.

9-2 Column Addition

pages 157–158

1 Getting Started

Objective
- To add three 2-digit numbers for sums through 199

Materials
hundred flat, tens rods, and ones cubes

Warm Up • Mental Math
Tell students to name the number.

1. 8 tens + 80 (160)
2. 70 − 2 tens (50)
3. 53 − 4 tens (13)
4. 9 tens − 6 ones (84)
5. 8 tens 2 ones + 8 ones (90)
6. 1 hundred 2 tens + 4 tens (160)

Warm Up • Number Sense
Have a student write any 2-digit number on the board. Have a second student write another 2-digit number and add the numbers. Have students use manipulatives to check the work. Repeat for more problems of 2-digit numbers plus 1- or 2-digit numbers.

Name ____________________

It's Algebra!

Column Addition

The students in Garden School sold cookies for charity. How many boxes of cookies did Holly, Keith, and Gloria sell altogether?

Boxes of Cookies SOLD	
Holly	54 boxes
Jason	43 boxes
Keith	37 boxes
Gloria	21 boxes

We want to know how many boxes of cookies Holly, Keith, and Gloria sold.

Holly sold <u>54</u> boxes.

Keith sold <u>37</u> boxes.

Gloria sold <u>21</u> boxes.

To find how many they sold altogether, we add <u>54</u>, <u>37</u>, and <u>21</u>.

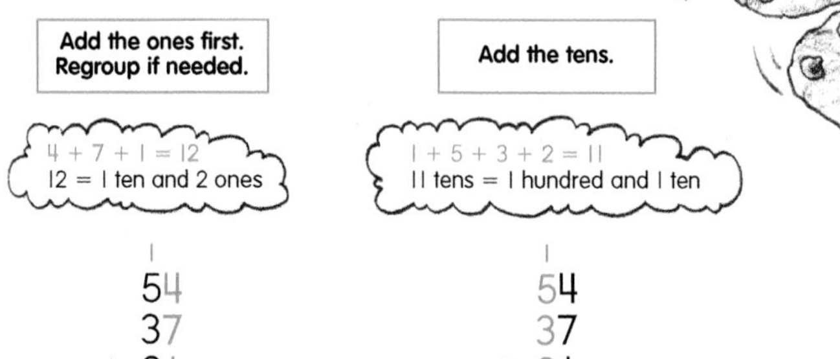


```
   1          1
  54         54
  37         37
+ 21       + 21
   2        112
```

They sold <u>112</u> boxes of cookies.

Getting Started

Add. Regroup if needed.

1. 16 + 72 + 35 = 123
2. 25 + 54 + 65 = 144
3. 41 + 37 + 96 = 174
4. 55 + 8 + 30 = 93
5. 14 + 24 + 36 = 74
6. 2 + 86 + 38 = 126

---

2 Teach

Develop Skills and Concepts Write **86 + 17 + 45** vertically on the board. Have students lay out 86 in tens rods and ones cubes. Repeat for 17 and 45. Ask students how many ones there are in all. (18) Tell students to regroup 10 ones for 1 ten and tell how many ones are left. (8) Ask the number of tens in all. (14) Tell students to trade 10 tens for 1 hundred flat and to tell how many tens are left. (4) Ask students how many hundreds there are. (1) Ask a student to write the sum in the problem on the board. (148) Remind students that looking for a ten is helpful in adding a column of numbers. Now, have a student add the columns from the bottom up in the problem on the board and show any regrouping to check the solution.

- Repeat for 29 + 38 + 11 (78), 51 + 8 + 92 (151), 45 + 15 + 65 (125), and 27 + 81 + 90 (198).

It's Algebra! The concept of this lesson prepares students for algebra.

3 Practice

Using page 157 Have a student read the example aloud and tell what is to be solved. (the total number of boxes of cookies sold by Holly, Keith, and Gloria) Ask students what information is needed. (Holly sold 54 boxes, Keith sold 37 boxes, and Gloria sold 21 boxes.) Ask what unnecessary information is given. (Jason sold 43 boxes.) Have students read and complete the information sentences. Work through the model with students and then have them complete the solution sentence. Have students add up the columns from the bottom up to check their answer.

- Help students with the Getting Started exercises if necessary.

Using page 158 Remind students to add the ones first and look for a ten when adding each column. Have students complete the rows of exercises independently.

Practice

Add. Regroup if needed.

1. 23 + 37 + 90 = 150	2. 40 + 30 + 70 = 140	3. 6 + 70 + 58 = 134	4. 13 + 33 + 76 = 122	5. 11 + 37 + 59 = 107	6. 49 + 10 + 68 = 127
7. 10 + 69 + 18 = 97	8. 59 + 61 + 3 = 123	9. 51 + 39 + 97 = 187	10. 31 + 6 + 52 = 89	11. 10 + 70 + 80 = 160	12. 54 + 34 + 25 = 113
13. 86 + 1 + 8 = 95	14. 35 + 30 + 35 = 100	15. 83 + 6 + 54 = 143	16. 30 + 19 + 88 = 137	17. 82 + 14 + 18 = 114	18. 72 + 23 + 98 = 193

Now Try This!

If you toss a coin 30 times, how many times do you think it will land tails up?

_____ times Answers will vary.

Try it.

Toss a coin 30 times.

How many heads did you get? _____

How many tails did you get? _____

Was your guess close? _____

Now Try This! Group students in pairs with one student tossing a coin and the other student recording the tosses.

Have students record their guesses and then complete the activity and record their results by using tally marks. Discuss with students that there are two possible outcomes of heads or tails and the most accurate guess would be 15 of each because 15 + 15 = 30.

4 Assess

Refer students to the art in the example on page 157. Ask them to find out how many cookies Holly, Jason, and Gloria sold. (118) Then, ask them to find out how many cookies Jason, Keith, and Gloria sold. (101)

For Mixed Abilities

Common Errors • Intervention

Some students may have difficulty keeping their numbers aligned properly and their trades shown in the proper columns when performing column addition. Have them write their problems on a place-value chart, which will help them keep hundreds, tens, and ones in the proper columns.

Enrichment • Algebra

Tell students to write and solve an addition problem to find the number of months they have lived since their birth.

More to Explore • Application

Invite a chef or dietician to speak to students about one or two of their favorite recipes. After explaining the recipe to the class, ask the chef or dietician to demonstrate how to increase the recipe to serve 50 or more people. Have that person chart the ingredients on the board to make it easier for students to understand. Ask the speaker to discuss other types of math problems encountered in his or her work.

ESL/ELL STRATEGIES

To help students with Now Try This!, distribute coins to students and ask them to identify the head (the side with a person's face on it) and the tail (the side without a person's face). Then, toss a coin as you say, *I'm tossing the coin.*

9-3 Subtracting With Regrouping

pages 159–160

1 Getting Started

Objective
- To subtract two 2-digit numbers

Materials
colored chalk

Warm Up • Mental Math
Ask students to name the following times:

1. 15 minutes after 2:00 (2:15)
2. 4 hours later than 6:25 (10:25)
3. 30 minutes after 6:26 (6:56)
4. 14 minutes later than 2:10 (2:24)
5. 15 minutes later than 11:50 (12:05)
6. 20 minutes after 4:30 (4:50)
7. 47 minutes after 3:00 (3:47)
8. 2 hours later than 7:36 (9:36)

Warm Up • Algebra
Write **62 = 6 tens 2 ones = 5 tens 12 ones** on the board. Have a student similarly rename 78 on the board. (78 = 7 tens 8 ones = 6 tens 18 ones) Continue for more practice in renaming 2-digit numbers.

Name ______________________

Subtracting With Regrouping

Greg sold 75 adult tickets to the school play. He sold 48 student tickets. How many more adult tickets did Greg sell?

We want to know how many more adult tickets were sold.

Greg sold __75__ adult tickets.

He sold __48__ student tickets.

To find how many more adult tickets were sold, we subtract __48__ from __75__.

REMEMBER Subtract the ones first.

Subtract the ones. Regroup if needed.	Subtract the tens.
15 − 8 = 7	6 − 4 = 2
$\begin{array}{r} \overset{6}{\cancel{7}}\,\overset{15}{\cancel{5}} \\ -\ 4\ 8 \\ \hline 7 \end{array}$	$\begin{array}{r} \overset{6}{\cancel{7}}\,\overset{15}{\cancel{5}} \\ -\ 4\ 8 \\ \hline 2\ 7 \end{array}$

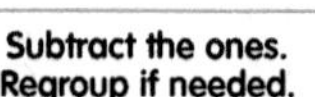

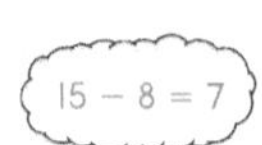

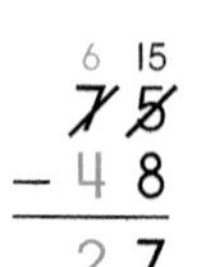

Greg sold __27__ more adult tickets.

Getting Started

Subtract. Regroup if needed.

1.	2.	3.	4.	5.	6.
74 − 26 = 48	47 − 33 = 14	71 − 51 = 20	89 − 76 = 13	80 − 52 = 28	91 − 27 = 64

2 Teach

Develop Skills and Concepts Write **87 − 49** on the board and use colored chalk to show the regrouping of 1 ten for 10 ones. Have a student complete the problem. (38) Have another student check by adding. (38 + 49 = 87) Now, write **92 − 59** on the board and have a student use colored chalk to show the regrouping and complete the problem. (33) Have another student check the work by adding. (33 + 59 = 92) Have students use colored chalk only if regrouping is needed as they continue practicing with the following problems: 91 − 80 (11), 77 − 49 (28), 63 − 34 (29), 54 − 27 (27), 86 − 53 (33), and 85 − 69 (16).

3 Practice

Using page 159 Have a student read the example aloud and tell what is to be found. (how many more adult tickets than student tickets Greg sold) Ask students what information is known. (He sold 75 adult tickets and 48 student tickets.) Have students read and complete the information sentences. Work through the model with students and then have them complete the solution sentence. Tell students to check their answer by adding.

- Have students complete the Getting Started exercises independently. Then, have them check their answers by adding.

Using page 160 Remind students to make a plan to solve each word problem and then assign the page to be completed independently.

Practice

Subtract. Regroup if needed.

1. 47 − 36 = 11	2. 66 − 34 = 32	3. 38 − 14 = 24	4. 75 − 68 = 7	5. 70 − 57 = 13	6. 61 − 44 = 17
7. 93 − 13 = 80	8. 32 − 15 = 17	9. 78 − 29 = 49	10. 61 − 28 = 33	11. 54 − 37 = 17	12. 63 − 29 = 34
13. 80 − 65 = 15	14. 52 − 30 = 22	15. 93 − 87 = 6	16. 17 − 11 = 6	17. 95 − 76 = 19	18. 75 − 59 = 16
19. 72 − 29 = 43	20. 87 − 42 = 45	21. 54 − 18 = 36	22. 31 − 29 = 2	23. 60 − 34 = 26	24. 82 − 20 = 62
25. 60 − 19 = 41	26. 55 − 23 = 32	27. 94 − 75 = 19	28. 27 − 20 = 7	29. 50 − 46 = 4	30. 37 − 11 = 26

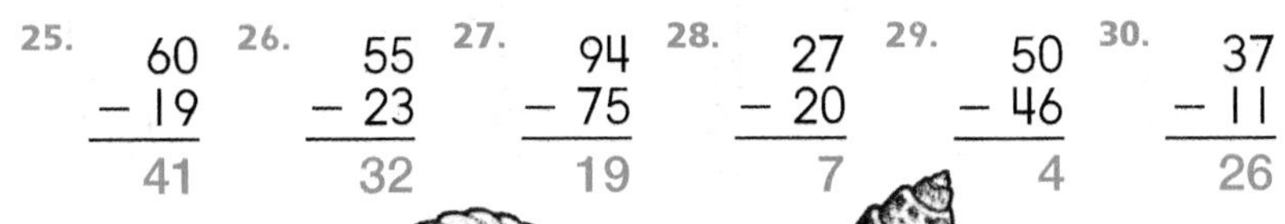

Problem Solving

Solve.

31. Martin found 37 shells. He gave 18 shells to Nell. How many shells does Martin have left?
19 shells

32. Rona poured 65 cups of juice. She sold 28 cups. How many cups of juice were not sold?
37 cups of juice

4 Assess

Tell students, *Mary has 45 stamps in her stamp collection. Martin has 62. How many more stamps does Martin have?* (17)

5 Mixed Review

1. 5 hundreds 4 tens 0 ones (540)
2. 27 ◯ 72 (<)
3. 5 + 4 (9)
4. 76, 77, 78, ____ (79)
5. 7¢ + 5¢ (12¢)
6. 8 − 5 (3)
7. 38 ◯ 28 (>)
8. 12¢ − 6¢ (6¢)
9. ____ + 4 = 12 (8)
10. 10 + 4 (14)

For Mixed Abilities

Common Errors • Intervention

Some students may get confused deciding when or when not to regroup. As they work each problem, have them first check to see whether the ones in the minuend are greater than the ones in the subtrahend. If not, then they know that they must regroup. Encourage them to verbalize this decision in the case of each place value until they feel comfortable with this skill.

Enrichment • Algebra

Tell students to write and solve four 2-digit subtraction problems that require regrouping and four problems that require no regrouping. Now, tell them to erase the number in the ones column of each minuend and to have a friend find the missing numbers.

More to Explore • Application

Bring in several different packages of crackers. Put a chart with these headings on the board:

Type of Cracker	Number in Package	Weight of Package	Price

Have students work in groups to copy the chart and fill it in after examining all the different packages. Now, ask them to compare the cost of the different kinds of crackers. Ask the following questions: *Which package gives you the most crackers? Which gives you the most weight? Why do some cost more than others? Which is the best buy?* Have students compare their answers.

9-4 Mixed Review

pages 161–162

1 Getting Started

Objective
- To add or subtract 2-digit numbers

Materials
*addition fact cards; *subtraction fact cards

Warm Up • Mental Math
Have students name the number that is

1. 100 less than 463 (363)
2. 10 more than 430 (440)
3. between 910 and 912 (911)
4. next in the sequence 18, 16, 14, 12, . . . (10)
5. 6 tens more than 50 (110)
6. 46 more than 200 (246)
7. less than 46, more than 40, and has the same number of tens and ones (44)

Warm Up • Number Sense
Show fact cards randomly for students to tell the operation and then give the sum or difference. Encourage students to increase their speed in answering.

Name ____________________

Mixed Review

Add or subtract. Regroup if needed.

1. 35 + 23 = 58
2. 74 + 96 = 170
3. 90 + 57 = 147
4. 54 + 29 = 83
5. 58 + 36 = 94
6. 32 + 99 = 131
7. 49 − 15 = 34
8. 86 − 34 = 52
9. 90 − 25 = 65
10. 41 − 28 = 13
11. 72 − 33 = 39
12. 91 − 59 = 32
13. 63 + 33 = 96
14. 86 + 46 = 132
15. 57 − 50 = 7
16. 90 − 67 = 23
17. 75 + 95 = 170
18. 51 − 26 = 25
19. 53 + 24 + 87 = 164
20. 65 + 4 + 38 = 107
21. 40 + 21 + 30 = 91
22. 7 + 52 + 73 = 132
23. 32 + 14 + 94 = 140
24. 74 + 44 + 4 = 122

Solve.

25. There are 33 puppies in the pet store. There are 17 kittens. How many more puppies than kittens are there?
 16 puppies

26. There are 75 goldfish and 85 guppies. How many fish are there altogether?
 160 fish

27. There are 18 canaries and 26 parakeets. How many birds are there altogether?
 44 birds

28. The pet store had 34 turtles. It sold 19. How many turtles were not sold?
 15 turtles

2 Teach

Develop Skills and Concepts Write **67 + 28** and **67 − 28** on the board. Have two students work the problems. (67 + 28 = 95, 67 − 28 = 39) Ask students if the answers are the same. (no) Ask why. (One problem is addition and one is subtraction.)

- Tell students a story about having 67 collector's cards and giving 28 away. Ask which problem on the board tells how many cards are left. (67 − 28 = 39) Have a student tell a story that is answered by the problem 67 + 28 = 95.
- Repeat the activity for 26 − 18 and 26 + 18.

3 Practice

Using page 161 Remind students to look at the operation sign of each exercise. Tell them to make a plan to solve each word problem and then assign the page to be completed independently.

Using page 162 Remind students to look at each operation sign before working the exercises. Tell students to make a plan to solve each word problem. Assign the page to be completed independently.

Practice

Add or subtract. Regroup if needed.

1.	2.	3.	4.	5.	6.
66 + 40 = 106	97 + 41 = 138	95 − 20 = 75	91 − 59 = 32	35 + 44 = 79	79 + 44 = 123

7.	8.	9.	10.	11.	12.
95 − 70 = 25	73 − 26 = 47	64 − 17 = 47	79 + 74 = 153	56 + 40 = 96	69 + 64 = 133

13.	14.	15.	16.	17.	18.
65 − 52 = 13	95 + 74 = 169	82 − 27 = 55	77 − 49 = 28	63 + 99 = 162	95 − 74 = 21

Problem Solving

Solve.

19. Clown School has 61 happy clowns and 45 sad clowns. How many more happy clowns are there?
16 happy clowns

20. The circus needs 23 horses, 14 lions, and 18 dogs. How many animals does it need?
55 animals

21. 89 girls and 94 boys went to the circus. How many children went to the circus?
183 children

22. Jumbo, an elephant, is 53 years old. Atlas, an elephant, is 38 years old. How many years older is Jumbo?
15 years

4 Assess

Write **55 + 62 =** (117), **97 + 58 =** (155), and **47 − 23 =** (24) on the board. Have students solve the problems.

5 Mixed Review

1. 8¢ − 5¢ (3¢)
2. 400, 500, 600, ____ (700)
3. 2 + 5 (7)
4. 64 ◯ 68 (<)
5. 10 + 5 (15)
6. 6 hundreds 3 tens 0 ones (630)
7. 15 − 8 (7)
8. 137 ◯ 371 (<)
9. 6 + 8 (14)
10. 15 − 9 (6)

For Mixed Abilities

Common Errors • Intervention

Some students may add when they should subtract or vice versa when working with a set of mixed problems. To help them become more aware of the operation signs, have them circle all the addition signs in one color and all the subtraction signs in another. This will help alert them to a change in operation.

Enrichment • Application

Have students use a calendar to find the total number of days in the first 6 months of the year. Then, tell them to find the number of days in the last 6 months of the year. Ask which 6-month period has more days. Why?

More to Explore • Logic

Provide students with a page from a monthly calendar. Have each student choose a 2 × 2 square of dates, for example Tuesday-Wednesday for two consecutive weeks. Have students add the numbers on one diagonal, then add the numbers for the other diagonal, and compare the sums. (The answers will be the same.) Ask students to choose other 2 × 2 squares and see if the results are the same. Challenge them to see if they can find any 2 × 2 square where the pattern does not exist.

This activity can be extended by using 3 × 3 and 4 × 4 squares.

9-5 Addition and Subtraction Sentences

pages 163–164

1 Getting Started

Objective

- To add or subtract when a problem is horizontal

Materials

tens rods and ones cubes

Warm Up • Mental Math

Tell students to give the sum and difference for the following:

1. 80, 20 (100, 60)
2. 66, 33 (99, 33)
3. 10¢, 8¢ (18¢, 2¢)
4. 19, 19 (38, 0)
5. 60, 50 (110, 10)
6. 42, 22 (64, 20)
7. 25¢, 10¢ (35¢, 15¢)

Warm Up • Number Sense

Write **86 + 45** and **86 − 45** on the board. Ask students which problem will have an answer less than 86. (86 − 45) Ask why. (because 45 is taken away from 86) Ask which will have an answer more than 86. (86 + 45) Ask why. (because 45 is added to 86) Continue for more problems having the same 2-digit numbers but different operational signs.

Name ______________________

Addition and Subtraction Sentences

Addition and subtraction problems are sometimes written as number sentences. If you cannot do the addition or subtraction in your head, copy the problem as shown below. Then you can add or subtract.

34 + 68 = ?

Copy. — Do. — Write the answer on the line.

$$\begin{array}{r} 34 \\ +\ 68 \\ \hline \end{array} \qquad \begin{array}{r} {}^{1}\\ 34 \\ +\ 68 \\ \hline 102 \end{array} \qquad 34 + 68 = \underline{102}$$

93 − 77 = ?

Copy. — Do. — Write the answer on the line.

$$\begin{array}{r} 93 \\ -\ 77 \\ \hline \end{array} \qquad \begin{array}{r} {}^{8\ 13}\\ \not{9}\not{3} \\ -\ 77 \\ \hline 16 \end{array} \qquad 93 - 77 = \underline{16}$$

Getting Started

Copy and add. Write the answer on the line.

1. 79 + 57 = 136
2. 47 + 12 + 96 = 155

---

2 Teach

Develop Skills and Concepts Write 29 + 78 = horizontally on the board. Tell students that a problem like this is easier to work if it is rewritten vertically. Rewrite the problem vertically on the board. Have a student solve the problem and then record the sum in the horizontal problem. (107)

- Repeat for 82 − 26. (56) Provide more horizontal addition and subtraction problems for students to copy vertically on the board and solve. Include some addition problems of three addends for sums less than 200.

3 Practice

Using page 163 Have a student read the paragraph at the top of the page aloud and tell about the picture. Work through both models with students as they complete the sentences by writing answers on the lines. Have students use tens rods and ones cubes to check both problems and then check the subtraction exercise again by adding.

- Help students with the Getting Started exercises if necessary.

Using page 164 Have students complete the exercises independently. Remind them to first copy each problem vertically in the space provided, work the problem, and then write the answer on the line.

Practice

Copy and do. Write the answer on the line.

1. 38 − 13 = 25
2. 80 − 5 = 75
3. 63 − 7 = 56
4. 62 + 14 = 76
5. 23 + 4 + 32 = 59
6. 99 + 99 = 198

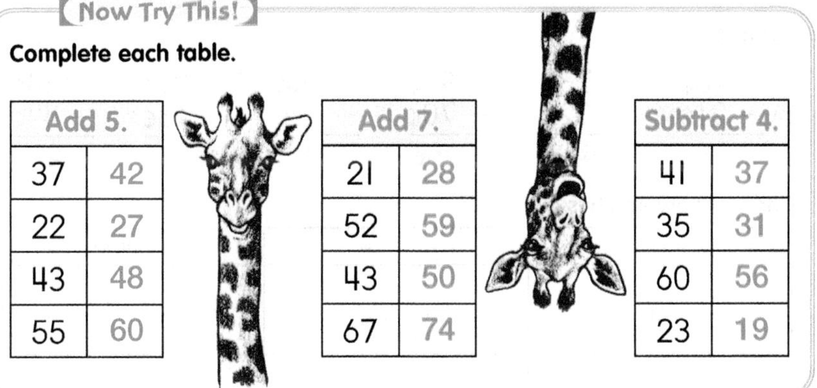

Now Try This!

Complete each table.

Add 5.	
37	42
22	27
43	48
55	60

Add 7.	
21	28
52	59
43	50
67	74

Subtract 4.	
41	37
35	31
60	56
23	19

Now Try This! Work through the first problem in the first and last tables with the students and then have them complete the tables independently. Allow students to work the exercises on another sheet of paper if needed.

4 Assess

Ask students when it is a good idea to rewrite a number sentence vertically to answer it. (when there are more than two addends or when there is regrouping in an addition or subtraction problem)

For Mixed Abilities

Common Errors • Intervention

If students have difficulty aligning the numbers properly as they write the problem in vertical form, have them use grid paper, where the lines and columns will help them keep the numbers in their proper places.

Enrichment • Number Sense

Tell students to write an addition sentence that tells the number of pennies in a half-dollar, quarter, dime, and nickel. Then, have them rewrite the problem vertically and solve it.

More to Explore • Application

Write the following on the board or duplicate it:

1. **Quarter + nickel + dime or quarter + quarter** (40¢, 50¢)
2. **Quarter + dime + half-dollar or quarter + quarter** (85¢, 50¢)
3. **Dime + dime + dime + nickel + quarter or half-dollar + nickel** (60¢, 55¢)
4. **Dollar or nickel + three quarters** ($1.00, 80¢)
5. **Quarter + dime + dime + dime or half-dollar** (55¢, 50¢)
6. **Five dollars + five dollars or five dollars + one dollar + one dollar + one dollar + fifty cents + dime + dime + dime + quarter** ($10, $9.05)
7. **Ten dollars or five dollars + fifty cents + fifty cents + dime + dime + dime + dime** ($10, $6.40)

Tell students to plan a shopping trip. Tell them to rewrite each money amount in numerals and then circle the amount in each choice that they would rather have to shop with.

9-6 Subtracting Money

pages 165–166

1 Getting Started

Objective

- To subtract amounts of money less than $1

Materials

tens rods and ones cubes; real or play dimes and pennies; colored chalk; classroom items with price tags

Warm Up • Mental Math

Tell students to name the following numbers:

1. 4 tens 16 ones (56)
2. 11 tens and 8 ones (118)
3. 6 ones 12 tens (126)
4. 19 tens 10 ones (200)
5. 2 hundreds 18 ones (218)
6. 19 ones + 2 tens (39)
7. 15 tens − 10 tens (50)

Warm Up • Number Sense

Write **68 − 49** horizontally on the board and have a student write and solve the problem vertically. (19) Have another student check the problem by adding. Continue with the following horizontal problems: 74 + 85 (159), 83 − 64 (19), 58 + 58 (116), 92 − 86 (6), and 60 − 49 (11).

Name ____________________

Subtracting Money

Mel had 85¢.
He bought a balloon.
How much does he have left?

Balloons 29¢

We want to find out how much money Mel has left.

Mel had 85¢.

The balloon cost 29¢.

To find out how much money Mel has left, we subtract 29¢ from 85¢.

Subtract the pennies first.	Subtract the dimes.
7 15 ~~8~~ ~~5~~¢ − 2 9¢ 6¢	7 15 ~~8~~ ~~5~~¢ − 2 9¢ 5 6¢

Mel has 56¢ left.

Getting Started

Subtract.

1.	2.	3.	4.	5.	6.
48¢ − 21¢ = 27¢	73¢ − 32¢ = 41¢	95¢ − 70¢ = 25¢	74¢ − 19¢ = 55¢	91¢ − 68¢ = 23¢	64¢ − 44¢ = 20¢

Find out how much is left.

	You had	You bought	How much is left?
7.	75¢	62¢	13¢
8.	83¢	58¢	25¢

2 Teach

Develop Skills and Concepts Write **85 − 26** and **85¢ − 26¢** on the board. Ask students how the two problems differ. (One has cent signs.) Have half the class use tens rods and ones cubes to work the first problem and the other half of the class use dimes and pennies. Talk through the regrouping of 1 ten or 1 dime for 10 ones or 10 pennies. Have students tell their solutions. (59 or 59¢) Help students show the regrouping with colored chalk as they work the problems on the board. Now, have two other students write and solve addition problems to check the subtraction.

- Have students alternate using coins and tens rods and ones cubes as you repeat the activity for the following: 91 − 45 (46) and 91¢ − 45¢ (46¢), 94 − 27 (67) and 94¢ − 27¢ (67¢), and 83 − 56 (27) and 83¢ − 56¢ (27¢).

3 Practice

Using page 165 Have a student read the example aloud and tell what is to be found. (how much money Mel has left) Ask students what information is needed. (amount of money Mel had and amount he spent) Ask what information is given. (Mel had 85¢ and spent 29¢.) Have students read and complete the information sentences. Work through the model with students and then have them complete the solution sentence. Have a student write and solve an addition problem on the board to check the answer. (56¢ + 29¢ = 85¢)

- Have students complete the Getting Started exercises independently. Remind them to add to check their answers.

Using page 166 Tell students to work the top rows of exercises and then solve Exercises 13 to 17 by writing and solving a subtraction problem for each. Have students complete the page independently.

Practice

Subtract.

1. 90¢ − 30¢ = 60¢	2. 50¢ − 36¢ = 14¢	3. 87¢ − 82¢ = 5¢	4. 33¢ − 9¢ = 24¢	5. 96¢ − 49¢ = 47¢	6. 70¢ − 17¢ = 53¢
7. 61¢ − 24¢ = 37¢	8. 93¢ − 78¢ = 15¢	9. 62¢ − 6¢ = 56¢	10. 28¢ − 16¢ = 12¢	11. 74¢ − 39¢ = 35¢	12. 44¢ − 18¢ = 26¢

Find out how much is left.

	You had	You bought	How much is left?
13.	75¢	18¢	57¢
14.	88¢	45¢	43¢
15.	67¢	Crayons 38¢	29¢
16.	50¢	18¢	32¢
17.	91¢	55¢	36¢

4 Assess

Give students several classroom items with price tags of less than 99¢ and 99¢ in 8 dimes and 19 pennies. Have students write problems to determine how much change they would have left if they purchased each of the items. They can use the coins to check their answers.

5 Mixed Review

1. ____ + 5 = 11 (6)
2. 250 ◯ 350 (<)
3. 687, 688, 689, ____ (690)
4. 3 tens 3 ones (33)
5. 13 − 9 (4)
6. 82 ◯ 79 (>)
7. 1 + 8 (9)
8. 10 + 2 (12)
9. 3¢ + 9¢ (12¢)
10. 13 − 5 (8)

For Mixed Abilities

Common Errors • Intervention

Some students may forget to write the cent sign in the answer. Discuss how the cent sign indicates that we are working with money. It may be helpful to students if they write the cent sign first before they subtract.

Enrichment • Application

Tell students to cut five items priced less than $1 from newspaper ads. Have them write and solve five problems to show how much money they would have left if they had 99¢ and bought one of the items. Ask how much money they would need to buy all five items.

More to Explore • Probability

Ask students if they know what is meant by the term *chance*. Explain that chance means "by luck" or "something over which we have no control," like the outcome of throwing the dice or flipping a coin. Whether you are born a boy or a girl is largely a matter of chance. Ask students in your class to name the number and gender of the children in their families. Write the students' answers on the board.

When the chart is finished, ask students to guess whether there are more boys or girls listed. Then, have volunteers count up the number of boys and girls to compare with the class estimate. Ask students to name something else in their lives that can happen by chance.

9-7 Adding Money

pages 167–168

1 Getting Started

Objective

- To add money amounts less than $1 for sums through $1.99

Materials

real or play dollars, dimes, and pennies; hundred flat, tens rods, and ones cubes

Warm Up • Mental Math

Tell students to name the number that comes next.

1. 18, 20, 22, 24 (26)
2. 10, 9, 8, 7 (6)
3. 163, 173, 183, 193 (203)
4. 708, 710, 712, 714 (716)
5. 7, 9, 11, 13 (15)
6. 165, 170, 175, 180 (185)

Warm Up • Pencil and Paper

Have a student lay out 8 dimes and 4 pennies. Ask the student to talk through the necessary regrouping to give another student 76¢. Ask how much money is left. (8¢) Have a student write and solve the subtraction problem. (84¢ − 76¢ = 8¢) Have another student write and solve an addition problem to check the subtraction. (8¢ + 76¢ = 84¢) Repeat for more subtraction of money amounts.

Name ________________________

Adding Money

Bear and Lion are putting their money together to buy a game. How much money do they have altogether?

We want to know how much money they have altogether.

Bear has 57¢.

Lion has 95¢.

To find how much they have altogether, we add 57¢ and 95¢.

Add the pennies first.	Add the dimes.
1 57¢ + 95¢ 2¢	1 57¢ + 95¢ 152¢

152¢ = $1.52

Bear and Lion have $1.52.

Getting Started

Add. Then write each answer in dollar notation.

1.	2.	3.	4.	5.
15¢ + 85¢ 100¢	63¢ + 25¢ 88¢	57¢ 32¢ + 57¢ 146¢	25¢ 3¢ + 75¢ 103¢	58¢ 20¢ + 49¢ 127¢
$1.00	$0.88	$1.46	$1.03	$1.27

---

2 Teach

Develop Skills and Concepts Write **120** on the board and have students lay out hundred flats, tens rods, and ones cubes to show the number. Now, write **120¢** on the board and have students lay out 1 dollar, 2 dimes, and 0 pennies. Write **120¢ = $1.20** on the board to remind students that 120 pennies can be written as $1.20.

- Have students lay out 93¢ and 48¢ and tell how many pennies there are in all. (11) Remind students that 10 pennies can be regrouped for 1 dime. Ask students how many pennies and dimes there are after the regroup. (14 dimes, 1 penny) Ask if a regrouping for $1 can be made. (yes) Tell students to regroup and then have a student write the sum of 93¢ and 48¢ on the board in total cents and then using the dollar sign and decimal point. (141¢, $1.41)
- Repeat to find the sum of 68¢, 24¢, and 51¢ ($1.43); 79¢ and 86¢ ($1.65); 48¢, 57¢, and 82¢ ($1.87); and 99¢ and 58¢. ($1.57)

3 Practice

Using page 167 Have a student read the example aloud and tell what is to be found. (how much money Bear and Lion have all together) Ask students what information is given in the problem or the picture. (Bear has 57¢ and Lion has 95¢.) Have students read and complete the information sentences. Work through the model with students and then have them complete the solution sentence. Have students lay out 57¢ and 95¢ and add the coins to check their solution.

- Have students complete the Getting Started exercises independently. Remind them to write the sum in cents and in dollars. If there are no dollars, tell students to write a zero in the dollar space.

Practice

Add. Then write each answer in dollar notation.

1.	2.	3.	4.	5.
75¢ + 52¢	98¢ + 95¢	61¢ + 89¢	50¢ + 41¢	83¢ + 42¢
127¢	193¢	150¢	91¢	125¢
$1.27	$1.93	$1.50	$0.91	$1.25

6.	7.	8.	9.	10.
92¢ + 69¢	88¢ + 63¢	12¢ + 98¢	55¢ + 45¢	77¢ + 37¢
161¢	151¢	110¢	100¢	114¢
$1.61	$1.51	$1.10	$1.00	$1.14

11.	12.	13.	14.	15.
87¢ + 62¢	56¢ + 39¢	86¢ 3¢ + 46¢	14¢ 34¢ + 26¢	55¢ 11¢ + 45¢
149¢	95¢	135¢	74¢	111¢
$1.49	$0.95	$1.35	$0.74	$1.11

Problem Solving

Write each answer.

☆ Lana has $1.25.
☆ Craig has 37¢.
☆ José has 75¢.

16. Who has the most money? Lana

17. Who has the least money? Craig

18. How much money do Craig and José have together? $1.12

19. How much more money does José have than Craig? 38¢

Using page 168 Tell students that they are to add in each problem, write the sum in cents, and then write the amount using the dollar sign and decimal point. For the Problem Solving exercises, tell students that they will be writing names for the first two answers and money amounts for the last two. Assign the page to be completed independently.

4 Assess

Have students write word problems for money sums. Tell students to include three addends in their problems. Then, have students exchange papers to answer each other's word problems.

For Mixed Abilities

Common Errors • Intervention

Some students may write money incorrectly because they misplace the decimal point. Review with them how 184 cents is the same as 1 dollar, 8 dimes, and 4 pennies and should be written as $1.84, where the decimal point separates the whole dollar from the part of a dollar. Be sure they understand that when a decimal point is used in money, it is always followed by two digits and no more.

Enrichment • Application

Tell students to cut out three items with prices under 70¢ from newspaper ads. Have them draw dimes and pennies to show how much money they would need to buy all three items. Then, tell them to draw the total amount using a dollar, dimes, and pennies.

More to Explore • Number Sense

Give students large paper, school glue, and colored rice or other small seeds. Write the Roman numerals for 1 through 10 on the board. (I, II, III, IV, V, VI, VII VIII, IX, X) Have students draw the Roman numerals with glue on their papers. Dust each paper with rice. Display their colorful numerals.

ESL/ELL STRATEGIES

Model formal ways of saying dollar amounts, for example: *one dollar and twelve cents, one dollar and twenty-five cents.* Then, model the more common form and ask students to repeat: *a dollar twelve, a dollar twenty-five.*

9-8 Estimating Sums

pages 169–170

1 Getting Started

Objective

- To estimate the sum of two 2-digit numbers

Warm Up • Mental Math

Have students add or subtract.

1. 8 plus 7 (15)
2. 5 plus 4 (9)
3. 6 plus 7 (13)
4. 10 minus 5 (5)
5. 13 minus 7 (6)
6. 14 minus 9 (5)

Warm Up • Number Sense

Write the following on the board for students to solve:

18 + 10 = (28)	16 − 9 = (7)
4 + 22 = (26)	15 − 10 = (5)
43 − 8 = (35)	11 + 37 = (48)
16 − 11 = (5)	12 + 12 = (24)
12 + 17 = (29)	17 − 6 = (11)

2 Teach

Develop Skills and Concepts Read the following word problem to students: *Jamal has 48 cents and Serena has 39 cents. Do they have enough money to buy a yo-yo for 70 cents?* Ask students what operation they need to use to find out how much money Jamal and Serena have together. (addition) Ask if they need to find an exact answer. (no) Ask them to explain. (Possible answer: The question does not ask how much money Jamal and Serena have together. The question asks if they have enough.)

- Introduce the rules for rounding money to the nearest 10 cents. Ask a volunteer to round 48 cents and 39 cents to the nearest 10 cents. (50 cents; 40 cents) Ask another volunteer to use these numbers to find the sum. (90 cents) Ask, *Do Jamal and Serena have enough money to buy a yo-yo for 70 cents?* (yes)

- Have students look back at the problem. Point out that the sum of the front-end digits is 7. Any amount of money over 40 cents and 30 cents will be enough for a yo-yo for 70 cents. Caution students to look back at the original amounts in any problem and adjust their estimate if needed. Explore what would happen if Jamal had 35 cents and Serena had 34 cents. Would they have enough? (no)

It's Algebra! The concepts in this lesson prepare students for algebra.

3 Practice

Using page 169 Have students look at the example at the top of the page. Ask students what information they need to solve the problem. (the cost of the doll and the cost of the softball) Then, ask, *What are you being asked to decide?* (if Sherri has enough money to buy the doll and the softball) Ask if they need an exact answer or an estimate. (estimate)

- Have students round each item to the nearest 10 cents. Then, find the estimate by adding the rounded addends.

- Help students complete the Getting Started exercises. Remind students to write their final answers in dollar notation.

Name ______________________

It's Algebra!

Estimating Sums

Sherri has $2.00. She wants to buy the doll and the softball. She does not know if she has enough money. She can estimate by rounding each item to the nearest ten cents to find out.

If the digit in the pennies place is 5 or greater, round up to the nearest ten cents.

If the digit in the pennies place is less than 5, round down to the nearest ten cents.

The cost of the softball is 91¢.

The cost of the doll is 65¢.

Round to the nearest 10 cents.		Estimate.
91¢ →	90¢	90¢
+ 65¢ →	+ 70¢	+ 70¢
		160¢ (160¢ = $1.60)

The estimate is $1.60. Sherri has enough money to buy the doll and the softball.

Getting Started

Estimate. Show how you rounded.

1. Mick has 87¢. Melissa has 75¢. About how much money do they have in all?
   90¢ + 80¢ = $1.70

2. Jamal has 68¢. Nadine has 88¢. About how much money do they have in all?
   70¢ + 90¢ = $1.60

3. Elise spent 42¢ to buy a pencil. She spent 53¢ to buy a pen. About how much did Elise spend in all?
   40¢ + 50¢ = 90¢

4. Suzie has 52¢ saved. Her mother gives her 75¢. About how much money does Suzie have now?
   50¢ + 80¢ = $1.30

Practice

Estimate. Show how you rounded.

1. 28¢ + 27¢
   30¢ + 30¢ = 60¢

2. 52¢ + 83¢
   50¢ + 80¢ = $1.30

3. 62¢ + 47¢
   60¢ + 50¢ = $1.10

4. 39¢ + 26¢
   40¢ + 30¢ = 70¢

Problem Solving

5. Jenny bought a birthday card for 83¢. She also bought a pin for 92¢. About how much did Jenny spend altogether?
   80¢ + 90¢ = $1.70

6. Max donated 38¢ to his sister's school band. He also donated 51¢ to the dog pound. About how much did Max donate in all?
   40¢ + 50¢ = 90¢

7. Ted bought a baseball for 93¢. He also bought a baseball cap for 95¢. About how much did Ted spend altogether?
   90¢ + $1.00 = $1.90

8. Laura saved 49¢. Her grandmother gave her 47¢. About how much money does Laura have?
   50¢ + 50¢ = $1.00

Now Try This!

What money amounts round to 70¢ when rounded to the nearest ten cents?

65¢, 66¢, 67¢, 68¢, 69¢,
70¢, 71¢, 72¢, 73¢, 74¢

For Mixed Abilities

Common Errors • Intervention

Some students may have difficulty determining how to round numbers to the nearest ten. Have students use a number line to determine which ten a given number is closer to. Have students highlight the number 5 on the number line. If the digit in the ones place is 5 or greater, tell students to go up to the next ten.

Enrichment • Number Sense

Tell students, *You have about 90 cents in your pants pockets. In your left pocket is 37 cents. What is the most and the least amount of money that you could have in your right pocket?* (most, 54 cents; least, 45 cents)

More to Explore • Number Sense

Have students work in pairs. Students can choose their own 2-digit numbers to add. One partner will find the exact sum and the other partner will find an estimate. Have pairs change roles so that each partner finds two sums and two estimates. Students can share their findings with the class to find how close estimates can be to the exact answer and to determine when this is likely to occur.

Using page 170 Have students look at Exercise 5. Read the problem aloud while students read along. Ask students for the given information. (Jenny bought a card for 83 cents and a pin for 92 cents.) Ask, *Which word in the question indicates whether you need an exact answer or an estimate?* (about) Ask, *Which word indicates which operation to use?* (*altogether*, indicating addition) Have the students complete the page.

Now Try This! Remind students that if the digit in the pennies place is less than 5¢, they round down, and if it is 5¢ or higher, they round up. Ask, *What is the highest amount that will round down to 70¢?* (74¢) *What is the lowest amount that will round up to 70¢?* (65¢)

4 Assess

Have students work in pairs. One student writes a story about a person buying two items that each cost less than $1.00 at a store and includes the amount of money the person has to spend. The other student determines if the person has enough money to make the purchase. Once the answer is checked, students should switch roles.

5 Mixed Review

1. 8¢ − 3¢ (5¢)
2. 695 ◯ 705 (<)
3. 585, 590, 595, ____ (600)
4. 58 ◯ 158 (<)
5. 7 hundreds 1 ten 5 ones (715)
6. 6 + ____ = 10 (4)
7. 11 − 3 (8)
8. 16 − 7 (9)
9. 0 + 3 (3)
10. 7 + 6 (13)

9-9 Problem Solving: Choose an Operation

pages 171–172

1 Getting Started

Objectives
- To choose the correct operations to solve problems
- To add or subtract amounts of money to solve problems

Materials
real or play dollars, dimes, and pennies

Warm Up • Mental Math
Ask students if they will add or subtract for problems that ask
1. how many in all? (add)
2. how many more? (subtract)
3. how many are left? (subtract)
4. how many altogether? (add)
5. how much change? (subtract)
6. what is the sum? (add)

Warm Up • Number Sense
Write **82¢ + 49¢ + 23¢** on the board. Have students work the problem independently on paper and write the sum using the cent sign and then in dollar notation. (154¢, $1.54) Have a student write the sum on the board in each notation. Remind students that amounts of $1 or more are generally written in dollar notation. Repeat for more addition problems of two or three money amounts.

Name ______________________

Problem Solving: Choose an Operation

Decide if you need to add or subtract. Then solve.

1. Melissa has 75¢. She bought a beach ball. How much does she have left?
32¢

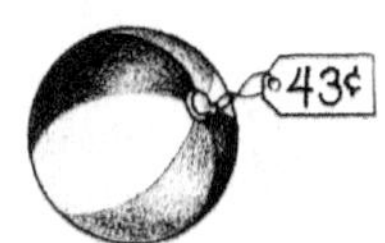

2. How much did Yong pay for both toys?
$1.44

3. Circle the toy that costs more. How much more does it cost?
23¢

4. Ashley bought a yo-yo. She gave the clerk 50¢. How much change did she get?
16¢

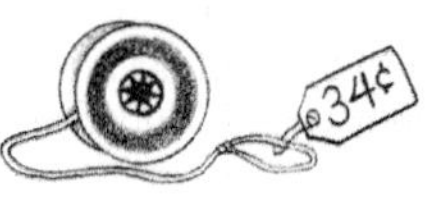

5. Steven had 95¢. He bought a top. How much does he have left?
27¢

6. Mr. Jon took his daughter to a movie. How much did he spend for the tickets?
$1.20

7. What is the cost of a bat and a ball together?
$1.52

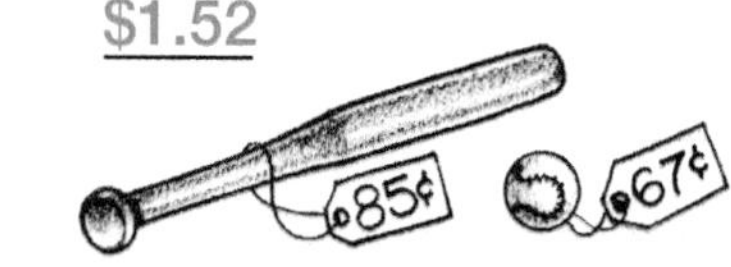

8. Kiku and Cathy each bought a glove. How much did they pay altogether?
$1.96

2 Teach

Develop Skills and Concepts Ask students, *I have 36¢ and I saved 54¢ more. How do I find out how much I have altogether?* (add) Have students answer the problem. (90¢)

- Ask, *I have 90¢. I buy a ball that costs 61¢. How do I find out how much I have left?* (subtract) Have students answer the problem. (29¢)
- Repeat until all students understand the difference between when to add and when to subtract.

3 Practice

Using page 171 Have students look at the direction line. Ask students what they will be doing. (deciding if they need to add or subtract for each exercise, then solving)

- Now, apply the four-step plan to Exercise 1. For SEE, ask, *What are you being asked to do?* (find out how much money Melissa has left) Then, *What information is given?* (how much money she has and how much the beach ball cost) For PLAN, ask students how they will find an answer. (subtract) For DO, have students solve Exercise 1. For CHECK, have them use manipulatives to check their answer to make sure Melissa has less money than she started with. They can also use addition to check their answers (32¢ + 43¢ = 75¢)
- Have students answer Exercises 2 to 8 independently. Remind students to write final answers in dollar notation where appropriate.

Practice

Decide if you need to add or subtract. Then solve.

1. How much more did Cary pay for the teddy bear?
29¢

2. How much did Dino pay for the scissors and crayons?
$1.60

3. How much did Al pay for the hammer and pliers?

$1.69

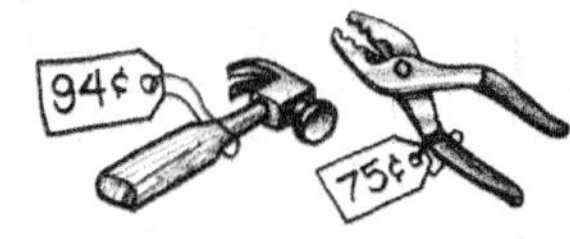

4. Kasey had 85¢. She bought a top. How much does she have left?
17¢

5. How much more did Rhea pay for the truck?

39¢

6. What is the cost for all three items?
$1.03

7. How much did Bart pay for all three toys?
$1.44

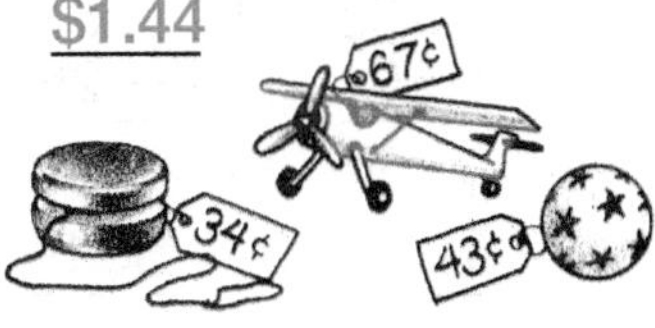

8. How much do the three toys cost altogether?
$1.68

Using page 172 Tell students to write and solve each problem and then record the answer on the line. Tell students to check each problem. Have students complete the page independently. Remind students to write final answers in dollar notation where appropriate.

4 Assess

Tell students to cut four items priced less than $1 from newspaper ads. Have them write one addition and one subtraction word problem about the priced items. Tell them to have a friend solve the problems. They should then check the friend's work.

For Mixed Abilities

Common Errors • Intervention

If students need more practice solving word problems, have them work in small cooperative groups where each member creates a word problem for adding or subtracting money. Members exchange problems, solve them, and then return them to the original writers to check the answers.

Enrichment • Algebra

Write the following problem on the board:

Darcy has 87¢. She bought a yo-yo for 27¢ and a balloon for 36¢. How much money does she have left?

Tell them that there are two steps to the problem. Ask students how they would solve this problem. (They would add the amount of money Darcy spent and subtract that amount from the amount she had.) Have students find the answer. (24¢)

More to Explore • Logic

Read or duplicate the following for students:

After her lunch break was over, a woman walked up to the cafe cash register to pay her bill. The cashier noticed the woman had carefully drawn a circle, a square, and a triangle along the left side of the bill. The cashier immediately looked up and said, "How long have you been a police officer?" How did the cashier know the lady was a police officer? (The police officer was wearing her uniform.)

Chapter 9 Test

page 173

Items	Objectives
1–12	To add two 2-digit numbers (see pages 155–156)
13–18	To subtract two 2-digit numbers (see pages 159–160)
19–30	To add three 2-digit numbers for sums through 199 (see pages 157–158)
31, 32, 34	To add money amounts less than $1 for sums through $1.99 (see pages 167–168)
33, 35	To subtract amounts of money less than $1 (see pages 165–166)

Name ______________________

Chapter 9 Test

Add or subtract.

1.	2.	3.	4.	5.	6.
38 + 19 = 57	46 + 21 = 67	15 + 83 = 98	24 + 63 = 87	25 + 38 = 63	46 + 26 = 72

7.	8.	9.	10.	11.	12.
87 + 62 = 149	32 + 77 = 109	77 + 43 = 120	69 + 66 = 135	83 + 58 = 141	67 + 63 = 130

13.	14.	15.	16.	17.	18.
86 − 23 = 63	75 − 14 = 61	67 − 17 = 50	93 − 24 = 69	51 − 39 = 12	75 − 48 = 27

19.	20.	21.	22.	23.	24.
23 + 14 + 42 = 79	10 + 50 + 70 = 130	13 + 65 + 63 = 141	43 + 73 + 6 = 122	45 + 50 + 55 = 150	32 + 27 + 93 = 152

25.	26.	27.	28.	29.	30.
34 + 21 + 22 = 77	53 + 72 + 8 = 133	32 + 42 + 26 = 100	20 + 60 + 40 = 120	40 + 51 + 69 = 160	16 + 75 + 60 = 151

Add or subtract. Then write each answer in dollar notation.

31.	32.	33.	34.	35.
35¢ + 75¢	57¢ + 98¢	97¢ − 65¢	75¢ + 50¢	83¢ − 25¢
110¢	155¢	32¢	125¢	58¢
$1.10	$1.55	$0.32	$1.25	$0.58

Alternate Chapter Test

You may wish to use the Alternate Chapter Test on page 323 of this book for further review and assessment.

Cumulative Assessment

Circle the letter of the correct answer.

1. 7 + 6 — a. 12 **(b.) 13** c. 14 d. NG

2. 8 + 9 = — **(a.) 17** b. 16 c. 18 d. NG

3. 12 − 5 — a. 17 b. 15 **(c.) 7** d. NG

4. 15 − 6 = — a. 8 b. 21 c. 11 **(d.) NG**

5. 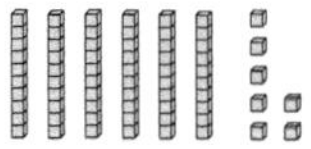
a. 76 b. 57 **(c.) 67** d. NG

6. 39 ◯ 41 — a. > **(b.) <**

7. 69 + 89 — **(a.) 158** b. 20 c. 148 d. NG

8. 25 + 34 + 17 — a. 66 b. 77 **(c.) 76** d. NG

9. 78 − 45 — a. 123 **(b.) 33** c. 113 d. NG

10. 91 − 25 — **(a.) 66** b. 74 c. 76 d. NG

11. 48 + 35 = — a. 82 **(b.) 83** c. 73 d. NG

12. 57 + 6 — a. 51 b. 53 **(c.) 63** d. NG

13. 71 − 29 = — a. 58 **(b.) 42** c. 52 d. NG

score

STOP

Cumulative Assessment

page 174

Items	Objectives
1–4	To review addition and subtraction facts with sums and minuends through 18 (see pages 3–12, 17–20, 23–28, 35–44, 53–56, 59–64)
5	To understand 2-digit numbers (see pages 71–74)
6	To find the greater or lesser of two 2-digit numbers; to use the < and > signs to compare 2-digit numbers (see pages 81–82)
7	To add two 2-digit numbers for a 3-digit sum (see pages 155–156)
8	To add three 2-digit numbers for sums through 199 (see pages 157–158)
9–10	To subtract two 2-digit numbers (see pages 137–146, 159–160)
11, 13	To add or subtract when a problem is horizontal (see pages 163–164)
12	To add 1-digit numbers to 2-digit numbers with some regrouping (see pages 123–124)

Alternate Cumulative Assessment

Circle the letter of the correct answer.

1. 6 + 5 — **(a) 11** b 10 c 9 d NG

2. 9 + 7 — a 14 b 15 **(c) 16** d NG

3. 16 − 8 — a 10 b 4 c 9 **(d) NG**

4. 14 − 7 — **(a) 7** b 8 c 9 d NG

5. 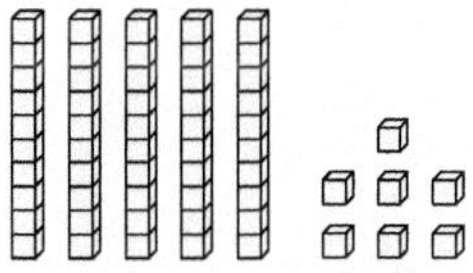
a 76 b 67 **(c) 57** d NG

6. 87 ◯ 76 — a < **(b) >**

7. 56 + 46 — a 912 **(b) 102** c 112 d NG

8. 24 + 12 + 63 — a 93 b 103 **(c) 99** d NG

9. 65 − 43 — a 28 **(b) 22** c 12 d NG

10. 76 − 48 — **(a) 28** b 38 c 22 d NG

11. 65 + 46 = — a 91 **(b) 111** c 119 d NG

12. 58 + 7 — **(a) 65** b 45 c 54 d NG

13. 81 − 14 — a 47 b 57 **(c) 67** d NG

10-1 Place Value Through 1,000

pages 175–176

1 Getting Started

Objective
- To understand place value through 1,000

Materials
hundred flats, tens rods, and ones cubes

Warm Up • Mental Math
Tell students to name the next ordinal number.

1. 7th, 8th, 9th (10th)
2. 215th, 216th, 217th (218th)
3. 11th, 10th, 9th (8th)
4. 1st, 3rd, 5th (7th)
5. 4th, 6th, 8th (10th)
6. 100th, 200th, 300th (400th)

Warm Up • Pencil and Paper
Tell students that you have 2 dimes and 6 pennies left after buying a book for 89¢. Ask a student to write and solve a problem to show the amount of money you had when you went shopping. (89¢ + 26¢ = $1.15) Now, tell students that you started with 8 dimes and 2 pennies and have 4 dimes and 3 pennies left. Ask a student to write and solve a problem to show the amount of money you spent. (82¢ − 43¢ = 39¢) Repeat for more problems.

Name ____________________

Adding 3-Digit Numbers

Chapter 10

Lesson 10-1

Place Value Through 1,000

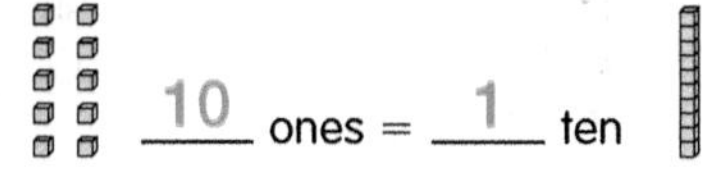
10 ones = 1 ten

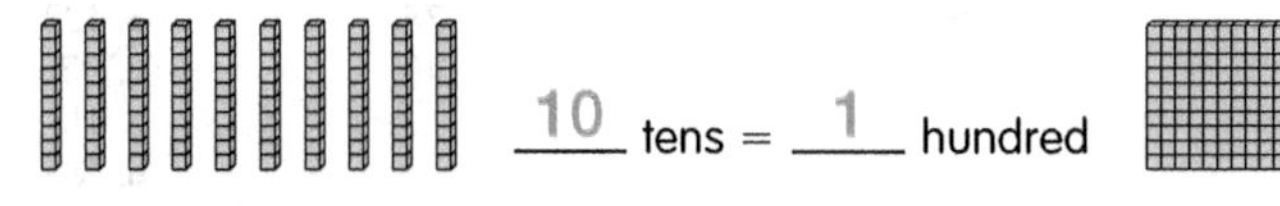
10 tens = 1 hundred

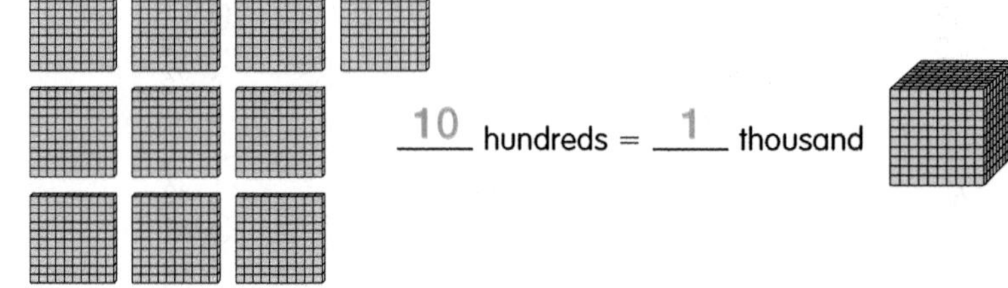
10 hundreds = 1 thousand

Count by tens. Write the missing numbers.

10 20 30 40 50 60 70 80 90 100

Count by hundreds. Write the missing numbers.

100 200 300 400 500 600 700 800 900 1,000

Getting Started

How many hundreds, tens, and ones are there? Write the numbers.

3 hundreds 2 tens 5 ones

325

2 Teach

Develop Skills and Concepts Lay out 3 hundred flats, 2 tens rods, and 6 ones cubes. Ask how many hundreds, tens, and ones there are. (3, 2, 6) Ask students to tell the number. (326) Repeat for more 2- or 3-digit numbers.

- Write **683** on the board and ask a student to lay out manipulatives to show the number. (6 hundred flats, 8 tens rods, 3 ones cubes) Continue for more numbers including those with no tens and/or no ones. Help students recognize that 10 hundreds equal 1,000.

3 Practice

Using page 175 Have students count the squares and complete the number sentences at the top of the page. Have students count by tens and hundreds orally as they fill in the missing numbers. Tell students to complete the Getting Started exercise independently.

Using page 176 Tell students to write the number of hundreds, tens, and ones and then write the number. Have students complete the page independently.

Practice

Write how many hundreds, tens, and ones there are. Write each number.

1. 1 hundred 8 tens 5 ones
185

2. 2 hundreds 7 tens 8 ones
278

3. 3 hundreds 0 tens 5 ones
305

4. 5 hundreds 2 tens 4 ones
524

5. 2 hundreds 3 tens 3 ones
233

6. 1 hundred 5 tens 9 ones
159

7. 4 hundreds 1 ten 0 ones
410

4 Assess

Write **176, 487,** and **926** on the board. Have students lay out hundred flats, tens rods, and ones cubes to represent each number.

5 Mixed Review

1. 13 − 6 (7)
2. 17 − 8 (9)
3. 3 + _____ = 12 (9)
4. 695 ◯ 700 (<)
5. 8¢ + 8¢ (16¢)
6. 570, 580, 590, 600, _____ (610)
7. 0 + 9 (9)
8. 93 ◯ 100 (<)
9. _____ + 6 = 10 (4)
10. 3 hundreds 2 tens 9 ones (329)

For Mixed Abilities

Common Errors • Intervention

If students have difficulty understanding hundreds, tens, and ones, have them work with partners and use hundred flats, tens rods, and ones cubes. Give each pair four cards, each card with a number on it such as 247. Have pairs use their place-value materials to model the number.

Enrichment • Number Sense

Tell students to write in a column the numbers from 0 to 1,000 that have 2 tens and 6 ones. Then, tell them to make another column of the numbers that have 8 tens and 7 ones.

More to Explore • Logic

Tell students that they are the city bus driver in the following problem: At the first stop, 11 passengers get on the bus. At the next stop, 3 get on and 4 get off. At the next stop, 7 get on and 2 get off. At the next stop, 9 get on and 2 get off. At the next stop, 4 get on and 5 get off. Now, ask students to tell you the driver's name. (They are the driver. What is their name?)

10-2 Review Adding 2-Digit Numbers

pages 177–178

1 Getting Started

Objective
- To review adding two 2-digit numbers for sums through 199

Materials
hundred flats, tens rods, and ones cubes

Warm Up • Mental Math
Tell students to name the number if they skipped 3 numbers after each.

1. 121 (125)
2. 706 (710)
3. 297 (301)
4. 87 (91)
5. 5, 10, 15, 20 (40)
6. 6, 8, 10, 12 (20)
7. 200, 300, 400 (800)

Warm Up • Logic
Have a student use manipulatives to lay out a 3-digit number. Have another student write the next number on the board. Have a third student lay out the number that follows the number on the board. Have a fourth student write the next number on the board. Continue for several more numbers and ask students to tell the pattern of the numbers on the board. (counting by 2s)

Name ______________________

Review Adding 2-Digit Numbers

The hardware store had a sale.
How many tools were for sale?

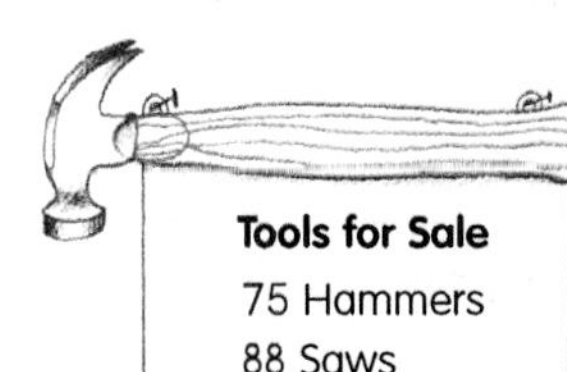

Tools for Sale
75 Hammers
88 Saws

We want to know the number of tools for sale.

The store had 75 hammers.

It had 88 saws.

To find how many tools were for sale, we add 75 and 88.

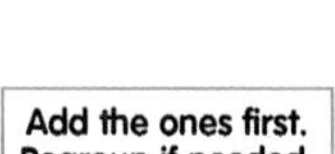

Add the ones first. Regroup if needed.	Add the tens.
$\begin{array}{r} ^{1} \\ 75 \\ +\ 88 \\ \hline 3 \end{array}$	$\begin{array}{r} ^{1} \\ 75 \\ +\ 88 \\ \hline 163 \end{array}$

The store had 163 tools for sale.

Getting Started
Add. Regroup if needed.

1.	2.	3.	4.	5.
37 + 82 = 119	96 + 44 = 140	39 + 99 = 138	81 + 85 = 166	27 + 73 = 100

6.	7.	8.	9.	10.
14 + 96 = 110	75 + 50 = 125	49 + 98 = 147	52 + 77 = 129	63 + 58 = 121

---

2 Teach

Develop Skills and Concepts Have students write the basic addition facts that have sums of 10. (9 + 1, 8 + 2, 7 + 3, . . . , 1 + 9) Remind students that 10 ones are regrouped for a ten and that 10 tens are regrouped for a hundred. Write **78 + 64** on the board and remind students that 8 ones + 4 ones = 12 ones, so 10 of the ones are regrouped for a ten, leaving 2 ones. Write the regrouping and the 2 ones. Remind students that 7 tens and 6 tens are added and then the 1 more ten for 14 tens. Tell students that 10 of the tens are regrouped for a hundred, leaving 4 tens. Write the regrouping and the 4 tens. Have a student record the number of hundreds. (1) Ask students to read the sum. (142)

- Repeat for 87 + 88 (175), 53 + 92 (145), and 78 + 99 (177), having students show the regroupings and write the sums.

3 Practice

Using page 177 Have a student read the example aloud and tell what is being asked. (the number of tools for sale) Ask students what information is given in the problem. (none) Ask what information is given in the picture. (75 hammers and 88 saws) Ask students what operation needs to be done to find the total number of tools. (addition) Have students read and complete the information sentences. Work through the model with students and then have them complete the solution sentence. Have students lay out 7 tens rods 5 ones cubes and 8 tens rods 8 ones cubes and tell the total tens and ones to check their answer.

- Have students complete the Getting Started exercises independently.

Using page 178 Have students complete the rows of exercises independently.

Practice

Add. Regroup if needed.

1. 42 + 83 = 125	2. 95 + 70 = 165	3. 84 + 29 = 113	4. 39 + 57 = 96	5. 79 + 83 = 162	6. 18 + 67 = 85
7. 68 + 54 = 122	8. 86 + 76 = 162	9. 22 + 54 = 76	10. 82 + 68 = 150	11. 56 + 55 = 111	12. 90 + 53 = 143
13. 63 + 82 = 145	14. 97 + 85 = 182	15. 78 + 79 = 157	16. 51 + 84 = 135	17. 68 + 24 = 92	18. 77 + 89 = 166

Now Try This!

It's Algebra!

Solve.

1. Add two numbers. The sum is 96. One number is 35. What is the other number? 61

2. Subtract two numbers. The answer is 38. The larger number is 96. What is the other number? 58

3. Add two numbers. The sum is 91. One number is 36. What is the other number? 55

4. Subtract two numbers. The answer is 57. The smaller number is 19. What is the larger number? 76

Now Try This! Write **26 + 42 = 68, 68 − 42 = 26,** and **68 − 26 = 42** vertically on the board. Remind students that the larger number (the sum in the first problem) minus one of the numbers equals the other number.

- Tell students that the sum of two numbers is 41 and one of the numbers is 26. Ask a student to write and solve a problem to find the other number. (41 − 26 = 15 or 26 + 15 = 41) Repeat for an answer of 73 if one number is 38. (73 − 38 = 35 or 38 + 35 = 73)
- Have students complete the exercises independently.

4 Assess

Have students write story problems with 2-digit addends. Then, have them switch papers with a partner to solve each other's problems.

For Mixed Abilities

Common Errors • Intervention

Some students may need additional practice in deciding when to regroup and when not to regroup when adding 2-digit numbers. Have them work with partners. Give the pair eight cards, each showing an addition problem, four that require regrouping and four that do not. Have pairs separate the cards into a regrouping pile and a nonregrouping pile. Be sure they verbalize how they decided into which group to put the problems. Then, have them perform the additions.

Enrichment • Logic

Tell students to write and solve problems to show all the numbers from 40 to 60 that, if added to 47, would require trading for a ten and/or a hundred.

More to Explore • Application

Arrange for an adding machine or cash register to be brought into the classroom. Invite a cashier, salesperson, or company representative to demonstrate the use of the machine. If possible, provide students with the opportunity to work at the machine for awhile. Have students list some of the jobs where they would be expected to know how to use one of these machines.

10-3 Adding a 3-Digit and a 1-Digit Number

pages 179–180

1 Getting Started

Objective

- To add a 3-digit and a 1-digit number with some regrouping

Materials

hundred flats, tens rods, and ones cubes

Warm Up • Mental Math

Ask students to name a number that

1. is less than 219 (218, . . . , 0)
2. has 8 tens (80, 180, 280, . . . , 980)
3. is greater than 468 (469, . . . , 999)
4. means 25 minutes after the hour on a clock (5)
5. has 3 digits and all are the same (111, 222, 333, . . . , 999)
6. reads the same backward and forward (111, 121, 131, etc.)

Warm Up • Pencil and Paper

Organize the class into pairs. Write **46 + 6** on the board and have one partner talk through the solution while the other partner records the work on a sheet of paper. (52) Repeat for 72 + 9 (81), 56 + 5 (61), 83 + 8 (91), 74 + 9 (83), and 68 + 8 (76). Have students switch roles with each problem.

Name ______________________

Lesson 10-3

Adding a 3-Digit and a 1-Digit Number

Some students and parents from Allen School went to Clown School. How many people studied clowning?

We want to know how many went to Clown School.

There were 154 students and 8 parents attending Clown School.

To find how many people were attending, we add 154 and 8.

Add the ones first. Regroup if needed.	Add the tens.	Add the hundreds.
$\begin{array}{r} \overset{1}{1}54 \\ +\ \ 8 \\ \hline 2 \end{array}$	$\begin{array}{r} \overset{1}{1}54 \\ +\ \ 8 \\ \hline 62 \end{array}$	$\begin{array}{r} \overset{1}{1}54 \\ +\ \ 8 \\ \hline 162 \end{array}$

There were 162 people attending Clown School.

Getting Started

Add. Regroup if needed.

1. $\begin{array}{r} 237 \\ +\ \ 5 \\ \hline 242 \end{array}$
2. $\begin{array}{r} 374 \\ +\ \ 7 \\ \hline 381 \end{array}$
3. $\begin{array}{r} 964 \\ +\ \ 6 \\ \hline 970 \end{array}$
4. $\begin{array}{r} 555 \\ +\ \ 5 \\ \hline 560 \end{array}$
5. $\begin{array}{r} 423 \\ +\ \ 9 \\ \hline 432 \end{array}$
6. $\begin{array}{r} 105 \\ +\ \ 8 \\ \hline 113 \end{array}$
7. $\begin{array}{r} 675 \\ +\ \ 6 \\ \hline 681 \end{array}$
8. $\begin{array}{r} 815 \\ +\ \ 7 \\ \hline 822 \end{array}$
9. $\begin{array}{r} 276 \\ +\ \ 2 \\ \hline 278 \end{array}$
10. $\begin{array}{r} 349 \\ +\ \ 8 \\ \hline 357 \end{array}$

---

2 Teach

Develop Skills and Concepts Dictate the following problems for students to write and solve on the board: 76 + 8 (84), 19 + 7 (26), and 25 + 5 (30). Now write **252 + 9** on the board and have students show the numbers with manipulatives. Have students tell the sum of 2 and 9. (11) Ask if regrouping is needed. (yes) Have a student show the regrouping and record the number of ones left. (1 one left) Have a student tell and record the number of tens and hundreds. (6 tens and 2 hundreds) Ask students the sum. (261) Repeat for the following problems: 456 + 7 (463), 8 + 709 (717), 345 + 4 (349), 7 + 208 (215), and 389 + 9 (398). Have students check each problem with manipulatives.

3 Practice

Using page 179 Have a student read the example aloud and tell what is being asked. (how many people studied clowning) Ask students what information is given in the problem or the picture. (154 students and 8 parents) Ask what needs to be done with the two numbers. (add) Have students read aloud with you as they complete the sentences, talk through the solution, and complete the solution statement. Have students use manipulatives to check their addition.

- Help students with the Getting Started exercises if necessary.

Using page 180 Remind students to add the ones first and then the tens and hundreds. Assign the page to be completed independently.

Practice

Add. Regroup if needed.

1. 774 + 9 783	2. 588 + 2 590	3. 517 + 9 526	4. 603 + 7 610	5. 357 + 4 361
6. 282 + 7 289	7. 156 + 6 162	8. 921 + 8 929	9. 813 + 9 822	10. 628 + 5 633
11. 487 + 4 491	12. 307 + 5 312	13. 156 + 6 162	14. 385 + 3 388	15. 906 + 8 914
16. 9 + 286 295	17. 986 + 6 992	18. 9 + 849 858	19. 383 + 8 391	20. 566 + 7 573

Problem Solving

Solve.

21. There were 335 circus tickets sold. Then 6 more tickets were sold. How many tickets were sold?
341 tickets

22. Pat sold 248 bags of popcorn at the circus. Then he sold 7 more bags. How many bags of popcorn did Pat sell?
255 bags

4 Assess

Write **574 + 6** on the board. Ask students if they need to regroup. (yes) Then, ask students to solve the problem. (580)

5 Mixed Review

1. 2 dimes 1 nickel (25¢)
2. 635, 640, 645, _____ (650)
3. 700 ◯ 600 (>)
4. 13¢ − 4¢ (9¢)
5. 8 hundreds 0 tens 5 ones (805)
6. 7 + 4 (11)
7. 805 ◯ 815 (<)
8. _____ + 5 = 14 (9)
9. 10 + 7 (17)
10. 2 + 9 (11)

For Mixed Abilities

Common Errors • Intervention

Some students have difficulty understanding regrouping when they add a 3-digit number and a 1-digit number. Draw a number line from 100 to 130 on the board with intervals of 1. Circle the decade number on the line, that is, 100, 110, 120, and 130. Tell students that each time a decade number is passed, a regrouping of 10 ones is made for 1 ten. Write **115 + 9** on the board. Have a student locate 115 on the number line, go 9 spaces forward and tell the number. (124) Ask, *Was a decade number passed?* (yes) Now, write on the board the addition problem for 115 + 9 in vertical form and discuss the regrouping as you solve it together. Repeat this procedure for other addition problems.

Enrichment • Logic

Tell students to write and solve a problem that tells the day of the year that is one week later than the 313th day.

More to Explore • Logic

Provide students with copies of this crossword puzzle. Do 1 across and 1 down together. Have students finish the puzzle independently.

ACROSS
1. subtract 4 from 38 (34)
2. subtract 9 from 26 (17)
4. subtract 20 from 60 (40)
6. subtract 30 from 50 (20)
7. subtract 15 from 39 (24)
9. subtract 27 from 42 (15)
10. subtract 48 from 62 (14)

DOWN
1. 38 minus 7 (31)
3. 83 minus 5 (78)
4. 70 minus 30 (40)
5. 45 minus 13 (32)
6. 60 minus 40 (20)
8. 65 minus 24 (41)
9. 72 minus 58 (14)

10-4 Adding a 3-Digit and a 2-Digit Number

pages 181–182

1 Getting Started

Objective
- To add 3-digit and 2-digit numbers with one regrouping

Materials
hundred flats, tens rods, and ones cubes

Warm Up • Mental Math
Ask students what 3-digit numbers read the same backward and forward and have the following:

1. 4 tens (141, 242, . . . , 949)
2. 9 ones (909, 919, 929, . . . , 999)
3. 6 hundreds (606, 616, 626, . . . , 696)
4. 0 tens (101, 202, 303, . . . , 909)
5. 3 ones (303, 313, 323, . . . , 393)
6. 7 tens (171, 272, 373, . . . , 979)
7. 8 hundreds (808, 818, 828, . . . , 898)

Warm Up • Pencil and Paper
Dictate the following problems for students to write and solve: 426 + 9 (435), 204 + 8 (212), 355 + 6 (361), 774 + 5 (779), and 563 + 7 (570).

Name ______________________

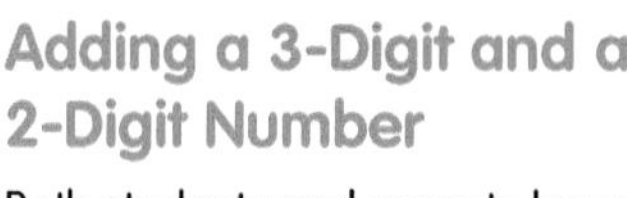

Adding a 3-Digit and a 2-Digit Number

Both students and parents bought tickets to the school carnival. How many tickets were sold?

There were 257 student tickets sold.

There were 82 adult tickets sold.

To find how many tickets were sold, we add 257 and 82.

Add the ones first. Regroup if needed.	Add the tens. Regroup if needed.	Add the hundreds.
7 + 2 = 9 ones No trade is needed.	5 + 8 = 13 tens 13 tens = 1 hundred and 3 tens	1 + 2 = 3 hundreds
257 + 82 = 9	257 + 82 = 39 (regrouped 1)	257 + 82 = 339 (regrouped 1)

There were 339 carnival tickets sold.

Getting Started
Add. Regroup if needed.

1. 580 + 87 = 667
2. 317 + 51 = 368
3. 271 + 46 = 317
4. 450 + 92 = 542
5. 694 + 32 = 726
6. 474 + 21 = 495
7. 425 + 84 = 509
8. 132 + 59 = 191
9. 230 + 87 = 317
10. 488 + 70 = 558

2 Teach

Develop Skills and Concepts Write **264 + 53** vertically on the board. Have students work in pairs to lay out the two numbers using manipulatives. Ask students the sum of the ones. (7) Ask if regrouping is needed. (no) Have a student write **7** in the ones answer column. Ask students the sum of 6 tens and 5 tens. (11 tens) Ask if regrouping is needed. (yes) Have students regroup and tell how many tens are left. (1) Have a student record the trade and the 1 ten. Ask students the total number of hundreds. (3) Have a student record the 3 in the answer on the board. Have students read the sum. (317)

- Repeat for the following problems, which require either no regrouping, a regrouping of 10 tens, or a regrouping of 10 ones: 815 + 92 (907), 420 + 58 (478), 746 + 83 (829), 278 + 18 (296), and 342 + 96 (438).

3 Practice

Using page 181 Have a student read the example aloud and tell what is to be solved. (the number of tickets sold) Ask what information is known. (257 student and 82 adult tickets were sold.) Ask what needs to be done with these numbers. (add) Have students read and complete the information sentences. Work through the model with students and then have them complete the solution sentence. Have students use manipulatives to check their solution.

- Help students with the Getting Started exercises if necessary.

Using page 182 Remind students that regrouping is needed in addition only if the sum is 10 or more. Have students complete the page independently.

Practice

Add. Regroup if needed.

1. 279 + 12 = 291	2. 478 + 14 = 492	3. 265 + 23 = 288	4. 343 + 49 = 392	5. 279 + 80 = 359
6. 189 + 80 = 269	7. 191 + 53 = 244	8. 149 + 20 = 169	9. 367 + 51 = 418	10. 186 + 21 = 207
11. 234 + 75 = 309	12. 339 + 53 = 392	13. 322 + 74 = 396	14. 407 + 54 = 461	15. 803 + 27 = 830
16. 725 + 15 = 740	17. 457 + 92 = 549	18. 559 + 24 = 583	19. 753 + 38 = 791	20. 442 + 93 = 535

Problem Solving

Solve.

21. Erin had 276 marbles. Devin gave her 70 more marbles. How many marbles does Erin have now?
346 marbles

22. Jason saved 358 stamps. His sister gave him 27 more stamps. How many stamps does Jason have now?
385 stamps

4 Assess

Write **136 + 71** on the board. Ask students if regrouping is needed. (yes) Ask what they are regrouping. (10 tens) Have them solve the problem. (207)

5 Mixed Review

1. 3 dimes, 3 nickels (45¢)
2. 7¢ + 7¢ (14¢)
3. 28 ○ 82 (<)
4. 15 − 6 (9)
5. 9 + _____ = 17 (8)
6. 170 ○ 710 (<)
7. 85, 90, 95, 100, _____ (105)
8. 6 + 7 (13)
9. 10 − 2 (8)
10. 13 − 8 (5)

For Mixed Abilities

Common Errors • Intervention

Some students may have difficulty adding a 2-digit number to a 3-digit number because they want to add a number to the hundreds. Have them work with partners and use place-value materials to model the problem.

Enrichment • Number Sense

Ask students to write and solve problems to find out which numbers from 20 to 30 require regrouping when added to 274.

More to Explore • Number Sense

Write the Roman numerals for 1 to 10. (I, II, III, IV, V, VI, VII, VIII, IX, X) Select one student to put his or her head down while another student erases two of the Roman numerals. The first student then goes to the board and writes in the correct missing numerals. If the student is correct, he or she can be the one to erase the numerals next while another student puts his or her head down. Extend the range of Roman numerals as the students' familiarity increases.

10-5 Adding With 2 Regroupings

pages 183–184

1 Getting Started

Objective

- To add a 3-digit and a 2-digit number with up to 2 regroupings

Materials

hundred flats, tens rods, and ones cubes

Warm Up • Mental Math

Ask students if regrouping is needed in addition for the following:

1. 7 tens + 1 ten + 3 tens (yes)
2. 2 ones + 1 one + 6 ones (no)
3. 5 tens + 5 tens (yes)
4. 75 + 5 (yes)
5. 60 + 40 (yes)
6. 2 ones + 2 ones + 2 ones (no)
7. 6 tens + 9 tens (yes)

Warm Up • Number Sense

Write **6 tens** on the board. Ask a student to write on the board the number of tens that can be added to 6 tens without regrouping. (0 through 3) Repeat for the number of tens that would require a regrouping. (4 through 9) Repeat for other numbers of tens or ones.

Name ______________________

Adding With 2 Regroupings

The school bookstore has 275 red pencils and 86 blue pencils. How many pencils does it have?

We are looking for the total number of pencils.

There are 275 red pencils and 86 blue pencils.

To find the total number of pencils, we add 275 and 86.

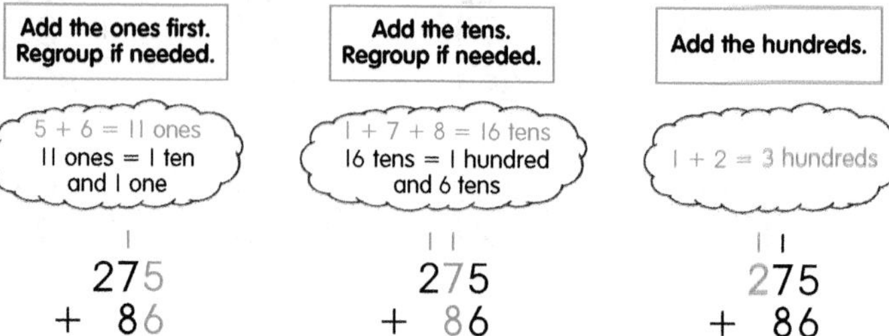

1	1 1	1 1
275	275	275
+ 86	+ 86	+ 86
1	61	361

The school book store has 361 pencils.

Getting Started

Add. Regroup if needed.

1.	2.	3.	4.	5.
326 + 79 = 405	542 + 88 = 630	384 + 16 = 400	794 + 59 = 853	453 + 98 = 551

6.	7.	8.	9.	10.
919 + 67 = 986	68 + 496 = 564	154 + 96 = 250	643 + 46 = 689	643 + 57 = 700

---

2 Teach

Develop Skills and Concepts Write the following problems vertically on the board: **254 + 35** (289), **254 + 39** (293), **254 + 73** (327), and **254 + 88** (342). Have students talk through each problem as you record the work. Students will see that the problems progress from no regrouping, regrouping for 1 ten, and regrouping for 1 hundred to regrouping for both 1 ten and 1 hundred.

- Repeat for the following series of problems: 726 + 33 (759), 726 + 34 (760), 726 + 82 (808), and 726 + 87 (813). Repeat for similar problems.

3 Practice

Using page 183 Have a student read the example aloud and tell what is to be found. (the total number of pencils) Ask what information is given. (There are 275 red and 86 blue pencils.) Ask what operation is used to find how many pencils there are in all. (addition) Have students read and complete the information sentences. Work through the model with students and then have them complete the solution sentence. Have students use manipulatives to check their solution.

- Help students with the Getting Started exercises if necessary.

Using page 184 Remind students that the problems may need 0, 1, or 2 regroupings. Have students complete the page independently.

Practice

Add. Regroup if needed.

1. 264 + 53 = 317	2. 486 + 45 = 531	3. 332 + 79 = 411	4. 517 + 98 = 615	5. 726 + 75 = 801
6. 154 + 95 = 249	7. 781 + 38 = 819	8. 857 + 69 = 926	9. 695 + 98 = 793	10. 201 + 99 = 300
11. 386 + 76 = 462	12. 850 + 92 = 942	13. 468 + 73 = 541	14. 729 + 58 = 787	15. 596 + 65 = 661
16. 271 + 27 = 298	17. 621 + 84 = 705	18. 586 + 76 = 662	19. 901 + 65 = 966	20. 153 + 73 = 226
21. 615 + 85 = 700	22. 723 + 68 = 791	23. 265 + 39 = 304	24. 37 + 685 = 722	25. 89 + 527 = 616

Now Try This!

Complete each Magic Square.

8	1	6
3	5	7
4	9	2

7	0	5
2	4	6
3	8	1

9	2	7
4	6	8
5	10	3

Now Try This! Help students complete the first square by guessing and checking. Have students complete the next two squares independently. Then, draw the squares on the board for students to write in their solutions.

4 Assess

Write the following problems on the board: **701 + 19, 648 + 65, 523 + 18,** and **148 + 72.** Have students copy the problems and circle the problems with 1 regrouping in blue (701 + 19, 523 + 18) and the problems with 2 regroupings in red (648 + 65, 148 + 72). Then, have students find the sums. (720, 713, 541, 220)

For Mixed Abilities

Common Errors • Intervention

Some students may regroup correctly but then simply drop the renamed value.

Incorrect	Correct
248 + 95 = 233	(1 1) 248 + 95 = 343

Correct students by having them work with partners and use place-value materials to model the problems.

Enrichment • Logic

Tell students to write and solve problems in which 99 is added to 99, 199, 299, 399, and so on, through 899. Ask what pattern can be seen.

More to Explore • Measurement

Introduce this activity with a recording of "The Inchworm" from the musical *Hans Christian Anderson*. Have each child trace, color, and cut out an inchworm made to scale.

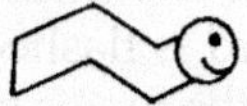

Then, have each student make four marigolds for a class bulletin-board garden with stems that are 2, 4, 8, and 16 inches high. Using the inchworm to measure, have the class discuss the progression of height. Point out that if the stems are in sequence, each stem is two times the height of the stem before.

ESL/ELL STRATEGIES

To help with the Now Try This! activity, explain that a magic square is a chart that is three cells high and three cells wide. The word *magic* is used because the sum of the three numbers in each vertical, horizontal, and diagonal row of cells is always the same.

10-6 Practice Adding With 1 or 2 Regroupings

pages 185–186

1 Getting Started

Objective
- To add 3-digit numbers to 2-digit numbers with regrouping

Materials
*addition fact cards; hundred flats, tens rods, and ones cubes

Warm Up • Mental Math
Tell students to rename the following numbers in hundreds, tens, and ones.

1. 999 (9 hundreds 9 tens 9 ones)
2. 182 + 2 (1 hundred 8 tens 4 ones)
3. 206 (2 hundreds 0 tens 6 ones)
4. 480 (4 hundreds 8 tens 0 ones)
5. 100 + 40 (1 hundred 4 tens 0 ones)
6. $1.62 (1 hundred 6 tens 2 ones)

Warm Up • Number Sense
Show addition fact cards in random order. As a card is flashed, tell students that the fact is showing addition of either tens or ones. Have students tell if a regrouping is needed, and if so, what the regrouping would be. For example, 6 tens + 9 tens requires a regrouping of 10 tens for 1 hundred.

Name ______________________

Practice Adding With 1 or 2 Regroupings

There were 355 books and 97 tapes checked out of the school library last week. How many books and tapes were checked out altogether?

We want to know how many items were checked out.

There were 355 books and 97 tapes.

To find out how many were checked out altogether, we add 355 and 97.

Add the ones first. Regroup if needed.	Add the tens. Regroup if needed.	Add the hundreds.
¹355 + 97 = 2	¹¹355 + 97 = 52	¹¹355 + 97 = 452

There were 452 books and tapes checked out of the library.

Getting Started

Add. Regroup if needed.

1.	2.	3.	4.	5.
347 + 46 = 393	275 + 82 = 357	586 + 97 = 683	164 + 76 = 240	795 + 55 = 850

6.	7.	8.	9.	10.
429 + 71 = 500	650 + 60 = 710	931 + 57 = 988	219 + 99 = 318	352 + 68 = 420

2 Teach

Develop Skills and Concepts Have students rewrite and solve the following horizontal problems: **476 + 24** (500), **82 + 327** (409), **253 + 86** (339), and **89 + 192** (281).

- Then, write **423** on the board and have a student complete the problem by writing a 2-digit addend. Have another student solve the problem and tell how many regroupings were needed. Repeat for more practice.

3 Practice

Using page 185 Have a student read the example aloud and tell what is to be found. (the total number of books and tapes checked out) Ask what information is known. (There were 355 books and 97 tapes checked out.) Ask what operation tells us how many in all. (addition) Have students read and complete the information sentences. Work through the model with students and then have them complete the solution sentence. Have students use manipulatives to check the solution.

- Help students complete the Getting Started exercises if necessary.

Using page 186 Remind students that any sum of 10 or more in these problems will require regrouping. Have students complete the rows of problems independently.

Practice

Add. Regroup if needed.

1.	2.	3.	4.	5.
127 + 31 = 158	275 + 18 = 293	756 + 87 = 843	635 + 87 = 722	362 + 89 = 451

6.	7.	8.	9.	10.
475 + 75 = 550	599 + 99 = 698	938 + 25 = 963	484 + 16 = 500	95 + 127 = 222

Now Try This!

Color each block blue. Then write your answer on the line.

1. 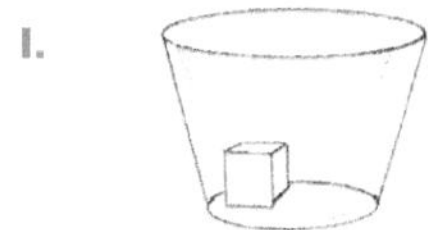 If I want to have an equal chance of drawing a red or blue, I would put in 1 red block(s).

2. 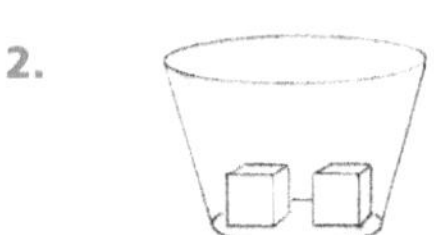 If I want blue to be more likely than red, I would put in 1 red block(s).

3. 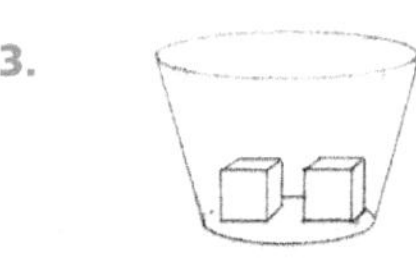 If I want blue to be less likely than red, I would put in 3 red blocks. or more

4. 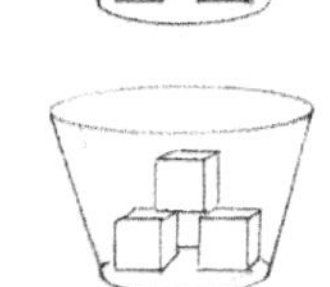 If I want an equal chance of drawing a red or blue, I would put in 3 red blocks.

Now Try This! Discuss the meanings of *equal chance, more likely chance,* and *less likely chance* with students. For there to be an equal chance, there must be the same number of each color block. For there to be a more likely chance of drawing blue, there must be more blue than red blocks. For there to be a less likely chance of drawing blue, there must be fewer blue than red blocks.

Have students color each block blue and complete the remaining exercises independently.

4 Assess

Organize the class into pairs. Have each student in the pair write three addition problems with 3-digit and 2-digit addends and at least 1 regrouping. Then, have students switch papers to answer each other's problems.

For Mixed Abilities

Common Errors • Intervention

Watch for students who write a renamed ten or hundred, even when a regrouping is not performed. Remind them to check the ones, or the tens, to see if regrouping is necessary. Encourage students to encircle the place-value digits that require regrouping before they start working the problem.

$$\begin{array}{r} 516 \\ +\ 75 \\ \hline \end{array}$$

Enrichment • Technology

Organize the class into pairs. Have one student in each pair find the sum for 85 + 59 (144) by writing the problem out. Have the other student find the sum by using a calculator. Have the two students compare their answers. If they do not match, have them redo the problem. When the answers match, have students switch roles and repeat the activity, using a problem found on page 186.

More to Explore • Measurement

Fill a box with foam packing material. Allow students to experiment with volumes of common household packages, for example, milk cartons, empty cereal boxes, and so on. Have them pour material from one container to another several times until they have a clear understanding of how much each container holds. Have the students make greater than and less than pictures using the information gathered from their experiments. (Hint: Antistatic spray or hairspray will keep the material from sticking.)

ESL/ELL STRATEGIES

Ask volunteers to explain in their own words the meaning of the phrases *an equal chance of, more likely than,* and *less likely than.* For example, *less likely than* means "it probably will not happen."

10-7 Adding Two 3-Digit Numbers

pages 187–188

1 Getting Started

Objective
- To add two 3-digit numbers for sums through 999 with regrouping

Materials
hundred flats, tens rods, and ones cubes

Warm Up • Mental Math
Tell students to compare the following numbers:

1. 482 ◯ 428 (>)
2. $3.75 ◯ $4.26 (<)
3. 29¢ ◯ $1.29 (<)
4. 901 ◯ 109 (>)
5. 141 ◯ 139 (>)
6. 777 ◯ 862 (<)
7. 311 ◯ 312 (<)
8. $9.00 ◯ $8.99 (>)

Warm Up • Pencil and Paper
Write **473 + 68** vertically on the board. Organize the class into pairs. Have one partner talk through the solution while the other partner records the work on a sheet of paper. (541) Repeat for 721 + 99 (820), 452 + 69 (521), 245 + 38 (283), 690 + 70 (760) and 288 + 46 (334). Have students switch roles after each problem.

2 Teach

Develop Skills and Concepts Write **473 + 268** vertically on the board. Have a student talk through the addition of the ones as you record the regrouping and the 1 one left. Repeat for the tens column, recording the regrouping and 4 tens left. Ask students how many hundreds there are in all. (7) Ask students to read the sum. (741)

- Repeat for 452 + 358 (810), 376 + 525 (901), 402 + 394 (814), 582 + 209 (791), and 643 + 158 (801).

Name ______________________

Adding Two 3-Digit Numbers

Plans were made by 128 parents of Lincoln School for a spring picnic. 375 children signed up to go. How many children and parents went to the picnic?

We want to know how many were at the picnic.

There were <u>375</u> children at the picnic.

There were <u>128</u> parents.

To find how many people were at the picnic, we add <u>375</u> and <u>128</u>.

Add the ones first. Regroup if needed.	Add the tens. Regroup if needed.	Add the hundreds.
$\begin{array}{r} {\scriptstyle 1} \\ 375 \\ +128 \\ \hline 3 \end{array}$	$\begin{array}{r} {\scriptstyle 1\,1} \\ 375 \\ +128 \\ \hline 03 \end{array}$	$\begin{array}{r} {\scriptstyle 1\,1} \\ 375 \\ +128 \\ \hline 503 \end{array}$

There were <u>503</u> people at the picnic.

Getting Started

Add. Regroup if needed.

1. $\begin{array}{r} 341 \\ +237 \\ \hline 578 \end{array}$
2. $\begin{array}{r} 655 \\ +329 \\ \hline 984 \end{array}$
3. $\begin{array}{r} 752 \\ +198 \\ \hline 950 \end{array}$
4. $\begin{array}{r} 437 \\ +463 \\ \hline 900 \end{array}$
5. $\begin{array}{r} 586 \\ +145 \\ \hline 731 \end{array}$
6. $\begin{array}{r} 176 \\ +532 \\ \hline 708 \end{array}$
7. $\begin{array}{r} 595 \\ +187 \\ \hline 782 \end{array}$
8. $\begin{array}{r} 215 \\ +675 \\ \hline 890 \end{array}$
9. $\begin{array}{r} 753 \\ +189 \\ \hline 942 \end{array}$
10. $\begin{array}{r} 375 \\ +275 \\ \hline 650 \end{array}$

---

3 Practice

Using page 187 Have a student read the example aloud and tell what is to be found. (number of children and parents who attended the picnic) Ask what information is given. (There were 375 children and 128 parents.) Ask students what needs to be done with these numbers to find the total. (add) Have students read and complete the information sentences. Work through the model with students and then have them complete the solution sentence. Have students use manipulatives to check their solution.

- Help students complete the Getting Started exercises if necessary.

Using page 188 Remind students to add the ones first, then the tens, and then the hundreds. Also, remind students to regroup only if the sum is 10 or more. Assign the page to be completed independently.

Practice

Add. Regroup if needed.

1. 128 + 239 = 367	2. 243 + 266 = 509	3. 154 + 186 = 340	4. 475 + 140 = 615	5. 500 + 250 = 750
6. 469 + 241 = 710	7. 428 + 395 = 823	8. 165 + 378 = 543	9. 752 + 108 = 860	10. 394 + 237 = 631
11. 417 + 230 = 647	12. 466 + 427 = 893	13. 352 + 248 = 600	14. 273 + 468 = 741	15. 116 + 599 = 715

Problem Solving

Solve.

16. The people at the spring picnic used 278 hot dog buns and 385 hamburger buns. How many buns were used?
663 buns

17. 325 cups of orange juice and 375 cups of milk were served. How many cups were served?
700 cups

18. 158 people swam and 263 rowed boats. How many people were swimming or rowing boats?
421 people

19. 185 children and 77 adults played bingo at the picnic. How many people played bingo?
262 people

4 Assess

Tell students, *There are 458 children going on Martin School's overnight field trip. There are 175 parents going. How many parents and children are going altogether?* (633)

5 Mixed Review

1. ____ + 7 = 15 (8)
2. 2 hundreds 9 tens 6 ones (296)
3. 4 nickels, 2 pennies (22¢)
4. 57 + 6 (63)
5. 3 + 6 (9)
6. 795 ◯ 98 (>)
7. 15 − 8 (7)
8. 91 + 5 (96)
9. 68 + 8 (76)
10. 16 − 9 (7)

For Mixed Abilities

Common Errors • Intervention

Watch for students who add incorrectly because they have not yet mastered their basic facts. Have them work with partners and basic-fact cards, practicing those that give them the most trouble more often than those that do not.

Enrichment • Algebra

Tell students to write and solve a problem to find out how many days are in 2 years. Then, tell them to write and solve a problem that finds the number of days in 3 years.

More to Explore • Geometry

Introduce the class to geoboards. If you do not have a classroom set of geoboards, you may want to use one class period to help students make them. Each board is a square of plywood with small nails arranged in a grid. You may make the board any convenient dimension. One common arrangement is a 10 × 10 grid.

In this first class, have students make as many different kinds of triangles as they can using a rubber band to outline the shapes on the geoboard. Have them experiment, and discover and list any other geometric shapes they can make.

10-8 Adding 3-Digit Numbers

pages 189–190

1 Getting Started

Objective
- To add any 3-digit numbers with regrouping

Materials
hundred flats, tens rods, and ones cubes

Warm Up • Mental Math
Ask students where the hour hand is when it is

1. 7:55 (almost on 8)
2. 2:40 (between 2 and 3)
3. 6:30 (between 6 and 7)
4. 12:00 (on 12)
5. 5:45 (between 5 and 6)
6. 3:50 (almost on 4)
7. 10:58 (almost on 11)

Warm Up • Number Sense
Write **2 hundreds 8 tens 6 ones + 3 hundreds 4 tens 5 ones** vertically on the board. Have students add the ones, regroup, add the tens, regroup, and add the hundreds. Write the sum as **6 hundreds 3 tens 1 one** on the board for students to read and then tell the number. (631) Repeat for more problems of 3-digit addends with 0, 1, or 2 regroupings.

Name ______________________

Lesson 10-8

Adding 3-Digit Numbers

Roger's grandfather works in a bakery. Each day he bakes 228 loaves of white bread and 198 loaves of wheat bread. How many loaves does he bake each day?

We want to know how many loaves he bakes each day.

He bakes 228 loaves of white bread and 198 loaves of wheat bread each day.

To find the total number of loaves, we add 228 and 198.

Add the ones first. Regroup if needed.	Add the tens. Regroup if needed.	Add the hundreds.
1 228 + 198 6	1 1 228 + 198 26	1 1 228 + 198 426

Roger's grandfather bakes 426 loaves of bread each day.

Getting Started

Add. Regroup if needed.

1. 357 + 548 = 905
2. 269 + 85 = 354

3. 296 + 313 = 609
4. 158 + 675 = 833
5. 391 + 193 = 584
6. 748 + 177 = 925
7. 624 + 257 = 881

2 Teach

Develop Skills and Concepts Write **215 + 326** horizontally on the board. Have a student write the problem vertically on the board. Have a student talk through the solution as another student records the work. (541) Repeat for 4 + 789 (793), 162 + 333 (495), 464 + 187 (651), 385 + 385 (770), 89 + 189 (278), and 101 + 889 (990), having students rewrite each problem vertically and then solve each problem.

3 Practice

Using page 189 Have a student read the example aloud and tell what is to be found. (number of loaves of bread baked each day) Ask what information is given. (Each day 228 white loaves and 198 wheat loaves are baked.) Ask what operation will find the total. (addition) Have students read and complete the information sentences. Work through the model with students and have them complete the solution sentence. Have students use manipulatives to check their solution.

- Help students complete the Getting Started exercises if necessary.

Using page 190 Tell students to rewrite each of the first problems vertically. Tell students to solve each problem and record the sum on the line in the number sentence. Have students complete the page independently. Remind students that they can check each problem with manipulatives.

Practice

Add. Regroup if needed.

1. 166 + 351 = 517
2. 449 + 276 = 725
3. 256 + 68 = 324
4. 159 + 681 = 840

5.	6.	7.	8.	9.
275 + 323 = 598	384 + 119 = 503	525 + 195 = 720	436 + 297 = 733	523 + 288 = 811

10.	11.	12.	13.	14.
35 + 265 = 300	96 + 875 = 971	105 + 196 = 301	57 + 288 = 345	441 + 82 = 523

15.	16.	17.	18.	19.
73 + 580 = 653	394 + 262 = 656	546 + 254 = 800	9 + 215 = 224	751 + 163 = 914

20.	21.	22.	23.	24.
95 + 438 = 533	526 + 175 = 701	253 + 288 = 541	615 + 173 = 788	252 + 308 = 560

4 Assess

Have students write word problems with two 3-digit addends and 2 regroupings. Then, have students switch papers to answer each other's problems.

5 Mixed Review

1. 35 + 28 (63)
2. 4 dimes, 2 nickels, 3 pennies (53¢)
3. 41 + 7 (48)
4. 10 + 4 (14)
5. 573 ◯ 375 (>)
6. 72 + 58 (130)
7. 5 hundreds 3 tens 8 ones (538)
8. 16 − 9 (7)
9. 28 + 9 (37)
10. 14 − 6 (8)

For Mixed Abilities

Common Errors • Intervention

Some students may have difficulty keeping the numbers aligned properly when they are adding two 3-digit numbers. Have them work their problems on grid paper, using the lines to keep the digits placed in their correct columns.

Enrichment • Number Sense

Tell students to write and solve an addition problem for a 3-digit sum in which 2 regroupings are needed. Then, tell them to write a problem requiring 1 regrouping and a problem requiring no regrouping.

More to Explore • Application

Have students collect cash register tapes from home shopping trips. Cover or remove the totals on the tapes. Tell students that they are the calculators and they must find the totals. Begin with shorter tapes and gradually have students advance to longer ones. Extend the activity by covering up some of the numbers within the column instead of covering the totals, and have students find the missing amounts in the problems.

10-9 Adding Money

pages 191–192

1 Getting Started

Objectives
- To add amounts of money for 3-digit sums in dollar notation
- To add amounts of money to solve word problems

Materials
real or play dollars, dimes, and pennies

Warm Up • Mental Math
Tell students to name the coins when

1. 2 coins equal 30¢ (1 quarter, 1 nickel)
2. 2 coins equal 50¢ (2 quarters)
3. 4 coins equal 40¢ (4 dimes)
4. 3 coins equal 75¢ (3 quarters)
5. 3 coins equal 30¢ (3 dimes)
6. 3 coins equal 40¢ (1 quarter, 1 dime, 1 nickel)
7. 3 coins equal 20¢ (1 dime, 2 nickels)

Warm Up • Number Sense
Dictate amounts of money through $9.99 for students to write in dollar notation. Remind students that the word *and* is said for the decimal point in reading amounts of money in dollar notation.

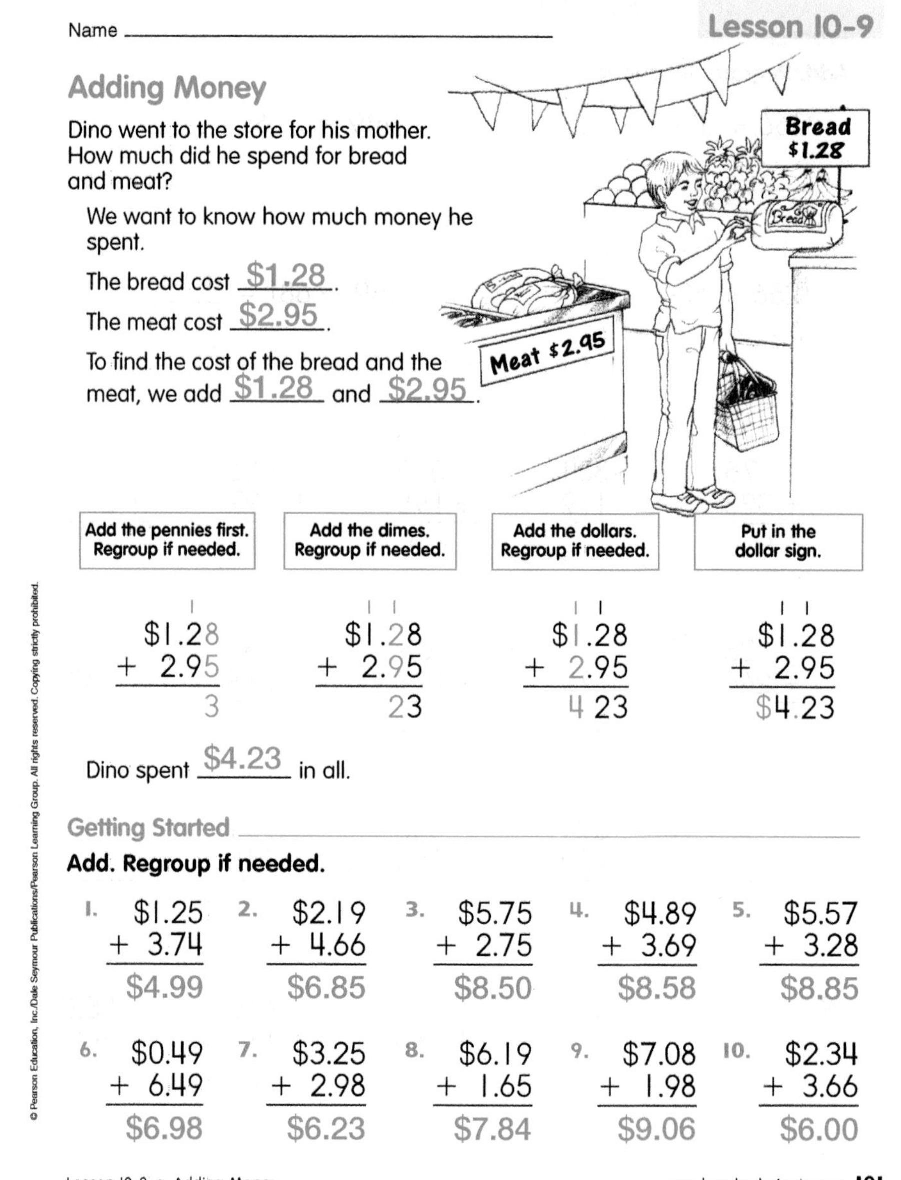
Name ______________________

Lesson 10-9

Adding Money

Dino went to the store for his mother. How much did he spend for bread and meat?

We want to know how much money he spent.

The bread cost $1.28.

The meat cost $2.95.

To find the cost of the bread and the meat, we add $1.28 and $2.95.

Add the pennies first. Regroup if needed.	Add the dimes. Regroup if needed.	Add the dollars. Regroup if needed.	Put in the dollar sign.
$1.28 + 2.95 = 3	$1.28 + 2.95 = 23	$1.28 + 2.95 = 4 23	$1.28 + 2.95 = $4.23

Dino spent $4.23 in all.

Getting Started

Add. Regroup if needed.

1. $1.25 + 3.74 = $4.99
2. $2.19 + 4.66 = $6.85
3. $5.75 + 2.75 = $8.50
4. $4.89 + 3.69 = $8.58
5. $5.57 + 3.28 = $8.85
6. $0.49 + 6.49 = $6.98
7. $3.25 + 2.98 = $6.23
8. $6.19 + 1.65 = $7.84
9. $7.08 + 1.98 = $9.06
10. $2.34 + 3.66 = $6.00

2 Teach

Develop Skills and Concepts Write **$2.64 + $3.46** vertically on the board. Ask students to read each amount orally with you. Have a student talk through the addition as another student records the work. (610) Remind students that the problem is about money and that the dollar sign and decimal point must be in the answer. Insert the signs in the answer. ($6.10) Have students note that the decimal point is placed after the number of dollars and before the number of cents.

- Repeat for $4.87 + $3.66 ($8.53), $0.28 + $2.45 ($2.73), $6.01 + $0.99 ($7.00), $5.98 + $2.43 ($8.41), and $7.59 + $1.43 ($9.02).

3 Practice

Using page 191 Have a student read the example and tell what is being asked. (amount of money Dino spent) Ask what information is given in the problem. (Dino bought bread and meat.) Ask what information is needed from the picture. (Bread costs $1.28 and meat costs $2.95.) Ask how the total cost of bread and meat can be found. (add) Have students read and complete the information sentences. Work through the example with students and then have them complete the solution sentence.

- Have students complete the Getting Started exercises independently. Encourage them to check their work using manipulatives.

Using page 192 Have students answer Exercises 1 to 5 independently. Next, have students read the items and their prices from the menu. Help students complete Exercise 6 and then tell them to complete Exercises 7 to 13 independently.

Practice

Add. Regroup if needed.

1.	2.	3.	4.	5.
$4.38	$3.15	$4.87	$2.65	$7.09
+ 1.28	+ 3.42	+ 3.76	+ 0.65	+ 1.95
$5.66	$6.57	$8.63	$3.30	$9.04

Problem Solving

Add to find the total cost.

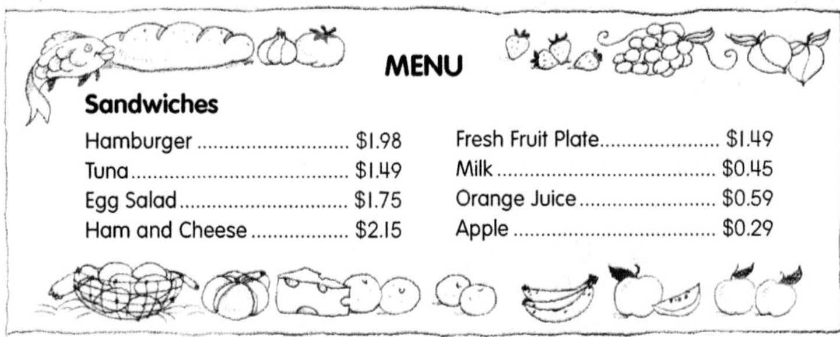

6. Hamburger, Milk: $1.98 + $0.45 = $2.43

7. Fresh Fruit Plate, Milk: $1.49 + $0.45 = $1.94

8. Tuna Sandwich, Orange Juice: $1.49 + $0.59 = $2.08

9. Ham and Cheese Sandwich, Apple: $2.15 + $0.29 = $2.44

10. Hamburger, Fresh Fruit Plate: $1.98 + $1.49 = $3.47

11. Tuna Sandwich, Fresh Fruit Plate: $1.49 + $1.49 = $2.98

12. Egg Salad Sandwich, Milk: $1.75 + $0.45 = $2.20

13. Ham and Cheese Sandwich, Orange Juice: $2.15 + $0.59 = $2.74

4 Assess

Organize the class into pairs. Give each pair a supermarket flier with sales and specials listed. Have each pair choose two favorite items from the flier and add to find out how much the items would cost altogether.

5 Mixed Review

1. 1 quarter, 2 dimes (45¢)
2. 65¢ + 27¢ (92¢)
3. 275 ◯ 265 (>)
4. 15 − 7 (8)
5. 43 + 18 (61)
6. 45, 50, 55, ____ (60)
7. ____ + 7 = 11 (4)
8. 95 + 8 (103)
9. 26 + 32 (58)
10. 16 − 8 (8)

For Mixed Abilities

Common Errors • Intervention

Some students may need more practice adding money. Have them work with partners and the menu on page 192 to plan each other's lunch. Then, have the pairs write and solve an addition problem to find the total cost for the two lunches.

Enrichment • Application

Have students make a menu having five or more priced items. Tell them to write three customers' orders and have a friend total the three bills. They should then check their friend's work.

More to Explore • Probability

Just as numbers and colors can be arranged in different combinations, so can letters. Write this on the board: **POT to TOP and PAT to TAP.**

Tell students that when the original three-letter words in each pair are rearranged, they take on a new meaning. Mathematicians would call it a permutation. Explain that you want the class over the next 2 days to list as many such three-letter word pairs as they can. Tell them to ask everyone in their family to help think of words that make sense spelled forward and backward.

10-10 Estimating Cost

pages 193–194

1 Getting Started

Objective
- To estimate the sum of two 3-digit numbers

Warm Up • Mental Math
Have students find the sums.

1. 18 + 10 (28)
2. 25 + 5 (30)
3. 30 + 22 (52)
4. 45 + 15 (60)
5. 58 + 8 (66)
6. 60 + 20 (80)

Warm Up • Number Sense
Write the following on the board and have students estimate:

1. **75 + 58** (140)
2. **47 + 42** (90)
3. **82 + 79** (160)
4. **93 + 77** (170)
5. **48 + 39** (90)
6. **38 + 85** (130)

Name ______________________

Lesson 10-10

It's Algebra!

Estimating Cost

Stephanie wants to buy the T-shirt and the pair of pants. She wants to know about how much she will have to pay. Stephanie can round to the nearest dollar.

If the digit in the dimes place is 5 or greater, round up.

If the digit in the dimes place is less than 5, round down.

The cost of the T-shirt is $3.85.

The cost of the pair of pants is $4.22.

Round to the nearest dollar.			Estimate.
$ 3.85 →	$ 4.00	round up	$ 4.00
+ 4.22 →	+ 4.00	round down	+ 4.00
			$ 8.00

Stephanie will spend about $8.00 to buy the T-shirt and pants.

Getting Started

Estimate. Show how you rounded.

1. Kathy has $5.26. Donna has $3.19. About how much money do they have in all?
   $5.00 + $3.00 = $8.00

2. Marcus earned $5.45 for delivering newspapers. He earned $3.82 for walking his neighbor's dog. About how much money did Marcus earn altogether?
   $5.00 + $4.00 = $9.00

3. Mrs. Wilkins spent $3.79 on orange juice and $4.92 on milk. About how much did Mrs. Wilkins spend altogether?
   $4.00 + $5.00 = $9.00

4. Samantha bought a skirt for $6.25. She bought a matching top for $2.45. About how much did Samantha spend in all?
   $6.00 + $2.00 = $8.00

---

2 Teach

Develop Skills and Concepts Review rounding with students. On the board, write **67 + 34.** Tell students that they do not need to find an exact answer, but an estimate. Have students explain how to round each of the numbers to the nearest ten in order to find the estimated sum. (67 rounds up to 70 and 34 rounds down to 30; 70 + 30 = 100)

- Now, write **325 + 489** on the board. Tell students that they are going to find the estimated sum by rounding to the nearest hundred. Ask, *Which place do you look at to round to the nearest hundred?* (tens) Explain that the same rule that they used to round to the nearest ten applies—if a number is 5 or greater round up, otherwise round down. Remind students that they are looking at the tens digit and not the ones digit when rounding to the nearest hundred.

It's Algebra! The concepts in this lesson prepare students for algebra.

3 Practice

Using page 193 Have students look at the example at the top of the page. Ask students what information they need to solve the problem. (the cost of the T-shirt and the cost of the pants) Ask, *What are you being asked to find?* (the estimated total cost of the T-shirt and pants) Ask students what operation they need to use to find the cost of the items. (addition) Have students round the cost of each item to the nearest dollar. Students can estimate by adding the rounded addends.

- Help students complete the Getting Started exercises if necessary.

Using page 194 Have students look at Exercise 1. Ask students what place they need to look at to round to the nearest dollar. (dimes) Help students complete Exercise 1 if necessary.

- Have students complete the remaining exercises independently.

Practice

Estimate. Show how you rounded.

1. $5.87 + 2.08
   $6.00 + $2.00 = $8.00

2. $4.29 + 4.88
   $4.00 + $5.00 = $9.00

3. $3.64 + 5.46
   $4.00 + $5.00 = $9.00

4. $6.31 + 1.87
   $6.00 + $2.00 = $8.00

Problem Solving

5. Rosie has $3.83 in her purse. Her grandmother gave her $4.25. About how much money does Rosie have now?
   $4.00 + $4.00 = $8.00

6. Artie has $1.83 in pennies and $4.20 in nickels in his piggy bank. About how much money does Artie have altogether?
   $2.00 + $4.00 = $6.00

Now Try This!

1. What is the greatest amount of money that rounds to $5.00 when rounded to the nearest dollar?
   $5.49

2. What is the least amount of money that rounds to $5.00 when rounded to the nearest dollar?
   $4.50

Now Try This! Remind students that when rounding to the nearest dollar, any amount over 50 cents is rounded up and any amount under 49 cents is rounded down. Have students work in pairs to solve these exercises.

4 Assess

Bring in takeout menus from a local restaurant. Have students pick any two items off the menu and estimate the total cost.

For Mixed Abilities

Common Errors • Intervention

Some students may have difficulty determining how to round numbers to the nearest dollar. Have students use a number line divided into ten-cent intervals to determine which dollar a given number is closer to. Have students highlight the number 50 on the number line. If the digit in the tens place is 5 or greater, tell students to go up to the next dollar.

Enrichment • Number Sense

Tell students, *Two items cost the same price. They cost about $5.80 rounded to the nearest 10 cents and about $6.00 rounded to the nearest dollar. What is the cost of each item?* (Possible answers: $2.85 through $2.94)

More to Explore • Logic

Read these sentences aloud: *Ruth is taller than John. John is shorter than Ruth. True or false?* (true) Now, read: *Sara got to school first. Sara arrived after Martin. Martin got to school last.* (false) Give students the following to identify as true or false:

1. Mrs. Morgan is John's mother. John is Mrs. Morgan's son. (true)
2. It is three miles from the school to the police station. It is two miles from the police station to the school. (false)
3. Allen is Mark's brother. Shirley is Allen's sister. Mark is Shirley's brother. (true)

10-11 Problem Solving: Use Information From a List

pages 195–196

1 Getting Started

Objective
- To use information from a list to solve problems

Materials
real or play dollars and coins

Warm Up • Mental Math
Tell students to name the number that tells the following:
1. 100 + 900 (1,000)
2. 40 minutes after the hour (8)
3. 80 − 60 (20)
4. what can be traded for 10 tens (1 hundred)
5. the total tens in 200 + 86 (8)
6. the value of 7 quarters ($1.75)

Warm Up • Number Sense
Lay out 2 dollars and 3 quarters in one group and 6 dollars, 4 dimes, and 1 quarter in another. Have a student write and solve an addition problem to tell how much money there is in the two groups. ($2.75 + $6.65 = $9.40) Repeat for other groups of bills and coins for sums through $9.99.

Name ______________________

Problem Solving: Use Information From a List

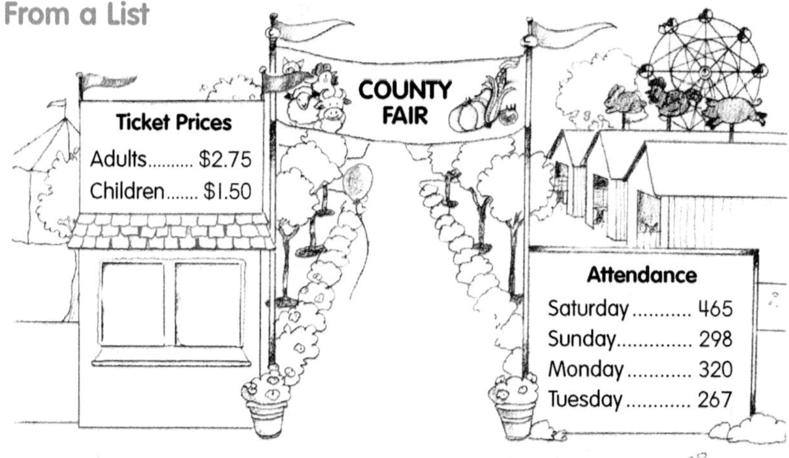

Use the information in the lists to solve each problem.

1. Mr. Brooks took his 8-year-old daughter to the county fair. How much did he pay for two tickets?
   $4.25

2. Mr. and Mrs. Velez went to the fair. How much did they pay for two adult tickets?
   $5.50

3. Robin and Peter went to the fair. How much did they pay for two children's tickets?
   $3.00

4. How many people went to the fair on Sunday and Monday?
   618

5. If Robin and Peter in Exercise 3 had $5.00, could they have bought one more child's ticket?
   yes

6. Were there more people at the fair on Saturday and Sunday or Monday and Tuesday?
   Saturday and Sunday

2 Teach

Develop Skills and Concepts On the board, write a simple list.

Prices for School Bake Sale

Cookies	$0.50 each
Cupcakes	$0.75 each
Apple pies	$5.00 per pie
Milk	$0.50 per container
Water	$1.00 per bottle

Ask students to tell you what information they can obtain from the list. (prices of items in a school bake sale) Next, ask students to find out how much a container of milk costs. ($0.50) Repeat for cookies and apple pies. Then, ask how much one cookie and a bottle of water would cost. ($1.50)

3 Practice

Using page 195 Have students tell about the picture and then discuss the students' experiences at county fairs or similar events. Have students tell the admission price for a child ($1.50) and an adult. ($2.75) Ask students how many people attended the fair on Monday (320) and then repeat for the other days noted.

- Now, have students apply the four-step plan to Exercise 1. For SEE, ask, *What are you asked to do?* (find out how much Mr. Brooks spent on a ticket for himself and his daughter) *What information is given?* (An adult ticket costs $2.75 and a child's ticket costs $1.50.) For PLAN, ask students how they will solve the problem. (add $2.75 and $1.50) For DO, have students find and write the sum. ($4.25) For CHECK, have students look at the ticket price list and check to be sure the numbers they used were correct.
- Have students complete the remaining exercises independently.

Use the information in the list to solve each problem.

1. How many horses and cows were shown at the fair?
   343 horses and cows

2. How many sheep and rabbits were shown at the fair?
   275 sheep and rabbits

3. How many horses and rabbits were shown at the fair?
   235 horses and rabbits

4. How many pigs and sheep were shown at the fair?
   234 pigs and sheep

5. How many pigs and rabbits were shown at the fair?
   255 pigs and rabbits

6. How many cows and sheep were shown at the fair?
   383 cows and sheep

Using page 196 Tell students to use information from the list in the picture to solve the exercises on this page. Also, remind students to check each problem and then record the answer on the answer line. Have students complete the page independently.

4 Assess

Have students look at the attendance list on page 195. Have them find out how many people attended the fair on Saturday and Sunday (763). Ask how many people attended on Wednesday. (cannot answer; there is no information for Wednesday in the list.)

For Mixed Abilities

Common Errors • Intervention

For students who need more practice solving word problems, change the data in the lists on pages 195 and 196 to create additional problems. Have students work with partners with whom they can discuss each problem before they cooperatively find the answer.

Enrichment • Number Sense

Tell students to use the list on page 195 to find the cost of tickets for the county fair for a family of 3 children, their mother, and their grandmother.

More to Explore • Application

This activity will help students learn to follow recipe directions on packages. Begin with a review of oven temperatures, degrees, how to use a timer, and how to measure with a cup measure, a teaspoon, and a tablespoon. Bring in several packages of corn muffin mix or other mix that can be simply made. Arrange the packages and the equipment that students will need in several stations around the room. Divide the class into groups and assign each group a station. Ask groups to work together to read the directions and put the ingredients together. Help them with words and procedures they do not understand. Arrange with the lunchroom staff to have the muffins baked so that students can enjoy the finished product. Finally, list the number of muffins each group made, and have a student count the total for the class.

page 197

Items	Objectives
1–5	To add a 3-digit and a 1-digit number with some regrouping (see pages 177–178)
6–13	To add 3-digit and 2-digit numbers with some regrouping (see pages 181–186)
14–20, 26	To add two 3-digit numbers for sums through 999 with regrouping (see pages 187–190)
21–24	To add amounts of money for 3-digit sums in dollar notation (see pages 191–192)
25	To add amounts of money for 3-digit sums in dollar notation (see pages 191–192)
	To add amounts of money to solve word problems (see pages 191–192)

Name ______________________

Add. Regroup if needed.

1. 341 + 7 = 348
2. 188 + 6 = 194
3. 259 + 4 = 263
4. 525 + 5 = 530
5. 707 + 9 = 716
6. 218 + 81 = 299
7. 175 + 16 = 191
8. 387 + 57 = 444
9. 696 + 73 = 769
10. 575 + 25 = 600
11. 27 + 365 = 392
12. 56 + 128 = 184
13. 75 + 250 = 325
14. 126 + 109 = 235
15. 361 + 278 = 639
16. 613 + 274 = 887
17. 338 + 255 = 593
18. 459 + 382 = 841
19. 175 + 328 = 503
20. 524 + 176 = 700
21. \$2.25 + 0.31 = \$2.56
22. \$3.36 + 1.47 = \$4.83
23. \$5.23 + 1.95 = \$7.18
24. \$3.37 + 5.63 = \$9.00

Solve.

25. Jaime spent \$2.75. Mona spent \$3.65. How much did they spend altogether? \$6.40

26. The Browns drove 245 miles on Saturday. They drove 188 miles on Sunday. How many miles did they drive altogether? 433 miles

Alternate Chapter Test

You may wish to use the Alternate Chapter Test on page 324 of this book for further review and assessment.

Circle the letter of the correct answer.

1. a. 1:25 b. 2:25 c. 3:25 d. NG

2. a. 36 b. 64 c. 46 d. NG

3. a. 204 b. 240 c. 402 d. NG

4. 38 ◯ 52 a. > b. <

5. a. $1.66 b. 60¢ c. $1.56 d. NG

6. $\begin{array}{r} 98 \\ -\ 26 \\ \hline \end{array}$ a. 124 b. 72 c. 36 d. NG

7. $\begin{array}{r} 84 \\ -\ 47 \\ \hline \end{array}$ a. 47 b. 131 c. 43 d. NG

8. $\begin{array}{r} 91 \\ -\ 27 \\ \hline \end{array}$ a. 74 b. 64 c. 76 d. NG

9. 38 + 99 = a. 127 b. 1217 c. 137 d. NG

10. $\begin{array}{r} 75 \\ +\ 85 \\ \hline \end{array}$ a. 150 b. 170 c. 160 d. NG

11. $\begin{array}{r} 346 \\ +\ 73 \\ \hline \end{array}$ a. 319 b. 419 c. 429 d. NG

12. $\begin{array}{r} 638 \\ +\ 267 \\ \hline \end{array}$ a. 905 b. 895 c. 805 d. NG

13. $\begin{array}{r} 135 \\ +\ 396 \\ \hline \end{array}$ a. 421 b. 531 c. 431 d. NG

score

STOP

Cumulative Assessment

page 198

Items	Objectives
1	To tell time in 5-minute intervals (see pages 95–96)
2	To read numbers through 100 (see pages 69–70)
3	To understand 3-digit numbers (see pages 71–74)
4	To find the greater or lesser of two 2-digit numbers (see pages 81–82)
5	To count money through $5 (see pages 75–76)
6–8	To subtract two 2-digit numbers (see pages 137–146, 159–160)
9	To add or subtract when a problem is horizontal (see pages 163–164)
10	To add two 2-digit numbers for a 3-digit sum (see pages 155–156)
11	To add 3-digit and 2-digit numbers with regrouping (see pages 181–186)
12–13	To add two 3-digit numbers for sums through 999 with regrouping (see pages 187–190)

Alternate Cumulative Assessment

Circle the letter of the correct answer.

1. 
a 11:10
b 4:45
c 12:00
d NG

2. a 45
b 25
c 54
d NG

3. a 107
b 130
c 137
d NG

4. 87 ◯ 98
a <
b >

5. 

a $2.41
b $2.36
c $2.28
d NG

6. $\begin{array}{r} 74 \\ -\ 52 \\ \hline \end{array}$
a 32
b 22
c 12
d NG

7. $\begin{array}{r} 65 \\ -\ 48 \\ \hline \end{array}$
a 27
b 23
c 13
d NG

8. $\begin{array}{r} 81 \\ -\ 25 \\ \hline \end{array}$
a 56
b 65
c 54
d NG

9. 14 + 52
a 38
b 56
c 66
d NG

10. $\begin{array}{r} 76 \\ +\ 48 \\ \hline \end{array}$
a 142
b 124
c 314
d NG

11. $\begin{array}{r} 436 \\ +\ 18 \\ \hline \end{array}$
a 454
b 444
c 544
d NG

12. $\begin{array}{r} 528 \\ +\ 297 \\ \hline \end{array}$
a 771
b 751
c 725
d NG

13. $\begin{array}{r} 472 \\ +\ 139 \\ \hline \end{array}$
a 617
b 511
c 611
d NG

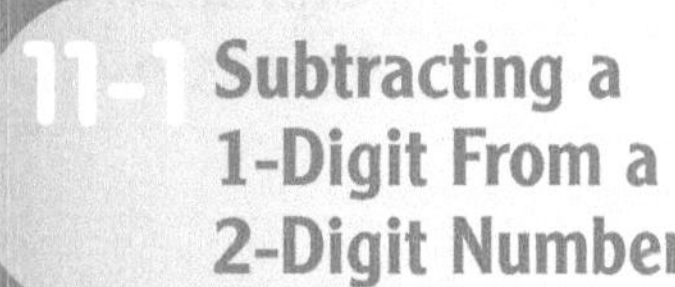

11-1 Subtracting a 1-Digit From a 2-Digit Number

pages 199–200

1 Getting Started

Objective

- To review subtracting a 1-digit number from a 2-digit number with regrouping

Materials

*addition and subtraction fact cards; *colored chalk

Warm Up • Mental Math

For each of the following, tell students to add 2 tens, subtract 5 ones, and tell the number.

1. 46 (61)
2. 80 (95)
3. 150 (165)
4. 21 (36)
5. 280 (295)
6. 55 (70)
7. 184 (199)

Warm Up • Number Sense

Write the following four headings across the board: **Sums Through 10**, **Sums of 11 and 12**, **Sums of 13, 14, and 15**, and **Sums of 16, 17, and 18**. Show addition fact cards, have students give the answers, and then place the cards on the chalk tray under the correct heading. Repeat for subtraction facts, changing the heading to **Minuends**.

Name ______________________

Subtracting 3-Digit Numbers

Lesson 11-1

Subtracting a 1-Digit From a 2-Digit Number

The Tidy Pet Shop had 33 finches. A total of 8 finches were sold. How many are left?

We are looking for the number not sold.

The pet shop had __33__ finches.

It sold __8__ finches.

To find how many are left, we subtract __8__ from __33__.

Subtract the ones. Regroup if needed.	Subtract the tens.
$\begin{array}{r} {\scriptstyle 2\ 13} \\ \not{3}\not{3} \\ -\ \ 8 \\ \hline 5 \end{array}$	$\begin{array}{r} {\scriptstyle 2\ 13} \\ \not{3}\not{3} \\ -\ \ 8 \\ \hline 25 \end{array}$

There are __25__ finches left.

Getting Started

Subtract. Regroup if needed.

1. $\begin{array}{r} 37 \\ -\ 5 \\ \hline 32 \end{array}$
2. $\begin{array}{r} 49 \\ -\ 7 \\ \hline 42 \end{array}$
3. $\begin{array}{r} 32 \\ -\ 6 \\ \hline 26 \end{array}$
4. $\begin{array}{r} 58 \\ -\ 9 \\ \hline 49 \end{array}$
5. $\begin{array}{r} 65 \\ -\ 7 \\ \hline 58 \end{array}$

2 Teach

Develop Skills and Concepts Write **26 − 8** vertically on the board. Remind students that 8 ones cannot be taken away from 6 ones, so a regrouping of 1 ten for 10 ones is made. Show the regrouping with colored chalk and have students then complete the subtraction. (18)

- Provide more problems on the board for added practice in subtracting a 1-digit number from a 2-digit number. Have students tell if regrouping is needed for each problem.

3 Practice

Using page 199 Have a student read the example and tell what is to be found. (the number of finches left) Ask students what information is given in the problem. (There were 33 finches and eight were sold.) Ask what will need to be done with the numbers. (subtract) Have students read and complete the information sentences. Work through the model with students and then have them complete the solution sentence. Remind students that to check subtraction, they should add the answer to the smaller number.

- Have students complete the Getting Started exercises independently.

Using page 200 Have students complete the page independently.

Practice

Subtract. Regroup if needed.

1. 18 − 5 = 13	2. 27 − 3 = 24	3. 13 − 4 = 9	4. 57 − 6 = 51	5. 41 − 8 = 33
6. 63 − 6 = 57	7. 45 − 2 = 43	8. 77 − 8 = 69	9. 88 − 6 = 82	10. 93 − 4 = 89
11. 25 − 5 = 20	12. 38 − 1 = 37	13. 57 − 9 = 48	14. 47 − 3 = 44	15. 63 − 7 = 56
16. 31 − 7 = 24	17. 87 − 8 = 79	18. 68 − 3 = 65	19. 44 − 8 = 36	20. 55 − 7 = 48

Problem Solving

Solve.

21. The pet shop had 42 kittens for sale. It sold 9 kittens. How many kittens are left?
33 kittens

22. The pet shop has 61 dog collars for sale. Sal sold 7 collars. How many collars are left?
54 collars

23. There were 55 fish. Trish bought 9. How many fish are left?
46 fish

24. There were 75 puppies for sale. Walter sold 6. How many puppies are left?
69 puppies

4 Assess

Write the following problems on the board. Have students say if regrouping is necessary and then solve the problems.

55 − 6	78 − 5	42 − 7	64 − 3	93 − 6
(yes, 49)	(no, 73)	(yes, 35)	(no, 61)	(yes, 87)

5 Mixed Review

1. 26 + 7 (33)
2. 1 quarter, 3 pennies (28¢)
3. 56 − 30 (26)
4. 9¢ + 9¢ (18¢)
5. 47 + 38 (85)
6. 695 ◯ 965 (<)
7. 49 − 32 (17)
8. _____ + 6 = 11 (5)
9. 98¢ + 26¢ ($1.24)
10. 17 − 9 (8)

For Mixed Abilities

Common Errors • Intervention

Some students may simply cross out numbers mechanically without understanding the regrouping process. Have them work with partners, using place-value materials to model trades where the goal is 1 less ten and 10 more ones. Write the following numbers on the board and have the partners first model the number with tens rods and ones cubes. Then, have them regroup a tens rod for 10 ones and verbalize the process and the result.

56 (5 tens 6 ones → 4 tens 16 ones)

28 (2 tens 8 ones → 1 ten 18 ones)

32 (3 tens 2 ones → 2 tens 12 ones)

45 (4 tens 5 ones → 3 tens 15 ones)

Enrichment • Number Sense

Tell students to write and solve problems to subtract 1 nickel from each amount of money from 80¢ to 92¢.

More to Explore • Geometry

Have students use geoboards and rubber bands to make as many quadrilaterals as possible, copying each one onto grid paper you have provided. Before students begin, have one student draw a square on the board and another draw a rectangle. Explain that both the square and the rectangle are quadrilaterals. However, point out that any figure that they make on the geoboards that has four sides is also a quadrilateral. Encourage them to find as many different kinds of figures as they can. If there is time, have students share their most unusual quadrilaterals, showing the shape on their geoboard as they hold up the matching grid-paper drawing. See if any made a concave or a twisted quadrilateral.

11-2 Subtracting 2-Digit Numbers

pages 201–202

1 Getting Started

Objective

- To review subtracting a 2-digit number from a 2-digit number with regrouping

Materials

*addition and subtraction fact cards

Warm Up • Mental Math

Tell students to use the following numbers to make a 3-digit number that reads the same backward and forward:

1. 3, 1 (131, 313)
2. 7, 8 (787, 878)
3. 6, 2 (626, 262)
4. 5, 6, (565, 656)
5. 4, 9, (949, 494)
6. 1, 2 (121, 212)

Warm Up • Number Sense

Flash a fact card for a sum from 11 to 18. Have one student give the answer. Call on other students to supply related addition or subtraction facts. Continue with more facts for sums and minuends through 18.

Name ______________________

Subtracting 2-Digit Numbers

Dana School had a roller skating party. There were 65 children and 27 adults skating. How many more children than adults were skating?

We want to know how many more children than adults were skating.

There were __65__ children and __27__ adults at the skating party.

To find how many more children than adults were skating, we subtract __27__ from __65__.

Subtract the ones. Regroup if needed.	Subtract the tens.
5 15 ~~6~~~~5~~ − 27 8	5 15 ~~6~~~~5~~ − 27 38

There are __38__ more children than adults skating.

Getting Started

Subtract. Regroup if needed.

1. 78 − 25 = 53
2. 96 − 71 = 25
3. 86 − 48 = 38
4. 51 − 22 = 29
5. 83 − 66 = 17

2 Teach

Develop Skills and Concepts Write the following problems vertically on the board: **67 − 32** (35), **95 − 54** (41), **52 − 25** (27), **76 − 59** (17), and **80 − 11** (69). Have a student record the work for each problem as other students talk through the subtraction. Now, have students tell which problems needed a regrouping of 1 ten for 10 ones. (the last 3 problems) Repeat for more problems if necessary.

3 Practice

Using page 201 Have a student read the example aloud and tell what is to be found. (how many more children than adults were skating) Ask what information is given. (There were 65 children and 27 adults.) Ask what needs to be done with the numbers. (subtract) Have students read and complete the information sentences. Work through the model with students and then have them complete the solution sentence. Have students check the answers by adding.

- Have students complete the Getting Started exercises independently.

Using page 202 Remind students that not all subtraction problems require regrouping. Have students complete the page independently.

Practice

Subtract. Regroup if needed.

1. 47 − 41 = 6	2. 67 − 17 = 50	3. 92 − 60 = 32	4. 96 − 89 = 7	5. 63 − 59 = 4
6. 73 − 26 = 47	7. 61 − 45 = 16	8. 96 − 78 = 18	9. 81 − 43 = 38	10. 65 − 47 = 18
11. 95 − 87 = 8	12. 88 − 83 = 5	13. 92 − 63 = 29	14. 49 − 25 = 24	15. 38 − 16 = 22
16. 62 − 14 = 48	17. 71 − 31 = 40	18. 66 − 49 = 17	19. 87 − 36 = 51	20. 64 − 16 = 48
21. 72 − 43 = 29	22. 52 − 30 = 22	23. 47 − 21 = 26	24. 63 − 39 = 24	25. 81 − 56 = 25

Problem Solving

Solve.

26. There were 41 girls and 24 boys skating. How many more girls than boys were skating?
17 more girls

27. Art skated around the rink 75 times. Ro skated around the rink 57 times. How many more times did Art skate around the rink?
18 times

4 Assess

Have students write a word problem that involves subtracting 2-digit numbers with regrouping. Have students switch papers to complete each other's problems.

5 Mixed Review

1. 45 + 83 (128)
2. 57 − 20 (37)
3. 68¢ + 56¢ ($1.24)
4. _____ + 5 = 12 (7)
5. 39 − 13 (26)
6. 291 ◯ 209 (>)
7. 5 hundreds 3 tens 7 ones (537)
8. 27 − 8 (19)
9. 79 + 4 (83)
10. 38 − 19 (19)

For Mixed Abilities

Common Errors • Intervention

Watch for students who regroup when it is not necessary or do not regroup when it is necessary. Before students begin to work a problem, have them check to see if the ones in the subtrahend are greater than the ones in the minuend. If yes, then have them write *yes* to indicate that regrouping is necessary. If not, have them write *no*.

Enrichment • Number Sense

Some of the problems on page 202 did not require regrouping. Tell students to rewrite those problems so that they would need a regrouping.

More to Explore • Statistics

Reinforce the concept of estimating to the class. Explain that some things can be counted exactly. Ask a student to tell how many people are in the classroom. Ask how the answer was calculated. (by counting) Ask another student to tell how many people are in a neighboring classroom. Ask how that number was calculated. (by guessing) Help students see that an estimation is made by using any data the student already knows. In the case of how many students are in a class, they know about how many students can be in a class. Ask students to gather the following information by estimating:

1. the number of rooms in their home
2. the number of leaves on a tree
3. the number of desks in the school
4. the number of people in their family
5. the number of pages in their math book

Then, ask which numbers could actually be counted.

11-3 Subtracting a 1-Digit From a 3-Digit Number

pages 203–204

1 Getting Started

Objective

- To subtract a 1-digit number from a 3-digit number with regrouping

Materials

colored chalk

Warm Up • Mental Math

Ask students if they will add or subtract to find the following:

1. how many are left (subtract)
2. the total of 64 and 36 (add)
3. how many more (subtract)
4. the difference (subtract)
5. how many altogether (add)
6. the sum (add)
7. how many remain (subtract)

Warm Up • Number Sense

Have students make 3-digit numbers using the numbers 3, 7, and 2. (327, 723, 237, 732, 372, or 273) Have students tell the number of hundreds, tens, and ones in the numbers they created. Repeat for 3-digit numbers using the numbers 9, 1, and 6. (916, 961, 169, 196, 691, or 619)

Name ______________________

Subtracting a 1-Digit From a 3-Digit Number

341 children went to the zoo.
9 parents went to the zoo.
How many more children than parents went to the zoo?

We want to know how many more children than parents went to the zoo.

There are 341 children.

There are 9 parents.

To find how many more children went, we subtract 9 from 341.

Subtract the ones. Regroup if needed.	Subtract the tens.	Subtract the hundreds.
3 4̸ 1̸ (3 11) − 9 = 2	3 4̸ 1̸ (3 11) − 9 = 32	3 4̸ 1̸ (3 11) − 9 = 332

There are 332 more children than parents.

Getting Started

Subtract. Regroup if needed.

1. 127 − 5 = 122
2. 252 − 8 = 244
3. 512 − 9 = 503
4. 331 − 6 = 325
5. 747 − 6 = 741

---

2 Teach

Develop Skills and Concepts Have students solve 357 − 5 (352) and 699 − 7 (692) at the board. Ask students if any regrouping was needed. (no) Now, write **476 − 8** on the board and ask if regrouping is needed. (yes) Ask why. (8 ones cannot be taken from 6 ones.) Have a student use colored chalk to show the regrouping. Have another student complete the subtraction and tell the answer. (468)

- Repeat for 271 − 8 (263), 906 − 5 (901), 472 − 3 (469), 555 − 6 (549), 338 − 3 (335), and 612 − 7 (605).

3 Practice

Using page 203 Have students tell about the picture and then discuss their own zoo experiences. Have a student read the example and tell what is to be found. (how many more children than parents went to the zoo) Ask what information is given. (341 children and 9 parents went.) Ask what needs to be done with the numbers. (subtract) Have students read and complete the information sentences. Work through the subtraction model with students and then have them complete the solution sentence. Have students add to check their subtraction.

- Help students complete the Getting Started exercises if necessary.

Using page 204 Tell students that some of the problems on this page do not need regrouping. Have students complete the rows of exercises independently.

Practice

Subtract. Regroup if needed.

1. 229 − 4 = 225
2. 636 − 8 = 628
3. 399 − 9 = 390
4. 851 − 7 = 844
5. 233 − 4 = 229
6. 137 − 5 = 132
7. 141 − 7 = 134
8. 725 − 6 = 719
9. 911 − 3 = 908
10. 673 − 5 = 668
11. 252 − 6 = 246
12. 341 − 9 = 332
13. 585 − 7 = 578
14. 463 − 9 = 454
15. 224 − 6 = 218

Now Try This!

1.

	4th inning
Blue Sox	5
Green Sox	7

Final Score: 9 to 6

Which team won? Green Sox

How do you know?

If the low score is six and the Green Sox already have 7 in the 4th inning, then the Green Sox must be the winner.

2.

	5th inning
Red Caps	8
Gold Caps	5

Final Score: 8 to 7

Which team won? Red Caps

How do you know?

If the low score is 7 and the Red Caps already have 8 in the 5th inning, then the Red Caps must be the winner.

Now Try This! Students are asked to use logic to solve these exercises. Have students discuss the information given in the first exercise. Help students, if necessary, discover that if the Green Sox had 7 runs at the end of the fourth inning, they could not end the game with only 6 runs. Therefore, they had to win the game with a score of 9. Help students apply the logic from the first exercise to see that if the Red Caps had 8 runs in the fifth inning, they could not have 7 runs at the end of the game. Therefore, they had to have won the game with 8 runs.

4 Assess

Write the following problems vertically on the board: **754 − 9 =** (745), **865 − 3 =** (862), and **232 − 8 =** (224). Have students find the differences.

For Mixed Abilities

Common Errors • Intervention

Watch for students who get confused when a 1-digit number is subtracted from a 3-digit number and try to subtract the subtrahend from all the top digits.

Incorrect	Correct
658	658
− 3	− 3
325	655

Have them work with a partner using hundred flats, tens rods, and ones cubes to model the problem.

Enrichment • Algebra

Tell students to write and solve problems to show all the 1-digit numbers that require a regrouping when subtracted from 715.

More to Explore • Number Sense

Write the following on the board, or duplicate for students:

Find the number that is:

1. the greatest number that has 4 in the hundreds place and 8 in the ones place (498)
2. the least number that has 2 in the hundreds place and 4 in the tens place (240)
3. the largest and the smallest 3-digit numbers that have the same number in the ones, tens, and hundreds place (111, 999)

11-4 Subtracting Multiples of 10

pages 205–206

1 Getting Started

Objective

- To subtract a 2-digit multiple of 10 from a 3-digit number

Materials

colored chalk; hundred flats, tens rods, and ones cubes

Warm Up • Mental Math

Ask students if the following are true or false:

1. Three quarters is 75¢. (T)
2. 6:30 means 6 minutes after 6. (F)
3. A square has three sides. (F)
4. A triangle has three sides. (T)
5. V means 5 in Roman numerals. (T)
6. 8 + 5 checks 13 − 5. (T)
7. 30 tens is 3 hundreds. (T)

Warm Up • Number Sense

Have students rename the following numbers in tens: 120 (12 tens), 240 (24 tens), 80 (8 tens), 840 (84 tens), 630 (63 tens), 960 (96 tens), and 100 (10 tens). Now, have students name numbers as you say the numbers in tens.

Name ____________________

Subtracting Multiples of 10

Morgan's Used Cars sold 256 cars in June and 80 cars in July. How many more cars were sold in June?

We want to know how many more cars were sold in June.

There were 256 cars sold in June and 80 cars sold in July.

To find how many more cars were sold in June, we subtract 80 from 256.

Subtract the ones. Regroup if needed.	Subtract the tens. Regroup if needed.	Subtract the hundreds.
6 − 0 = 6 ones	15 − 8 = 7 tens	1 − 0 = 1 hundred

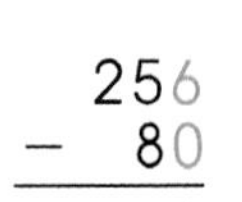

256 − 80 = 6

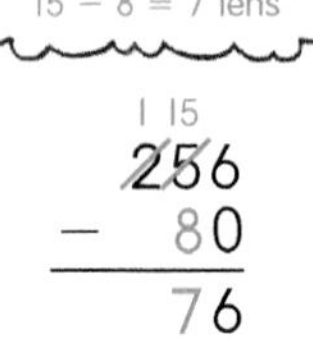

256 − 80 = 76 (1 15 regrouped)

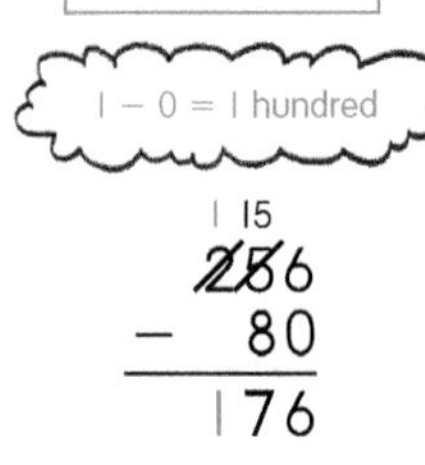

256 − 80 = 176 (1 15 regrouped)

There were 176 more cars sold in June.

Getting Started

Subtract. Regroup if needed.

1. 342 − 20 = 322
2. 563 − 50 = 513
3. 245 − 40 = 205
4. 326 − 60 = 266
5. 681 − 90 = 591

2 Teach

Develop Skills and Concepts Write the following problems on the board: **565 − 40** (525), **385 − 50** (335), **732 − 70** (662), and **428 − 90** (338). Have students use manipulatives to solve them. Now, use colored chalk to show the regrouping of 1 hundred for 10 tens in each of the last two problems on the board.

- Write the following problems on the board: **276 − 80** (196), **955 − 90** (865), **104 − 20** (84), **332 − 10** (322), and **720 − 60** (660). Have students use the colored chalk to show any regrouping and then solve the problems.

3 Practice

Using page 205 Have a student read the example aloud and tell what is to be found. (how many more cars were sold in June) Ask students what information is given. (There were 256 cars sold in June and 80 cars in July.) Ask what needs to be done with the numbers to find how many more. (subtract) Have students read and complete the information sentences. Work through the model with students and then have them complete the solution sentence. Have students use manipulatives or add to check their solution.

- Have students complete the Getting Started exercises independently. Have them use addition to check their solutions if necessary.

Using page 206 Have students complete the page independently.

Practice 

Subtract. Regroup if needed.

1. 636 − 80 = 556	2. 521 − 20 = 501	3. 561 − 80 = 481	4. 327 − 50 = 277	5. 613 − 20 = 593
6. 399 − 30 = 369	7. 229 − 50 = 179	8. 168 − 70 = 98	9. 852 − 90 = 762	10. 355 − 50 = 305
11. 512 − 70 = 442	12. 303 − 50 = 253	13. 756 − 30 = 726	14. 230 − 30 = 200	15. 646 − 60 = 586
16. 116 − 20 = 96	17. 663 − 80 = 583	18. 550 − 70 = 480	19. 909 − 40 = 869	20. 855 − 60 = 795
21. 532 − 50 = 482	22. 763 − 40 = 723	23. 877 − 90 = 787	24. 145 − 30 = 115	25. 315 − 70 = 245

Problem Solving

Solve.

26. During July there were 325 cars and 70 vans sold. How many more cars than vans were sold?
255 more cars

27. There were 257 used cars on the lot. Andrew sold 80. How many cars were left?
177 cars

4 Assess

Have students work in small groups to write a series of subtraction problems with 3-digit numbers and multiples of 10. Have groups exchange problems to solve.

5 Mixed Review

1. 46 − 31 (15)
2. 32¢ − 15¢ (17¢)
3. 92 + 9 (101)
4. 6 dimes, 1 nickel (65¢)
5. 527 ◯ 659 (<)
6. 56 + 7 (63)
7. 56¢ + 27¢ (83¢)
8. 86 − 27 (59)
9. 78 − 53 (25)
10. 630, 635, 640, ____ (645)

For Mixed Abilities

Common Errors • Intervention

If students have difficulty subtracting multiples of 10, have them practice on a number line with 100 to 300 marked off in intervals of 10. Give them problems such as 256 − 40. They first find 256 on the number line and then count back by 10s for 40. (216) Help them see the pattern that the digit in the ones place remains the same.

Enrichment • Algebra

Tell students to write and solve a problem to find the number of days left in 1 year when 10 days have passed since January 1. Then, have them find how many days are left when 30, 70, and 90 days have passed.

More to Explore • Measurement

Have students work in pairs to cut a piece of adding machine tape the length of their bodies and label the tape with their names. Take students outside in the morning and have them help each other cut a piece of tape the length of their shadow, labeling the tapes with their names and "shadow morning." Have them repeat the shadow measurement in the afternoon and label those shadows. Finally, have them measure the three tapes in inches or centimeters and compare. Discuss with students why there is a difference between the morning and afternoon shadows.

11-5 Subtracting a 2-Digit From a 3-Digit Number

pages 207–208

1 Getting Started

Objective
- To subtract a 2-digit number from a 3-digit number with some regrouping

Materials
*colored chalk; hundred flats, tens rods, and ones cubes

Warm Up • Mental Math
Tell students to name the number that is

1. the largest 3-digit number (999)
2. the smallest 2-digit number (10)
3. the largest 2-digit number (99)
4. the smallest 4-digit number (1,000)
5. the smallest 3-digit number (100)
6. 2 more than the largest 2-digit number (101)
7. 9 tens more than the smallest 3-digit number (190)

Warm Up • Number Sense
Have students write and solve problems to subtract each 2-digit multiple of 10 from 760. Have students tell if regrouping is needed in each problem.

Name ______________________

Subtracting a 2-Digit From a 3-Digit Number

Tyler School played Bell School in a soccer game. There were 225 students from Tyler and 93 students from Bell attending the game. How many more students from Tyler School attended the game?

We want to know how many more students were from Tyler.

Tyler School had 225 students at the game.

Bell School had 93 students at the game.

To find how many more children were from Tyler, we subtract 93 from 225.

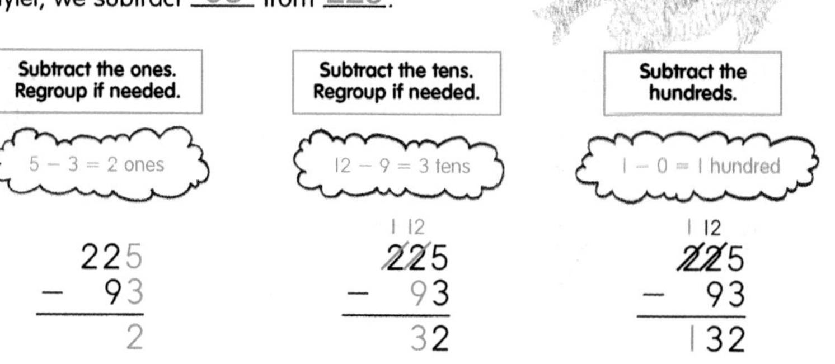

Subtract the ones. Regroup if needed.	Subtract the tens. Regroup if needed.	Subtract the hundreds.
5 − 3 = 2 ones	12 − 9 = 3 tens	1 − 0 = 1 hundred
225 − 93 = 2	1 12 / 225 − 93 = 32	1 12 / 225 − 93 = 132

There were 132 more students from Tyler School.

Getting Started

Subtract. Regroup if needed.

1. 346 − 23 = 323
2. 346 − 38 = 308
3. 346 − 84 = 262
4. 579 − 95 = 484
5. 718 − 78 = 640

2 Teach

Develop Skills and Concepts Write **488 − 79** on the board. Ask students if regrouping for more ones is needed in order to subtract the ones. (yes) Show the regrouping with colored chalk and have a student then subtract the ones. (9) Ask if regrouping is needed to subtract the tens. (no) Have a student complete the subtraction. (409)

- Repeat the procedure for 488 − 94, where regrouping is needed to subtract the tens. Continue to have students solve the following problems where no regrouping or 1 regrouping is needed: 263 − 48 (215), 903 − 82 (821), 679 − 42 (637), 333 − 28 (305), and 564 − 81 (483).

3 Practice

Using page 207 Have a student read the example aloud and tell what is to be solved. (how many more students from Tyler School attended the game) Ask students what information is given. (There were 225 Tyler students and 93 Bell students at the game.) Ask what needs to be done with the numbers. (subtract) Have students read and complete the information sentences. Work through the subtraction model with students and then have them complete the solution sentence. Have students check their work with manipulatives or by adding.

- Help students complete the Getting Started exercises if necessary.

Using page 208 Remind students to regroup in subtraction only when needed. Assign the page to be completed independently.

Practice

Subtract. Regroup if needed.

1. 286 − 54 = 232	2. 192 − 78 = 114	3. 375 − 43 = 332	4. 422 − 81 = 341	5. 623 − 42 = 581
6. 518 − 27 = 491	7. 742 − 92 = 650	8. 891 − 85 = 806	9. 566 − 75 = 491	10. 327 − 95 = 232
11. 963 − 39 = 924	12. 462 − 62 = 400	13. 319 − 58 = 261	14. 294 − 85 = 209	15. 601 − 71 = 530
16. 708 − 46 = 662	17. 643 − 28 = 615	18. 840 − 37 = 803	19. 677 − 70 = 607	20. 575 − 49 = 526
21. 350 − 25 = 325	22. 517 − 86 = 431	23. 999 − 95 = 904	24. 741 − 29 = 712	25. 802 − 82 = 720

Problem Solving

Solve.

26. Mark jumped rope 395 times. Angie jumped rope only 89 times. How many more times did Mark jump rope?
306 times

27. Liz sold 329 tickets to the ballgame. Harry sold 95 tickets. How many more tickets did Liz sell?
234 tickets

4 Assess

Write the following problems vertically on the board. Have students tell if they need to regroup ones or tens, and then solve.

943 − 51 (tens, 892), **753 − 49** (ones, 704), **826 − 43** (tens, 783), **129 − 35** (tens, 94), **682 − 24** (ones, 658)

5 Mixed Review

1. 75¢ + 37¢ ($1.12)
2. 87 + 26 (113)
3. 75 − 41 (34)
4. 41 + 93 (134)
5. 2 quarters, 2 dimes, 3 nickels (85)
6. _____ + 8 = 11 (3)
7. 56 − 39 (17)
8. 84¢ − 38¢ (46¢)
9. 921 ◯ 937 (<)
10. 68 + 40 (108)

For Mixed Abilities

Common Errors • Intervention

Watch for students who forget to decrease the digit to the left by one after regrouping.

Incorrect	Correct
2 4̸ 2 (14 above) − 9 1 = 2 5 1	2̸ 4̸ 2 (1 14 above) − 9 1 = 1 5 1

Have them practice rewriting numbers in the hundreds as 1 less hundred and 10 more tens, for example, 327 = 3 hundreds 2 tens 7 ones or 2 hundreds 12 tens 7 ones, aligning one form of the number under the other.

Enrichment • Number Sense

Tell students to write and solve a problem to find out how many more students than teachers are in their school.

More to Explore • Statistics

A fairly common genetically determined trait is the ability to curl your tongue. Ask students to try to curve the edges of their tongue upward so that their tongue forms a tiny circle. Count the number who can curl their tongue and the number who cannot. Put the results on the board. Now, ask the class to predict how many tongue curlers they would expect to find out of every 30 people, then out of every 15. (Answers will vary.) Ask them to survey 15 different people, outside the class. Have them keep track of the number of curlers and the number of noncurlers. Compare the results of their surveys. Remind students that this is not a test of skill, nor is it something they can practice. It is an inherited characteristic. They might want to try the test at home to see which members of their families can curl their tongue.

11-6 Subtracting 3-Digit Numbers

pages 209–210

1 Getting Started

Objective

- To subtract two 3-digit numbers for up to two regroupings

Materials

*colored chalk; hundred flats, tens rods, and ones cubes

Warm Up • Mental Math

Ask students if the following are true or false:

1. 6 tens + 4 tens is 64 tens. (F)
2. 30 + 180 = 220 (F)
3. The present year has 4 digits. (T)
4. 5 hundreds + 10 tens = 600 (T)
5. Subtraction always needs regrouping. (F)
6. Addition never needs regrouping. (F)

Warm Up • Number Sense

Write **186 − 49 = 137** on the board. Have a student write and solve an addition problem to check the subtraction problem. Continue for the following problems: 235 − 94 = 141 (141), 379 − 89 = 290 (290), 490 − 68 = 420 (422), 519 − 29 = 490, and 360 − 90 = 280 (270). Have students correct and check any problems that have errors.

Name ______________________

Subtracting 3-Digit Numbers

The Green River Adventures store rents rafts, kayaks, and canoes. How many more rafts than canoes were rented during August?

We want to know how many more rafts than canoes were rented.

There were 420 rafts rented.

There were 225 canoes rented.

To find how many more rafts were rented, we subtract 225 from 420.

Subtract the ones. Regroup if needed.	Subtract the tens. Regroup if needed.	Subtract the hundreds.
10 − 5 = 5 ones	11 − 2 = 9 tens	3 − 2 = 1 hundred
420 − 225 = 5	420 − 225 = 95	420 − 225 = 195

There were 195 more rafts rented.

Getting Started

Subtract. Regroup if needed.

1. 465 − 243 = 222
2. 389 − 164 = 225
3. 572 − 155 = 417
4. 249 − 164 = 85
5. 628 − 139 = 489

2 Teach

Develop Skills and Concepts Write **376 − 197** on the board. Ask students if regrouping is needed to subtract the ones. (yes) Use colored chalk to show the regrouping and then have a student subtract the ones. (9) Ask if regrouping is needed to subtract the tens. (yes) Show the regrouping with colored chalk and have a student complete the problem. (179) Repeat the procedure for 926 − 278 (648), 453 − 327 (126), 849 − 678 (171), 655 − 432 (223), 895 − 576 (319), and 753 − 269 (484) where one, two, or no regroupings are needed.

3 Practice

Using page 209 Have students tell about the picture. Have a student read the example aloud and tell what is to be found. (how many more rafts than canoes were rented in August) Ask students what information is needed from the picture. (There were 420 rafts and 225 canoes rented in August.) Ask students if the information about kayaks is needed. (no) Ask what operation needs to be done. (subtraction) Have students read and complete the information sentences. Work through the subtraction model with students and then have them complete the solution sentence. Have students use manipulatives or add to check their solution.

- Help students complete the Getting Started exercises if necessary.

Using page 210 Remind students to regroup in subtraction only when needed. Tell students that some of these problems will need no regrouping whereas some will need one or two regroupings. Have students complete Exercises 1 to 15 independently.

Practice

Subtract. Regroup if needed.

1.	2.	3.	4.	5.
965 − 234 = 731	782 − 357 = 425	359 − 165 = 194	417 − 186 = 231	531 − 167 = 364

6.	7.	8.	9.	10.
361 − 172 = 189	619 − 285 = 334	999 − 578 = 421	843 − 357 = 486	775 − 298 = 477

11.	12.	13.	14.	15.
375 − 185 = 190	658 − 459 = 199	583 − 196 = 387	417 − 208 = 209	625 − 357 = 268

Now Try This!

Complete.

1. 100 = 10 tens
   104 = 10 tens 4 ones
   307 = 30 tens 7 ones
   208 = 20 tens 8 ones
   701 = 70 tens 1 one

Trade 1 ten for 10 ones.

2.

tens	ones
69	11
~~70~~	~~1~~

tens	ones
49	18
50	8

tens	ones
29	12
30	2

tens	ones
79	10
80	0

Subtract.

3.

tens	ones
80	6
− 34	7
45	9

4.

tens	ones
50	7
− 15	8
34	9

5.

tens	ones
60	0
− 25	5
34	5

6.

tens	ones
80	5
− 59	8
20	7

Now Try This! Have students complete the number sentences and then regroup 1 ten for 10 ones in the exercises. Tell students to solve the four exercises in the bottom row by subtracting 1 ten from 80, 1 ten from 50, and so on.

4 Assess

Write the following problems vertically on the board. Have students copy the problems on a sheet of paper. Tell them to circle the problems with one regrouping in blue and the problems with two regroupings in red. Then, have students solve them.

963 − 225 (one, 738), **842 − 359** (two, 483), **712 − 549** (two, 163), **698 − 129** (one, 569)

For Mixed Abilities

Common Errors • Intervention

Some students may always write either 10 tens or 10 ones when they are regrouping and not add regrouped values to existing numbers.

Incorrect	Correct
10 / 2 ~~3~~ 10 / ~~346~~	13 / 2 ~~3~~ 16 / ~~346~~
−187	− 187
123	159

Correct students by having them work in pairs, using place-value materials to model the problems so they see that 10 tens or 10 ones must be added to the number already in the place.

Enrichment • Algebra

Ask students if 543 minus 277 equals 276. Tell them to show their work to support their answer.

More to Explore • Measurement

Have students make paper chains that are equal to their height by gluing circular strips together. Ask students to estimate the length of the chain in centimeters or inches. Then, have students measure and record their own chain measurement. Connect the individual chains to make a class chain. Have students first estimate the length of the class chain and then measure and record the length.

ESL/ELL STRATEGIES

Use simple line drawings on the board to show the difference between a *raft*, a *kayak*, and a *canoe*.

11-7 Practice Subtracting With 1 or 2 Regroupings

pages 211–212

1 Getting Started

Objective

- To practice subtraction with regrouping

Materials

*colored chalk; addition and subtraction fact cards; hundred flats, tens rods, and ones cubes

Warm Up • Mental Math

Tell students to complete each statement.

1. A four-sided figure is a ____. (square or rectangle)
2. A clock tells us the ____. (time)
3. A coin worth 50¢ is a ____. (half-dollar)
4. 726 is ____ more than 696. (30)
5. A three-sided figure is a ____. (triangle)

Warm Up • Number Sense

Distribute all addition fact cards to students so that each student has several. Show a subtraction fact card and ask students to show the addition fact or facts that would be used to check the subtraction fact. Continue with more cards.

Name ______________________

Lesson 11-7

Practice Subtracting With 1 or 2 Regroupings

In the holiday parade, there were 452 people marching in bands and 298 in drill teams. How many more people were marching in bands?

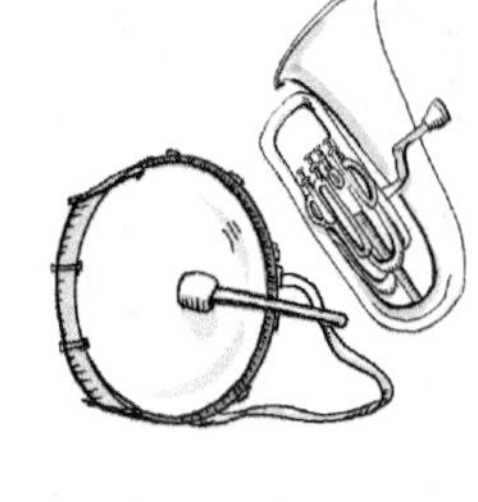

We want to know how many more people were in bands.

There were 452 people in bands, and 298 people in drill teams.

To find how many more people were marching in bands, we subtract 298 from 452.

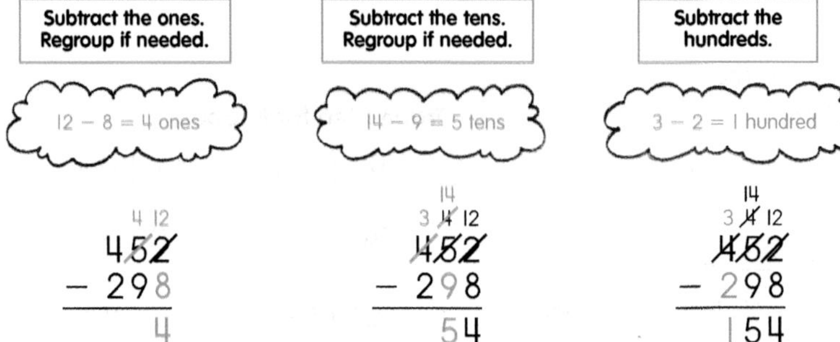

There were 154 more people marching in bands.

Getting Started

Subtract. Regroup if needed.

1.	2.	3.	4.	5.
342 − 29 = 313	561 − 71 = 490	492 − 175 = 317	382 − 7 = 375	825 − 598 = 227

---

2 Teach

Develop Skills and Concepts Write the following on the board: **423 − 9** (414), **708 − 26** (682), **354 − 296** (58), **966 − 589** (377), and **458 − 272** (186). Have students tell if regrouping is needed in the first problem and what regrouping is needed. (yes, 1 ten for 10 ones) Use colored chalk to draw a small arrow above the 3 in the first expression to denote a regrouping is needed. Continue through the other problems, noting with an arrow where regroupings are needed. Have students talk through each problem as it is being solved.

3 Practice

Using page 211 Have a student read the example aloud and tell what is to be solved. (how many more people were in bands) Ask what information is given in the problem. (452 people were in bands and 298 were in drill teams.) Ask what operation is used to find how many more. (subtraction) Have students read and complete the information sentences. Work through the model with students and then have them complete the solution sentence. Have students add to check their answer.

- Have students complete the Getting Started exercises. Allow them to use manipulatives to check their answer if necessary.

Using page 212 Remind students to regroup only when needed. Have students solve the exercises independently.

Practice

Subtract. Regroup if needed.

1. 342 − 8 = 334	2. 561 − 80 = 481	3. 478 − 96 = 382	4. 658 − 167 = 491	5. 725 − 286 = 439
6. 786 − 451 = 335	7. 892 − 355 = 537	8. 669 − 278 = 391	9. 315 − 192 = 123	10. 669 − 580 = 89
11. 419 − 269 = 150	12. 915 − 400 = 515	13. 643 − 258 = 385	14. 695 − 555 = 140	15. 947 − 589 = 358
16. 456 − 8 = 448	17. 316 − 93 = 223	18. 695 − 636 = 59	19. 721 − 345 = 376	20. 926 − 387 = 539
21. 350 − 75 = 275	22. 736 − 258 = 478	23. 840 − 375 = 465	24. 624 − 398 = 226	25. 261 − 243 = 18

Now Try This!

It's Algebra!

Put in the missing digits.

1. 3 5 [4] − 1 [2] 2 = 2 3 2

2. 4 [7] 6 − [2] 4 [1] = 2 3 5

3. 7 [5] 7 − 3 8 [4] = [3] 7 3

For Mixed Abilities

Common Errors • Intervention

If students have difficulty keeping all three numbers aligned properly and their regroupings in the correct places, have them work their problems on grid paper so that the lines and columns can help them place everything correctly.

Enrichment • Algebra

Tell students to write and solve a subtraction problem of two 3-digit numbers where a regrouping of 1 hundred for 10 tens is needed, but no regrouping for more ones is needed.

More to Explore • Graphing

Explain to students that one way to show a tally of information is with a picture graph. Have students divide a large sheet of paper into three sections. Have them label each with a title: Refrigerator, Freezer, Cupboard. Have them use old magazines to cut out pictures of food and glue them under the correct category according to how they would be stored. Have them display their finished graphs. Ask: *Is it easy or difficult to get information from a picture graph? Which category had the most food? Which items fit under more than one category?*

Now Try This! Write the following on the board:

```
  4 2 (6)
− (2) 1 8
  2 0 8
```

Tell students that there are two missing numbers to be found. Ask students how many ones would 8 ones be taken from to have 8 ones left. (16) Write 6 in the ones place and ask students if a ten needed to be regrouped for ones. (yes) Help students see that 1 ten would be left and 1 from 1 is 0. Ask if 1 of the 4 hundreds was regrouped. (no) Ask the number of hundreds that would be taken from 4 hundreds to have 2 hundreds left. (2) Record the 2 and help students check the problem by adding. Tell students to work each exercise to find the missing numbers.

It's Algebra! The concepts presented in this activity prepare students for algebra.

4 Assess

Have students write two subtraction problems, one with one regrouping and one with two regroupings. Have students switch papers to solve each other's problems.

11-8 Subtracting Money

pages 213–214

1 Getting Started

Objective
- To subtract amounts of money through $9.99

Materials
real or play dollars, dimes, and pennies; hundred flats, tens rods, and ones cubes

Warm Up • Mental Math
Tell students to name the number for

1. the third Tuesday this month
2. the present year
3. 1 penny less than $1 (99¢)
4. the number of months until January
5. 40 more than 68 (108)
6. the last Sunday in next month
7. yesterday's date
8. 100 more than 799 (899)

Warm Up • Number Sense
Have students lay out 1 one cube and tell what piece of money has the same value. (a penny) Repeat for students to relate the hundred flat and tens rod to the dollar and dime, respectively. Dictate amounts of money through $9.99 and have students show each amount with money and then with hundred flats, tens rods, and ones cubes.

Name ______________________

Subtracting Money

Teresa saved $5.46.
She bought a paint set.
How much money does she have left?

We want to find out how much money Teresa has left.

She had __$5.46__.

She spent __$2.57__.

To find the amount of money she has left, we subtract __$2.57__ from __$5.46__.

Subtract the pennies. Regroup if needed.	Subtract the dimes. Regroup if needed.	Subtract the dollars.	Put in the dollar sign and decimal point.
$5.46 (regrouped 3 16) − 2.57 = 9	$5.46 (regrouped 4 13 16) − 2.57 = 89	$5.46 (regrouped 4 13 16) − 2.57 = 2 89	$5.46 (regrouped 4 13 16) − 2.57 = $2.89

Teresa has __$2.89__ left.

Getting Started

Subtract. Regroup if needed.

1. $2.94 − 1.23 = $1.71
2. $5.82 − 2.65 = $3.17
3. $4.65 − 1.83 = $2.82
4. $3.14 − 1.92 = $1.22
5. $5.31 − 3.45 = $1.86

---

2 Teach

Develop Skills and Concepts Have students lay out $7.47, subtract $3.28 from it, and tell the amount left. ($4.19) Have a student write and solve the problem on the board. Remind students that the decimal point separates the dollars and cents and that the dollar sign goes before the number of dollars. Ask students why this answer would not be written using the cent sign. (The amount is more than $1.)

- Continue for $2.63 − $0.96 ($1.67), $8.98 − $3.59 ($5.39), $7.18 − $4.49 ($2.69), $6.02 − $1.99 ($4.03), and $5.50 − $3.26 ($2.24).

3 Practice

Using page 213 Have students tell about the picture. Have a student read the example and tell what is to be solved. (the amount of money Teresa has left) Ask what information is given in the problem. (She saved $5.46 and bought a paint set.) Ask what information is needed from the picture. (The paint set costs $2.57.) Ask students what operation tells us how much is left. (subtraction) Have students read and complete the information sentences. Work through the model with students and then have them complete the solution sentence. Tell students to add to check their answer.

- Have students complete the Getting Started exercises independently. Have them use addition or manipulatives to check their answers if necessary.

Practice

Subtract. Regroup if needed.

1.	2.	3.	4.	5.
$1.07	$4.71	$6.35	$1.98	$7.45
− 0.75	− 1.89	− 2.75	− 0.98	− 1.49
$0.32	$2.82	$3.60	$1.00	$5.96

Problem Solving

PAT'S DINER

Hamburger	$2.95	Salad Plate	$3.49
Ham Sandwich	$3.25	Milk	$0.65
Egg Salad Sandwich	$1.88	Chocolate Milk	$0.75
Tuna Sandwich	$2.59	Iced Tea	$0.49

Use the menu above.

6. How much more did Jack pay for a hamburger than an egg salad sandwich? $1.07

   $2.95 − 1.88 = $1.07

7. How much more is chocolate milk than iced tea? $0.26

   $0.75 − 0.49 = $0.26

8. How much did Joe pay for a hamburger and a glass of milk? $3.60

   $2.95 + 0.65 = $3.60

9. How much less is a tuna sandwich than a ham sandwich? $0.66

   $3.25 − 2.59 = $0.66

10. How much more is a ham sandwich than an egg salad sandwich? $1.37

    $3.25 − 1.88 = $1.37

11. How much is a salad plate and a chocolate milk? $4.24

    $3.49 + 0.75 = $4.24

Using page 214 Have students complete the top row of exercises independently.

- Tell students to use the menu shown to solve the word problems. Tell students that some of the problems require addition and some require subtraction. Have students read each problem and look for clue words that suggest the operation needed. Help students reword Exercise 9, if necessary, so that the problem asks how much more the ham sandwich costs. Assign the remainder of the page to be completed independently.

4 Assess

Bring in copies of take-out menus. Have students pick one item on the menu and see how much change they would have left over if they started with $9.99.

For Mixed Abilities

Common Errors • Intervention

Some students may have difficulty using all their subtraction procedures when working with money. Have students work with partners to act out a problem such as $6.56 − $2.98 using real or play money. (dollars, dimes, pennies) Have them talk through the regroupings and then solve the problem by writing the subtraction as they have done in other lessons in the chapter.

Enrichment • Algebra

Tell students to find an amount of money greater than $1.10 that can be subtracted from or added to $2.26 without requiring any regrouping.

More to Explore • Estimation

Have students work in pairs. Students may choose their own 3-digit numbers to subtract. One partner will find the exact difference and the other partner will find an estimate. Have pairs change roles so that each partner finds two differences and two estimates. Students may share their findings with the class to find how close estimates can be to the exact answer.

ESL/ELL STRATEGIES

After completing the money exercises in Lesson 11-8, call on different students to practice reading the problems and answers aloud using dollar amounts. For example, "Five dollars and forty-six cents minus two dollars and fifty-seven cents equals two dollars and eighty-nine cents."

11-9 Estimating Differences

pages 215–216

1 Getting Started

Objective

- To estimate differences to solve money problems

Warm Up • Mental Math

Have students find the sum or difference.

1. 45 + 30 (75)
2. 58 + 4 (62)
3. 37 + 20 (57)
4. 55 − 25 (30)
5. 38 − 20 (18)
6. 60 − 20 (40)

Warm Up • Number Sense

Write the following on the board and have students estimate the difference.

1. 32 − 15 (10)
2. 63 − 29 (30)
3. 83 − 31 (50)
4. 67 − 48 (20)
5. 80 − 52 (30)
6. 93 − 61 (30)

Name ________________

Estimating Differences

It's Algebra!

Maria has $3.02. She buys a ball for $1.08. About how much money does Maria have left?

Round to the nearest ten cents to find out.

Round to the nearest 10 cents.		Estimate.
$3.02 →	$3.00	$3.00
− 1.08 →	− 1.10	− 1.10
		$1.90

Maria has about $1.90 left.

Getting Started

Estimate. Show how you rounded.

1. Sally has $2.00. She buys a sandwich for $1.38. About how much money does Sally have left? Round to the nearest ten cents.
   $2.00 − $1.40 = $0.60
2. Mr. Washington has $5.65. He buys a fruit juice for $1.79. About how much money does Mr. Washington have left? Round to the nearest dollar.
   $6.00 − $2.00 = $4.00
3. Michele has $7.85. She buys a movie ticket for $2.75. About how much money does Michelle have left? Round to the nearest dollar.
   $8.00 − $3.00 = $5.00
4. Billy spent $3.15 at lunch today. He had $6.92 before lunch. About how much money does Billy have left? Round to the nearest dollar.
   $7.00 − $3.00 = $4.00

2 Teach

Develop Skills and Concepts Review rounding with students. On the board, write **82 − 57**. Tell students that they do not need to find an exact answer but an estimate. Have students explain how to round each of the numbers to the nearest ten in order to find the estimated difference. (82 rounds down to 80 and 57 rounds up to 60; 80 − 60 = 20)

- Now, write **468 − 139** on the board. Tell students that they are going to find the estimated difference by rounding to the nearest hundred. Ask, *Which place do you look at to round to the nearest hundred?* (tens) Have students explain how to round each of the numbers to the nearest hundred and give the estimated difference. (468 rounds up to 500 and 139 rounds down to 100; 500 − 100 = 400)

It's Algebra! The concepts presented in this lesson prepare students for algebra.

3 Practice

Using page 215 Have students look at the example at the top of the page. Ask students what information they need to solve the problem. (the amount of money that Maria has and the cost of the ball) Then, ask, *What are you being asked to find?* (about how much money Maria will have left after she buys the ball) Point out that the word *about* tells you to estimate. The problem is not looking for an exact answer. Ask students what operation they need to use to find about how much money Maria will have left. (subtraction) Have students round each number in the problem to the nearest ten cents. Students can estimate by subtracting the rounded numbers.

- Help students complete Exercise 1 if necessary. Then, have students complete the page independently.

Practice

Estimate. Round to the nearest ten cents.

1. $5.49 − 2.04 → $5.50 − 2.00 = $3.50
2. $6.31 − 3.02 → $6.30 − 3.00 = $3.30
3. $7.84 − 2.17 → $7.80 − 2.20 = $5.60
4. $4.57 − 1.92 → $4.60 − 1.90 = $2.70
5. $9.57 − 4.82 → $9.60 − 4.80 = $4.40
6. $3.35 − 2.11 → $3.40 − 2.10 = $1.30

Estimate. Round to the nearest dollar.

7. $7.22 − 2.38 → $7.00 − 2.00 = $5.00
8. $9.39 − 3.77 → $9.00 − 4.00 = $5.00
9. $7.41 − 2.99 → $7.00 − 3.00 = $4.00
10. $4.21 − 1.83 → $4.00 − 2.00 = $2.00
11. $8.45 − 3.52 → $8.00 − 4.00 = $4.00
12. $6.51 − 3.89 → $7.00 − 4.00 = $3.00

Problem Solving

Estimate. Show how you rounded.

13. The CD that Millie wants to buy is on sale for $7.97. Millie has $9.25. About how much money will Millie have left? Round to the nearest ten cents.
$9.30 − $8.00 = $1.30

14. Alex was given $7.15 to spend at the mall. He came home with $1.89. About how much did Alex spend? Round to the nearest dollar.
$7.00 − $2.00 = $5.00

Using page 216 Have students look at Exercise 1. Ask students to which place they need to look to round to the nearest ten cents. (pennies) Repeat the question for the nearest dollar. (dimes) Have students write the subtraction sentence for Exercise 1 and then review the estimation as a class.

- Have students complete the remaining exercises independently.

4 Assess

Have students work in pairs. One partner writes a story about a person who has from $5 to $9.99, and wants to buy an item that costs less than $5.00. The other partner finds about how much change the person will receive. Once the answer is checked, partners should switch roles.

For Mixed Abilities

Common Errors • Intervention

Some students may confuse rounding to the nearest ten cents with rounding to the nearest dollar. When the problem asks students to round a number to the nearest ten cents, have students circle the digits for the number of dimes. Then, draw a box around the digit for the number of pennies. Have students focus on the digit in the box. If it is 5 or greater, they change the digit in the circle to the next higher number. They then write a 0 in the cents column. If it is less than 5, the digit in the circle remains the same and they write a 0 in the cents column.

Enrichment • Number Sense

Tell students, *You have $6.75. You buy a magazine for $3.48. Which gives a better estimate, rounding to the nearest dollar or to the nearest ten cents? Why?* (10 cents; the estimated difference is $6.80 − $3.50 = $3.30. This is close to the actual difference of $3.27.)

More to Explore • Statistics

Before class begins, cut out a paragraph of type for each student from magazines or newspapers. Each paragraph should have about 50 words. Give students graph paper with quarter-inch squares. Tell them to read through the paragraph and count the number of times each letter appears. Suggest that they cross out each letter as they count it. Show them how to set up the graph paper with the alphabet printed along the bottom. Explain that they will keep count of the letters by filling in one square for each letter counted.

```
X           X
X   X     X   X
A   B   C   D   E   F . . . Z
```

Some students will count all the As first; others will go through the paragraph coloring in a square for each letter in turn. Have them compare their graphs at the end. Ask what letters appear most often.

11-10 Problem Solving: Use Logical Reasoning

pages 217–218

1 Getting Started

Objective
- To use logical reasoning to solve problems

Materials
hundred chart; hundred flats, tens rods, and ones cubes

Warm Up • Mental Math
Ask students how many
1. minutes there are between 7 and 8 on a clock (5)
2. ones are gained when regrouping a ten (10)
3. cents are in 13 dimes (130)
4. nickels make $1.00 (20)
5. half-dollars are in $8 (16)
6. tens are in $8.26 (2)
7. places are after the decimal point in a money amount (2)

Warm Up • Number Sense
Tell a story of John having $2.70 and losing 23¢. Have a student write and solve a problem to tell how much money John has left. ($2.47) Tell more stories of dollar amounts for students to decide if addition or subtraction is needed. Then, have them write and solve the problems.

Name ______

Problem Solving
Lesson 11-10

It's Algebra!

Problem Solving: Use Logical Reasoning

Here is a riddle:
When you subtract 18 from me, you get 35.
Who am I?

What do you know?

What is the difference? 35

What is the number being subtracted? 18

You can write an addition problem to find the mystery number.	You can check your answer by using subtraction.

$$\begin{array}{r} 35 \\ +\ 18 \\ \hline 53 \end{array} \qquad \begin{array}{r} 53 \\ -\ 35 \\ \hline 18 \end{array}$$

I am 53.

Getting Started

Solve each riddle.

1. When you subtract me from 28, you get the same number as me.

   Who am I? 14

2. When you subtract 32 from me, you get 45.

   Who am I? 77

3. When you subtract me from 42, you get a number with 1 in the tens place and 2 in the ones place.

   Who am I? 30

4. When 25 is subtracted from me, you get 25.

   Who am I? 50

2 Teach

Develop Skills and Concepts Have students take out their hundred charts. Then, read the following problem to students: *My number has 6 tens. The ones digit is between 5 and 9. My number is odd.* Now, reread the first sentence and ask students what numbers the answer could be. (any number from 60 to 69) Reread the second sentence and ask what numbers could the answer be. (66, 67, 68) Reread the third sentence and ask what is the number. (67)

It's Algebra! The concepts in this lesson prepare students for algebra.

3 Practice

Using page 217 Read with students the example at the top of the page.

- Now, apply the four-step plan to the example. For SEE, ask, *What are you being asked to do?* (find the missing number) Then, *What information is given?* (The difference is 35.) For PLAN, ask students how they can go about finding the mystery number. (find what number minus 18 equals 35 by adding 18 and 35) For DO, have students solve the problem. For CHECK, have students use manipulatives to check their answers.
- Have students complete the page independently.

Using page 218 Have students look at Exercise 1. Read the problem aloud while students read along. Ask students for the given information. (Some number minus 35 is equal to 47.) Ask students what operation they can use to check subtraction. (addition) Have students add to solve the riddle. Then, students can write the subtraction sentence to check their answer.

- Have students write the number sentence for Exercise 2 and then review the riddle as a class. Now, have students complete the page.

Practice

Solve each riddle.

1. If you subtract 35 from me, you get 47.
   Who am I? 82

2. The difference between 60 and me is 20. I am less than 60.
   Who am I? 40

3. If you subtract 22 from me, you get 22.
   Who am I? 44

4. If you subtract 15 from me and then subtract 12 more, you get 43.
   Who am I? 70

5. If you subtract me from 36, you get the same number as me.
   Who am I? 18

6. If you subtract 32 from me and then subtract 23 more, you get 41.
   Who am I? 96

7. If you subtract me from 35, you get 25.
   Who am I? 10

8. If you subtract 17 from me, you get 44.
   Who am I? 61

Now Try This!

Complete each Magic Square.

1.

8	1	6
3	5	7
4	9	2

2.

2	9	4
7	5	3
6	1	8

3.

2	7	6
9	5	1
4	3	8

Now Try This! Remind students that they have worked Magic Squares before. Help students see that the sum of every row and column will be the same. Then, have students complete independently.

4 Assess

Tell students, *Solve this riddle. If you subtract 72 from me, you get 125. Who am I?* (197)

For Mixed Abilities

Common Errors • Intervention

Some students may be having difficulty solving the riddles. After students read each riddle, have them write a subtraction sentence in vertical form. Students can place the numbers in the place they need to go in the problem. Remind students that they can use addition to check subtraction and vice versa.

Enrichment • Logic

Have students work in pairs. Each partner should write a riddle using subtraction to subtract a 2-digit number from a larger 2-digit number. Students can switch papers and solve each other's riddles.

More to Explore • Number Sense

Have students work in pairs. Have one student pick a number from 101 to 999. Have the other student pick a number less than the first number. Then, tell students to subtract the smaller number from the larger number and compare answers. Have one partner write an addition sentence to check the answer. Finally, students may write a word problem using their numbers to give to another set of partners.

Chapter 11 Test

page 219

Items	Objectives
1–2	To review subtracting a 1-digit number from a 3-digit number with regrouping (see pages 203–204)
3–5, 7	To subtract a 2-digit multiple of 10 from a 3-digit number (see pages 205–206)
6, 8–12	To subtract a 2-digit number from a 3-digit number with some regrouping (see pages 207–208)
13–20, 26	To subtract two 3-digit numbers for up to 2 regroupings (see pages 209–210)
21–25, 27	To subtract amounts of money through $9.99 (see pages 217–218)

Alternate Chapter Test

You may wish to use the Alternate Chapter Test on page 325 of this book for further review and assessment.

Name ______________________

Chapter 11 Test

Subtract. Regroup if needed.

1. 348 − 9 = 339	2. 273 − 6 = 267	3. 781 − 50 = 731	4. 528 − 70 = 458	5. 417 − 60 = 357
6. 465 − 81 = 384	7. 278 − 90 = 188	8. 847 − 35 = 812	9. 750 − 23 = 727	10. 641 − 78 = 563
11. 687 − 55 = 632	12. 566 − 59 = 507	13. 318 − 135 = 183	14. 628 − 435 = 193	15. 919 − 378 = 541
16. 475 − 149 = 326	17. 721 − 254 = 467	18. 833 − 126 = 707	19. 715 − 359 = 356	20. 454 − 168 = 286
21. $3.18 − 0.15 = $3.03	22. $2.75 − 1.50 = $1.25	23. $5.75 − 1.56 = $4.19	24. $7.15 − 4.91 = $2.24	25. $6.35 − 2.98 = $3.37

Solve.

26. The pet store had 251 goldfish. Alison sold 163 of them. How many goldfish are left?
88 goldfish

27. Kiel had $7.35. He bought a toy boat for $2.45. How much money does he have left?
$4.90

Circle the letter of the correct answer.

Item	Problem	Choices	Item	Problem	Choices
1	7 + 8	a. 16 b. 14 (c.) 15 d. NG	7	57 + 38	a. 21 (b.) 95 c. 85 d. NG
2	13 − 6 =	(a.) 7 b. 3 c. 19 d. NG	8	35 + 68	a. 915 b. 33 (c.) 103 d. NG
3		a. 55 (b.) 145 c. 154 d. NG	9	275 + 465	a. 630 (b.) 740 c. 730 d. NG
4		(a.) 2:18 b. 2:08 c. 3:18 d. NG	10	71 − 24	(a.) 47 b. 53 c. 57 d. NG
5		a. 42¢ b. 57¢ c. 47¢ (d.) NG	11	93 − 27	a. 74 b. 76 (c.) 66 d. NG
6		a. $1.51 (b.) $1.76 c. $1.71 d. NG	12	435 − 162	a. 333 (b.) 273 c. 373 d. NG

score

STOP

Cumulative Assessment

page 220

Items	Objectives
1–2	To review addition and subtraction facts with sums and minuends through 18 (see pages 3–12, 17–20, 23–28, 35–44, 53–56, 59–64)
3	To understand 3-digit numbers (see pages 71–74)
4	To tell time to the minute (see pages 101–102)
5–6	To count money through $5 (see pages 113–114)
7–8	To add two 2-digit numbers with some regrouping (see pages 125–126, 155–156)
9	To add two 3-digit numbers for sums through 999 with regrouping (see pages 187–190)
10–11	To subtract two 2-digit numbers (see pages 137–146, 159–160)
12	To subtract two 3-digit numbers for up to 2 regroupings (see pages 209–210)

Alternate Cumulative Assessment

Circle the letter of the correct answer.

1. 6 + 5
   a 10 (b) 11 c 12 d NG

2. 15 − 9
   a 4 b 5 (c) 6 d NG

3. 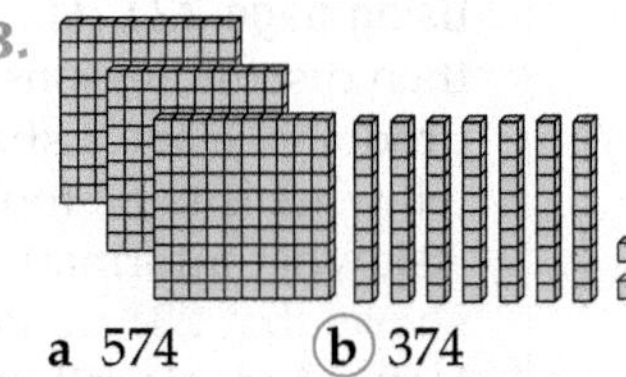 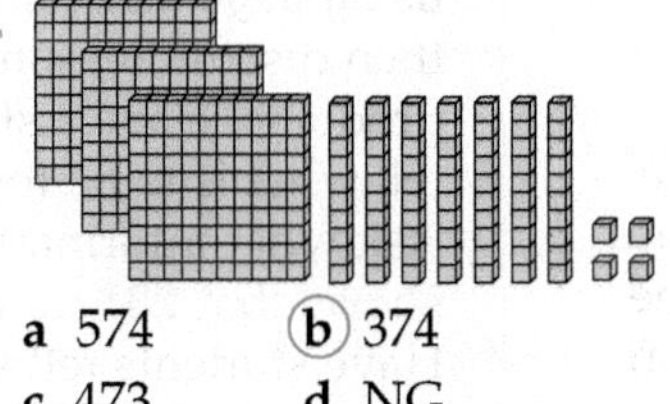
   a 574 (b) 374 c 473 d NG

4. 
   (a) 11:18 b 3:45 c 10:24 d NG

5. 
   a 81¢ (b) 86¢ c 96¢ d NG

6. 
   a $2.41 b $2.36 (c) $2.28 d NG

7. 74 + 19
   a 95 b 815 c 85 (d) NG

8. 65 + 26
   a 811 b 41 c 81 (d) NG

9. 281 + 199
   a 380 (b) 480 c 840 d NG

10. 76 − 48
    a 38 b 32 (c) 28 d NG

11. 47 − 18
    (a) 29 b 39 c 21 d NG

12. 528 + 297
    a 771 b 751 (c) 825 d NG

12-1 Adding 3-Digit Numbers

pages 221–222

1 Getting Started

Objective

- To add 3-digit numbers for sums through 999

Materials

hundred flats, tens rods, and ones cubes

Warm Up • Mental Math

Ask students what should be done.

1. first in addition (add the ones)
2. to find how many more (subtract)
3. to show a money amount (use cent or dollar notation)
4. to check subtraction (add)
5. to find how many are left (subtract)
6. first in subtraction (subtract the ones)
7. when there are not enough tens to subtract (regroup 1 hundred for 10 tens)

Warm Up • Number Sense

Write **284** on the board. Have students write and solve problems on the board to add various multiples of 10 to 284. Dictate the multiples of 10 as 12 tens, 24 tens, 6 tens, and so on.

Name ______________________

Adding and Subtracting 3-Digit Numbers

Chapter 12

Lesson 12-1

Adding 3-Digit Numbers

Marilyn and Thomas helped collect paper for the senior citizens' paper drive. How much paper did they collect?

We want to find out how much paper was collected.

Marilyn collected 237 pounds of paper.

Thomas collected 285 pounds of paper.

To find how much paper they collected, we add 237 and 285.

285

237 pounds

Add the ones. Regroup if needed.	Add the tens. Regroup if needed.	Add the hundreds.
1 237 + 285 2	1 1 237 + 285 22	1 1 237 + 285 522

Marilyn and Thomas collected 522 pounds of paper.

Getting Started

Add.

1.	2.	3.	4.	5.
347 + 212 = 559	375 + 374 = 749	561 + 327 = 888	77 + 18 = 95	752 + 95 = 847

6.	7.	8.	9.	10.
96 + 323 = 419	606 + 239 = 845	154 + 515 = 669	809 + 88 = 897	343 + 457 = 800

2 Teach

Develop Skills and Concepts Write **6 + 7** on the board. Have students lay out 6 ones and 7 ones, regroup for a ten, and tell the number. (13) Write **66 + 47** on the board and have students lay out 6 tens and 4 tens and tell the total number of tens and ones. (11, 3) Ask if 10 tens can be regrouped for 1 hundred. (yes) Have students make the regrouping and tell the number. (113) Write **266 + 447** on the board and have students lay out 2 hundreds and 4 hundreds and tell the total number of hundreds, tens, and ones. (7, 1, 3) Write **592 + 389** (981) on the board and repeat the process. Continue to develop more addition problems.

3 Practice

Using page 221 Have students tell about the picture and then discuss reasons for recycling paper or other products. Have a student read the example aloud and tell what is to be found. (total weight of paper collected) Ask what information is given and where. (The picture shows that 237 pounds and 285 pounds were collected.) Have students tell what operation is needed to find the total. (addition) Have students read and complete the information sentences. Work through the example with students and then have them complete the solution sentence. Have students use manipulatives to check their answer.

- Have students complete the Getting Started exercises independently.

Practice

Add.

1. 618 + 135 = 753	2. 515 + 87 = 602	3. 156 + 372 = 528	4. 612 + 279 = 891	5. 350 + 350 = 700
6. 175 + 175 = 350	7. 149 + 289 = 438	8. 649 + 329 = 978	9. 233 + 565 = 798	10. 578 + 9 = 587
11. 219 + 356 = 575	12. 317 + 483 = 800	13. 86 + 75 = 161	14. 529 + 91 = 620	15. 490 + 390 = 880
16. 96 + 78 = 174	17. 775 + 189 = 964	18. 89 + 367 = 456	19. 455 + 224 = 679	20. 496 + 287 = 783
21. 634 + 275 = 909	22. 398 + 198 = 596	23. 758 + 163 = 921	24. 239 + 467 = 706	25. 683 + 192 = 875

Problem Solving

Solve.

26. Clark School has 345 students. Polk School has 488 students. What is the total number of students at both schools?
345 + 488 = 833
833 students

27. Bonnie collected 159 stickers. Her sister collected 258 stickers. How many stickers did they collect together?
159 + 258 = 417
417 stickers

Using page 222 Remind students to add the ones column first. Tell students that some of the problems on this page need no regrouping, whereas others will need one or two regroupings. Remind students to record each word problem answer on the line under the problem. Have students complete the page independently.

4 Assess

Have students write their own word problems with two 3-digit addends. Then, have students switch papers to solve each other's problems.

5 Mixed Review

1. 72¢ + 38¢ ($1.10)
2. 65 + 9 (74)
3. 48 − 32 (16)
4. 31 + 57 (88)
5. 3 + 5 + 7 (15)
6. 16 − 8 (8)
7. 38 ◯ 380 (<)
8. 270, 280, 290, ____ (300)
9. ____ + 6 = 15 (9)
10. 48 + 93 (141)

For Mixed Abilities

Common Errors • Intervention

Watch for students who are regrouping incorrectly because they are adding from left to right.

Incorrect	Correct
1 1	1
495	495
+ 852	+ 852
258	1,347

Have students use counters and a place-value chart to show the two addends. Then, have them join the counters in each place, from right to left, regrouping as they go along. Remind them to work toward the operation sign rather than away from it.

Enrichment • Algebra

Tell students to find the greatest 1-digit number that can be added to 643 without requiring a regrouping. (6) Then, tell students to find the greatest 2-digit number that, when added to 643, requires no regrouping. (56)

More to Explore • Geometry

Draw a pentagon on the board and ask students to copy the five-sided figure on their geoboards with a rubber band. Tell them to make as many different pentagons as they can and copy them onto graph paper. Show them how to take a pentagon and divide it into triangles using more rubber bands. Have students illustrate these dissected pentagons on the graph paper as well. This activity is preliminary to later work in geometry in which students will show that many-sided plane figures can be made rigid by dividing them into triangles. Have students collect their work, staple it together, and label it the **Pentagon Book**.

ESL/ELL STRATEGIES

As you encounter them, discuss with students words and phrases used when adding up numbers. These words include *total, sum, together,* and *in all.* Model sentences using each word and ask students to repeat them. Write sample sentences on the board.

12-2 Column Addition

pages 223–224

1 Getting Started

Objective

- To add three 2- or 3-digit numbers for sums through 999

Warm Up • Mental Math

Tell students to repeat these numbers in order and tell the sum.

1. 4, 6, 3 (13)
2. 9, 2, 8 (19)
3. 11, 6, 1 (18)
4. 7, 7, 2 (16)
5. 9, 3, 5 (17)
6. 8, 9, 2 (19)

Warm Up • Number Sense

Write **7 + 3 + 2** in a column on the board. Remind students that in column addition, it is helpful to find a sum of 10 if possible. Have a student talk through the addition of 7 and 3 for a sum of 10 and then 10 and 2 for a sum of 12. Remind students to add up the column to check the sum. Have students find more sums of three 1-digit numbers whose sums are less than 20.

Name ______________________

Lesson 12-2

It's Algebra!

Column Addition

How many baseball cards did Bobby, Cathleen, and Keith collect altogether?

We want to know how many cards were collected.

Bobby collected 126 cards.

Cathleen collected 252 cards.

Keith collected 375 cards.

To find how many cards in all, we add 126, 252, and 375.

Add the ones. Regroup if needed.	Add the tens. Regroup if needed.	Add the hundreds.
126 252 + 375 3	126 252 + 375 53	126 252 + 375 753

They collected 753 baseball cards altogether.

Getting Started

Add.

1. 113 + 231 + 442 = 786
2. 143 + 46 + 51 = 240
3. 314 + 122 + 351 = 787
4. 442 + 136 + 55 = 633
5. 165 + 225 + 365 = 755
6. 251 + 315 + 178 = 744
7. 423 + 74 + 186 = 683
8. 142 + 436 + 219 = 797
9. 323 + 265 + 188 = 776
10. 504 + 193 + 268 = 965

2 Teach

Develop Skills and Concepts Write **168 + 222 + 537** vertically on the board. Ask students the total number of ones. (17) Remind students to look for a ten when adding a column of numbers. Talk through the addition of 8 and 2 for 10 and then 10 and 7 for 17. Ask if a regrouping for a ten should be done. (yes) Have students regroup 10 ones for a ten and tell how many ones are left as you record the regrouping and the 7 remaining ones. Continue the procedure for adding the tens, regrouping for 1 hundred, and adding the hundreds. Ask students the sum of the three 3-digit numbers. (927) Have students add up each column with you to check the addition.

- Repeat the activity for 710 + 139 + 87 (936), 215 + 333 + 345 (893), 649 + 28 + 170 (847), and 452 + 327 + 206 (985). Note: The sum of the ones or tens column does not exceed 19.

3 Practice

Using page 223 Have a student read the example aloud and tell what is to be found. (the total number of baseball cards collected) Ask what information is given. (Bobby collected 126 cards, Cathleen collected 252, and Keith collected 375.) Ask students what operation is used to find the total number of cards. (addition) Have students read and complete the information sentences. Work through the model with students and then have them complete the solution sentence. Have students add up each column to check their answer.

- Help students complete the Getting Started exercises if necessary.

Using page 224 Remind students to check each answer by adding up the columns. Have students complete the page independently.

Practice

Add.

1. 511 + 330 + 145 = 986	2. 232 + 27 + 47 = 306	3. 314 + 85 + 200 = 599	4. 125 + 54 + 397 = 576	5. 325 + 132 + 538 = 995
6. 534 + 134 + 237 = 905	7. 415 + 162 + 244 = 821	8. 241 + 367 + 179 = 787	9. 321 + 465 + 212 = 998	10. 165 + 316 + 273 = 754
11. 923 + 56 + 19 = 998	12. 86 + 202 + 658 = 946	13. 192 + 505 + 247 = 944	14. 434 + 143 + 309 = 886	15. 107 + 581 + 270 = 958

Now Try This!

It's Algebra!

Fill in the missing numbers.

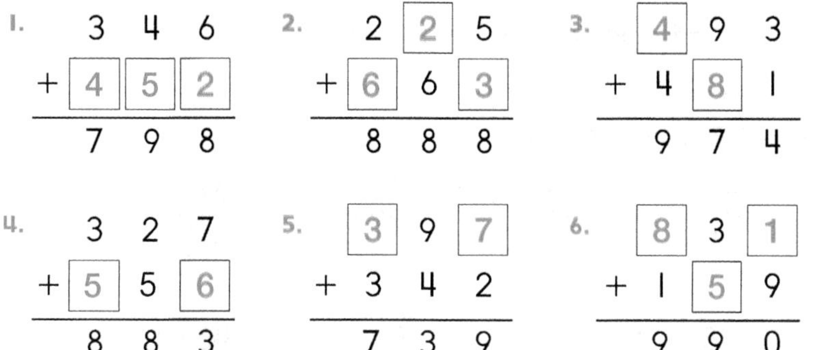

Now Try This! Help students complete the first exercise if necessary and then have students complete the problems independently.

It's Algebra! The concepts in this activity prepare students for algebra.

4 Assess

Organize the class into groups of four. Have three members of each group write a 3-digit number and have the fourth member find the sum. Have students switch roles until each student has had a chance to find the sum.

For Mixed Abilities

Common Errors • Intervention

Some students will have difficulty doing column addition because they become confused going from one partial sum to the other. Suggest to them that they can help themselves by thinking of only two digits at a time and by writing down partial sums so that they do not forget them.

Enrichment • Algebra

Tell students to write and solve problems to show all the ways that three 1-digit numbers can have a sum of 19.

More to Explore • Probability

Ask students to tell the last four digits in their telephone numbers and list these on the board in columns. Have students look at these numbers to see if they can find any pattern. (Except for the fact that each is four digits long, the numbers will be unrelated.) Explain that these are random numbers. Many things in the world are random. Ask students if they all have the same arm span, or reach. (no) Point out that although they are all in the same grade, they each have a slightly different arm length. Explain that there is not one set arm length for a second grader. Instead, there is an average arm length calculated by measuring the random arm spans of many children and calculating the most common. Demonstrate the random distribution of arm spans by having all the students line up and mark their farthest reach, from outstretched arms, with chalk on the board. From their seats, have students look at the collection of random spans. Ask them to pick one reach that seems to be an average.

12-3 Subtracting 3-Digit Numbers

pages 225–226

1 Getting Started

Objective

- To subtract from 3-digit minuends

Materials

addition and subtraction fact cards

Warm Up • Mental Math

Have students complete each comparison, that 2 is to 5 as 7 is to 10 as

1. 61 is to ____ (64)
2. 23 is to ____ (26)
3. 8 is to ____ (11)
4. ____ is to 22 (19)
5. 253 is to ____ (256)
6. ____ is to 45 (42)

Warm Up • Number Sense

Have students help sort subtraction fact cards into groups of facts related to sums through 10, facts related to sums 11 through 18 and facts that are doubles. Then, have students find and show a subtraction fact related to an addition fact card you show. Repeat to pair more related addition and subtraction facts.

Name ____________________

Lesson 12-3

Subtracting 3-Digit Numbers

How much farther is it from Kent to Benson than from Benson to Jackson?

We want to find out how much farther it is from Kent to Benson.

It is 635 miles from Kent to Benson.

It is 457 miles from Benson to Jackson.

To find how much farther, we subtract 457 from 635.

Subtract the ones. Regroup if needed.	Subtract the tens. Regroup if needed.	Subtract the hundreds.
635 − 457 = 8 (regrouped: 2 15)	635 − 457 = 78 (regrouped: 5 12 15)	635 − 457 = 178 (regrouped: 5 12 15)

It is 178 miles farther from Kent to Benson.

Getting Started

Subtract. Regroup if needed.

1. 347 − 212 = 135
2. 845 − 428 = 417
3. 561 − 327 = 234
4. 877 − 18 = 859
5. 752 − 95 = 657
6. 275 − 198 = 77
7. 323 − 96 = 227
8. 515 − 154 = 361
9. 457 − 289 = 168
10. 635 − 436 = 199

2 Teach

Develop Skills and Concepts Ask students how to find how much greater 9 is than 6. (subtract) Have a student solve the problem on the board. (9 − 6 = 3) Repeat to find how much greater 26 is than 19 (7) and so on, for more subtraction problems of 1-, 2-, or 3-digit numbers. Have students check their subtraction by adding. Remind students that questions of how much farther, how much greater, how many more, what is the difference, and so on will require subtraction.

- Present more dictated problems using the above questions for students to gain practice in writing and solving problems. Help students recognize that in subtraction problems, the larger number of the two must always be the minuend, or the top number. Have students continue to check each problem by adding.

3 Practice

Using page 225 Have students tell about the map. Have a student read the example aloud and tell what is to be found. (how much farther it is from Kent to Benson than from Benson to Jackson) Ask what information is given. (It is 635 miles from Kent to Benson and 457 miles from Benson to Jackson.) Have students read and complete the information sentences. Work through the model with students and then have them complete the solution sentence.

- Have students complete the Getting Started exercises independently. Encourage them to use addition to check their answers.

Using page 226 Remind students to regroup only when necessary. Assign the page to be completed independently.

Practice

Subtract. Regroup if needed.

1.	2.	3.	4.	5.
648 − 234 = 414	435 − 365 = 70	741 − 329 = 412	318 − 175 = 143	526 − 143 = 383

6.	7.	8.	9.	10.
227 − 88 = 139	398 − 200 = 198	921 − 567 = 354	847 − 436 = 411	733 − 227 = 506

11.	12.	13.	14.	15.
490 − 170 = 320	529 − 91 = 438	654 − 234 = 420	465 − 165 = 300	624 − 375 = 249

16.	17.	18.	19.	20.
647 − 432 = 215	518 − 279 = 239	422 − 87 = 335	882 − 693 = 189	753 − 275 = 478

Problem Solving

Solve.

21. Some fishing boats brought in 256 fish on Thursday and 428 fish on Friday. How many more fish were caught on Friday?
428 − 256 = 172
172 fish

22. Gene's father stacked 375 logs. Gene stacked 187 logs. How many more logs did his father stack?
375 − 187 = 188
188 logs

4 Assess

Write the following problems on the board. Have students tell how many regroupings are needed and then find the difference.

751 − 179	842 − 313	854 − 755	613 − 478
(two, 572)	(one, 529)	(two, 99)	(two, 135)

5 Mixed Review

1. 83 − 47 (36)
2. 15 + 17 + 21 (53)
3. 49 tens (490)
4. 58 + 27 (85)
5. 75¢ − 48¢ (27¢)
6. 68 − 43 (25)
7. 86¢ + 43¢ ($1.29)
8. 93 − 40 (53)
9. 37 + 8 (45)
10. 108 ◯ 180 (<)

For Mixed Abilities

Common Errors • Intervention

Watch for students who always subtract the lesser digit from the greater digit to avoid regrouping.

Incorrect	Correct
423 − 194 = 371	423 (regrouped: 3 11 13) − 194 = 229

Have students work with partners and place-value materials to model the problem.

Enrichment • Number Sense

Tell students to write a word problem that requires subtraction of two 3-digit numbers. Tell them to have a friend solve the problem and then check the friend's work by adding.

More to Explore • Measurement

Remind students that an estimate is a good guess. In one corner of the room, arrange a variety of large containers: dishpans, kettles, and pots. Put a 1-cup measuring cup on your own desk where students can see it but not use it. Ask students to estimate the number of cups of water, for example, it would take to fill each container. Have each student divide a paper into three columns with the following headings: **Container, Estimated Number of Cups,** and **Actual Number of Cups to Fill.** When they have had an opportunity to examine the containers and make their estimations, have students fill the containers and see how close the estimates were to the actual capacity of each container. Have students write the number of cups it took to fill each container to the right of their estimate.

ESL/ELL STRATEGIES

Point out that *how much* is used with questions we cannot answer using just a number. For example, how much paper . . . ? The phrase *how many* is used with questions we can answer using just a number. For example, how many sheets of paper are there?

12-4 Practice Subtracting 3-Digit Numbers

pages 227–228

1 Getting Started

Objective
- To subtract 3-digit numbers

Materials
hundred flats, tens rods, and ones cubes

Warm Up • Mental Math
Ask students to supply answers for the following:

1. 6:42 means (42) minutes after 6.
2. 54 is (6) more than 48.
3. The difference of 100 and 75 is (25).
4. The total of 8 and 90 is (98).
5. 2 dimes are (5¢) less than a quarter.
6. 4 hours later than 2:15 is (6:15).
7. 6 + 18 is 2 more than (22).

Warm Up • Pencil and Paper
Help students make a list of questions that are commonly found in subtraction word problems. The list may include, but not be limited to, the following: How much more? How many more? What is the difference? How much greater? How much older? How many are left? How much change?

Name ______________________

Practice Subtracting 3-Digit Numbers

During the spring sale, the Sports Store sold 325 baseballs and 179 footballs. How many more baseballs were sold?

We want to know how many more baseballs were sold.

There were 325 baseballs sold.

There were 179 footballs sold.

To find how many more baseballs were sold, we subtract 179 from 325.

Subtract the ones. Regroup if needed.	Subtract the tens. Regroup if needed.	Subtract the hundreds.
325 − 179 = 6	325 − 179 = 46	325 − 179 = 146

The store sold 146 more baseballs than footballs.

Getting Started

Subtract. Regroup if needed.

1. 465 − 128 = 337
2. 819 − 96 = 723
3. 752 − 329 = 423
4. 530 − 156 = 374
5. 738 − 299 = 439
6. 561 − 9 = 552
7. 678 − 496 = 182
8. 788 − 298 = 490
9. 937 − 447 = 490
10. 825 − 466 = 359

2 Teach

Develop Skills and Concepts Have students work in pairs at the board to gain practice in writing and solving subtraction problems as you dictate problems such as the following: *How many more than 127 is 642?* (642 − 127 = 515) *How many miles farther is a town that is 306 miles away than a town that is 88 miles away?* (306 − 88 = 218) *How much greater is the number 990 than the number 694?* (990 − 694 = 296) Have one student solve the problem and the second student check the problem with manipulatives or by adding.

3 Practice

Using page 227 Have a student read the example aloud and tell what is to be found. (how many more baseballs than footballs were sold) Ask what information is given. (325 baseballs and 179 footballs were sold.) Ask what operation is used to find how many more. (subtraction) Have students read and complete the information sentences. Work through the model with students and then have them complete the solution sentence. Have students check their answer by adding.

- Have students complete the Getting Started exercises independently. Encourage students to check their answers by adding or using manipulatives.

Using page 228 Have students complete the rows of exercises independently.

Practice

Subtract. Regroup if needed.

1. 578 − 294 = 284	2. 428 − 183 = 245	3. 687 − 269 = 418	4. 824 − 470 = 354	5. 633 − 156 = 477
6. 258 − 85 = 173	7. 755 − 255 = 500	8. 515 − 347 = 168	9. 786 − 395 = 391	10. 678 − 493 = 185
11. 714 − 529 = 185	12. 337 − 165 = 172	13. 758 − 132 = 626	14. 621 − 279 = 342	15. 582 − 298 = 284

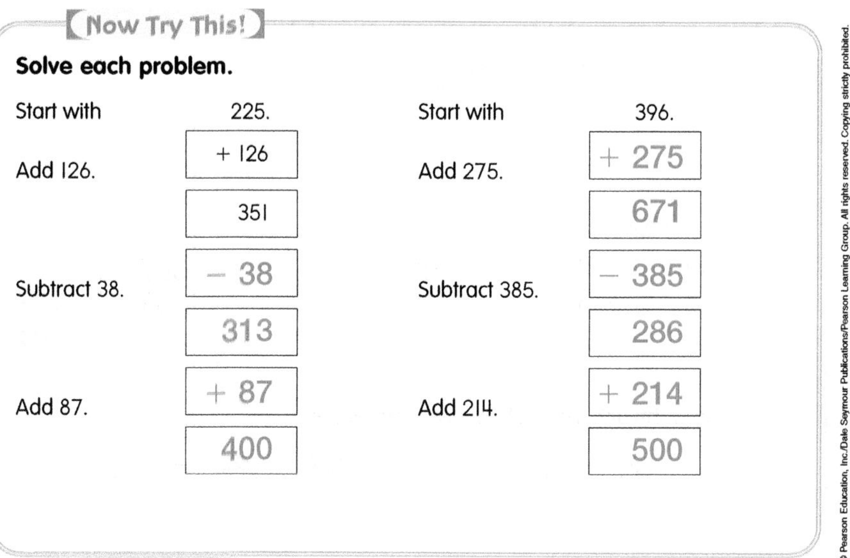

Now Try This!

Solve each problem.

Start with	225.	Start with	396.
Add 126.	+ 126	Add 275.	+ 275
	351		671
Subtract 38.	− 38	Subtract 385.	− 385
	313		286
Add 87.	+ 87	Add 214.	+ 214
	400		500

Now Try This! Write the following on the board: **Start with 100, add 264, subtract 78, add 126.** Tell students that to solve this problem, we must go step by step. Write **100 + 264** vertically on the board and find the sum. (364) Write **− 78** under 364 and find the difference. (286) Write **+ 126** under 287 and find the sum. (412)

- Have students complete the exercises independently.

4 Assess

Write the following problems vertically on the board. Have students copy the problems on a sheet of paper. Tell them to circle the problems with one regrouping in blue and the problems with two regroupings in red. Then, have them solve the problems.

912 − 809 (one, 103), **624 − 445** (two, 179), **712 − 149** (two, 563), **698 − 569** (one, 129)

For Mixed Abilities

Common Errors • Intervention

Watch for students who subtract incorrectly because they do not know their basic subtraction facts. Have them work with partners using the fact cards for those facts that give them trouble and practice quizzing each other.

Enrichment • Number Sense

Tell students to cut pictures from catalogs or newspapers to make a store display with a sign that shows there were 550 of one item and 287 of another item for sale. Then, tell them to find out how many of each item were left after the store sold 199 of each.

More to Explore • Statistics

Bring a collection of toy cars and trucks to class. Have students graph the total number of wheels, starting with one car, then adding another and another. Give each student graph paper and help them set up the paper for a bar graph. Have them graph their wheel counts.

Number of Cars: 5, 4, 3, 2, 1

Number of Wheels: 4 8 12 16 20 24 . . .

Pin up all the bar graphs so that students can see each other's work. Ask students to describe the pattern made. (The bars increase in length in a constant way.) Later, this kind of graph will be called a linear graph.

12-5 Checking Subtraction

pages 229–230

1 Getting Started

Objective
- To check subtraction by adding

Materials
*subtraction fact cards; hundred flats, tens rods, and ones cubes

Warm Up • Mental Math
Ask students how many pennies are in the following:

1. $2.63 (263)
2. 5 quarters (125)
3. 6 dimes (60)
4. 4 half-dollars (200)

Ask how many dollars and dimes equal the following:

5. $6.90 (6, 9)
6. 340 pennies (3, 4)
7. 4 quarters and 2 nickels (1, 1)
8. 20 nickels (1, 0)

Warm Up • Pencil and Paper
Show a subtraction fact card and have students write the addition fact that uses the same numbers on a sheet of paper. Remind students that the two facts are related and that the addition fact is used to check the subtraction fact. Continue for more practice.

Name ____________________

Lesson 12-5

Checking Subtraction

You can check subtraction by adding.

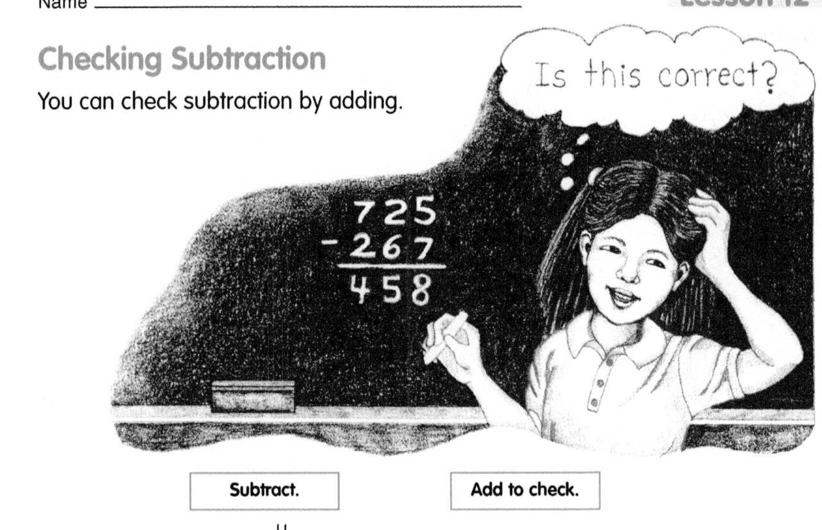

Subtract.	Add to check.
725 − 267 = 458	458 + 267 = 725

Getting Started

Subtract. Check your answers.

1. 83 − 35 = 48; 48 + 35 = 83
2. 145 − 18 = 127; 127 + 18 = 145
3. 367 − 139 = 228; 228 + 139 = 367

Copy and subtract. Then check your answers.

4. 348 − 127 = 221; 348 − 127 = 221; 221 + 127 = 348
5. 475 − 298 = 177; 475 − 298 = 177; 177 + 298 = 475

2 Teach

Develop Skills and Concepts Have students lay out manipulatives to show 132. Tell students to move 64 away and tell the number left as you write **132 − 64** on the board. (68) Have a student show the regroupings and record the answer in the problem on the board.

- Tell students to now add the 68 left and the 64 removed to see if the total is 132. (yes) Have a student write and solve **68 + 64** on the board. (132) Ask students how we know that the subtraction problem is correct. (The sum of the number left and the number removed is the same as the number in all.)
- Repeat the procedure for 375 − 219 (156), 708 − 649 (59), 573 − 386 (187), and 921 − 84 (837).

3 Practice

Using page 229 Have students read the statement about checking subtraction. Work through the solution of the example with students. Ask students what numbers are used in the addition problem to check subtraction. (the answer and the smaller number) Work through the addition problem together and discuss how to find out if the problem is correct. (The sum is the same number as the top number in the subtraction problem.)

- Help students with the Getting Started exercises if necessary.

Using page 230 Tell students to solve each subtraction problem in the first two rows and then write and solve an addition problem to check the subtraction. Remind students that the next group of exercises needs to be written vertically. Tell students to solve each subtraction problem and then check by adding. Have students complete the exercises independently.

Practice ______

Subtract. Check your answers.

1.	522 − 271 = 251	251 + 271 = 522	2.	78 − 43 = 35	35 + 43 = 78	3.	157 − 29 = 128	128 + 29 = 157
4.	645 − 298 = 347	347 + 298 = 645	5.	849 − 587 = 262	262 + 587 = 849	6.	731 − 285 = 446	446 + 285 = 731

Copy and subtract. Then check your answers.

7. 627 − 345 = 282
627 − 345 = 282 | 282 + 345 = 627

8. 517 − 209 = 306
517 − 209 = 308 | 308 + 209 = 517

9. 839 − 468 = 371
839 − 468 = 371 | 371 + 468 = 839

10. 755 − 388 = 367
755 − 388 = 367 | 367 + 388 = 755

Now Try This!

It's Algebra!

Use these digits to complete each subtraction problem. 4 8 6

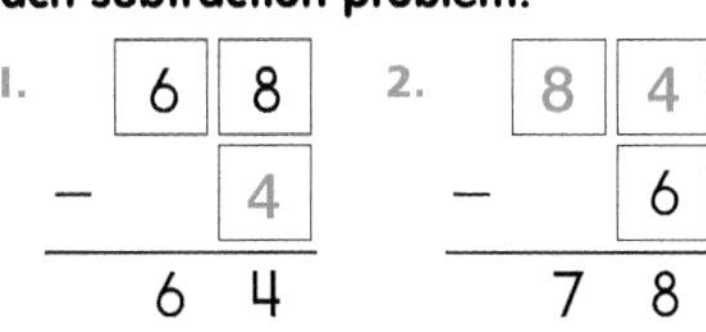

1. 68 − 4 = 64
2. 84 − 6 = 78
3. 46 − 8 = 38

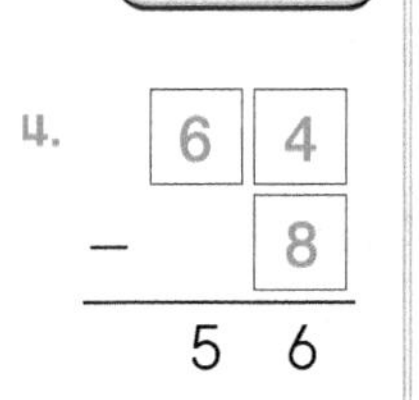

4. 64 − 8 = 56

Now Try This! Write **2, 8,** and **3** on the board. Tell students to arrange the three digits in the following problem so that each is used only once and the problem makes sense:

(3)(8) − (2) = 3 6

As students experiment with the numbers, show them how to keep a record of which number combinations have been tried by listing each number that does not work. Repeat for (2) (3) − (8) = 15. Tell students to solve the exercises independently.

It's Algebra! The concepts presented in this activity prepare students for algebra.

4 Assess

Have students write a subtraction problem for another student to solve. Have students use addition to check their solution.

For Mixed Abilities

Common Errors • Intervention

Some students may get confused and simply add the minuend and subtrahend to check. Have them work with partners and place-value materials to model a subtraction problem, such as 456 − 234. After they show 222 as the answer, have them add the place-value materials they have removed, 234, to those left, 222, to get those they started with, 456.

Enrichment • Number Sense

Tell students to write three subtraction problems of 2- and 3-digit numbers. Have them solve the problems so that at least one solution is incorrect. Tell them to have a friend find and correct any errors made.

More to Explore • Number Sense

Tell students that they are going to make a Numeral Nancy. Put the following example on the board:

Point out that the 3s form the head, the eyes are made with 9s and the number 8, and the nose is formed with a 0. Ask students to identify that the mouth, chin, and neck are formed with the numbers 6, 7, and 11. Ask students to add the numbers to find the age of Numeral Nancy. (59)

12-6 Subtracting Money

pages 231–232

1 Getting Started

Objective

- To add or subtract money for sums and minuends through $9.99

Materials

hundred flats, tens rods, and ones cubes; real or play dollars and coins

Warm Up • Mental Math

Ask students what page would come first in a book.

1. 26 or 35 (26)
2. 310 or 301 (301)
3. 224 or 186 (186)
4. 92 or 116 (92)
5. 15 or 51 (15)
6. 143 or 35 (35)
7. 200 or 315 (200)
8. 90 or 62 (62)

Warm Up • Number Sense

Have students lay out a hundred flat and then lay out one piece of money that is the same. (1 dollar) Have a student write **$1.00** and **100** on the board. Repeat for other 1- through 3-digit numbers to be shown and written as money amounts.

Name ______________________

Subtracting Money

How much more does the car cost than the boat?

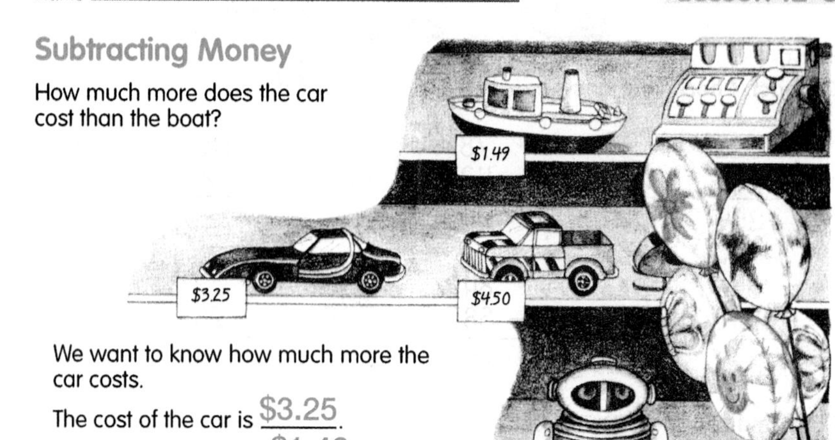

We want to know how much more the car costs.

The cost of the car is $3.25.

The cost of the boat is $1.49.

To find how much more the car costs, we subtract $1.49 from $3.25.

Copy the problem. Line up the points.	Subtract. Regroup if needed.	Put in the dollar sign and decimal point.	Add to check.
$3.25 − 1.49	$3.25 − 1.49 = 1 76 (regrouped: 2 11 15)	$3.25 − 1.49 = $1.76 (regrouped: 2 11 15)	$1.76 + 1.49 = $3.25

The car costs $1.76 more than the boat.

Getting Started

Subtract. Then check your answers.

1. $4.27 − 1.15 = $3.12; $3.12 + 1.15 = $4.27
2. $5.32 − 2.29 = $3.03; $3.03 + 2.29 = $5.32
3. $6.25 − 4.75 = $1.50; $1.50 + 4.75 = $6.25

2 Teach

Develop Skills and Concepts Have a student solve the following problem at the board: **326 − 145.** (181) Next have a student solve this problem at the board: **$3.26 − $1.45.** ($1.81) Ask students how the two answers differ. (The second one has a dollar sign and decimal point.) Have students check the problems by writing and solving addition problems at the board. Now, write **$2.59 − $0.88** on the board and tell students to subtract the numbers and then insert the dollar sign and decimal point to show the problem is about money. ($1.71) Repeat for more money problems.

3 Practice

Using page 231 Have a student read the example and tell what is to be solved. (how much more the car costs than the boat) Ask what information is needed. (the cost of the car and the cost of the boat) Ask what information is given in the picture but is not needed to solve this problem. (The truck costs $4.50.) Ask students what operation is needed to find how much more. (subtraction) Have students read and complete the information sentences. Work through the model with students to solve and check the problem. Then, have them complete the solution sentence.

- Have students complete the Getting Started exercises independently.

Using page 232 Tell students that the first three exercises are to be solved and checked. Tell students that they are to use the priced items to solve the word problems and that some of the word problems require addition and some require subtraction. Have students complete the page independently.

Practice

Subtract. Then check your answers.

1.	$7.46 − 3.98 = $3.48	$3.48 + 3.98 = $7.46	
2.	$9.29 − 6.37 = $2.92	$2.92 + 6.37 = $9.29	
3.	$8.54 − 5.75 = $2.79	$2.79 + 5.75 = $8.54	

Problem Solving

Solve.

4. How much would you pay for a book and a game? $9.14
   $3.85 + 5.29 = $9.14

5. How much more would you pay for a robot than a boat? $5.52
   $7.50 − 1.98 = $5.52

6. How much more does a game cost than a book? $1.44
   $5.29 − 3.85 = $1.44

7. If you bought a game and you gave the clerk $5.50, how much change would you get? $0.21
   $5.50 − 5.29 = $0.21

8. How much would you pay for a robot and a boat? $9.48
   $7.50 + 1.98 = $9.48

9. How much more would you pay for a book than a boat? $1.87
   $3.85 − 1.98 = $1.87

4 Assess

Bring in copies of take-out menus. Have students choose two items on the menu that cost less than $9.99 each and see how much more one item is than the other.

5 Mixed Review

1. 83¢ + 27¢ ($1.10)
2. _____, 120, 130, 140, (110)
3. 91 − 74 (17)
4. 8 + _____ = 13 (5)
5. 651 ◯ 647 (>)
6. 3 quarters, 2 pennies (77¢)
7. 75 + 6 (81)
8. 27 + 13 + 35 (75¢)
9. 83 − 28 (55)
10. 15 − 8 (7)

For Mixed Abilities

Common Errors • **Intervention**

If students need more practice subtracting with money, change the prices of the items on page 232 to provide more practice. Have students check all sums by using play or real money and all subtraction problems by using addition.

Enrichment • Money

Tell students to cut pictures of three items costing less than $10 each from magazines or catalogs. Tell them to arrange the pictures in order from the least expensive to the most expensive. Have them write and solve a problem to find how much money would be needed to buy all three items.

More to Explore • Number Sense

Have students cut 30 small squares of tagboard. Number each card from 0 to 9, making three cards that show each number. Then, have students write **ones** under each number in one set, **tens** under each number in the second set, and **hundreds** under each number in the third set. Pass out the cards to several students. Have a student call out a 3-digit number. Those students holding the correct number and place-value cards to make that number, go to the front of the room and hold up their cards. Check to make sure students have the correct place value and are in the right order. Repeat for each student to call out a number.

12-7 Problem Solving: Use Data From a Picture

pages 233–234

1 Getting Started

Objectives
- To use data from a picture to solve problems
- To add or subtract 2- and 3-digit numbers to solve problems

Warm Up • Mental Math
Ask if the following are true or false:
1. A square has four corners. (T)
2. A circle has four corners. (F)
3. Some clocks have Roman numerals. (T)
4. 10 is X in Roman numerals. (T)
5. I, V, and Y are Roman numerals. (F)

Warm Up • Number Sense
Write **728** and **169** on the board. Have a student show and tell why it is important to know whether to add or subtract these numbers. (728 + 169 = 897, 728 − 169 = 559, the answers are very different.) Have students make up word problems using the same numbers for each operation. Repeat for more pairs of 2- or 3-digit numbers.

Name ________________________

Problem Solving: Use Data From a Picture

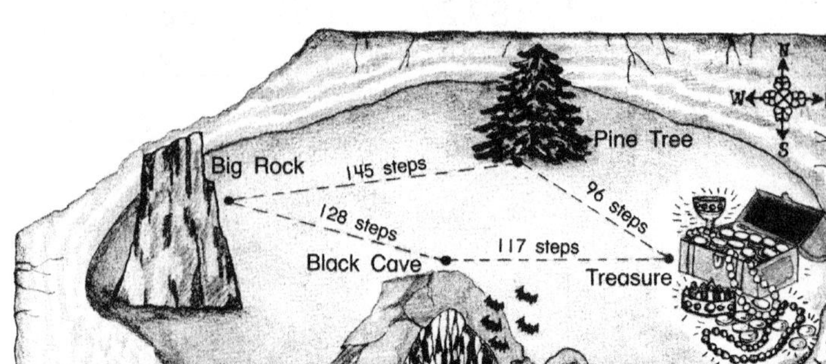

Solve.

1. How many steps would you walk from Big Rock to Pine Tree to the Treasure? 241 steps — 145 + 96 = 241
2. How many steps is it from Big Rock to Black Cave to the Treasure? 245 steps — 128 + 117 = 245
3. How much farther is it from Big Rock to Pine Tree than from Pine Tree to the Treasure? 49 steps — 145 − 96 = 49
4. How much farther is it from Big Rock to Black Cave than from Black Cave to the Treasure? 11 steps — 128 − 117 = 11
5. How much farther is it from Big Rock to Pine Tree than from Big Rock to Black Cave? 17 steps — 145 − 128 = 17
6. How much farther is it from Black Cave to the Treasure than from Pine Tree to the Treasure? 21 steps — 117 − 96 = 21

2 Teach

Develop Skills and Concepts Explain that a map is a bird's-eye view of a place. Depending on the type of map it is, we can gather information about the place depicted on the map. We can learn if there are geographical features or the names of streets in a neighborhood. Show students several different types of maps and ask them to list the different kinds of information they can gather from each.

3 Practice

Using page 233 Have students look at the map at the top of the page. Review the information given. Then, have students look at Exercise 1.

- Now, use the four-step plan. For SEE, ask, *What are you asked to do?* (find out how many steps it would take to walk from Big Rock to Pine Tree to the Treasure) *What information is given?* (The picture shows it is 145 steps from Big Rock to Pine Tree and 96 steps from Pine Tree to the Treasure.) For PLAN, ask students how they will solve the problem. (add the two distances) For DO, have students write the addition fact and solve. (241) For CHECK, have students make sure they used the correct information from the picture.
- Help students complete Exercise 2. Then, have them complete the remaining exercises independently.

Apply

Solve.

1. How many steps would you walk from the school to the store to the post office?

   $174 + 136 = 310$

   310 steps

2. How many steps would you walk from the post office to the park and back to the post office?

   $109 + 109 = 218$

   218 steps

3. How many steps would you walk from the park to the school to the store?

   $201 + 174 = 375$

   375 steps

4. How much farther is it from the school to the store than from the store to the post office?

   $174 - 136 = 38$

   38 steps

5. How much farther is it from the school to the park than from the post office to the park?

   $201 - 109 = 92$

   92 steps

6. How much farther is it from the store to the post office than from the park to the post office?

   $136 - 109 = 27$

   27 steps

Using page 234 Review the information from the map with students. Help students complete Exercise 1 if necessary. Then, have them complete the remaining exercises independently.

4 Assess

Organize the class into pairs. One student will write a word problem about the map on page 233 while the other writes a word problem about the map on page 234. Have students switch papers with another pair to answer them.

For Mixed Abilities

Common Errors • Intervention

If students have difficulty interpreting visuals, have them work with partners and take turns retelling what each picture shows in their own words. Then, have them answer questions about the picture before asking them to perform operations based on data in the picture.

Enrichment • Number Sense

Tell students to use the map on page 233 to find the distance from Black Cave to the Treasure if one went by way of Big Rock and Pine Tree. (369 steps) Ask how many more steps this is than if one went directly to the Treasure from Black Cave. (252 steps)

More to Explore • Number Sense

Provide students with two dice. Tell students to work in pairs, taking turns throwing the dice and recording the sum. Students continue to throw the dice and add to their total until they reach 75. The student coming closest to the number without going over, is the winner.

page 235

Items	Objectives
1–2, 4–5, 9	To add 2- or 3-digit numbers for sums through 999 (see pages 221–222)
6–8	To add three 3-digit numbers for sums through 999 (see pages 223–224)
3, 10–13, 19	To subtract from 3-digit minuends (see pages 225–226)
14–18, 20–22	To add or subtract money for sums and mineunds through $9.99 (see pages 231–232)
18–20	To check subtraction by adding (see pages 229–230)

Name ______________________________

Add or subtract.

1. 276 + 23 = 299
2. 357 + 28 = 385
3. 515 − 48 = 467
4. 148 + 347 = 495
5. 259 + 620 = 879
6. 468 + 132 + 375 = 975
7. 206 + 280 + 214 = 700
8. 383 + 115 + 129 = 627
9. 685 + 133 = 818
10. 767 − 258 = 509
11. 873 − 395 = 478
12. 931 − 567 = 364
13. 472 − 274 = 198
14. $3.95 + 1.22 = $5.17
15. $5.25 + 3.29 = $8.54
16. $8.34 − 2.49 = $5.85
17. $6.15 − 2.37 = $3.78

Subtract. Then check your answers.

18. $5.69 − 2.87 = $2.82; check: $2.82 + 2.87 = $5.69
19. 346 − 157 = 189; check: 189 + 157 = 346
20. $7.53 − 2.75 = $4.78; check: $4.78 + 2.75 = $7.53

Solve.

21. Ling had $5.75. He spent $1.89. How much money does he have left?
$5.75 − 1.89 = $3.86
Ling has $3.86 left.

22. Jane had $3.75. She earned $2.95. How much money does she have now?
$3.75 + 2.95 = $6.70
Jane has $6.70.

Alternate Chapter Test

You may wish to use the Alternate Chapter Test on page 326 of this book for further review and assessment.

Circle the letter of the correct answer.

1. 7 + 8 =
 a. 1
 (b.) 15
 c. 14
 d. NG

2. 16 − 7
 (a.) 9
 b. 23
 c. 19
 d. NG

3. 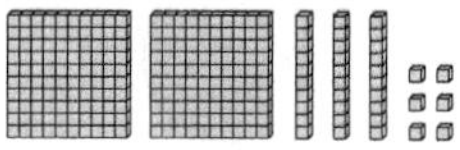
 a. 326
 b. 263
 (c.) 236
 d. NG

4. 
 (a.) $1.88
 b. $1.28
 c. $1.83
 d. NG

5. 
 a. 4:45
 (b.) 3:45
 c. 9:18
 d. NG

6. 85 + 67
 a. 12
 b. 142
 (c.) 152
 d. NG

7. 238 + 475
 a. 703
 b. 603
 (c.) 713
 d. NG

8. 91 − 48
 a. 53
 (b.) 43
 c. 57
 d. NG

9. 315 − 197
 (a.) 118
 b. 512
 c. 328
 d. NG

10. 563 − 274
 a. 281
 b. 311
 c. 399
 (d.) NG

11. $3.25 + 2.75
 (a.) $6.00
 b. $5.90
 c. $5.00
 d. NG

12. $5.25 − 2.98
 a. $8.23
 (b.) $2.27
 c. $3.37
 d. NG

STOP

score

Cumulative Assessment

page 236

Items	Objectives
1–2	To review addition and subtraction facts with sums and minuends through 18 (see pages 3–12, 17–20, 23–28, 35–44, 53–56, 59–64)
3	To understand 3-digit numbers (see pages 71–74)
4	To count money through $5 (see pages 113–114)
5	To tell time to the minute (see pages 101–102)
6	To add two 2-digit numbers for a 3-digit sum (see pages 155–156, 221–222)
7, 11	To add two 3-digit numbers, including money, with regrouping (see pages 187–190, 221–223)
8	To subtract 2-digit numbers (see pages 137–146, 159–160)
9–10, 12	To subtract 3-digit numbers, including money, for up to two regroupings (see pages 209–210, 225–226, 231–232)

Alternate Cumulative Assessment

Circle the letter of the correct answer.

1. 8 + 6
 (a) 14
 b 15
 c 16
 d NG

2. 16 − 7
 a 11
 b 10
 (c) 9
 d NG

3. 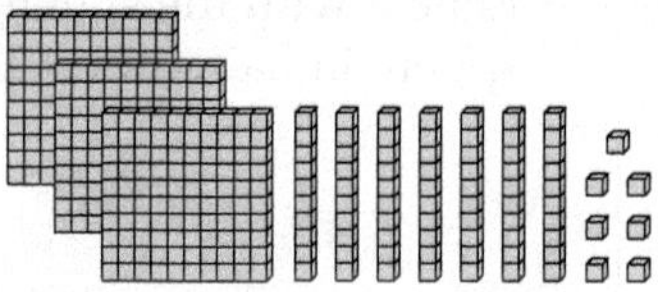
 a 773
 b 737
 (c) 377
 d NG

4. 
 a $2.04
 (b) $2.36
 c $2.21
 d NG

5. 
 a 4:35
 (b) 7:23
 c 5:40
 d NG

6. 47 + 37
 a 74
 (b) 84
 c 714
 d NG

7. 773 + 182
 (a) 955
 b 615
 c 855
 d NG

8. 65 − 26
 a 81
 b 41
 c 31
 (d) NG

9. 281 − 199
 (a) 82
 b 92
 c 182
 d NG

10. 315 − 218
 a 87
 b 107
 c 197
 (d) NG

11. $4.75 + 3.64
 a $7.39
 b $9.81
 (c) $8.39
 d NG

12. $5.82 − $2.79
 (a) $3.03
 b 3.13
 c $3.53
 d NG

13-1 Solid Figures

pages 237–238

1 Getting Started

Objectives
- To identify solid figures
- To match solid shapes

Materials
*geometric solids; dot paper

Warm Up • Mental Math
Tell students to name the number that is the following:

1. 70 tens + 2 ones (702)
2. 200 less than 563 (363)
3. 6 hours later than 4:22 (10:22)
4. 1 of 4 equal parts ($\frac{1}{4}$)
5. 3 half-dollars + 2 quarters ($2.00)
6. 3 hours past 11:47 (2:47)
7. 36 + 90 tens (936)
8. 5 dollars + 10 nickels ($5.50)

Warm Up • Geometry
Have students draw half of a figure on dot paper. Have students exchange papers to complete the figure by drawing the matching half.

Name ______________________

Geometry and Fractions

Chapter 13

Lesson 13-1

Solid Figures

Match each shape to its name.

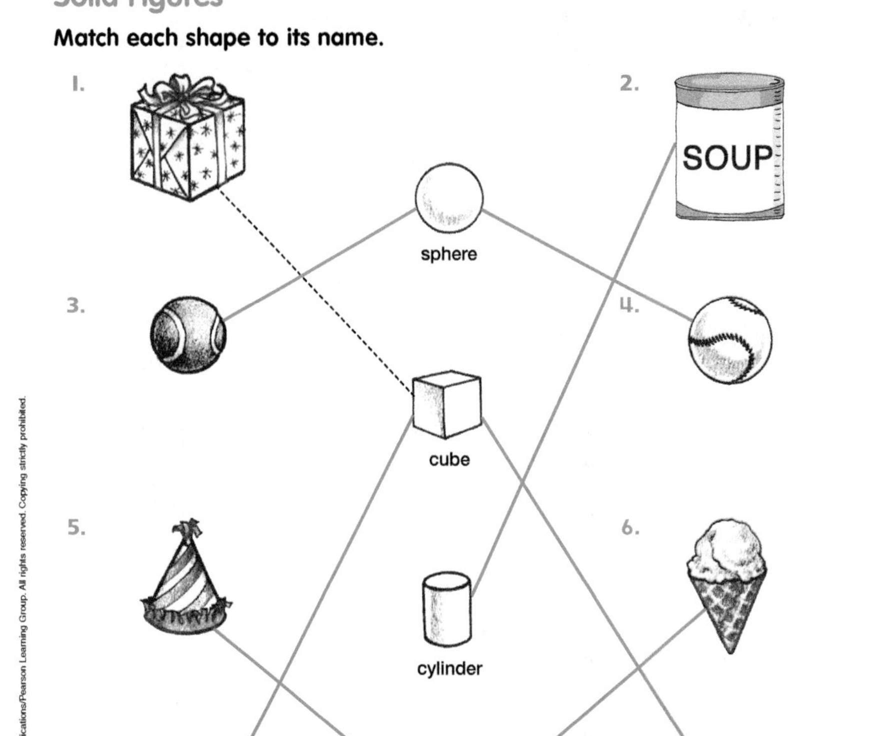

2 Teach

Develop Skills and Concepts Display a sphere, cube, cylinder, and cone on the chalk tray and write the name of each above it. Have students read the names aloud with you as you hold up each figure. Tell students that these are called solid figures because they have depth, or space, through them.

- Hold up the cube. Have students tell you the things they observe about the cube. Point out the 6 square faces, 12 edges, and 8 vertices. Show that a cube can slide.
- Next, hold up the cylinder. Have students tell you things they observe about the cylinder. Point out that the cylinder has two circular bases and a body that is a rolled rectangle. Show that a cylinder rolls or slides, depending on how it is placed.
- Hold up the cone. Have students tell you things they observe about the cone. Point out that the cone has a circular base. Show that it can either slide or roll.
- Repeat with the sphere. Tell students that if you cut a sphere in half, they will see a circle.

3 Practice

Using page 237 Have students name examples of spheres, cubes, cylinders, and cones such as the following: spheres—globe, tennis ball, golf ball; cubes—building blocks, dice; cylinders—some cups, soup cans, soda cans; cones—party hats, ice-cream cones. Note: Some boxes are cubes but only if all sides are equal and all corners are squares. Boxes with unequal sides are prisms. Tell students that they are to draw a line from each numbered object to the figure in the center of the page that matches its shape. Have students complete the page independently.

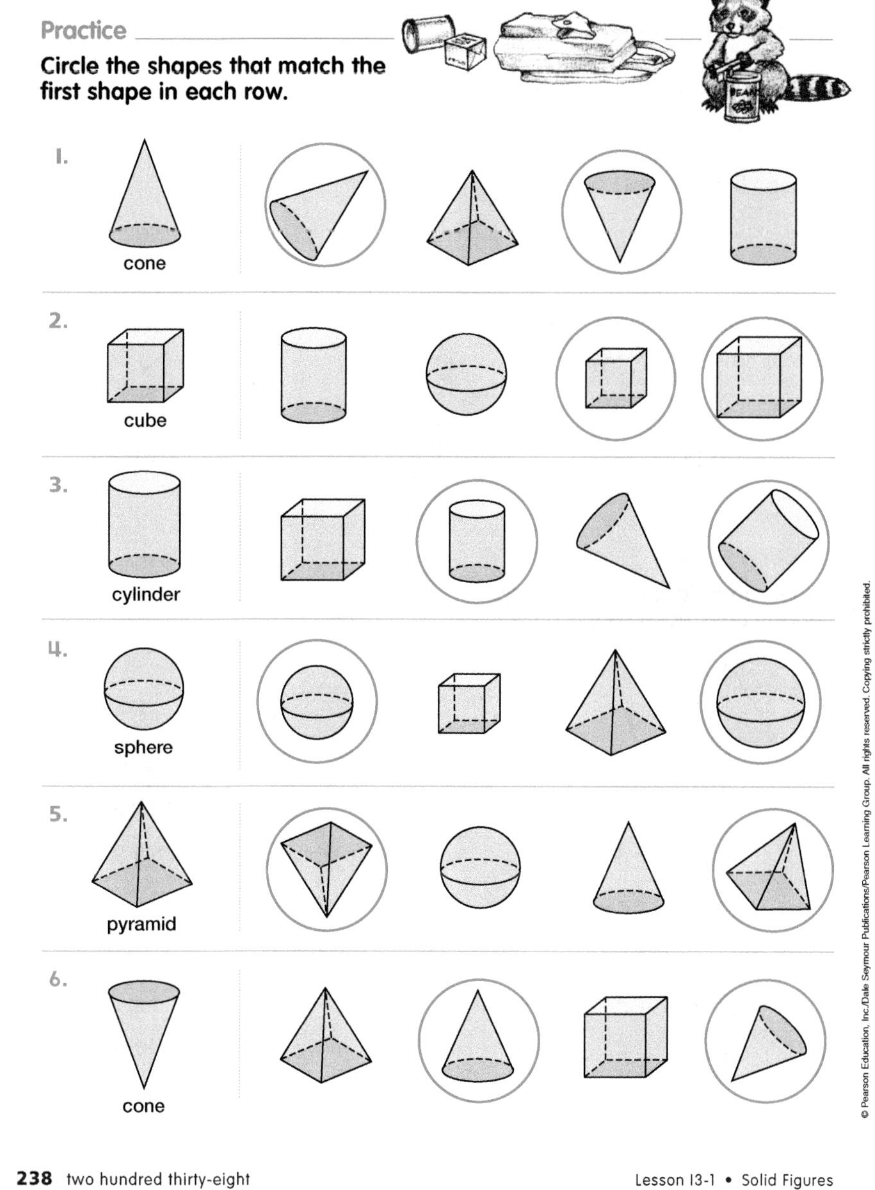

Using page 238 Tell students that they are to circle all the shapes in each row that are the same shape as the numbered shape. Have students complete the page independently.

4 Assess

Hold up some common items and have students determine what shape they are. Some suggestions are dice for cubes, an oatmeal container for a cylinder, a basketball for a sphere, and an ice-cream cone for a cone.

5 Mixed Review

1. 393 ◯ 387 (>)
2. 83¢ − 29¢ (54¢)
3. 653 + 86 (739)
4. 47 − 9 (38)
5. _____ + 8 = 12 (4)
6. 36 + 15 + 43 (94)
7. 8 + 7 (15)
8. 4 dimes, 5 nickels, 2 pennies (67¢)
9. 6 + 6 + 6 (18)
10. 78¢ + 26¢ ($1.04)

For Mixed Abilities

Common Errors • Intervention

For students who have difficulty identifying solid figures from two-dimensional drawings, have them work with partners to find and name models of solid figures in the classroom. For each figure, have them write comments to describe it, for example, *Sphere: smooth, no flat parts, no corners, round like a ball, and so on.*

Enrichment • Geometry

On the board, draw a circle, rectangle, triangle, and square. Ask students to match the two-dimensional shape on the board to a part of the three-dimensional shape of the geometric solids. Students should see the circle related to the cone, cylinder, and sphere; the rectangle related to the rectangular prism and the cylinder; the square related to the cube and the pyramid; the triangle related to the pyramid. Use a penny to represent a circle. Stack a set of pennies and ask students what solid figure is formed. (cylinder) Repeat with a stack of squares or rectangles.

More to Explore • Geometry

The Chinese tangram puzzle is made up of seven pieces: two small triangles, a medium-sized triangle, two large triangles, a square, and a parallelogram. At least one tangram set is needed for this lesson. To make individual sets from an original set, trace the pieces carefully, reproduce the tracings, and give each student a sheet. Have students cut out the pieces carefully. Give students time to play with the pieces, fitting them together in any way they choose. Then, have them make as many squares as they can, using as many pieces as they like. They should be able to make at least two squares using each set of triangles. Some will be able to make larger squares. Challenge the class to make a square using all the pieces.

13-2 Faces, Vertices, and Edges

pages 239–240

1 Getting Started

Objective

- To identify the number of faces, vertices, and edges on a solid figure

Vocabulary

faces, vertex

Materials

geometric solids

Warm Up • Mental Math

Ask how long Ed worked if he started at 4:20 and ended at

1. 6:20 (2 hours)
2. 5:00 (40 minutes)
3. 5:10 (50 minutes)
4. 4:47 (27 minutes)
5. 1:20 (9 hours)
6. 5:25 (65 minutes)

Warm Up • Geometry

Show geometric solids at random and have students identify each figure.

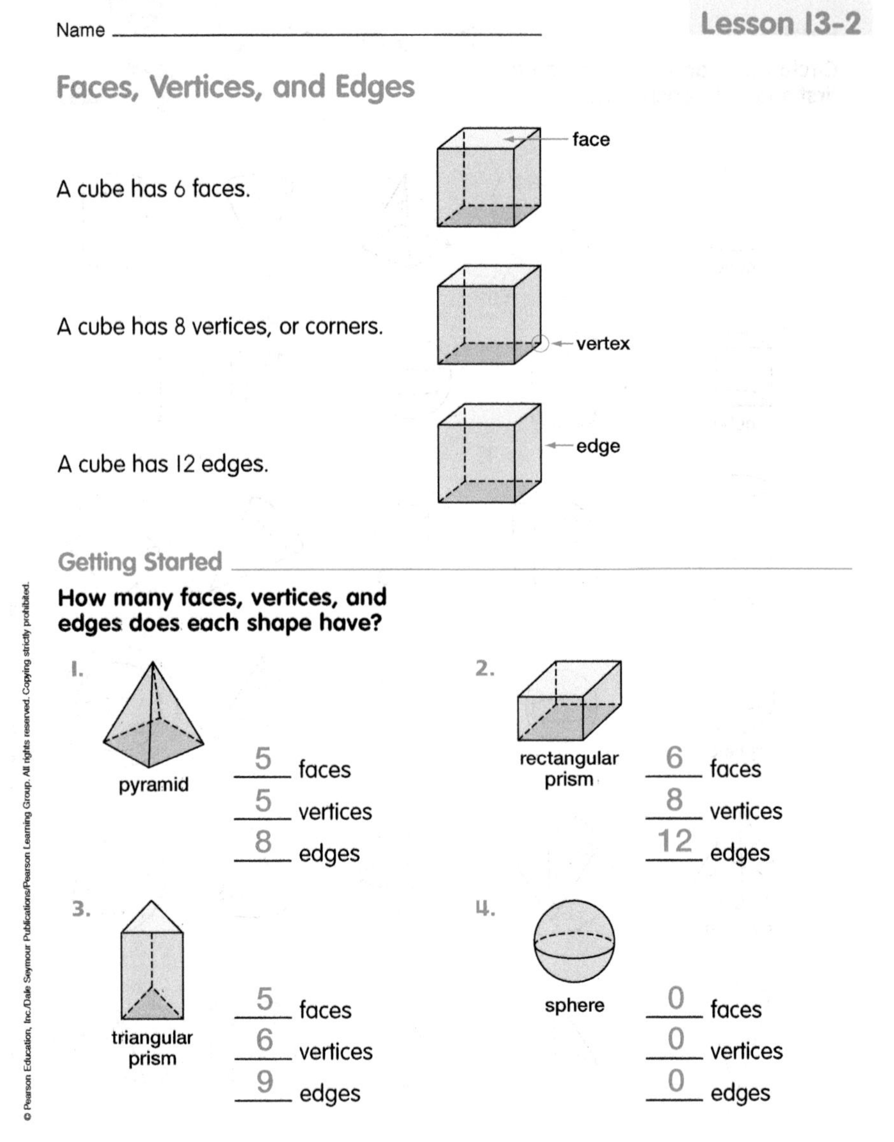

Name ______________________

Lesson 13-2

Faces, Vertices, and Edges

A cube has 6 faces.

A cube has 8 vertices, or corners.

A cube has 12 edges.

Getting Started

How many faces, vertices, and edges does each shape have?

1. pyramid — 5 faces, 5 vertices, 8 edges

2. rectangular prism — 6 faces, 8 vertices, 12 edges

3. triangular prism — 5 faces, 6 vertices, 9 edges

4. sphere — 0 faces, 0 vertices, 0 edges

2 Teach

Develop Skills and Concepts Give students geometric solids and have them count how many sides and corners each has. Then, explain what faces, edges, and vertices are. Use the different shapes as models. Have students find the faces, edges, and vertices on each shape. Note: Not all shapes have a face, edge, or vertex. Mention that a cone has a circular base and one vertex called an apex.

3 Practice

Using page 239 Read the example at the top of the page with students. Help students complete the Getting Started exercises. Allow students to use geometric solids to complete the exercises.

Using page 240 Have students complete Exercises 1 and 2 independently. Explain that for Exercises 3 to 5, they will be looking to determine what two solid figures make up each figure.

Practice

Count the number of faces, vertices, and edges in each shape.

1.

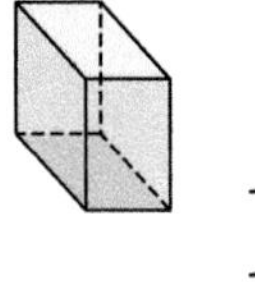

6 faces
8 vertices
12 edges

2.

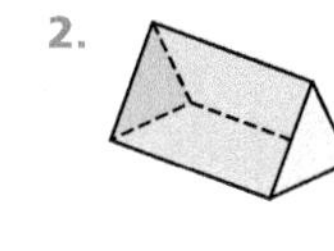

5 faces
6 vertices
9 edges

Each object is made up of two solid shapes. Name each shape.

3.

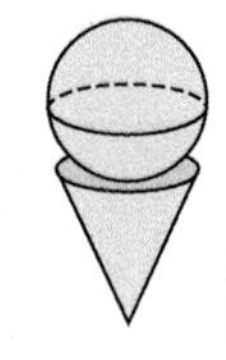

cone and sphere

4.

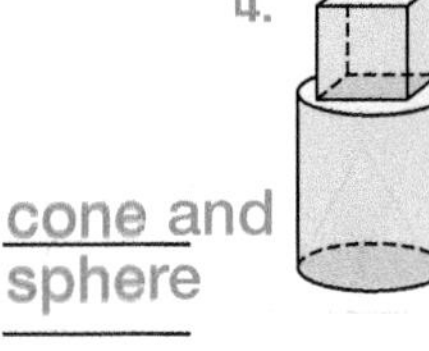

cube and cylinder

5.

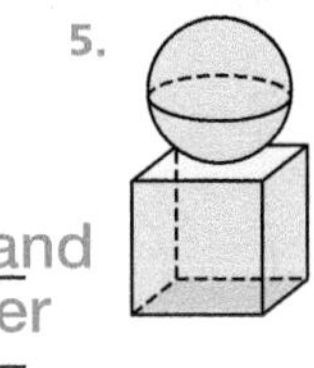

cube and sphere

Now Try This!

Answer each riddle. Then draw the shape.

1. I have 5 faces, 6 vertices, and 9 edges. What shape am I?

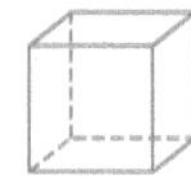

triangular prism

2. I have no faces, vertices, and edges. What shape am I?

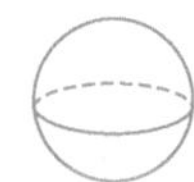

sphere

3. I have 6 faces, 8 vertices, and 12 edges. What shape am I?

cube

4. I have 5 faces, 5 vertices, and 8 edges. What shape am I?

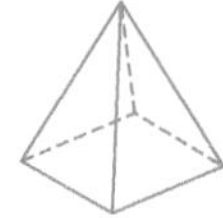

pyramid

Now Try This! Read the first exercise aloud. Ask students which solid figure has 5 faces, 6 vertices, 9 edges. (triangular prism) *Do any other solid figures match this description?* (no) Tell students that the answer to Exercise 1 is triangular prism. Have students complete the remaining exercises independently. Tell them to use the same deductive process that you used to find the answer to Exercise 1.

4 Assess

Draw three solid figures on the board and have students count the faces, vertices, and edges on each one.

For Mixed Abilities

Common Errors • Intervention

Some students may have difficulty identifying faces, vertices, and edges. Have them work with partners with geometric solids. Have them use their fingers to trace around each figure and tell the number of faces, vertices, and edges. Encourage students to place a green sticker on each face, a red sticker on each vertex, and a blue sticker on each edge to make them easier to count.

Enrichment • Geometry

Have students make a list of geometric shapes in the classroom and tell the number of faces, vertices, and edges each one has.

More to Explore • Logic

Draw the following on the board:

hamster	dog
cat	bike

Ask students to tell you something about the items. (Three of the things are related. The hamster, dog, and cat are all pets.) Ask which item does not belong. (bike) Tell each student to make up three of these diagram games of their own. They may write the names of the objects in each quarter of the diagram, or they may draw pictures of the items. Have students do the work at home, cutting pictures from magazines to illustrate the items for their puzzle. Then, have students exchange puzzles and try to guess which item does not belong. Have the author of the puzzle help if no one can guess the answer.

ESL/ELL STRATEGIES

Preteach the words *vertices* and *face*. Point out these elements in the illustrations. Say the word *vertices* several times and ask students to repeat. Explain that *vertices* is plural for *vertex*; one vertex or many vertices.

13-3 Plane Figures

pages 241–242

1 Getting Started

Objective
- To identify circles, triangles, squares, and rectangles

Materials
*different sizes of squares, rectangles, triangles, and circles; blank cards

Warm Up • Mental Math
Tell students to name the number.
1. 480 − 6 (474)
2. 20 tens (200)
3. 149 + 5 (154)
4. 770 + 12 (782)
5. 45 + 45 (90)
6. 16 tens + 6 (166)

Warm Up • Number Sense
Give each student two blank cards. Have students write an addition problem and a subtraction problem using 2- or 3-digit numbers. Write the following across the board: **No regrouping, One regrouping, Two regroupings**. Have students place their problems under the proper heading. Then, have each student select two cards and solve the problems. Have students replace the cards under their proper headings and then select two problems that have been solved and check the answers.

Name ______________________

Plane Figures

circle | triangle | square | rectangle

Put C inside each circle. **Put S inside each square.**
Put T inside each triangle. **Put R inside each rectangle.**

2 Teach

Develop Skills and Concepts Hold up one circle. Help students tell about circles as you write the following identifying features of a circle in phrases or sentences on the board: **round, no corners, may be different sizes**. Repeat for the other figures, stressing their features as follows: triangle—three sides, three corners, may be different sizes; rectangle—four sides, opposite sides are same length, four corners, corners are same size, may be different sizes; square—a special kind of rectangle, four sides, sides are equal, four corners, corners are equal, may be different sizes. Leave sample shapes on the chalk tray of the board as you mix the other figures and show one at a time for students to identify. Continue until students are readily able to name each shape. Then, remove the samples from the board and have students again identify randomly presented shapes.

3 Practice

Using page 241 Display one circle, one triangle, one rectangle, and one square across the chalk tray of the board. Write the name of each figure under or above it, using an uppercase letter to begin each shape's name. Help students read each word. Show another circle and have students tell the name of the shape as you place it under the circle. Continue to show more of each shape for students to identify and then place on the chalk tray next to its respective sample shape.

- Read directions aloud to students. Have students complete the page independently.

Using page 242 Tell students to color all the shapes as indicated in the directions. Have students complete the page independently.

Practice

Color the circles green. **Color the triangles purple.**

Color the squares red. **Color the rectangles orange.**

4 Assess

Have students draw their own pictures, similar to the picture on page 242. Tell them that their pictures must include a circle, a square, a triangle, and a rectangle.

5 Mixed Review

1. 23 + 46 + 31 (100)
2. 253 + 6 (259)
3. 729 ◯ 279 (>)
4. 57 − 29 (28)
5. _____ + 6 = 15 (9)
6. 78¢ + 53¢ ($1.31)
7. 469 + 4 (473)
8. 38¢ + 29¢ (67¢)
9. 65 − 32 (33)
10. 5 + 9 + 5 (19)

For Mixed Abilities

Common Errors • **Intervention**

Some students may have difficulty identifying plane figures because their everyday life experiences are not two-dimensional. Use paper cutouts of the five figures in this lesson as flashcards. Have students identify the figure and then identify an object or, more likely, part of an object in the classroom that has the same shape. Drawing a figure on an overhead may help students to understand how a figure could have length and width but not depth.

Enrichment • Geometry

To help students see the relationship between two-dimensional and three-dimensional figures, get models of cylinders, cones, cubes, rectangular prisms, and spheres. These can be models or actual objects such as a can, a funnel, a block, a box, and a ball. For the cone, cylinder, rectangular prism, and cube, have students make an impression of the flat surface of the solid in clay and identify the two-dimensional shape that results.

More to Explore • Logic

On the board, write a simple code for the alphabet. Assign a number to each letter of the alphabet. For example,

A	B	C	D	. . .
1	2	3	4	. . .

Tell students to write addition problems using the letters as addends. Tell them to exchange papers with a partner and solve each other's problems. Have them exchange papers again to check. Tell them to try writing more problems, changing the code by varying the numbers assigned to each letter.

13-4 Slides, Flips, and Turns

pages 243–244

1 Getting Started

Objective
- To perform a slide, flip, or turn on an object and identify the resulting orientation

Vocabulary
slide, flip, turn

Materials
pattern blocks

Warm Up • Mental Math
Have students find the sum or difference.

1. 30 plus 51 (81)
2. 28 plus 40 (68)
3. 13 plus 50 (63)
4. 53 minus 23 (30)
5. 37 minus 10 (27)
6. 44 minus 30 (14)

Warm Up • Geometry
Draw the following figures on the board. Have students identify each figure.

triangle	rectangle
square	circle

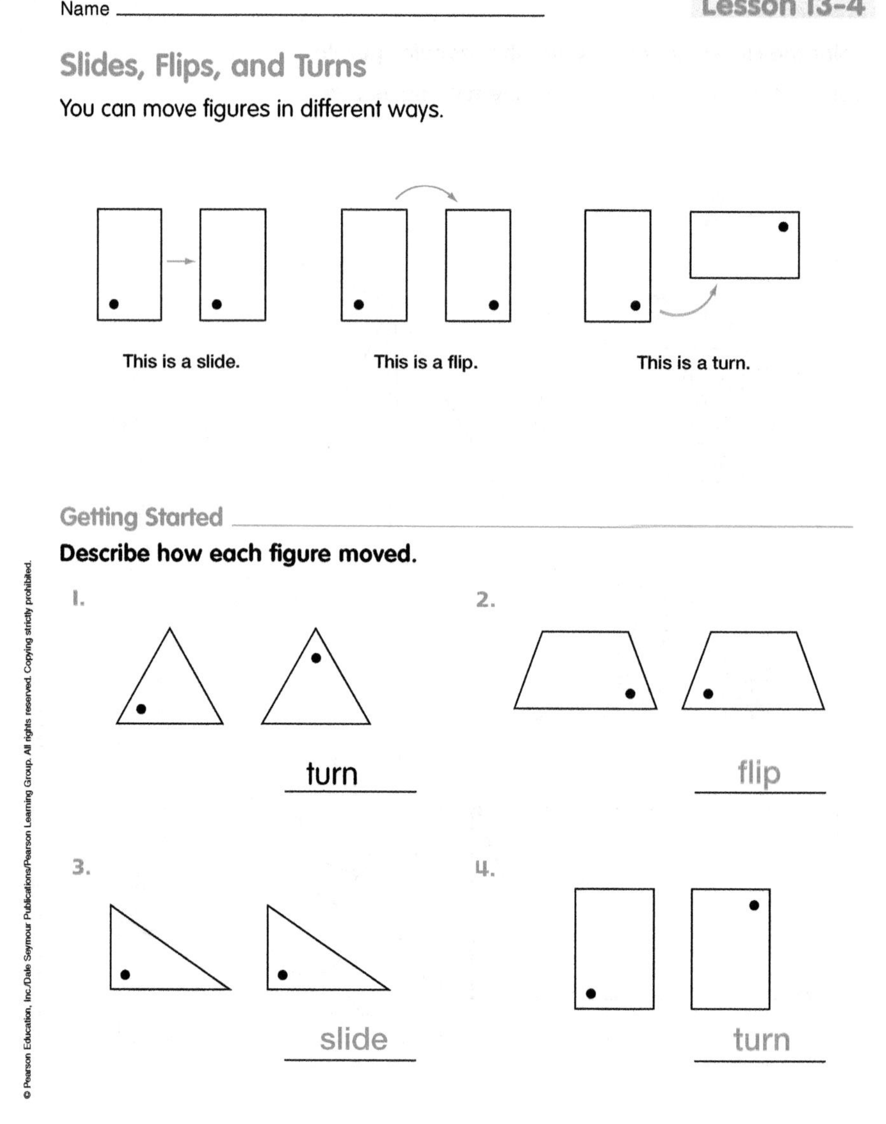

2 Teach

Develop Skills and Concepts In the front of the room, hold up two identical pattern blocks but not a regular figure such as an equilateral triangle or a square. Tell students that there are three basic ways that a figure can be moved: the slide, the flip, and the turn. First, demonstrate that a slide moves a figure either left or right or up or down. Then, demonstrate that a turn moves a figure around a point. Finally, demonstrate that a flip is a mirror image of a figure; the two identical figures are pointed in opposite directions. Have two students go to the front of the room to demonstrate each type of movement.

3 Practice

Using page 243 Read with students the example at the top of the page.

- Point to the rectangles that show a slide. Ask, *How do you know that this is a slide?* (The rectangle has been moved to the right. It has not been turned.) Point to the rectangles that show a flip. Ask, *How do you know that this is a flip?* (The rectangles are facing in different directions.) Point to the rectangles that show a turn. Ask, *How do you know that this is a turn?* (The rectangle has been rotated to a different direction.)
- Have students determine the movement of the equilateral triangle in Exercise 1 and then review the answer with the class. Now, have students complete the page independently.

Using page 244 Have students look at Exercise 1. Have them determine the movement of the hexagons and then review the answer with the class. Now, have students complete the page independently.

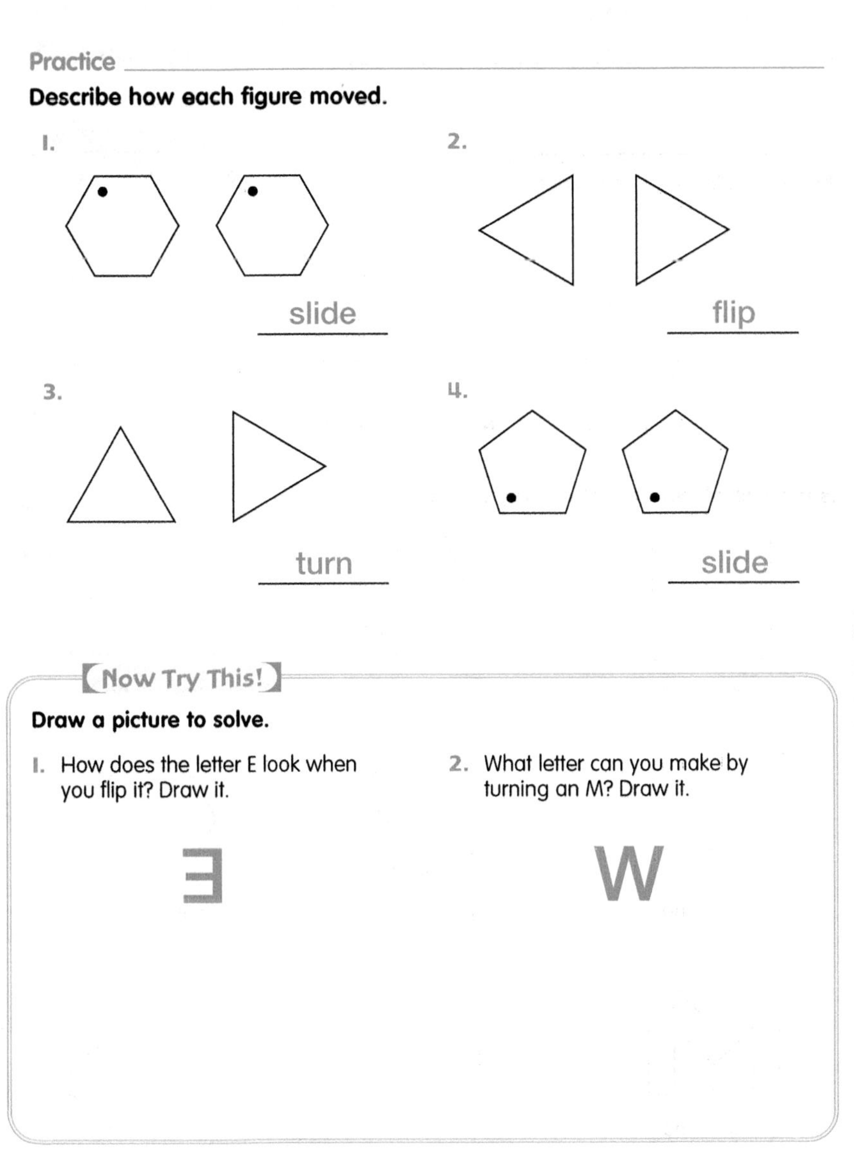

Now Try This! Write the letter **P** on the board. Ask a student volunteer to go to the board to draw what the *P* would look like flipped. Repeat with other letters and slides and turns. Then, have students complete the activity.

4 Assess

Ask students to show what happens to a figure when it is slid, flipped, or turned.

For Mixed Abilities

Common Errors • Intervention
Some students may be having difficulty differentiating between slides, flips, and turns. Have the students use pattern blocks to show how a figure moves when it is slid, flipped, or turned.

Enrichment • Geometry
Ask students to draw the capital letters that look the same when flipped. (A, H, I, M, O, T, U, V, W, X, Y) Then, have them draw the capital letters that look the same if they are turned less than a full turn. (H, I, O, X)

More to Explore • Geometry
Have students work in pairs. Partners are to pick a shape they can draw and then use flips, slides, and turns to form a pattern. When partners have finished drawing, have them exchange patterns with another pair for the other pair to determine the pattern.

ESL/ELL STRATEGIES

Point out the illustrations on page 243 and discuss the meaning of *slide, flip,* and *turn* with students. Then, help students find everyday examples of each movement. (Possible answer: You *slide* a window open. You *flip* a pancake. You *turn* a doorknob.)

13-5 Symmetry

pages 245–246

1 Getting Started

Objectives
- To identify a line of symmetry
- To create the other part of a symmetrical figure

Vocabulary
symmetry, line of symmetry, congruent, symmetric

Materials
*various sizes of paper; *symmetric paper figures; *asymmetric paper figures; *large sheet of dotted paper; *straightedge; *colored pencils; *geometric solids and shapes; scissors

Warm Up • Mental Math
Ask students what question is answered when solving a problem by

1. checking (Does the solution make sense?)
2. deciding to add (What operation needs to be done?)
3. finding the numbers given (What do we know?)
4. telling what is asked (What is to be found?)

Warm Up • Geometry
Show various geometric solids and have students tell how many faces, vertices, and edges each has.

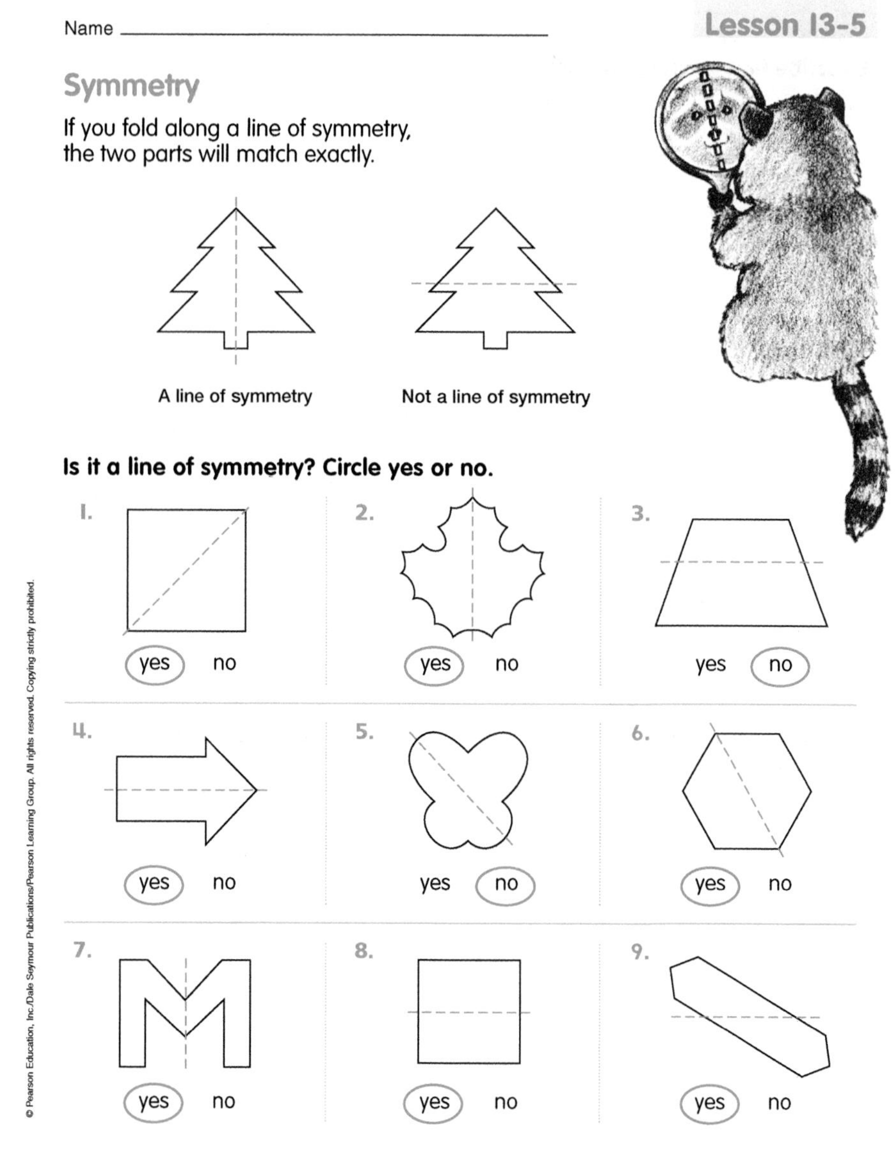

Name ____________________

Lesson 13-5

Symmetry

If you fold along a line of symmetry, the two parts will match exactly.

A line of symmetry | Not a line of symmetry

Is it a line of symmetry? Circle yes or no.

1. (yes) no
2. (yes) no
3. yes (no)
4. (yes) no
5. yes (no)
6. (yes) no
7. (yes) no
8. (yes) no
9. (yes) no

2 Teach

Develop Skills and Concepts Demonstrate folding a sheet of paper in half and cutting a shape such as a tree or a heart. Open the paper and show students how the part on each side of the fold is the same size and shape. Fold the paper again and run your finger along the edge of the shape to show students that both sides have the same edge. Open the paper and tell students that the fold is called the line of symmetry because it divides the shape into two parts that are the same size and shape. Tell students that the two parts are called congruent because they are the same size and shape. Tell students that a figure is called symmetrical if a line of symmetry can be drawn down the middle to form two congruent parts.

3 Practice

Using page 245 Fold a rectangular sheet of typing or colored paper in half, open it, and ask students to name the line of symmetry (the fold) and the two congruent parts. (each half) Repeat for more shapes folded in half in different ways to form congruent parts. Now, fold the paper so that the parts are not congruent and have students tell if each fold is a line of symmetry (no) and if the two parts are congruent. (no) Help students fold a sheet of paper to form congruent parts and then fold the paper in half and cut out shapes with congruent parts.

- Have students read the sentences about the two tree shapes with you. Then, tell students that in each of the problems they are to circle the word *yes*, if the line is a line of symmetry or circle the word *no* if it is not. Have students complete the page independently.

Using page 246 Display the large sheet of dotted paper. Use a colored pencil and a straightedge to draw a vertical or horizontal line to connect some dots. Then, use a

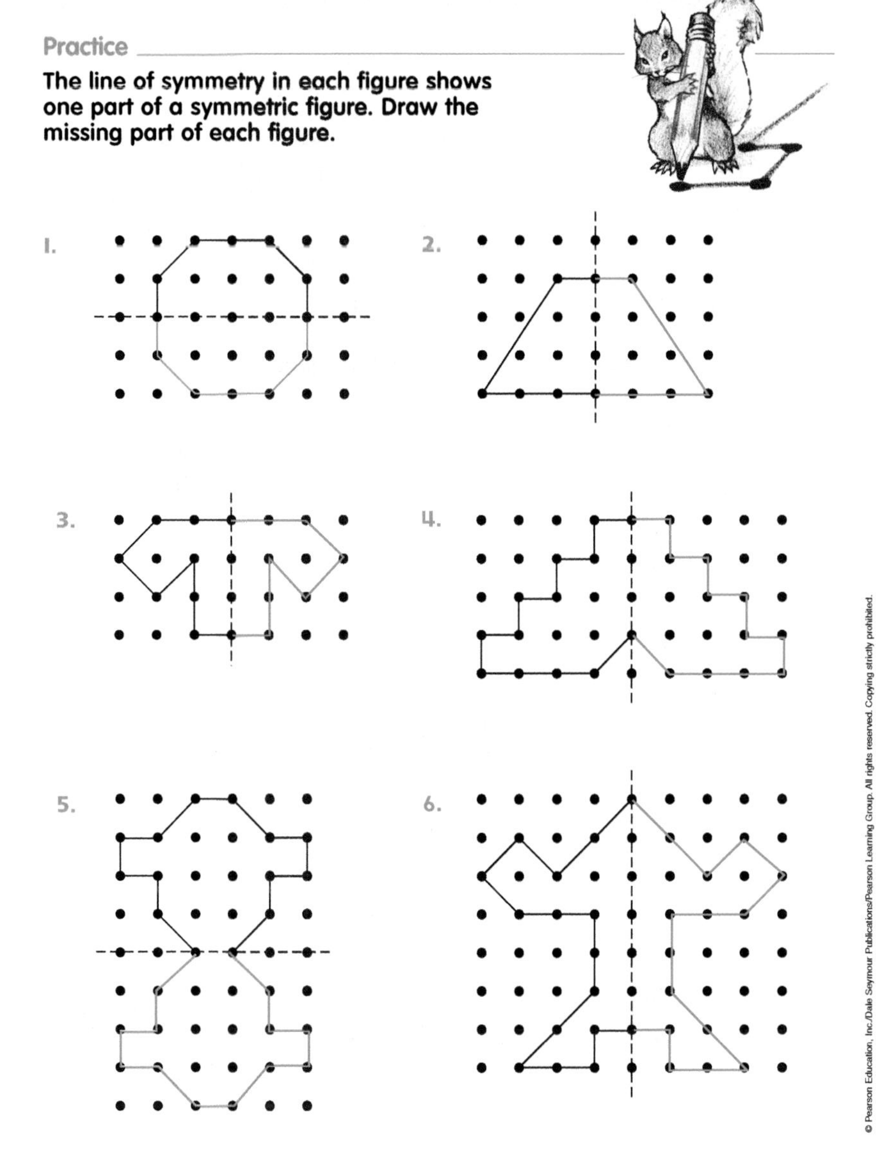
Practice

The line of symmetry in each figure shows one part of a symmetric figure. Draw the missing part of each figure.

1\.

2\.

3\.

4\.

5\.

6\.

different-colored pencil to connect dots to draw half of a square on one side of the line. Tell students that we want to draw the other half of the square to form congruent parts. Show students how to count the dots up and across to be sure the other half is exactly the same size and shape as the first.

- Repeat for more examples and then have students complete Exercise 1. If students need more practice, use the dotted paper to give more examples. Then, have students complete the page independently.

4 Assess

Give students several geometric shapes. Have them draw a line of symmetry through each.

For Mixed Abilities

Common Errors • Intervention

Some students may have difficulty understanding the concept of symmetry. Have them work with partners with figures similar to those shown in the lesson with a line of symmetry drawn. Have them cut out the figures and fold them along the line of symmetry to see how the two sides match exactly. Encourage students to cut figures of any shape from folded sheets of paper. They should see that the fold has become a line of symmetry for the flattened figure.

Enrichment • Application

Explain that living things also have a line of symmetry. Display photographs of raccoons, butterflies, and humans, and show students the line of symmetry. Then, have students draw a picture of another animal and show the line of symmetry for that animal.

More to Explore • Geometry

Have students work in pairs. Give each pair a set of pattern blocks and a sheet of paper with a vertical line drawn down the center. The first student in the pair uses the pattern blocks to build a shape on the paper to the left of the line. Using the line as a line of symmetry, the second student must complete the design using the same pattern blocks. When the shape is completed, students should see that the two halves are congruent but that one is the mirror image of the other.

13-6 Fractions

pages 247–248

1 Getting Started

Objective

- To identify $\frac{1}{2}$, $\frac{1}{3}$, and $\frac{1}{4}$ fractional parts of a whole

Vocabulary

fraction, unit fractions, one-half, one-third, one-fourth, one-fifth, one-twelfth

Materials

paper; scissors

Warm Up • Mental Math

Tell students that a nickel is to 5 as

1. a dime is to _____ (10)
2. a dollar is to _____ (100)
3. a half-dollar is to _____ (50)
4. a quarter is to _____ (25)
5. a penny is to _____ (1)
6. 2 quarters are to _____ (50)
7. 9 dimes are to _____ (90)
8. 3 dollars are to _____ (300)

Warm Up • Geometry

Have students fold a sheet of paper and cut a symmetrical figure of their own design. Encourage students to create a unique design to be displayed in the classroom.

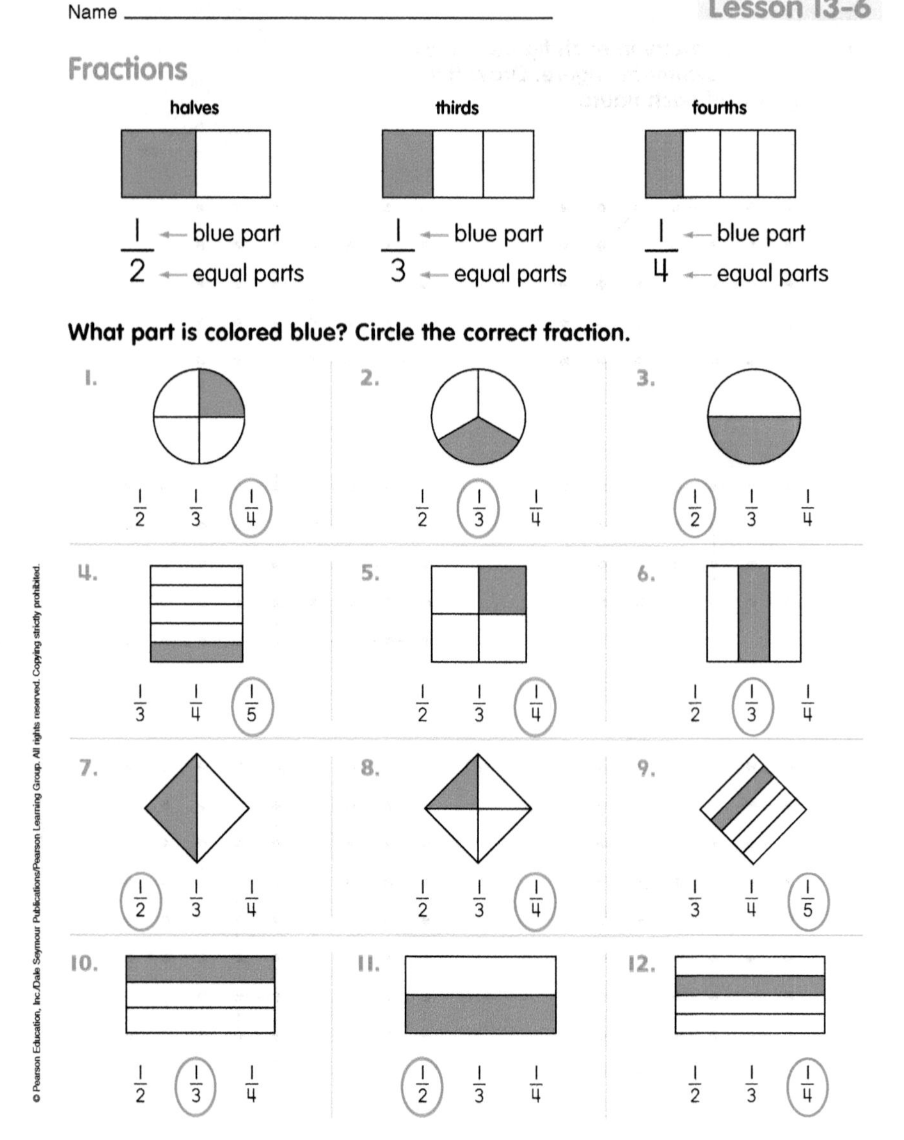

Name ______________________ Lesson 13-6

Fractions

halves	thirds	fourths
$\frac{1}{2}$ ← blue part / ← equal parts	$\frac{1}{3}$ ← blue part / ← equal parts	$\frac{1}{4}$ ← blue part / ← equal parts

What part is colored blue? Circle the correct fraction.

1. $\frac{1}{2}$ $\frac{1}{3}$ $\frac{1}{4}$
2. $\frac{1}{2}$ $\frac{1}{3}$ $\frac{1}{4}$
3. $\frac{1}{2}$ $\frac{1}{3}$ $\frac{1}{4}$
4. $\frac{1}{3}$ $\frac{1}{4}$ $\frac{1}{5}$
5. $\frac{1}{2}$ $\frac{1}{3}$ $\frac{1}{4}$
6. $\frac{1}{2}$ $\frac{1}{3}$ $\frac{1}{4}$
7. $\frac{1}{2}$ $\frac{1}{3}$ $\frac{1}{4}$
8. $\frac{1}{2}$ $\frac{1}{3}$ $\frac{1}{4}$
9. $\frac{1}{3}$ $\frac{1}{4}$ $\frac{1}{5}$
10. $\frac{1}{2}$ $\frac{1}{3}$ $\frac{1}{4}$
11. $\frac{1}{2}$ $\frac{1}{3}$ $\frac{1}{4}$
12. $\frac{1}{2}$ $\frac{1}{3}$ $\frac{1}{4}$

2 Teach

Develop Skills and Concepts Fold a sheet of paper in half lengthwise, unfold it, and ask students to tell how many parts there are. (2) Tell students that 1 part is 1 part of 2 as you write $\frac{1}{2}$ on the board. Tell students that $\frac{1}{2}$ is called a fraction and that fractional parts are always equal parts. Fold the paper on the fold to stress that the 2 parts are equal. Next, fold the paper in half lengthwise again, unfold it, and ask how many parts there are in all. (4) Tell students that 1 of the parts is 1 part of 4 equal parts or one-fourth as you write $\frac{1}{4}$ on the board. Now, fold a sheet of paper into thirds, point to 1 part and ask students the fraction for that part. ($\frac{1}{3}$) Write $\frac{1}{3}$ on the board.

3 Practice

Using page 247 Tell students that $\frac{1}{2}$, $\frac{1}{4}$, and $\frac{1}{3}$ are called unit fractions because we are talking about 1 part of the whole, or 1 unit. Help students fold sheets of paper to show halves, fourths, and thirds. Have students write a unit fraction on each part of each paper to show its part of the whole.

- Have students read aloud with you through the illustrated unit fractions at the top of the page. Ask students how many equal parts are in the circle in Exercise 1. (4) Ask how many parts are blue. (1) Ask students which fraction below the circle tells what part of the circle is blue. ($\frac{1}{4}$) Have students circle $\frac{1}{4}$. Tell students to circle the unit fraction under each figure that tells the part of the whole colored blue.
- Have students complete the page independently.

Using page 248 Tell students to read the unit fraction and then color that part of the figure. Help students complete the first problems, if necessary, before assigning the page to be completed independently. Note: Students may color any one of the parts in each figure.

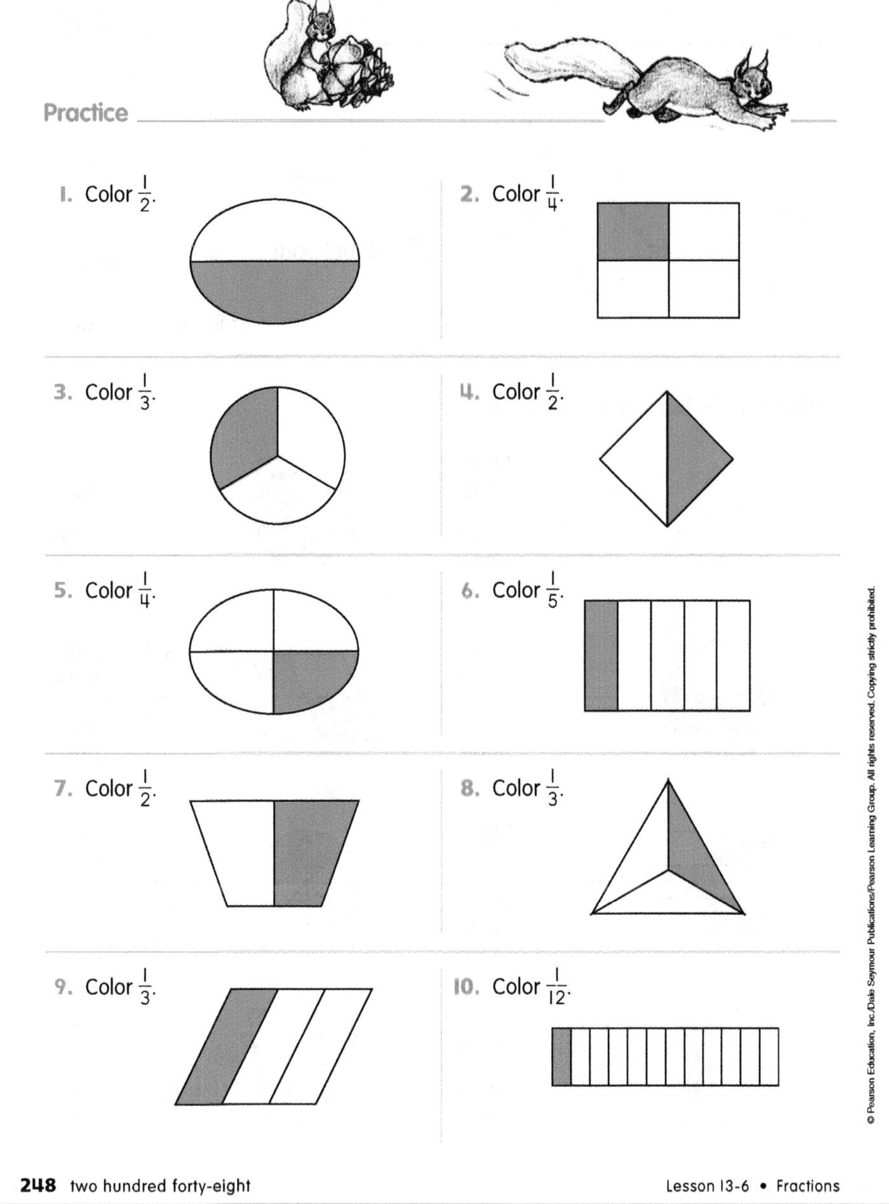

Practice

1. Color $\frac{1}{2}$.

2. Color $\frac{1}{4}$.

3. Color $\frac{1}{3}$.

4. Color $\frac{1}{2}$.

5. Color $\frac{1}{4}$.

6. Color $\frac{1}{5}$.

7. Color $\frac{1}{2}$.

8. Color $\frac{1}{3}$.

9. Color $\frac{1}{3}$.

10. Color $\frac{1}{12}$.

4 Assess

Have students draw a pizza. Tell them to divide the pizza into equal parts for 8 people. Ask what one piece fraction is called. ($\frac{1}{8}$) Have them shade in $\frac{1}{8}$ of the pizza.

5 Mixed Review

1. 61 − 43 (18)
2. 58 − 33 (25)
3. 7 hundreds 2 tens 5 ones (725)
4. 68¢ − 42¢ (26¢)
5. 473 + 86 (559)
6. 92¢ − 73¢ (19¢)
7. 39 + 47 + 21 (107)
8. 656 ◯ 566 (>)
9. 46¢ + 28¢ (74¢)
10. _____ + 3 = 11 (8)

For Mixed Abilities

Common Errors • Intervention

Some students may have difficulty understanding the concept of fractions. Have them work in groups of four with four equal parts of a circle. Ask, *If each of you takes a part, did anyone get a part larger or smaller than someone else?* (no) Let them physically compare parts to confirm the answer. Ask, *How many equal parts of the whole does each of you have?* (1) Write $\frac{1}{4}$ on the board. Ask, *Which number tells how many equal parts are in the whole?* (4) *Which number tells how many parts each of you has?* (1) Encourage students to use the fraction $\frac{1}{4}$ to describe other common situations that exist or may exist in their experience. Repeat this process with other unit fractions.

Enrichment • Fractions

Tell students to draw objects to show how they could be shared so that a student would have $\frac{1}{4}$ and then $\frac{1}{3}$ and then $\frac{1}{2}$ of them.

More to Explore • Geometry

Have students use the tangrams they made in the Lesson 13-1 More to Explore activity. Tell them to remove the two large triangles from the set and use the remaining five pieces. Give students paper and pencils and have them work with a partner. Have each student arrange the pieces in a simple pattern, trace the outside of the figure, and give the tracing to the other student. When each partner has received an outline from the other, have students arrange the five pieces so that they all fit within the tracing. Have students make at least two outlines to exchange and solve. Collect all the patterns and leave them in one spot in the classroom. Allow students time to try to solve classmates' puzzles.

13-7 Fractional Parts

pages 249–250

1 Getting Started

Objective
- To identify a non-unit fractional part of a figure

Vocabulary
numerator, denominator

Materials
fractional part pieces for halves through eighths; paper; scissors; colored chalk

Warm Up • Mental Math
Tell students to name the number that is described by the following:

1. less than 500 but more than 498 (499)
2. 1 part of 6 equal pieces ($\frac{1}{6}$)
3. 1 inch more than 7 inches (8 inches)
4. corners in a triangle (3)
5. sides in a square (4)
6. square corners in a rectangle (4)
7. corners on a circle (0)

Warm Up • Number Sense
Have students fold sheets of paper into halves, thirds, and fourths and then cut on the folds. Have students place all pieces in a group and then reassemble the wholes. Ask students to hold up $\frac{1}{4}$, $\frac{1}{3}$, $\frac{1}{2}$, and another $\frac{1}{4}$, $\frac{1}{3}$, and so on, as you dictate a unit fraction. Write each unit fraction on the board.

Name ____________________

Lesson 13-7

Fractional Parts

3 blue parts

4 equal parts

$\frac{3}{4}$ (3 ← blue parts; 4 ← equal parts)

$\frac{3}{4}$ of the circle is blue.

What part is blue? Write the fraction.

1.	$\frac{2}{3}$ (2 ← blue parts; 3 ← equal parts)	2.	$\frac{5}{6}$ (5 ← blue parts; 6 ← equal parts)
3.	$\frac{3}{5}$ (3 ← blue parts; 5 ← equal parts)	4.	$\frac{2}{4}$ (2 ← blue parts; 4 ← equal parts)
5.	$\frac{3}{6}$ (3 ← blue parts; 6 ← equal parts)	6.	$\frac{3}{8}$ (3 ← blue parts; 8 ← equal parts)
7.	$\frac{1}{3}$ (1 ← blue parts; 3 ← equal parts)	8.	$\frac{3}{6}$ (3 ← blue parts; 6 ← equal parts)

---

2 Teach

Develop Skills and Concepts Have students lay out cut fractional parts that show fourths. Have students show $\frac{1}{4}$ of the whole as you write $\frac{1}{4}$ on the board. (1 part) Remind students that $\frac{1}{4}$ is 1 part of 4 equal parts. Now, have students hold up 2 parts of the whole as you write $\frac{2}{4}$ on the board. Tell students that this fraction is not a unit fraction because we are now talking about 2 parts of 4 equal parts. Have students hold up 3 parts of the whole and tell the fraction. ($\frac{3}{4}$) Write $\frac{3}{4}$ on the board. Have students hold up 4 parts and tell the fraction. ($\frac{4}{4}$) Write $\frac{4}{4}$ on the board and tell students that $\frac{4}{4}$ is the whole figure because we are talking about all 4 of the 4 parts.

3 Practice

Using page 249 Repeat the Develop Skills and Concepts activity for halves and thirds. Now, have students cut out the parts of a figure marked in fifths and hold up $\frac{1}{5}$, $\frac{3}{5}$, $\frac{5}{5}$, and so on. Repeat the activity to show various fractions in eighths. Have students look at the top of the page and fill in the answers for red parts (3) and equal parts. (4)

- Help student complete the first one or two exercises before assigning the page to be completed independently.

Using page 250 Ask students what they are to do in the first exercise. (color $\frac{2}{3}$ of the figure) Ask how many equal parts are in the figure. (3) Ask what number in the fraction tells how many of the equal parts are to be colored. (2) Have students complete the page independently.

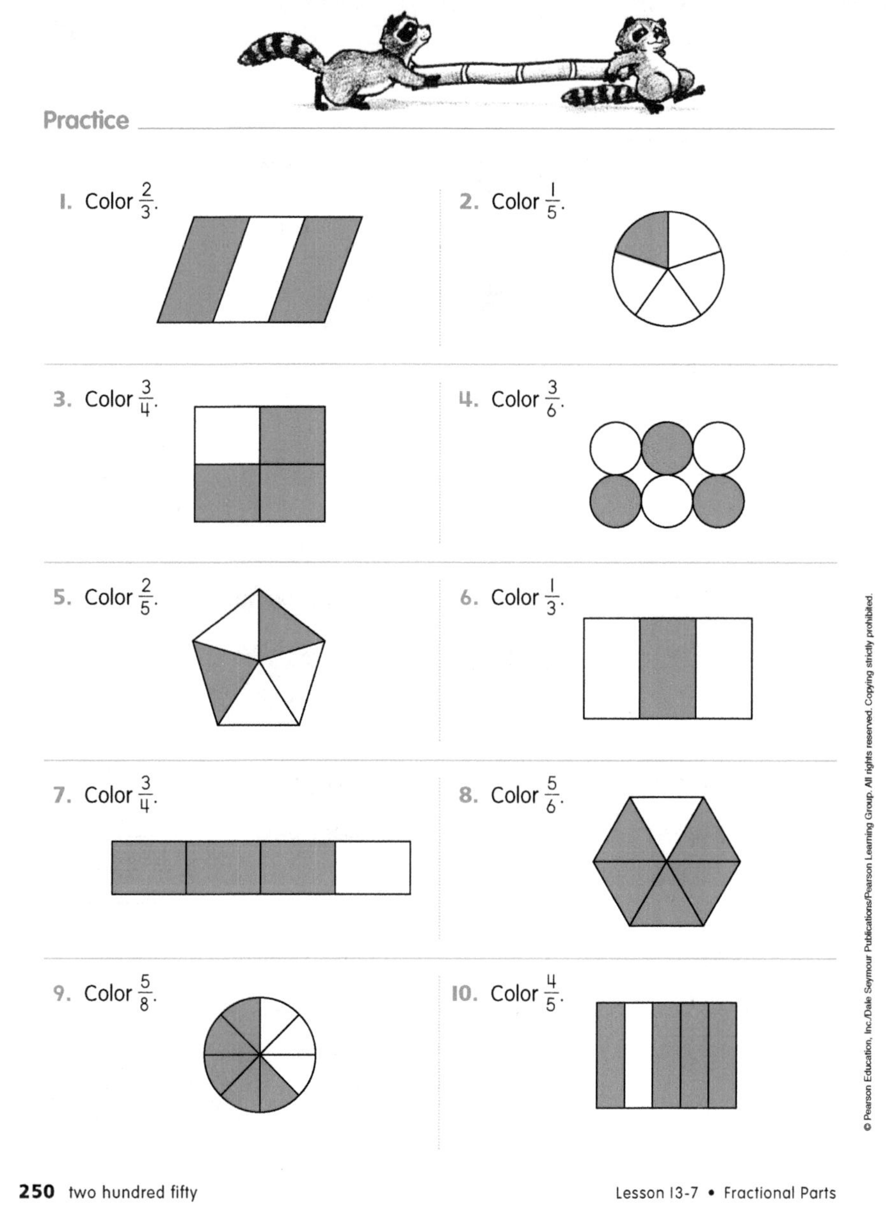
Practice

1. Color $\frac{2}{3}$.

2. Color $\frac{1}{5}$.

3. Color $\frac{3}{4}$.

4. Color $\frac{3}{6}$.

5. Color $\frac{2}{5}$.

6. Color $\frac{1}{3}$.

7. Color $\frac{3}{4}$.

8. Color $\frac{5}{6}$.

9. Color $\frac{5}{8}$.

10. Color $\frac{4}{5}$.

4 Assess

Draw several geometric shapes on the board and divide them into equal parts. Then, have students go to the board and use colored chalk to shade in fractional parts for each shape and write the fraction represented by each shading.

5 Mixed Review

1. _____ + 7 = 12 (5)
2. 47 − 21 (26)
3. 526 + 318 (844)
4. 76 − 58 (18)
5. 6 dimes, 3 nickels, 2 pennies (77¢)
6. 27 − 20 (7)
7. 755 + 108 (863)
8. 656 ◯ 566 (>)
9. 9 + 3 + 2 (14)
10. 68¢ + 47¢ ($1.15)

For Mixed Abilities

Common Errors • Intervention

Some students may have difficulty relating the numerator and denominator to the parts of a whole. Before they color fractional parts of a figure in Exercises 1 to 10, have them discuss the meaning of the numerator and denominator in relation to the figure. For example, $\frac{2}{3}$ means there are 3 equal parts in the whole and 2 of them are to be colored.

Enrichment • Number Sense

Tell students to make drawings that show the following fractions: $\frac{2}{7}$, $\frac{4}{5}$, $\frac{6}{9}$, $\frac{5}{15}$, and $\frac{11}{12}$.

More to Explore • Logic

On large paper, draw a branching tree like this one.

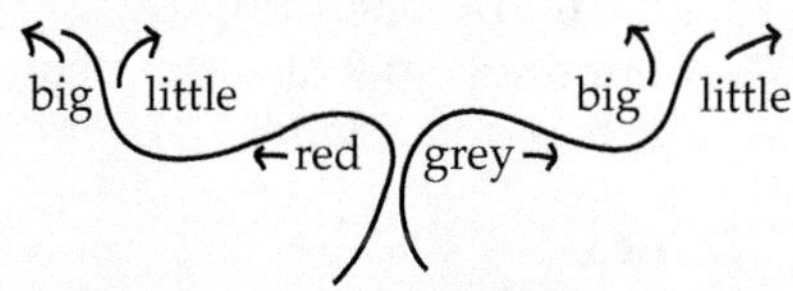

At the first intersection put a sign indicating red one way and gray the other. At the next intersections, put signs that indicate big one way and little the other. Pin the tree on a bulletin board. Then, put several cardboard squirrels (red and gray, big and little) at the base of the tree. Have students take turns helping the squirrels up the tree and onto the right branch. Let them use thumbtacks to pin the squirrels in place.

13-8 Parts of a Whole

pages 251–252

1 Getting Started

Objective

- To identify unit and non-unit parts of a whole

Materials

scissors; papers marked in fifths, sixths, eighths, and tenths; *colored chalk

Warm Up • Mental Math

Ask students how to get from

1. 462 to 356 (subtract)
2. 75 to 253 (add)
3. 4:00 to 7:00 (add)
4. $3.26 to $9.00 (add)
5. 630 to 603 (subtract)
6. 40 + 6 to 8 tens (add)
7. 4 hundreds to 9 tens (subtract)
8. 50¢ to a dollar (add)

Warm Up • Number Sense

Have a student write the fraction on the board that tells about 2 parts of 6 equal parts. ($\frac{2}{6}$) Continue having students write fractions as you name the number of parts of wholes.

Name ______________________ Lesson 13-8

Parts of a Whole

$\frac{1}{4}$ is white.

$\frac{3}{4}$ is blue.

Color the parts.

1. Color $\frac{1}{6}$ red. Color $\frac{5}{6}$ blue.

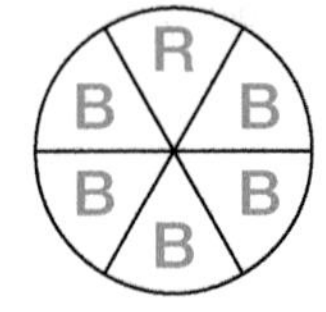

2. Color $\frac{2}{3}$ purple. Color $\frac{1}{3}$ yellow.

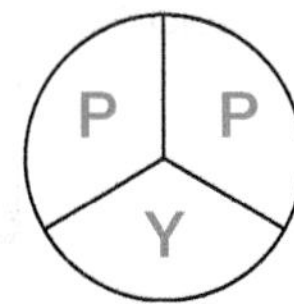

3. Color $\frac{3}{8}$ blue. Color $\frac{5}{8}$ green.

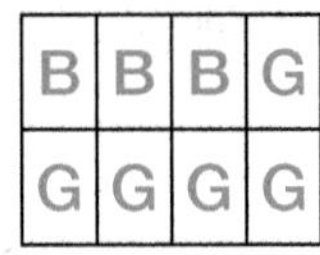

4. Color $\frac{7}{10}$ brown. Color $\frac{3}{10}$ yellow.

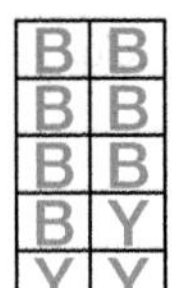

5. Color $\frac{3}{5}$ purple. Color $\frac{2}{5}$ yellow.

6. Color $\frac{2}{4}$ red. Color $\frac{2}{4}$ blue.

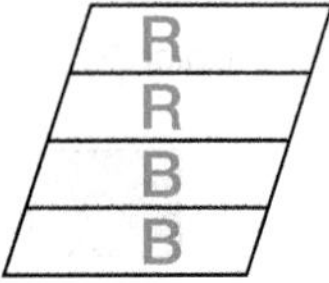

7. Color $\frac{1}{3}$ red. Color $\frac{2}{3}$ blue.

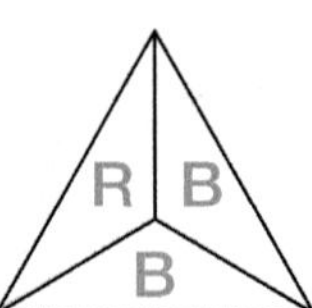

8. Color $\frac{5}{12}$ purple. Color $\frac{7}{12}$ yellow.

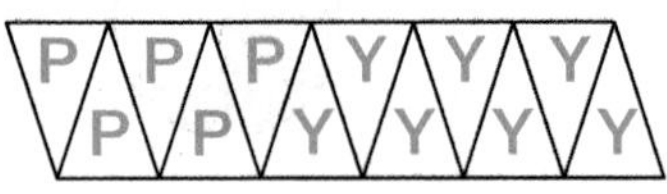

2 Teach

Develop Skills and Concepts Have students fold a sheet of paper into fourths and cut out the 4 parts. Have students hold up $\frac{1}{4}$ of their figure and then tell what fraction tells about the other parts. ($\frac{3}{4}$) Next, have students hold up $\frac{2}{4}$ and tell what fraction tells about the rest of the figure. ($\frac{2}{4}$) Repeat for showing $\frac{3}{4}$ with $\frac{1}{4}$ remaining. Repeat the activity for papers marked in tenths and sixths. Now have students hold up 2 parts of 6 and write on the board the fraction that tells the parts being shown ($\frac{2}{6}$) and then the fraction telling about the remaining parts. ($\frac{4}{6}$) Repeat for eighths and fifths.

3 Practice

Using page 251 Have students read aloud with you the sentences about the white and blue parts of the figure at the top. Ask students what number in each fraction tells how many parts there are in all. (4) Ask students what number in each fraction tells about the white and blue parts. (1 and 3)

- Help students complete the first exercise before assigning the page to be completed independently.

Using page 252 Tell students to write the fractions that tell about the blue and white parts of each figure. Have students complete the first exercise together and then write the fractions on the board. ($\frac{2}{5}$ and $\frac{3}{5}$) Then, have students complete the page independently.

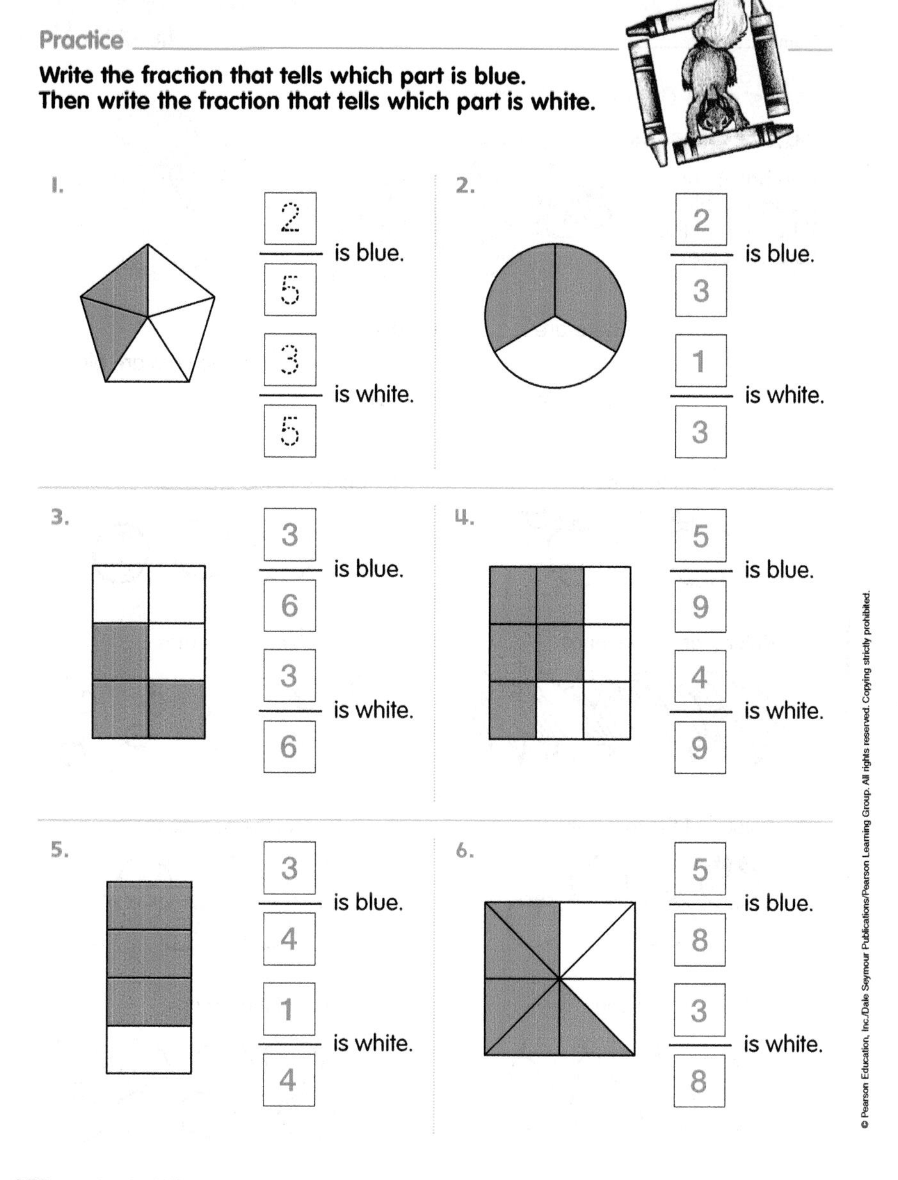

Practice

Write the fraction that tells which part is blue.
Then write the fraction that tells which part is white.

1. $\frac{2}{5}$ is blue. $\frac{3}{5}$ is white.

2. $\frac{2}{3}$ is blue. $\frac{1}{3}$ is white.

3. $\frac{3}{6}$ is blue. $\frac{3}{6}$ is white.

4. $\frac{5}{9}$ is blue. $\frac{4}{9}$ is white.

5. $\frac{3}{4}$ is blue. $\frac{1}{4}$ is white.

6. $\frac{5}{8}$ is blue. $\frac{3}{8}$ is white.

For Mixed Abilities

Common Errors • Intervention

Some students may need practice naming fractional parts. Have them work with partners, each with a sheet of paper divided into 8 equal parts. Have each partner color some of the equal parts, exchange papers, and then write the fraction for the part that is colored and the fraction for the part that is not colored.

Enrichment • Application

Tell students to find uses of fractions in newspapers, magazines, cookbooks, and so on to share with the class. Have them tell about each fraction.

More to Explore • Statistics

Survey students and list on the board how many different things they had for breakfast. Then, have a volunteer ask how many students ate each of the foods while a second student writes the numbers on the board. Help them set up a graph with the number of students along one axis and the types of food along the other. Ask them to transfer the information from the board to a bar graph. Extend the activity by discussing nutritious foods that should be eaten for breakfast.

4 Assess

Draw geometric shapes on the board and use colored chalk to color in parts of each shape. Have students tell you which fraction of the shape is colored and which fraction is not.

5 Mixed Review

1. 68 − 37 (31)
2. 84¢ − 36¢ (48¢)
3. \$2.59 + \$5.36 (\$7.95)
4. 709 ◯ 709 (=)
5. 368 + 135 (503)
6. 4 hundreds 8 tens 2 ones (482)
7. 6 + 8 + 3 (17)
8. _____ + 2 = 11 (9)
9. 40 − 27 (13)
10. 305 + 208 (513)

13-9 Parts of a Group With the Same Objects

pages 253–254

1 Getting Started

Objective
- To identify fractional parts of a group of objects

Materials
*fractional part pieces for halves through eighths; buttons that are the same size in two different colors

Warm Up • Mental Math
Ask students the following:
1. What is today's date?
2. What is the present year?
3. What time is it?
4. What ordinal number tells the present month?
5. What is tomorrow's date?
6. What time will it be in 2 hours?
7. What was yesterday's date?

Warm Up • Number Sense
Show students 3 of 8 equal parts and have a student write the fraction on the board. Continue for other parts of wholes.

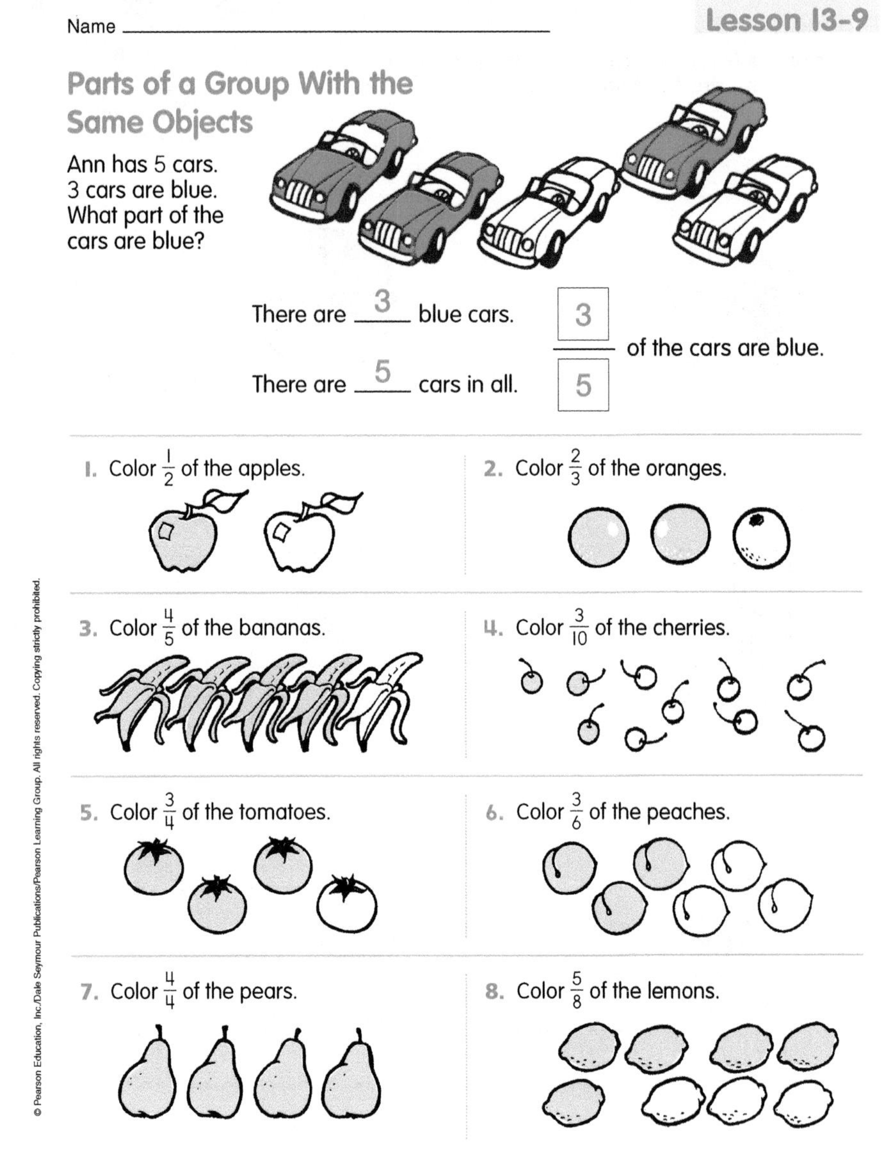

2 Teach

Develop Skills and Concepts Draw 6 circles on the board and have a student fill in 4 of them. Ask students how many circles are filled in. (4) Ask students how many circles there are in all. (6) Write $\frac{4}{6}$ on the board and tell students that $\frac{4}{6}$ is the fraction that tells that 4 of the 6 circles are filled in. Ask students to tell what part of the circles is filled in as you fill in another circle. (5 of 6 or $\frac{5}{6}$) Write $\frac{5}{6}$ on the board. Draw 10 Xs on the board and draw a circle around 4 of them. Ask students how many Xs are circled. (4) Ask how many there are in all. (10) Write $\frac{4}{10}$ on the board and tell students that $\frac{4}{10}$ is the fraction that tells that 4 of the 10 Xs are circled. Continue with Xs or circles to show $\frac{5}{7}$, $\frac{2}{5}$, $\frac{3}{8}$, and $\frac{4}{9}$, having students write the fractions for each.

3 Practice

Using page 253 Have a student read the example aloud and tell what is to be found. (the part of the cars that are blue) Ask what information is given. (There are 5 cars in all and 3 are blue.) Have students read and complete the information sentences and then write the fraction.

- Have students complete the page independently.

Using page 254 Tell students to write a fraction in each problem to show what part of the group is blue. Remind students that the top number in each fraction tells how many are blue and the bottom number tells how many there are in all. Help students complete the first few exercises, if necessary, before assigning the page to be completed independently.

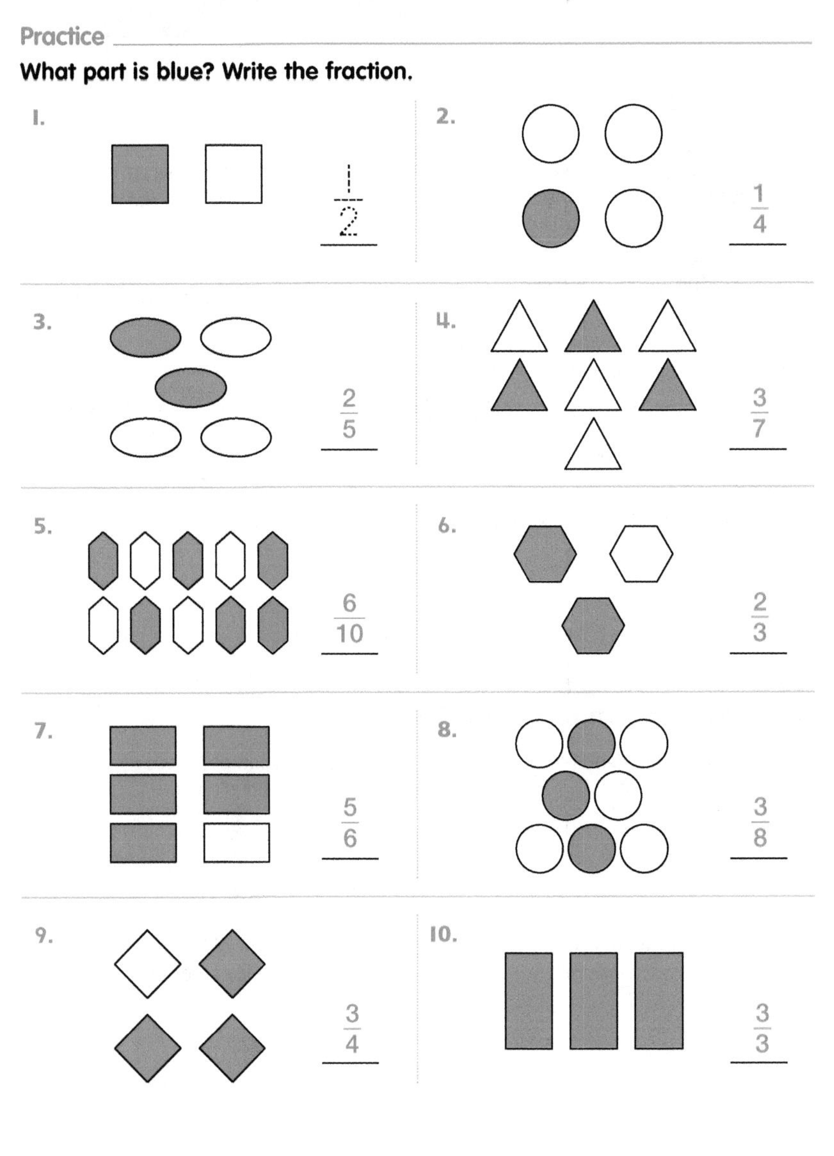

Practice

What part is blue? Write the fraction.

1. $\frac{1}{2}$
2. $\frac{1}{4}$
3. $\frac{2}{5}$
4. $\frac{3}{7}$
5. $\frac{6}{10}$
6. $\frac{2}{3}$
7. $\frac{5}{6}$
8. $\frac{3}{8}$
9. $\frac{3}{4}$
10. $\frac{3}{3}$

4 Assess

Set up 6 buttons, using different amounts of two different colors. Have students tell you the fraction of buttons that are one color. Repeat with 8, 10, and 12 buttons.

5 Mixed Review

1. 15 + 18 + 22 (55)
2. 47¢ + 28¢ (75¢)
3. 270 − 6 (264)
4. 263 + 408 (671)
5. 7 + _____ = 13 (6)
6. 270 ◯ 207 (>)
7. 78 − 30 (48)
8. 73¢ − 37¢ (36¢)
9. $2.95 + $3.08 ($6.03)
10. 94 + 38 (132)

For Mixed Abilities

Common Errors • Intervention

Some students may confuse the numerator and denominator when writing a fraction. Encourage them to first count all the objects in the group and write this number as the denominator. The denominator tells them how many there are in the "whole" group. Then, they should count the objects that are red and write this number as the numerator. The numerator tells how many parts of the whole are colored.

Enrichment • Number Sense

Tell students to draw objects to show $\frac{5}{6}$ and $\frac{3}{6}$ and to tell which fraction is greater and why.

More to Explore • Fractions

Have students select different but even-numbered related items found in the classroom, such as books, toys, writing and drawing utensils, and so on. Tell them to arrange the articles in sets on a table. Ask each student to come up when other work is finished and arrange the articles into each of the following parts of each set: $\frac{1}{2}$, $\frac{1}{3}$, $\frac{1}{4}$, and so on. Have students list on their papers the number of objects contained in each fraction of the set. At the end of the day, have students take turns showing each correct fraction by rearranging the object according to their lists.

13-10 Parts of a Group With Different Objects

pages 255–256

1 Getting Started

Objectives

- To identify fractional parts of a group with different objects
- To use a Venn diagram to solve problems involving fractions

Vocabulary

Venn diagram

Warm Up • Mental Math

Ask students the following:

1. 1 part of 10 equal parts $(\frac{1}{10})$
2. 3 parts of 4 equal parts $(\frac{3}{4})$
3. 2 parts of 8 equal parts $(\frac{2}{8})$
4. 6 parts of 7 equal parts $(\frac{6}{7})$

Ask students how many are equal parts in the whole:

5. $\frac{6}{9}$ (9)
6. $\frac{7}{10}$ (10)
7. $\frac{1}{2}$ (2)
8. $\frac{4}{5}$ (5)

Name ______

Parts of a Group With Different Objects

Alfredo asked 10 of his friends which flavor of ice cream they like. He made a Venn diagram from the information.

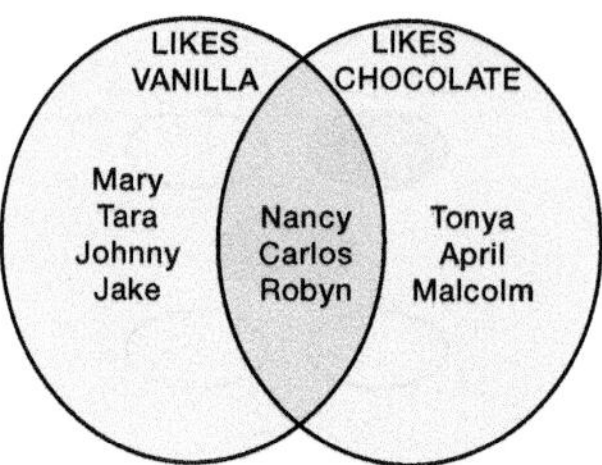

We can use the Venn diagram to find what fraction of his friends like vanilla.

How many friends are there in all? 10

How many friends like only vanilla? 4

How many friends like both vanilla and chocolate? 3

What fraction of students like vanilla? $\frac{7}{10}$

Getting Started

Use the Venn diagram to find each fraction.

1. What fraction of friends like both vanilla and chocolate ice cream? $\frac{3}{10}$ friends
2. What fraction of friends like only chocolate ice cream? $\frac{3}{10}$ friends
3. What fraction of friends like chocolate ice cream? $\frac{6}{10}$ friends
4. What fraction of friends like only vanilla ice cream? $\frac{4}{10}$ friends

2 Teach

Develop Skills and Concepts Draw 5 circles and 4 Xs on the board. Ask students how many objects there are in all. (9) Ask how many objects are Xs. (4) Write $\frac{4}{9}$ on the board. Tell students that $\frac{4}{9}$ is the fraction that tells what part of the whole group of objects is Xs. Now, ask students how many objects are circles. (5) Write $\frac{5}{9}$ on the board. Tell students that 5 of the 9 objects are circles, so $\frac{5}{9}$ is the fraction that tells what part of the group is circles. Add 2 more Xs and have students tell how many objects there are in all. (11) Ask how many of the objects are Xs now. (6) Write $\frac{6}{11}$ on the board and ask students what this fraction tells. (that 6 of the 11 objects are Xs) Have a student write a fraction on the board to tell what part of the whole group is circles. $(\frac{5}{11})$

3 Practice

Using page 255 Read with students the example at the top of the page. Explain that a Venn diagram is often used to compare two things. Explain that in this case, the Venn diagram is comparing members of a group who like two different flavors of ice cream.

- Ask, *How many circles make up the Venn diagram?* (2) Then, *What does the left circle represent?* (the friends that like vanilla but not chocolate) *What does the overlapping circle represent?* (the friends that like vanilla and chocolate) *What does the right circle represent?* (the friends that like chocolate but not vanilla) *How many students did Alfredo ask?* (10) Help students realize that 10 will be the denominator of any fraction asked about this Venn diagram.
- Help students complete the questions.

Practice

Use the Venn diagram to find each fraction.

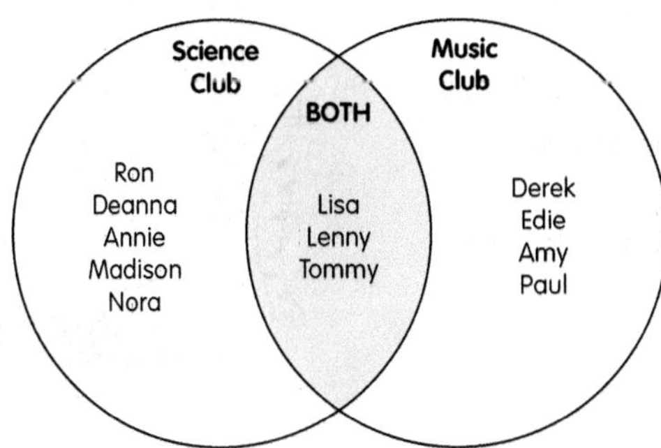

1. What fraction of students are only in the Science Club?

   $\frac{5}{12}$ students

2. What fraction of students are in the Science Club?

   $\frac{8}{12}$ students

3. What fraction of students are only in the Music Club?

   $\frac{4}{12}$ students

4. What fraction of students are in the Music Club?

   $\frac{7}{12}$ students

5. What fraction of students are involved in both clubs?

   $\frac{3}{12}$ students

6. What fraction of students belong to at least 1 club?

   $\frac{12}{12}$ students

For Mixed Abilities

Common Errors • Intervention

Some students may be having difficulty interpreting the overlapping circle of the Venn diagram. In addition to the Venn diagram, students can make a two-column table with those names in the overlapping circle in both columns.

Enrichment • Statistics

Have students write a survey question in which they will use the answers in a Venn diagram with three overlapping circles to record the answer. (Possible answer: Do you like math, reading, social studies, two of them, or all three?)

More to Explore • Statistics

Have students work in pairs. Students may use information from the Venn diagram on page 256 to make a line plot and a tally table. Students can pick the categories that they are going to tally and display in the line plot. When pairs have finished making their line plots and tally tables, have them write a question and answer to share with the class.

- Work through Exercise 1 with students. Review that the denominator will be the total number of students and the numerator will be the part of the group that likes a certain flavor. Now, help students complete the page if necessary.

Using page 256 Have students look at Exercise 1. Ask students to determine the denominator. (12) Have them explain why 12 is the denominator. (Twelve is the total number of students listed in the Venn diagram.) Ask students how they can determine what fraction of the students are in the Science Club only. Use the number of students from the Science Club circle only. Review the fraction with the class. Now, have students complete the page.

4 Assess

Draw a Venn diagram on the board, such as the one shown on page 255. Ask students if they like apples or bananas or both. Fill in the Venn diagram with the information. Then, ask students questions about the fraction parts.

(Possible answer:

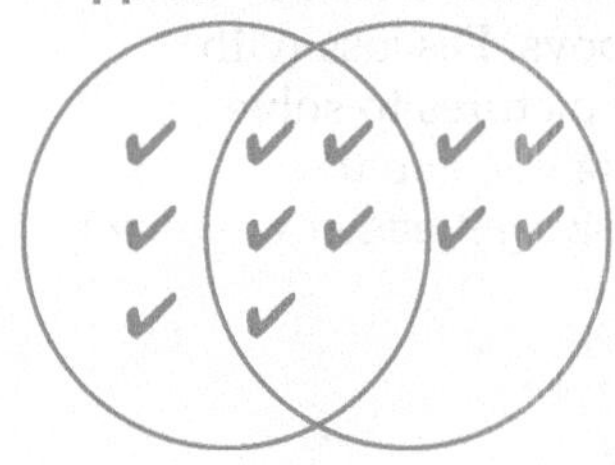

$\frac{3}{12}$ like apples only, $\frac{5}{12}$ like both, $\frac{4}{12}$ like bananas only.)

13-11 Problem Solving: Draw a Picture

pages 257–258

1 Getting Started

Objectives

- To solve word problems about fractions by drawing a picture
- To identify parts of a group with different objects

Warm Up • Mental Math

Have students find the sum or difference.

1. 10 + 24 (34)
2. 17 + 30 (47)
3. 32 + 20 (52)
4. 44 − 30 (14)
5. 63 − 60 (3)
6. 58 − 18 (40)

Warm Up • Paper and Pencil

Have students draw a diagram showing each fraction.

1. $\frac{3}{5}$
2. $\frac{2}{8}$
3. $\frac{1}{6}$
4. $\frac{3}{3}$
5. $\frac{3}{4}$
6. $\frac{2}{5}$

Name ______________________

Problem Solving: Draw a Picture

There are 4 cats. 3 of the cats have stripes. What fraction of the cats have stripes? You can use a picture to show the fraction.

How many cats are there? 4

How many of the cats have stripes? 3

What fraction of the cats have stripes? $\frac{3}{4}$

Getting Started

Draw a picture to solve.

1. There are 3 coins. 2 of the coins are quarters. What fraction of the coins are quarters? $\frac{2}{3}$

   Student drawings should show 2 quarters and one coin that is not a quarter.

2. There are 5 balls. 3 of the balls are footballs. The rest are baseballs. What fraction of the balls are footballs? $\frac{3}{5}$

   Student drawings should show 3 footballs and 2 baseballs.

3. There are 4 students on the team. 2 of the students are girls. What fraction of the team are girls? $\frac{2}{4}$

   Student drawings should show 2 girls and 2 boys.

2 Teach

Develop Skills and Concepts Read the following word problem to students: *Patti is having a bowling party. Three girls and two boys go bowling with Patti. What fraction of the guests are boys?* Now, allow students time to solve. ($\frac{2}{5}$) Ask students what they were thinking about as you read the problem and how they solved it. (Possible answer: I was picturing the people in my head; I just counted the total and the number of boys.) Draw the people on the board and have students count the total number of guests and the number that are boys. Discuss with students the benefits to drawing pictures to solve problems. (Possible answer: It lets you see the information from the problem, making it easier to solve.)

3 Practice

Using page 257 Read with students the example at the top of the page.

- Now, apply the four-step plan. For SEE, ask, *What are you being asked to do?* (find what fraction of the cats have stripes) Then, *What information is given?* (There are 4 cats and 3 have stripes.) For PLAN, ask students how they can go about writing the fraction. (draw a picture of the information in the problem to determine which number is the numerator and which is the denominator) For DO, have students look at the picture and solve the problem. For CHECK, ask, *Is the denominator greater than the numerator?* (yes) *Is the denominator equal to the number of cats?* (yes)
- Have students complete the page independently. Be sure they draw a picture using the given information before solving.

Practice

Draw a picture to solve.

1. A pizza has 8 slices. Juan ate $\frac{3}{8}$ of a pizza. What fraction of the pizza did he leave? $\frac{5}{8}$

Student drawings should show a pizza divided into eighths with 3 parts shaded.

2. There are 5 children on the basketball team. 4 are boys. What fraction of the team are girls? $\frac{1}{5}$

Student drawings should show 4 boys and 1 girl.

3. There are 6 circles. 2 of the circles are shaded. What fraction of the circles are shaded? $\frac{2}{6}$

Student drawings should show 2 shaded circles and 4 unshaded circles.

4. Brian has 8 shirts. $\frac{6}{8}$ of his shirts have stripes. What fraction of Brian's shirts do not have stripes? $\frac{2}{8}$

Student drawings should show 6 shirts with stripes and 2 shirts without stripes.

5. A rectangle is divided into 4 equal parts. One part is shaded. What fraction of the rectangle is not shaded? $\frac{3}{4}$

Student drawings should show a rectangle divided into fourths with 1 part shaded and 3 parts unshaded.

Using page 258 Have students look at Exercise 1. Read the problem aloud while students read along. Ask students for the given information. (Juan ate $\frac{3}{8}$ of a pizza.) Ask students to draw a picture from the given information. Ask, *How many slices of pizza were there before Juan ate?* (8)

- Have students draw a picture for Exercise 2. Review the picture as a class and then have students solve the problem. ($\frac{1}{5}$) Review the answer as a class.
- Have students complete the page independently.

4 Assess

Have students work in pairs. Give each pair a number of red and blue crayons so that they have 8 crayons in all. One partner can pick any number of the crayons and say, for example, "I have 8 crayons. Five of the crayons are red. What fraction of the crayons is blue?" Partners can use any or all of the crayons and switch roles.

For Mixed Abilities

Common Errors • Intervention

Some students may be having difficulty finding all the relevant information given in a word problem. After students read each word problem, have them underline the question. Then, students should go back into the word problem and circle information as they draw it.

Enrichment • Probability

Ask students, *A number cube has 6 faces. What fraction of a number cube contains the number 1?* ($\frac{1}{6}$) *What fraction of a number cube contains a number less than 4?* ($\frac{3}{6}$)

More to Explore • Number Sense

Have students work in pairs. Tell students to spell each of their first and last names. Have students count the letters in each of their names and then count the vowels and consonants in their names. Have one partner write a question such as, What fraction of the letters in my first name are vowels? Then, the other partner can ask another question about the name. Partners can repeat the process for each of their names and the total number of letters in both their names. Then, the class can share some of its findings about fractions.

Chapter 13 Test

page 259

Items	Objectives
1–4	To identify circles, triangles, squares, and rectangles (see pages 241–242)
5–7	To identify faces, vertices, and edges (see pages 239–240)
8–9	To identify a line of symmetry (see pages 245–246)
10–11	To identify fractional parts of a whole (see pages 247–252)
12	To identify fractional parts of a group with the same objects (see pages 253–254)
13	To identify fractional parts of a group with different objects (see pages 255–258)

Alternate Chapter Test

You may wish to use the Alternate Chapter Test on page 327 of this book for further review and assessment.

Name ______________________

Chapter 13 Test

How many of each shape are there? Write the number.

1. 4 circles
2. 3 triangles
3. 4 squares
4. 2 rectangles

Write the number for each.

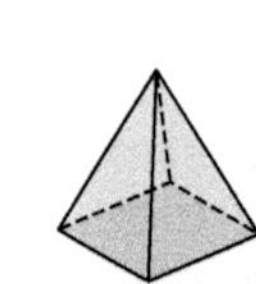

5. 5 faces
6. 5 vertices
7. 8 edges

Is the line a line of symmetry? Circle yes or no.

8. 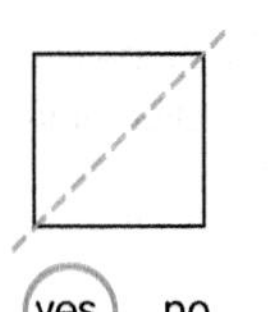

(yes) no

9. yes (no)

Write the fraction for the blue parts of each figure.

10. 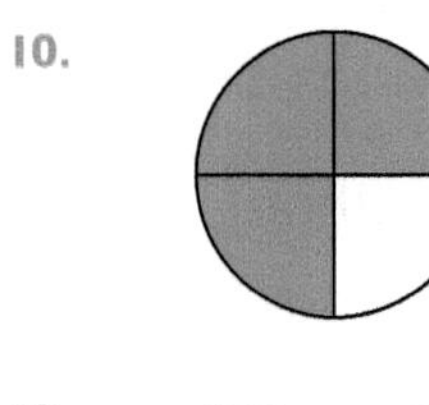 $\frac{3}{4}$

11. 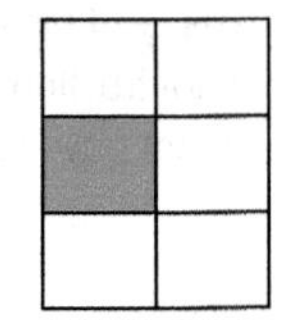 $\frac{1}{6}$

12. 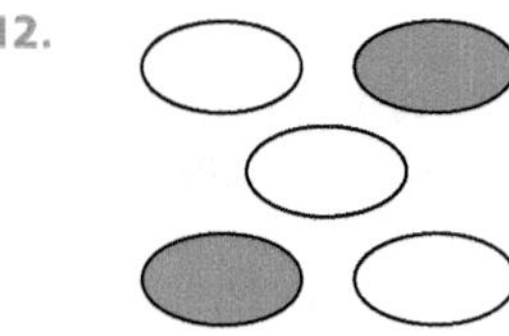 $\frac{2}{5}$

13. 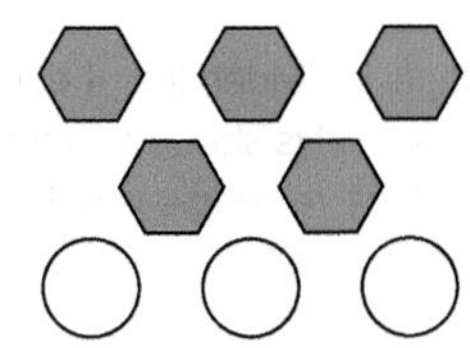 $\frac{5}{8}$

Circle the letter of the correct answer.

1. 5 + 7 =
   a. 2 **(b.) 12** c. 13 d. NG

2. 15 − 8
   a. 23 b. 3 **(c.) 7** d. NG

3. 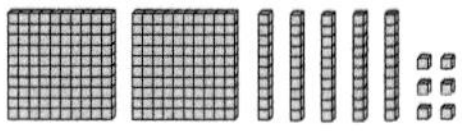
   a. 352 b. 235 c. 523 **(d.) NG**

4. 35 + 27 =
   a. 52 b. 8 **(c.) 62** d. NG

5. 473 + 75
   a. 448 **(b.) 548** c. 398 d. NG

6. 265 + 376
   (a.) 641 b. 631 c. 541 d. NG

7. 85 − 26
   a. 61 **(b.) 59** c. 69 d. NG

8. 526 − 85
   a. 561 b. 541 **(c.) 441** d. NG

9. 725 − 298
   a. 573 **(b.) 427** c. 537 d. NG

10. What part is blue?
   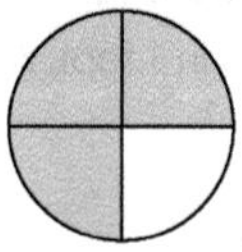
   (a.) $\frac{3}{4}$ b. $\frac{4}{3}$ c. $\frac{1}{4}$ d. NG

11. 455 + 345
   (a.) 800 b. 750 c. 700 d. NG

12. \$4.59 + 2.82
   a. \$7.31 b. \$6.41 **(c.) \$7.41** d. NG

13. \$7.15 − 0.48
   (a.) \$6.67 b. \$6.77 c. \$7.33 d. NG

score

STOP

page 260

Items	Objectives
1–2	To review addition and subtraction facts with sums and minuends through 18 (see pages 3–12, 17–20, 23–28, 35–44, 53–56, 59–64)
3	To understand 3-digit numbers (see pages 71–74)
4	To add a horizontal problem (see pages 163–164)
5	To add 3-digit and 2-digit numbers with regrouping (see pages 181–186)
6, 11–12	To add two 3-digit numbers, including money, with regrouping (see pages 187–190, 221–223, 231–232)
7	To subtract two 2-digit numbers (see pages 137–146, 159–160)
8	To subtract a 2-digit number from a 3-digit number with regrouping (see pages 207–208)
9, 13	To subtract two 3-digit numbers, including money, with regroupings (see pages 209–210, 225–226, 231–232)
10	To identify fractional parts of a whole (see pages 247–252)

Alternate Cumulative Assessment

Circle the letter of the correct answer.

1. 7 + 6
   a 14 **(b) 13** c 12 d NG

2. 16 − 9
   a 6 **(b) 7** c 8 d NG

3. 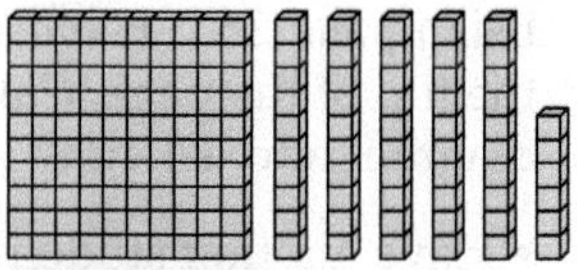
   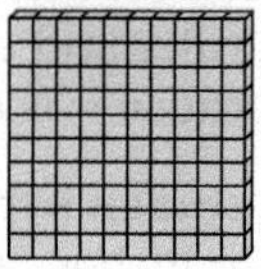
   a 626 b 508 **(c) 256** d NG

4. 31 + 58
   a 98 **(b) 89** c 78 d NG

5. 417 + 74
   a 591 **(b) 491** c 481 d NG

6. 247 + 663
   (a) 910 b 810 c 800 d NG

7. 73 − 18
   a 65 **(b) 55** c 52 d NG

8. 625 − 26
   a 559 b 509 c 501 **(d) NG**

9. 812 − 199
   (a) 613 b 683 c 783 d NG

10. What part is blue?
   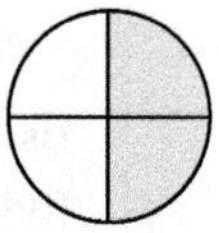
   a $\frac{2}{5}$ b $\frac{2}{3}$ **(c) $\frac{2}{4}$** d NG

11. 315 + 218
   (a) 533 b 523 c 513 d NG

12. \$6.75 + 2.56
   a \$9.39 **(b) \$9.31** c \$8.31 d NG

13. \$5.28 − 3.59
   (a) \$1.69 b \$1.79 c \$2.69 d NG

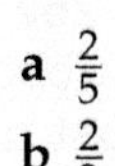

14-1 Inches and Feet

pages 261–262

1 Getting Started

Objective

- To measure length in inches, half-inches, and feet

Vocabulary

inch, foot

Materials

*paper; 12-inch ruler; paper strips cut into inch and half-inch lengths through 12 inches; objects that are exact to the inch or half-inch; scissors; *yardstick

Warm Up • Mental Math

Tell students to name the number.

1. 42 more than 410 (452)
2. 90 − 25 (65)
3. 7 hundreds − 699 (1)
4. 5 parts of 7 equal parts ($\frac{5}{7}$)
5. 45 + 100 + 5 (150)

Warm Up • Spatial Sense

Show students a sheet of paper folded in half lengthwise. Ask if the 2 parts are congruent. (yes) Write $\frac{1}{2}$ on the board and remind students that 1 part of 2 equal parts is written as $\frac{1}{2}$. Have students identify $\frac{1}{2}$ of more sheets of paper folded in half in different ways.

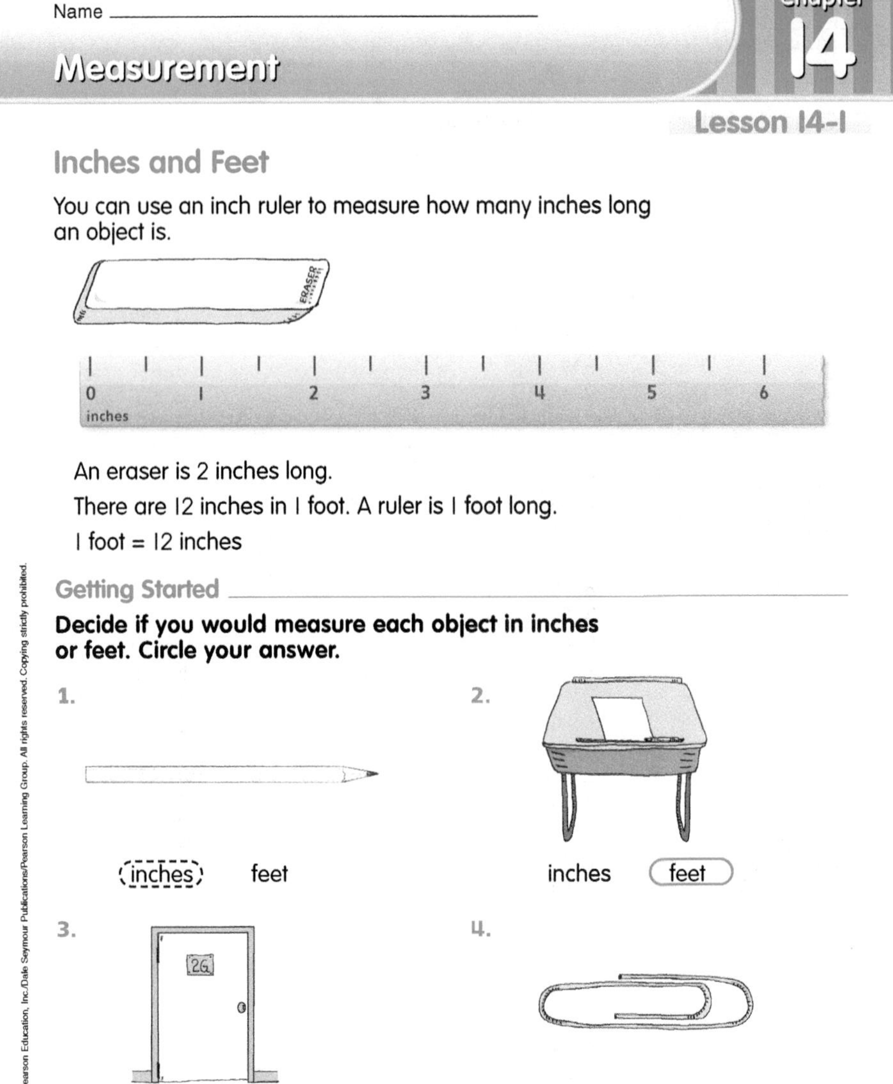

2 Teach

Develop Skills and Concepts Discuss the need for a standard unit of measure. Tell students that the inch is a standard unit of measure. Explain that a ruler is used to measure inches. Have students find the 1-, 2-, 3-inch marks, and so on, on their rulers. Place a ruler on the board and show students how you start at zero or the edge of the ruler to draw a bar 5 inches long. Continue for 2-, 3-, 4-, and 6-inch bars. Now, show students the half-inch marks on the ruler for measuring half-inches. Draw a bar that is $1\frac{1}{2}$ inches long and have several students measure the bar to check your work. Repeat for more lengths. Have students measure various objects and tell the length of each in inches or half-inches.

3 Practice

Using page 261 Have a student read the first sentence at the top of the page. Call students' attention to the diagram and ask how long the eraser is. (2 inches)

- Have another student read the next sentence. Show students a ruler and explain that the length of the ruler is 1 foot because it is equal to 12 inches.
- Explain to students that smaller items would be measured in inches, whereas larger items are measured in feet. Then, help students complete Exercise 1. If necessary, help students complete the remaining exercises.

Using page 262 For Exercises 1 to 4, tell students to mark each ribbon where it is to be cut. Help students mark the first ribbon and then tell students to complete the page independently.

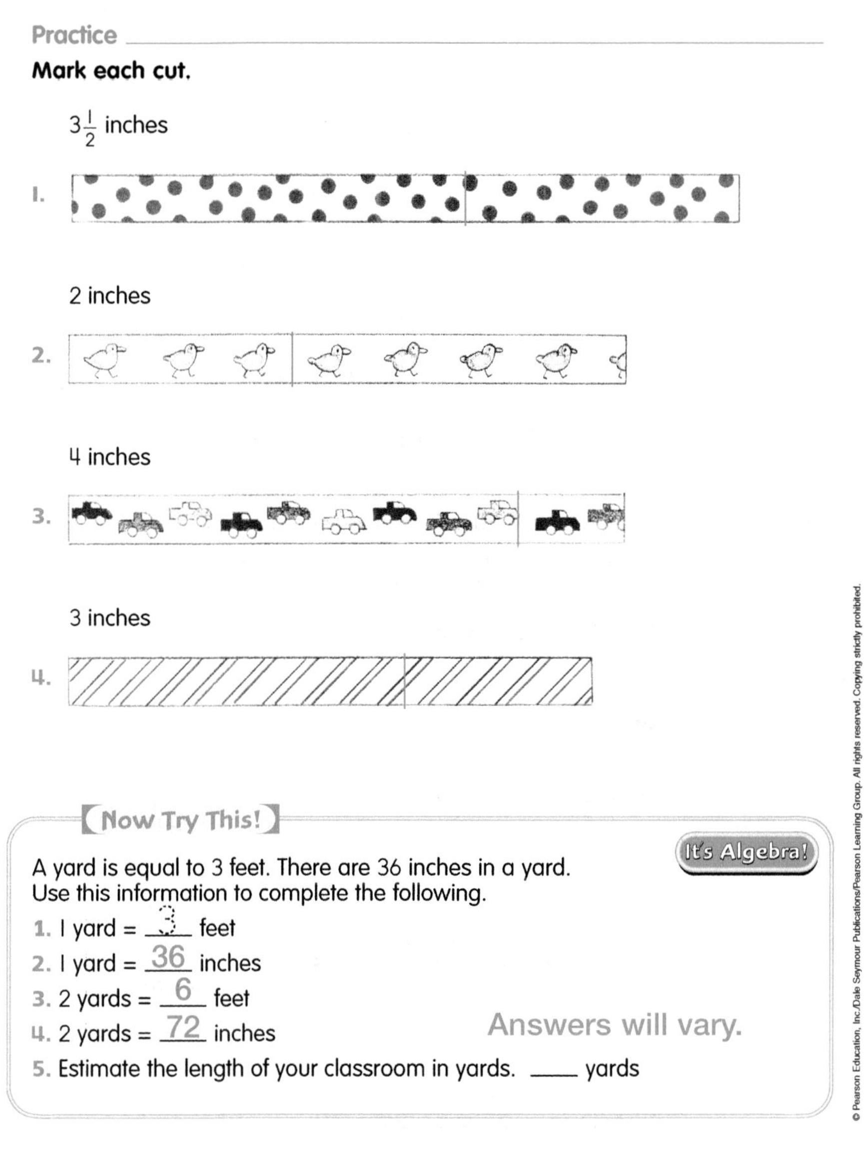

Practice

Mark each cut.

$3\frac{1}{2}$ inches

1.

2 inches

2.

4 inches

3.

3 inches

4.

Now Try This!

It's Algebra!

A yard is equal to 3 feet. There are 36 inches in a yard. Use this information to complete the following.

1. 1 yard = 3 feet
2. 1 yard = 36 inches
3. 2 yards = 6 feet
4. 2 yards = 72 inches
5. Estimate the length of your classroom in yards. ____ yards

Answers will vary.

262 two hundred sixty-two — Lesson 14-1 • Inches and Feet

Now Try This! Show students a yardstick and a ruler. Then, read the sentences with students. Show how the length of three rulers equals the length of a yardstick. Review the first exercise with students. Then, have students complete Exercises 2 to 4 independently. Finally, help students estimate the size of your classroom for Exercise 5.

4 Assess

Draw lines of different lengths on the board. Have students use a ruler to measure the lengths. Be sure to include some lines that are 12 inches or more in length.

For Mixed Abilities

Common Errors • Intervention

Some students measure incorrectly because they do not properly align the end of their rulers or the mark for 0 with the end of the object that they are measuring. Have these students work in pairs to measure line segments, checking each other to make sure that the ruler is correctly placed.

Enrichment • Measurement

Have students work in pairs. Give each pair of students three objects to measure, such as a new pencil, a crayon, and a sheet of paper. Also, give students a ruler and a small paper clip. Ask students to first measure the length of the pencil using the paper clip. (about 5 or 6 paper clip lengths) Have students record this number. Ask them to measure the pencil again, this time using a ruler. (about 7 inches) Have them record this number as well. Repeat for the other objects. Pairs should compare their results with their classmates. Ask students which measure they feel is more accurate. Explain that using a standard unit of measurement, like the inch, is more accurate than a nonstandard unit, like the paper clip, because the paper clip may vary slightly in length.

More to Explore • Probability

One way probability is used in everyday life is in the prediction of the weather. Explain that the prediction is usually made in terms of percents. Point out that 100% means that something is certain and that 0% means that something is completely unlikely. The weather forecaster might say that there is a 90% chance of rain. Ask the class to explain why the numbers between 0 and 100 show increasing probability so that 90% is very likely, whereas 10% is very unlikely. Ask students to listen to the nightly weather report and record any probabilities given. The next day, have individuals report on the weather forecast and ask the class if the weather report was accurate after looking at the day's actual weather conditions.

14-2 Measuring to the Nearest Inch

pages 263–264

1 Getting Started

Objective

- To measure length to the nearest inch

Materials

*objects to be measured to the nearest inch; *paper strips; objects that are exact to the inch or half-inch; 12-inch rulers; ribbons cut to different lengths

Warm Up • Mental Math

Ask students how many:

1. more than 10 is 60 (50)
2. months are between May and September (3)
3. hours there are from 2:00 to 12:00 (10)
4. days are between Monday and Saturday (4)
5. objects are in a dozen (12)
6. days are in a year (365)

Warm Up • Measurement

Review how to place the ruler edge or zero mark at one end of an object when measuring length. Have students measure various objects 6 inches or less in length and tell each length in inches or half-inches.

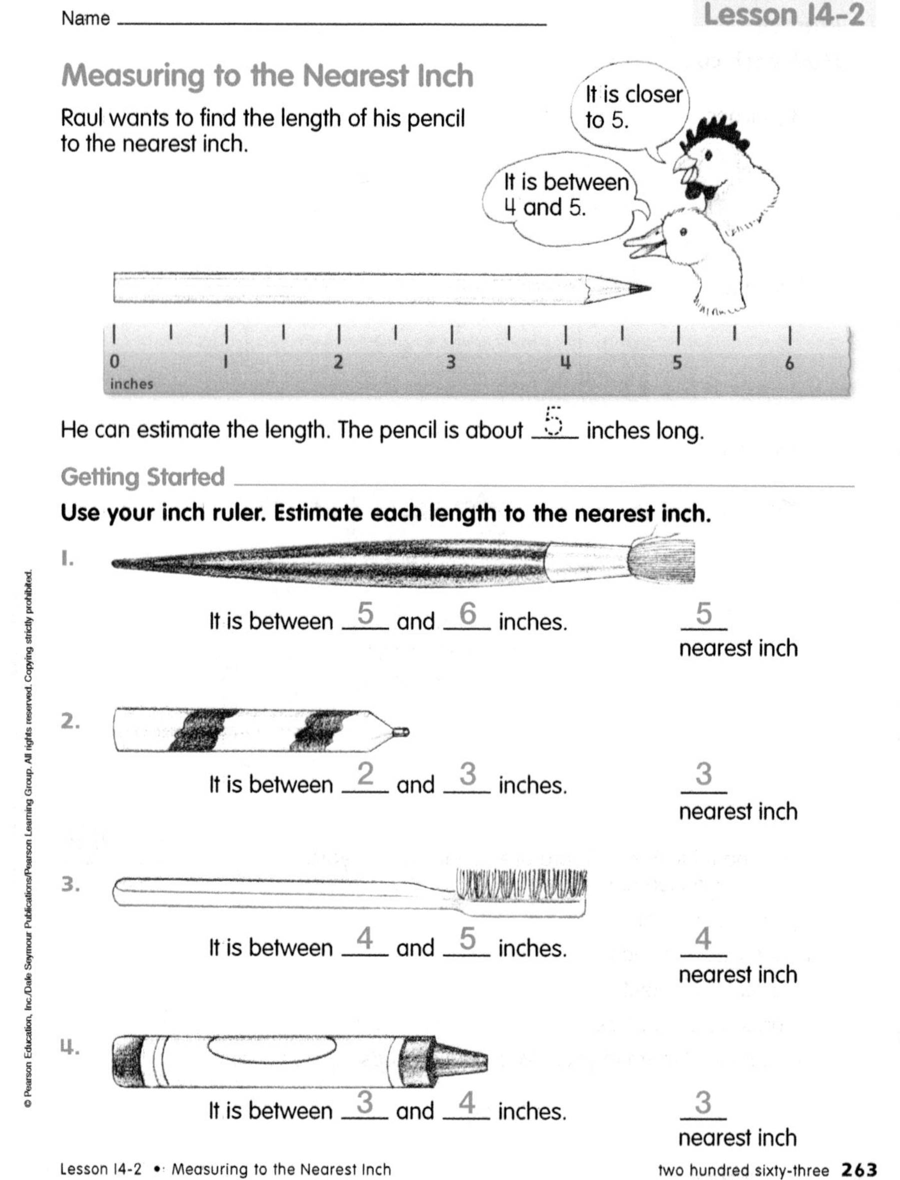

2 Teach

Develop Skills and Concepts Tell students that there are times when we do not need to know the exact length of an object and that knowing it is *about* 4 inches or *about* 6 inches is enough information. Attach a $4\frac{3}{4}$-inch strip of paper to the board or bulletin board. Use a ruler to measure the strip and ask students if the paper is exactly $4\frac{1}{2}$ inches. (no) Ask if it is exactly 5 inches. (no) Tell students that the paper is between $4\frac{1}{2}$ and 5 inches, so it is closer to 5 inches than to 4 inches. Tell students that we say that the paper is about 5 inches long to the *nearest inch*. Now, show students a strip of paper that is $4\frac{1}{4}$ inches long and ask if it is closer to the 4-inch mark or the 5-inch mark. (4-inch) Tell students that the paper is between 4 and $4\frac{1}{2}$ inches, so we say it is about 4 inches long. Tell students that the strip of paper is about 4 inches to the nearest inch. Have students use their rulers to measure more strips of paper to tell each length to the nearest inch.

3 Practice

Using page 263 Have a student read the example aloud and tell what is to be found. (the length of the pencil to the nearest inch) Ask what is known. (The pencil is between 4 and 5 inches in length.) Ask students to tell the length of the pencil to the nearest inch. (5) Have students read and complete the solution sentence.

- Help students complete Exercise 1 before assigning the rest of the page to be completed independently.

Using page 264 Have students complete the page independently.

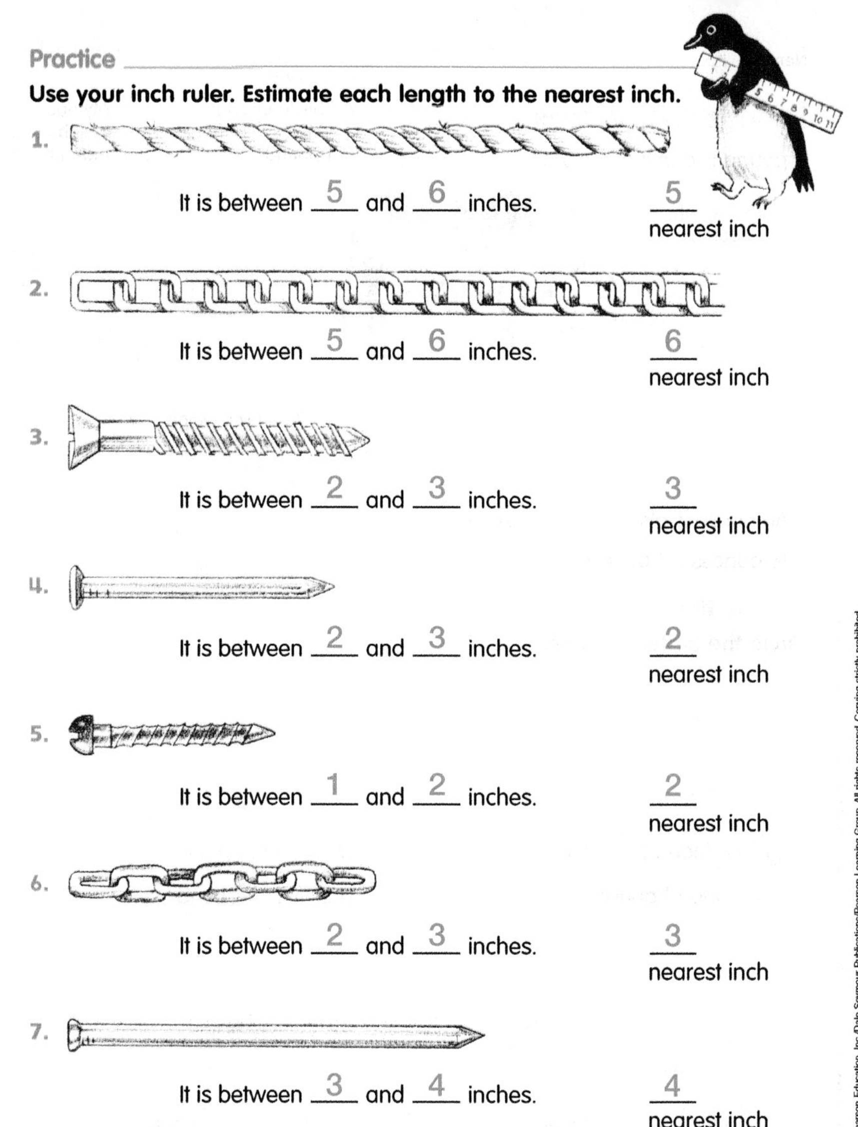

Practice

Use your inch ruler. Estimate each length to the nearest inch.

1. It is between 5 and 6 inches. 5 nearest inch

2. It is between 5 and 6 inches. 6 nearest inch

3. It is between 2 and 3 inches. 3 nearest inch

4. It is between 2 and 3 inches. 2 nearest inch

5. It is between 1 and 2 inches. 2 nearest inch

6. It is between 2 and 3 inches. 3 nearest inch

7. It is between 3 and 4 inches. 4 nearest inch

4 Assess

Cut different lengths of ribbon and give each student three pieces. Have them estimate and then measure the length of each piece of ribbon.

5 Mixed Review

1. 207 ◯ 270 (<)
2. 63 + 21 + 15 (99)
3. 438 − 246 (192)
4. $3.56 + $4.94 ($8.50)
5. 16 − 5 (11)
6. 105, 110, 115, _____ (120)
7. 195 − 168 (27)
8. 326 + 53 (379)
9. 68 − 15 (53)
10. 306 − 219 (87)

For Mixed Abilities

Common Errors • Intervention

If students have difficulty telling to which of two numbers of inches a measure is closer, have them place their finger at the end of the object. Then, have them move their finger back and forth across the ruler to determine whether the end of the object is to the left or to the right of the half-way mark between the inches. If it is to the left, they choose the smaller number of inches; if it is to the right, they choose the larger number of inches.

Enrichment • Measurement

Tell students to locate four objects that are about 6 inches to the nearest inch and four objects that are about 2 inches to the nearest inch.

More to Explore • Logic

Display a chart on the board that assigns a dollar value to each letter of the alphabet.

A = $1, B = $2, C = $3, . . .
Z = $26.

Ask students to find

1. the value of their name
2. the value of the teacher's name
3. the most expensive three-letter word
4. the least expensive three-letter word
5. $10 words
6. $100 words

14-3 Pounds and Ounces

pages 265–266

1 Getting Started

Objective
- To estimate weight in pounds and ounces

Vocabulary
pound, ounces

Materials
*balance scale; *1-pound and 1-ounce weights; *items weighing about 1 pound and about 1 ounce

Warm Up • Mental Math
Have students tell the perimeter of a figure whose sides are

1. 4, 3, 6 centimeters (13 cm)
2. 50, 50, 40 inches (140 in.)
3. equal and one of four sides is 2 inches (8 in.)
4. 1, 2, 3, 4, and 5 centimeters (15 cm)
5. equal and one of three sides is 5 centimeters (15 cm)
6. 1, $2\frac{1}{2}$, $2\frac{1}{2}$ inches (6 in.)

Warm Up • Measurement
Have students tell you how many inches are in 2 feet (24), 3 feet (36), and 4 feet (48). Ask how they figured it out. (Possible answer: I know there are 12 inches in a foot, so I added 12 + 12 to find out how many inches are in 2 feet and so on.)

Name ______________________

Lesson 14-3

Pounds and Ounces

A pound is a unit of weight.

An ounce is also a unit of weight.

16 ounces = 1 pound

Getting Started

Circle the better estimate.

1. (More than 1 pound) Less than 1 pound
2. More than 1 pound (Less than 1 pound)
3. (2 pounds) 2 ounces
4. 4 pounds (4 ounces)

2 Teach

Develop Skills and Concepts Tell students that one unit we use to measure the weight of an object is the pound. Another is the ounce. Sixteen ounces equal 1 pound. Explain that the tool we use to measure weight is a scale. A bathroom scale is used to measure pounds. Small kitchen scales are often used to measure ounces.

- Have students hold the 1-pound weight to get a feel for its weight. Place the 1-pound weight on the balance scale and tell students that the scale will tip to the side of the heavier object. Show several items weighing about 1 pound and have students place each on the scale to see if they weigh more or less than 1 pound. Have students group the objects for more than and less than 1 pound.
- Repeat for the 1-ounce weight and objects that weigh about 1 ounce. Now, have students hold the pound weight in one hand and an object in the other and tell if the object feels to be more or less than 1 pound. Repeat for 1 ounce. Show two books and ask students if the books might weigh 2 pounds or 2 ounces. (2 pounds) Repeat for students to estimate if objects would be weighed in pounds or ounces.

3 Practice

Using page 265 Have students read the captions and sentences aloud. Ask how many ounces are in 1 pound. (16) Ask students if a dog or a tennis ball weighs more. (dog) Ask if 9 pennies would weigh more or less than a dog. (less) Ask how many ounces the butter would weigh. (16)

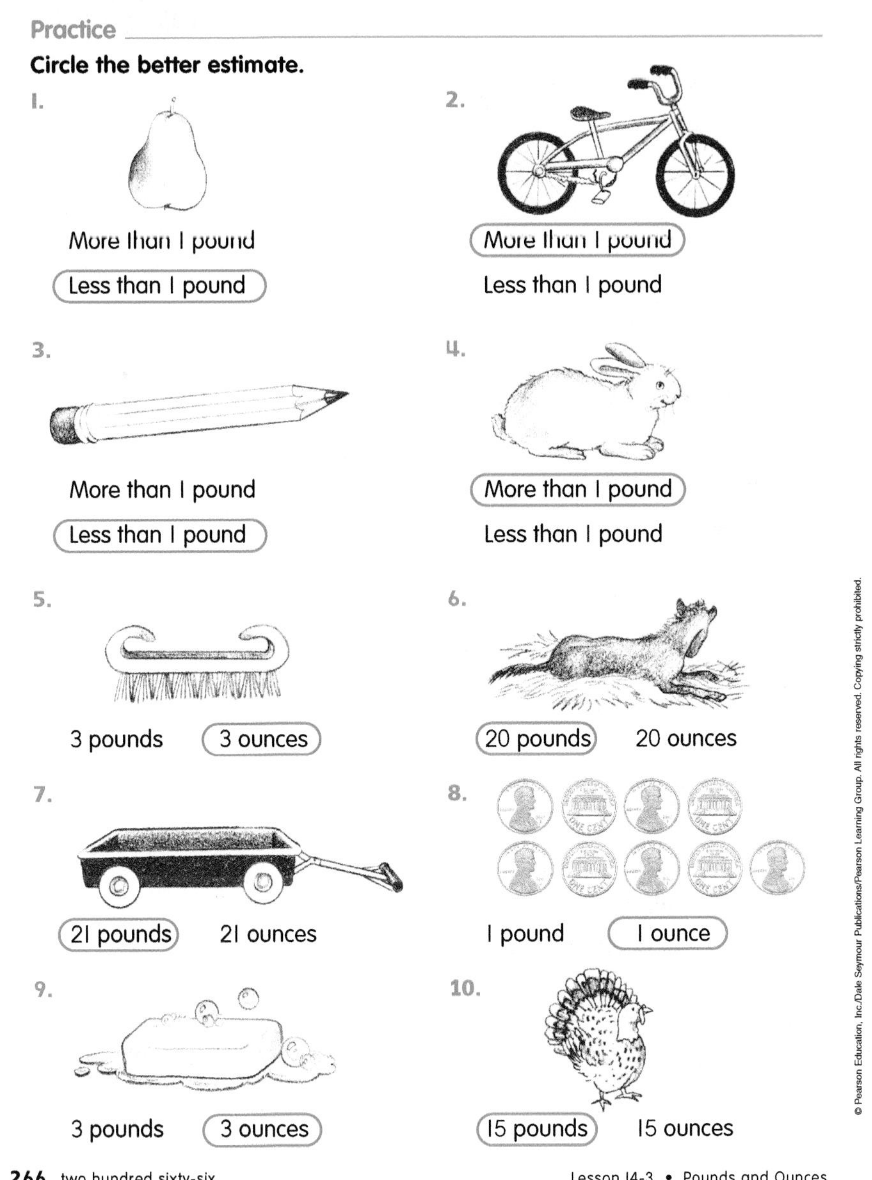

- Have students tell which measure of weight would be the better guess for each item in the Getting Started exercises and then circle their answer.

Using page 266 Have students complete the page independently.

4 Assess

Choose several common classroom items and have students estimate if the weight is more than a pound or less than a pound.

5 Mixed Review

1. 397 + 18 (415)
2. 600 − 173 (427)
3. 3 dimes, 3 nickels, 5 pennies (50¢)
4. 105 + 306 + 219 (630)
5. 38 + 46 (84)
6. 75 − 48 (27)
7. 410 − 38 (372)
8. 5 hundreds 0 tens 0 ones (500)
9. \$2.56 − \$1.77 (\$0.79)
10. 6 + _____ = 14 (8)

For Mixed Abilities

Common Errors • Intervention

Some students may have difficulty deciding whether an object weighs more or less than a pound. Have them work in cooperative groups with a bag of sugar or loaf of bread weighing one pound. Let each of them, in turn, hold it in one hand and another object in the other hand to determine whether the object weighs more than or less than 1 pound. Then, have them work together to make a list of five objects in the classroom that weigh more than 1 pound and five objects that weigh less than 1 pound.

Enrichment • Measurement

Tell students to make a list of items in their bedrooms that would be measured in pounds and items that would be measured in ounces.

More to Explore • Geometry

Have students trace their right hand on a sheet of graph paper. Have students count and label the number of squares covered by their hand. Tell them to count every square that is included or drawn through, as one whole square. Have students repeat the process for their right foot. Ask students to compare the areas of their hand with that of their foot. Discuss the results. Ask students for the mathematical problem that would be a way to find the area of a pair of hands and a pair of feet.

14-4 Cups, Pints, and Quarts

pages 267–268

1 Getting Started

Objectives

- To compare the capacities of cups, pints, and quarts
- To estimate capacities of a cup, pint, and quart

Vocabulary

cup, pint, quart, capacity

Materials

*various-sized containers; cup, pint, and quart containers; *measuring cups; water or plastic foam packing filler; magazines or newspapers

Warm Up • Mental Math

Tell students to name the day or month.

1. eleventh month (November)
2. last month of the year (December)
3. last day of the week (Saturday)
4. month between March and May (April)
5. fifth day of the week (Thursday)

Warm Up • Measurement

Write the following on the board: **16 ounces = 1 pound**. Have students add 16 and 16 to find out how many ounces are in 2 pounds and write it on the board. (32 ounces = 2 pounds) Have students find the number of ounces in 3, 4, 5 pounds and so on.

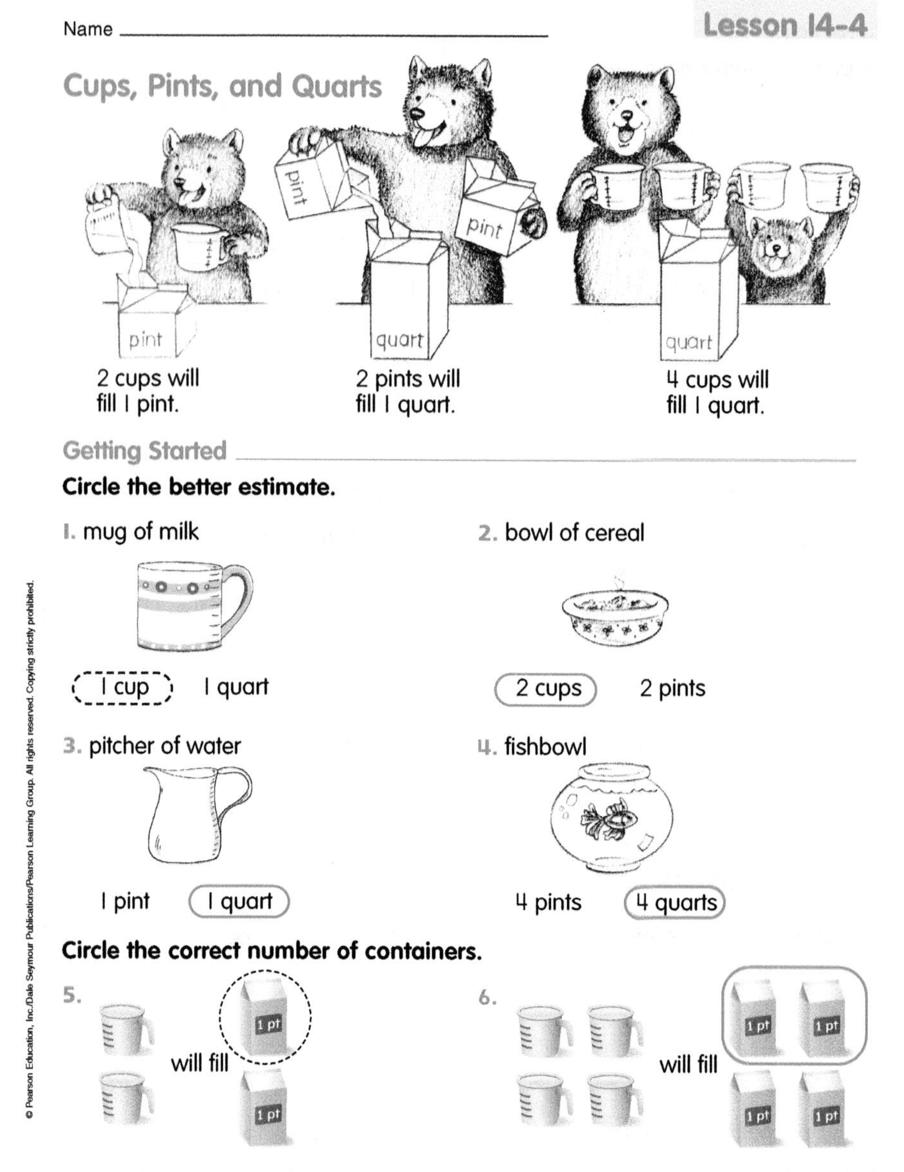

Name ____________________ Lesson 14-4

Cups, Pints, and Quarts

2 cups will fill 1 pint.

2 pints will fill 1 quart.

4 cups will fill 1 quart.

Getting Started

Circle the better estimate.

1. mug of milk — 1 cup / 1 quart
2. bowl of cereal — 2 cups / 2 pints
3. pitcher of water — 1 pint / 1 quart
4. fishbowl — 4 pints / 4 quarts

Circle the correct number of containers.

5. [2 cups] will fill [1 pt] [1 pt]
6. [4 cups] will fill [1 pt] [1 pt] [1 pt] [1 pt]

2 Teach

Develop Skills and Concepts Show students the cup and pint containers. Have a student fill the cup with water or plastic foam filler and pour it into the pint. Ask if the pint will hold more. (yes) Have the student pour another cupful into the pint and tell how many cups equal 1 pint. (2) Repeat for filling the quart container from a pint container. (2 pints = 1 quart) Continue for students to see that 4 cups equal 1 quart. Repeat each measurement and write the following on the board:

2 cups = 1 pint
2 pints = 1 quart
4 cups = 1 quart

- Ask students how they can use these measurements to find out how many cups are in 2 pints. (add 2 cups and 2 cups) Write the following on the board:

1 pint = 2 cups
+ 1 pint = 2 cups
2 pints = 4 cups

- Continue to find how many cups are in 2 quarts, pints in 2 quarts, and so on. Now, show students various-sized containers to estimate the capacity each would hold. Have students measure to check each estimate.

3 Practice

Using page 267 Ask students to read the three sentences silently. Ask how many pints will fill 1 quart. (2) Ask how many cups will fill 1 pint. (2) Ask how many cups will fill 1 quart. (4)

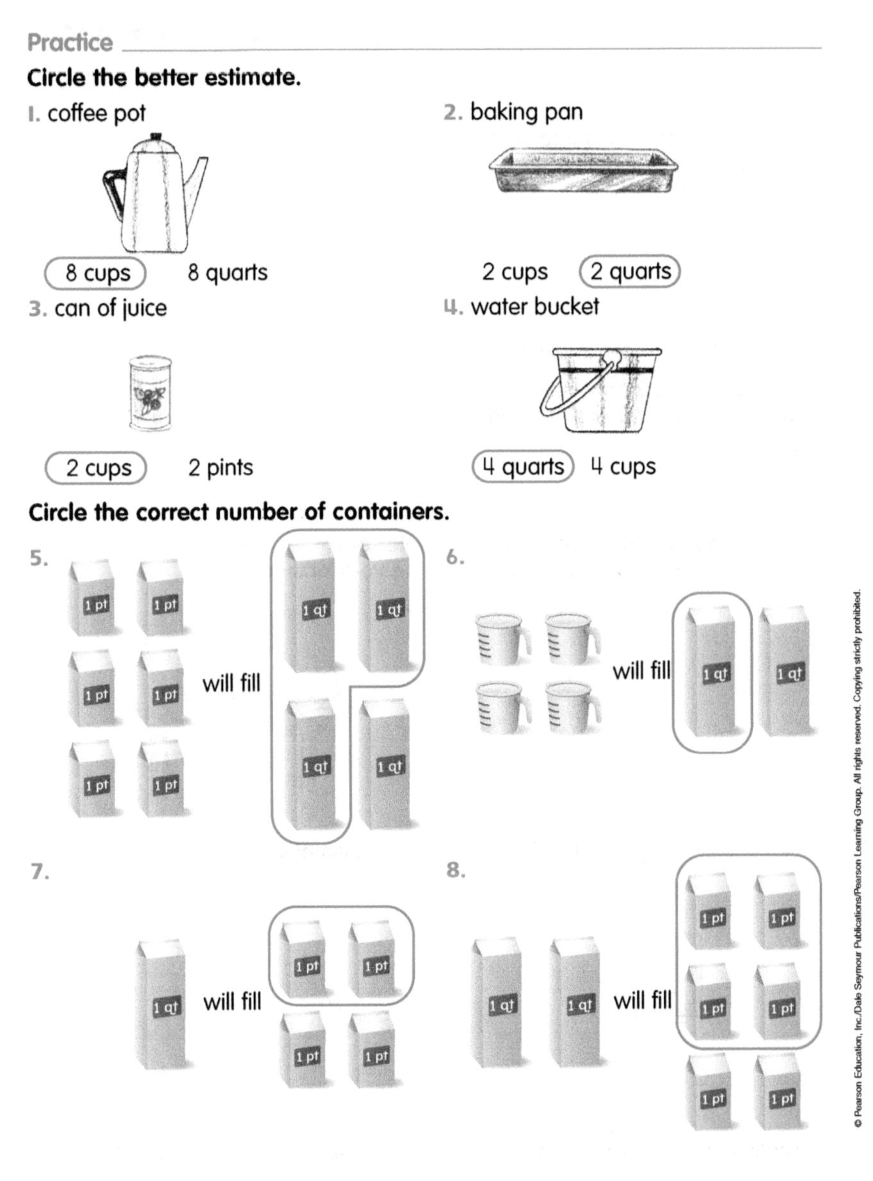

Practice

Circle the better estimate.

1. coffee pot — (8 cups) 8 quarts
2. baking pan — 2 cups (2 quarts)
3. can of juice — (2 cups) 2 pints
4. water bucket — (4 quarts) 4 cups

Circle the correct number of containers.

5. 1 pt 1 pt 1 pt 1 pt 1 pt 1 pt will fill 1 qt 1 qt 1 qt 1 qt
6. will fill 1 qt 1 qt
7. 1 qt will fill 1 pt 1 pt 1 pt 1 pt
8. 1 qt 1 qt will fill 1 pt 1 pt 1 pt 1 pt 1 pt 1 pt

- Ask students if the mug of milk in Exercise 1 would hold about 1 cup or 1 quart of liquid. (1 cup) Have students trace the correct answer for Exercise 1 and complete Exercises 2 to 4 independently. Then, tell students to look at Exercise 5 and tell how many of the pint containers can be filled with the contents of the cups. (1 pint) Have students complete Exercise 6 independently.

Using page 268 Tell students to estimate the better guess of measurement for Exercises 1 to 4 and then find which containers can be filled in Exercises 5 to 8. Have students complete the page independently.

4 Assess

Tell students to cut from magazines or newspapers items that are commonly measured in cups, pints, or quarts. Have them use the pictures to make a chart telling the number of cups in a pint, pints in a quart, and cups in a quart.

For Mixed Abilities

Common Errors • Intervention

Some students may have difficulty choosing the appropriate unit to measure liquid capacity. Have them work in cooperative groups with models of a cup, pint, and quart. Have them use water or sand to see how many of each unit it takes to fill the next larger unit. Then, let them fill various nonstandard containers with water or sand from the models. This provides everyday life models for estimating and comparing capacities.

Enrichment • Measurement

Tell students that another unit used to measure capacity is the gallon. There are 4 quarts in a gallon. Ask them to find how many cups are in a gallon (16) and how many pints (8). Repeat the activity for 2 and 3 gallons.

More to Explore • Measurement

Give students one drinking straw each and tell them to cut it to any length they want. Tell them that they have created a new nonstandard measuring unit that they must then name, for example, "squinch." Tell students to measure items you name, such as desktop, length and width of a textbook, their forearm, and so on, with their nonstandard unit of measure and record each measure. Then, have them repeat each measurement, using a standard unit of measurement, and record the data. Have students compare and discuss their two sets of measurements. Ask them to explain why standard units of measurement are necessary.

14-5 Centimeters and Meters

pages 269–270

1 Getting Started

Objectives

- To measure length in centimeters
- To determine when to use centimeters or meters to measure

Vocabulary

centimeter, meter

Materials

*10-centimeter paper strip; objects with lengths in whole centimeters; centimeter ruler; 6-inch ruler; paper strips; colored chalk

Warm Up • Mental Math

Tell students to name the ordinal number for the following:

1. the tenth plus eighteenth (twenty-eighth)
2. the month of October (tenth)
3. today's date
4. your age in order in your family from the oldest
5. 5 less than twentieth (fifteenth)
6. 11 more than eighty-eighth (ninety-ninth)

Warm Up • Measurement

Display several paper strips that are not exact to the inch. Have students measure the strips to the nearest inch and tell about how long each strip is.

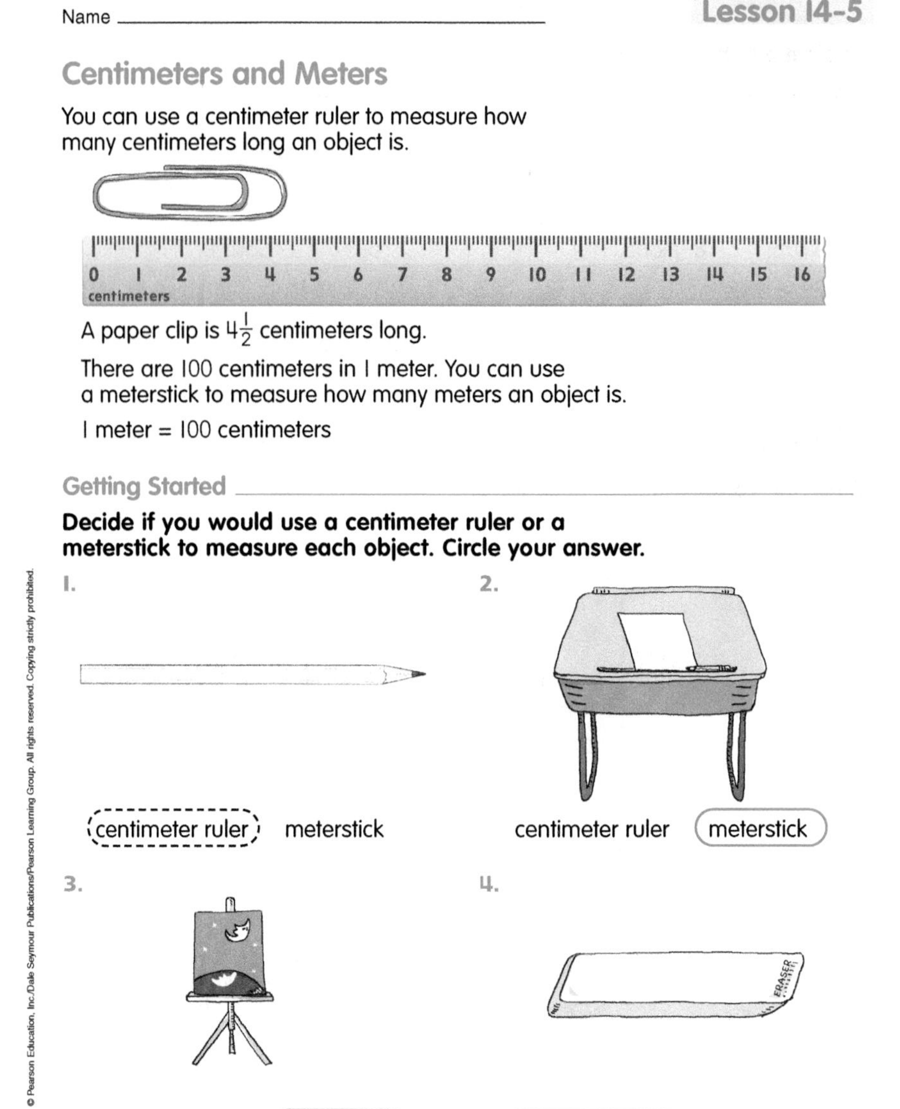

Name ______________________

Lesson 14-5

Centimeters and Meters

You can use a centimeter ruler to measure how many centimeters long an object is.

A paper clip is $4\frac{1}{2}$ centimeters long.

There are 100 centimeters in 1 meter. You can use a meterstick to measure how many meters an object is.

1 meter = 100 centimeters

Getting Started

Decide if you would use a centimeter ruler or a meterstick to measure each object. Circle your answer.

1. centimeter ruler meterstick
2. centimeter ruler meterstick
3. centimeter ruler meterstick
4. centimeter ruler meterstick

2 Teach

Develop Skills and Concepts Tell students that the centimeter is a metric unit of measure for length. It is measured with a centimeter ruler. Have students read the numbers in order across a centimeter ruler. Have students work in pairs to measure various objects and record their measurements. When all students have had time to measure several objects, have students measure each object as other students check their work. Attach a 10-centimeter paper strip on the board or bulletin board and ask a student to measure it and tell its length in centimeters. (10 centimeters) Have another student measure and make a mark on the strip at 8 centimeters. Continue for 5 centimeters, 9 centimeters, 3 centimeters, and so on.

3 Practice

Using page 269 Read the first sentence aloud. Then, have students look at the drawing and tell how long the paper clip is. ($4\frac{1}{2}$ centimeters) Then, have a student read the next set of sentences aloud. Display a meterstick and explain that this is a tool we use to measure meters.

- Have students tell whether they would use a centimeter ruler or a meterstick to measure a pencil. (centimeter ruler) Have them trace the dashed circle around the answer for Exercise 1 before completing Exercises 2 to 4 independently.

Using page 270 Tell students to make a mark for each cut in the first group of exercises and then measure and write the centimeters for each item in Exercises 4 to 6. Assign the page to be completed independently.

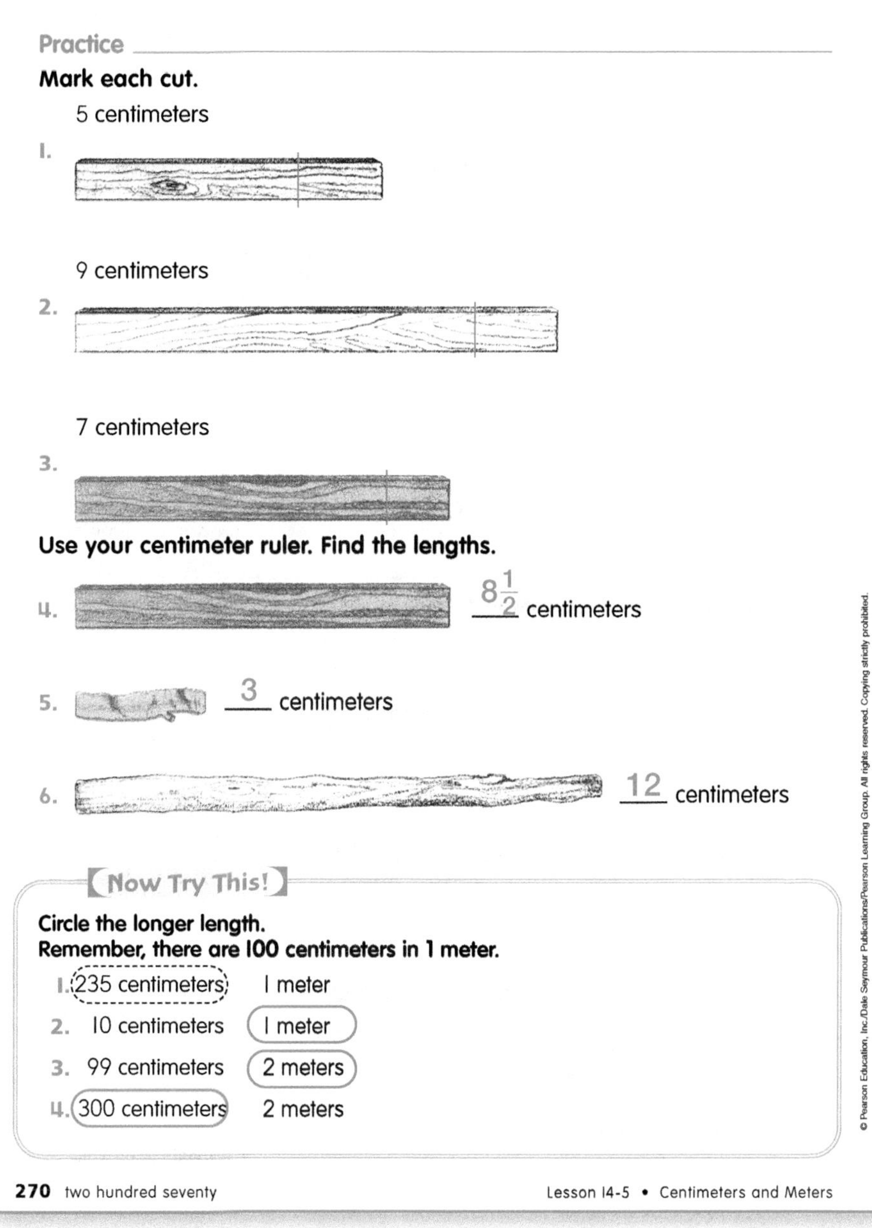

Practice

Mark each cut.

1. 5 centimeters

2. 9 centimeters

3. 7 centimeters

Use your centimeter ruler. Find the lengths.

4. $8\frac{1}{2}$ centimeters

5. 3 centimeters

6. 12 centimeters

Now Try This!

Circle the longer length.
Remember, there are 100 centimeters in 1 meter.

1. (235 centimeters) 1 meter
2. 10 centimeters (1 meter)
3. 99 centimeters (2 meters)
4. (300 centimeters) 2 meters

For Mixed Abilities

Common Errors • Intervention

If students need more practice measuring to the nearest centimeter, have them work in pairs to cut various lengths from paper strips. Then, they should share the strips equally, measure each to the nearest centimeter, mark the measurement on the back, and then trade them to check each other's answers.

Enrichment • Measurement

Tell students to draw a picture that has objects in it that are 1, 3, 6, and 9 centimeters in length.

More to Explore • Application

Ask a local deli that serves breakfast to let you use a current or no longer used menu. Tell students that they each have $9.99 to spend on breakfast and lunch for the next day. Have students use the menu and plan their meals. Tell them to write out their choices, the prices, and the total bill for each meal. Have them add all meals together for a day's total. Have them make note of any things that strongly influenced their decisions on how to spend the money.

Now Try This! Read the directions with students. Then, review the first exercise. Remind students that there are 100 centimeters in 1 meter. Given this, 235 centimeters is a longer length than 1 meter. Have students trace the answer before completing the remaining exercises independently.

4 Assess

Have pairs of students use colored chalk to draw lines that are 50 centimeters, 1 meter, and $1\frac{1}{2}$ meters long.

5 Mixed Review

1. 6 + 8 + 4 (18)
2. $7.02 − $5.31 ($1.71)
3. 96 − 27 (69)
4. 87¢ + 46¢ ($1.33)
5. 226 ◯ 262 (<)
6. 175 + 225 + 108 (508)
7. 368 + 402 (770)
8. 9 hundreds 2 tens 5 ones (925)
9. 408 − 28 (380)
10. 756 − 235 (521)

14-6 Measuring to the Nearest Centimeter

pages 271–272

1 Getting Started

Objective
- To measure length to the nearest centimeter

Materials
*paper strips not cut to the exact centimeter or half-centimeter; *straightedge; centimeter ruler

Warm Up • Mental Math
Tell students to name the closest hour to

1. 2:03 (2:00)
2. 6:48 (7:00)
3. 12:40 (1:00)
4. 9:25 (9:00)
5. 11:57 (12:00)
6. 7:35 (8:00)
7. 10:15 (10:00)
8. 1:01 (1:00)

Warm Up • Measurement
Use a straightedge to draw the following lengths on the board: 5 centimeters, 9 centimeters, 4 centimeters, 1 centimeter, and 11 centimeters. Have students measure and record each length. Repeat for more lengths in centimeters.

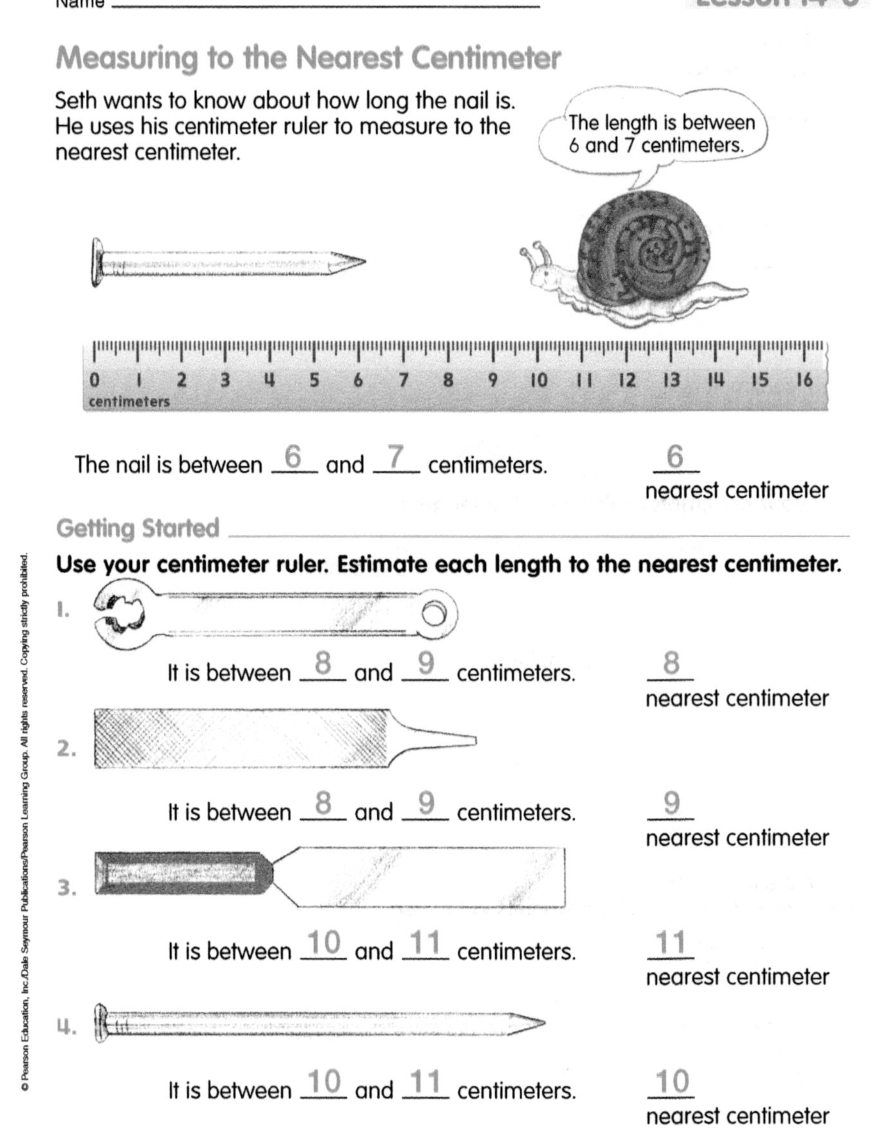

2 Teach

Develop Skills and Concepts Have students find the mark between 2 and 3 on the centimeter ruler. Tell students that the mark is halfway between 2 and 3 and means a measure of $2\frac{1}{2}$ centimeters. Have students locate other half marks on the ruler and tell each length.

- Give each student a paper strip that is slightly longer than 8 centimeters. Have students measure and tell if the length is exactly 8 centimeters. (no) Tell students that we then look to see if the length is closer to 8 or to 9 centimeters as you write **between 8 and 9 centimeters** on the board. Tell students that if the length is between 8 and the $8\frac{1}{2}$ mark, then it is closer to 8 centimeters; however, if it is between the $8\frac{1}{2}$ mark and the 9, it is closer to 9 centimeters. Ask students which whole centimeter is closer to the end of the strip. (8) Write **nearest centimeter** on the board and have a student write **8** on the board. Repeat with more paper strips.

3 Practice

Using page 271 Have a student read the example and tell what is to be found. (about how long the nail is) Ask what is known. (The nail is more than 6 centimeters.) Have students read the caption and then complete the sentence. Have students check the centimeter ruler to see if the length of the nail is closer to 6 or 7 and then write the nearest centimeter on the line. (6)

- Help students with Exercise 1 if necessary. Then, have them complete the remaining exercises independently.

Using page 272 Tell students that they are to measure each length to the nearest centimeter. Assign the page to be completed independently.

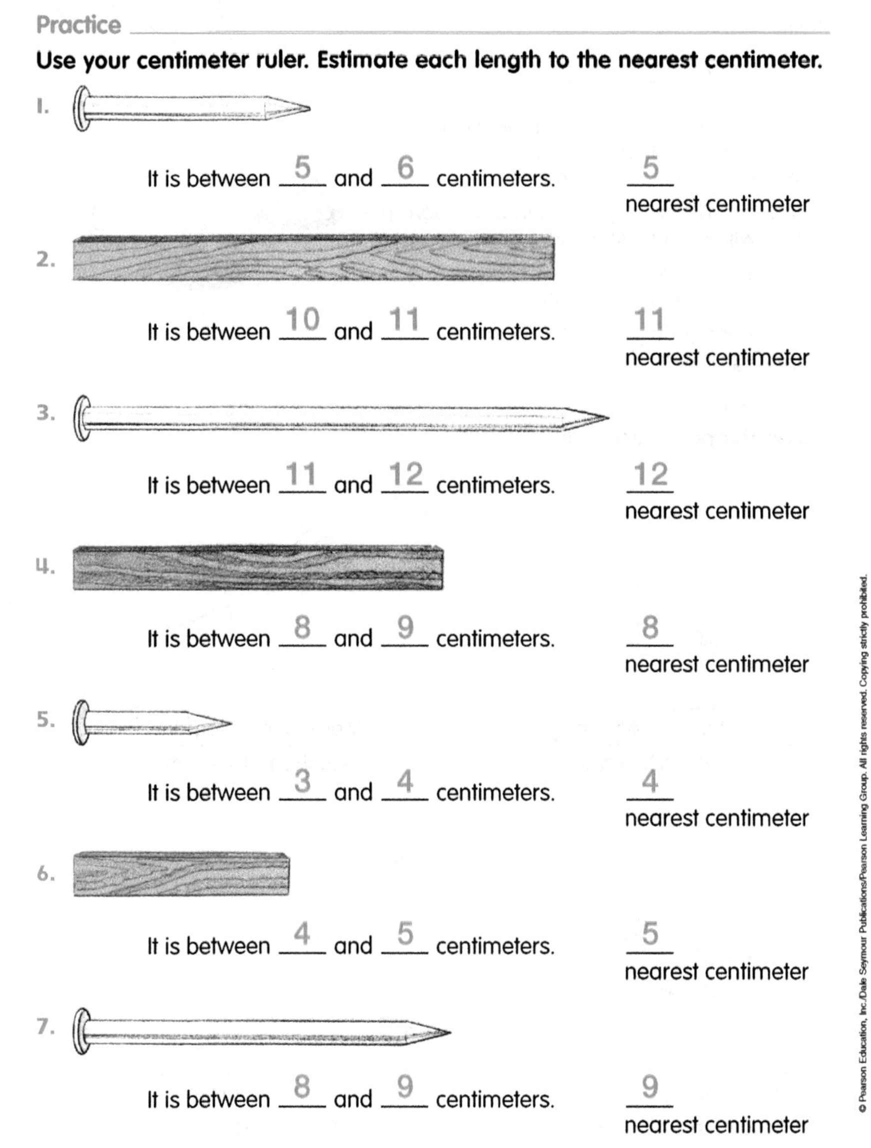

Practice

Use your centimeter ruler. Estimate each length to the nearest centimeter.

1. It is between 5 and 6 centimeters. 5 nearest centimeter
2. It is between 10 and 11 centimeters. 11 nearest centimeter
3. It is between 11 and 12 centimeters. 12 nearest centimeter
4. It is between 8 and 9 centimeters. 8 nearest centimeter
5. It is between 3 and 4 centimeters. 4 nearest centimeter
6. It is between 4 and 5 centimeters. 5 nearest centimeter
7. It is between 8 and 9 centimeters. 9 nearest centimeter

4 Assess

Cut strips of paper to $8\frac{3}{4}$ centimeters, $5\frac{1}{8}$ centimeters, and $6\frac{2}{3}$ centimeters. Have students say what lengths each piece is between. (8 and 9 cm, 5 and 6 cm, 6 and 7 cm)

5 Mixed Review

1. 773 ◯ 377 (>)
2. 651 − 68 (583)
3. 83 − 41 (42)
4. 205, 210, 215, _____ (220)
5. $3.93 − $2.96 ($0.97)
6. 5 dimes, 1 quarter, 1 nickel (80¢)
7. 27¢ + 46¢ (73¢)
8. 63 + 29 + 42 ($1.34)
9. 17 − 6 (11)
10. _____ + 7 = 15 (8)

For Mixed Abilities

Common Errors • Intervention

If students have difficulty measuring objects to the nearest centimeter, have them work with partners to measure paper strips. If they put a paper strip very close to the edge of the ruler, it will be easier to see where the end of the strip meets the ruler and to which of the two numbers of centimeters it is closer. A ruler is also easier to read if the person using it sits squarely in front of and looks down over the ruler.

Enrichment • Measurement

Tell students to draw a five-sided figure and then measure each side to the nearest centimeter and record the length.

More to Explore • Application

Discuss with the class the reasons for planning ahead and budgeting when handling money for a family or business. Make sure students understand what a budget is. Invite someone who works with budgeting daily, such as an accountant or homemaker, to speak to the class about how he or she deals with planning and budgeting on the job. Encourage students to ask their parents about their family budget.

14-7 Grams and Kilograms

pages 273–274

1 Getting Started

Objective
- To compare and estimate the weights of objects in grams and kilograms

Vocabulary
gram, kilogram

Materials
gram weight; kilogram weight; balance scale

Warm Up • Mental Math
Have students tell how many.

1. inches are in a foot (12)
2. feet are in a yard (3)
3. ounces are in a pound (16)
4. centimeters are in a meter (100)
5. pints are in a quart (2)
6. cups are in a pint (2)

Warm Up • Measurement
Have students tell what tool they should use to measure the following:

1. time (watch or clock)
2. length in inches (ruler)
3. length in centimeters (centimeter ruler)
4. weight (scale)
5. capacity (measuring cup)

Name ______________________

Lesson 14-7

Grams and Kilograms

A kilogram is a metric unit for measuring how much something weighs.
The book weighs 1 kilogram.

A baseball bat weighs less than 1 kilogram.
A bowling ball weighs more than 1 kilogram.

A gram is also a metric unit for measuring how much something weighs.

There are 1,000 grams in a kilogram.
1,000 grams = 1 kilogram

Getting Started

Circle the better estimate.

1.

More than 1 kilogram (circled)
Less than 1 kilogram

2.

More than 1 kilogram
Less than 1 kilogram (circled)

3.

More than 1 kilogram (circled)
Less than 1 kilogram

4.

More than 1 gram (circled)
Less than 1 gram

2 Teach

Develop Skills and Concepts Explain that we can measure how much something weighs in metric or customary units. The metric units are grams and kilograms. [Note: These units are actually units of mass. Mass will not change based on gravity. However, for purposes of discussion, we will assume all measurements are on Earth, so saying *weight* is acceptable.]

- If possible, allow students to handle a weight of 1 gram and another of 1 kilogram. Use a balance scale to put the weights on for students to see that a kilogram "weighs" more than a gram. Then, use the scale to test the weight of classroom items against the kilogram. Students can use the kilogram as a benchmark for determining whether an object weighs more or less than 1 kilogram.

3 Practice

Using page 273 Read the sentences at the top of the page with students and make sure they understand that there are 1,000 grams in a kilogram. Call their attention to the art and ask, *What has a weight of about 1 kilogram?* (a book)

- Work with students to complete Exercise 1. *Does a large dog weigh more than a book?* (yes) Have students trace the dashed circle. Have students complete the remaining exercises independently.

Using page 274 Have students look at Exercise 1. Say, *A baseball bat weighs less than 1 kilogram. Does a pencil weigh more than a baseball bat?* (no)

- Have students complete Exercise 2 and then review their answers with the class. Now, have students complete the remaining exercises independently.

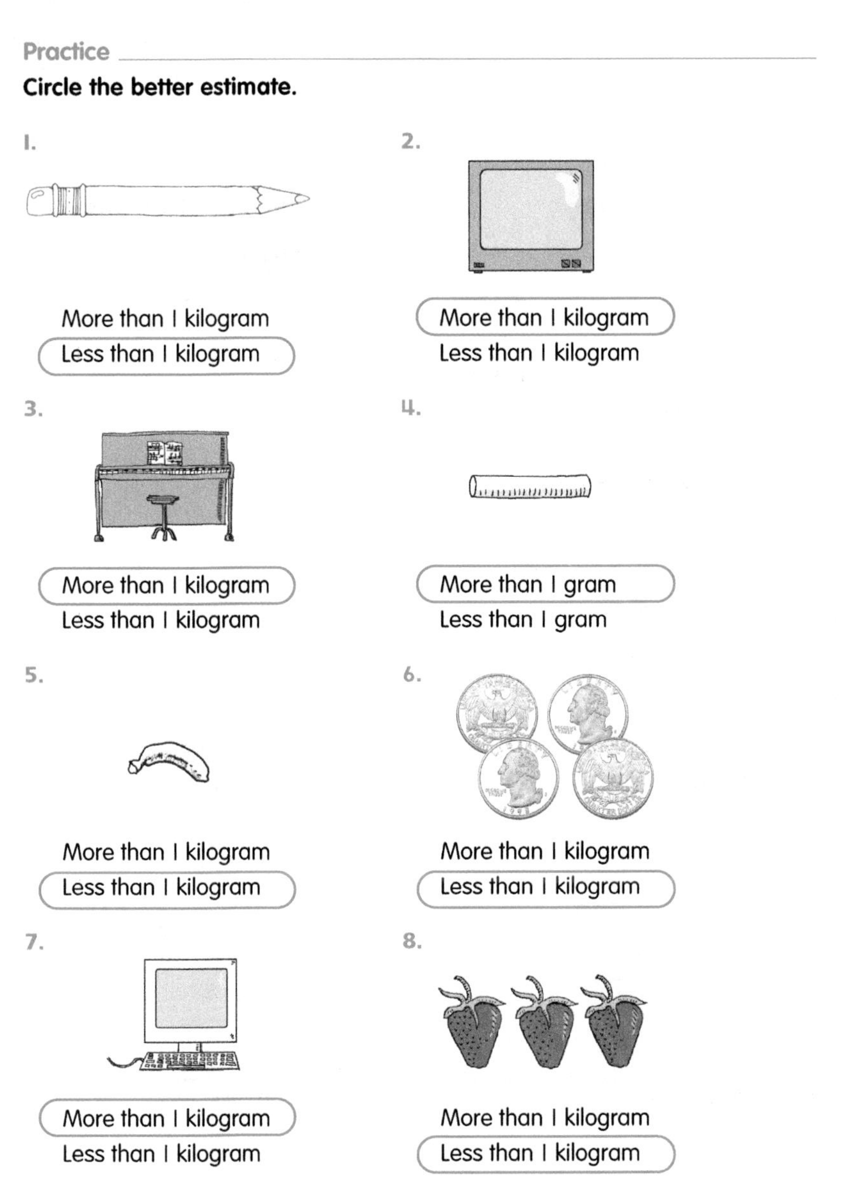

Practice

Circle the better estimate.

1. More than 1 kilogram / Less than 1 kilogram
2. More than 1 kilogram / Less than 1 kilogram
3. More than 1 kilogram / Less than 1 kilogram
4. More than 1 gram / Less than 1 gram
5. More than 1 kilogram / Less than 1 kilogram
6. More than 1 kilogram / Less than 1 kilogram
7. More than 1 kilogram / Less than 1 kilogram
8. More than 1 kilogram / Less than 1 kilogram

For Mixed Abilities

Common Errors • Intervention

Some students may think that the larger the object, the more it weighs. Have students handle tall and large objects that are light and short or small objects that are heavy.

Enrichment • Measurement

Have students name five objects that can be measured in grams. (Possible answers: feather, paper clip, CD, sheet of paper, pen) Then, have them name five objects that weigh about 1 kilogram. (Possible answers: stapler, tape dispenser, stuffed animal, doll, notebook)

More to Explore • Measurement

Have students work in groups to determine which classroom objects weigh more than 1 kilogram, about 1 kilogram, and less than 1 kilogram. A recorder can make a list of the group's findings. For those classroom items that weigh less than 1 kilogram, groups can determine how many of the items it would take to weigh about 1 kilogram.

4 Assess

Ask students which weighs more, a kilogram of rocks or a kilogram of paper. Have students explain their answer.

5 Mixed Review

1. 8 + 5 + 9 (22)
2. 26 + 18 + 21 (65)
3. 565 − 20 (545)
4. 1 quarter, 1 dime, 1 nickel (40¢)
5. 295 + 430 (725)
6. 91 − 37 (54)
7. 372 − 80 (292)
8. 78¢ + 45¢ ($1.23)
9. 650 ◯ 560 (>)
10. 6 + _____ = 10 (4)

14-8 Milliliters and Liters

pages 275–276

1 Getting Started

Objective

- To estimate and measure capacity in milliliters and liters

Vocabulary

liter, milliliter

Materials

liter bottle; milliliter dropper

Warm Up • Mental Math

Have students tell which is the greater unit.

1. inch or foot (foot)
2. yard or foot (yard)
3. pound or ounce (pound)
4. gram or kilogram (kilogram)
5. centimeter or meter (meter)
6. cup or pint (pint)

Warm Up • Measurement

Have students tell if each item weighs more or less than 1 kilogram.

1. truck (more)
2. pencil (less)
3. DVD player (more)
4. DVD (less)
5. sticky note (less)
6. cat (more)

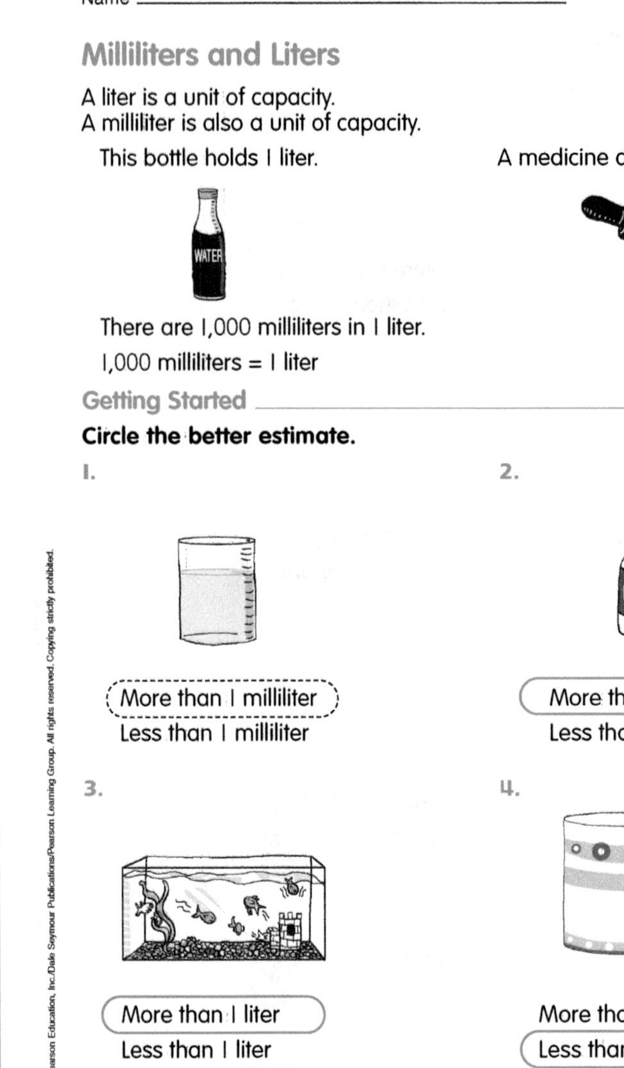

Name ______________________ Lesson 14-8

Milliliters and Liters

A liter is a unit of capacity.
A milliliter is also a unit of capacity.

This bottle holds 1 liter. A medicine dropper holds 1 milliliter.

There are 1,000 milliliters in 1 liter.
1,000 milliliters = 1 liter

Getting Started

Circle the better estimate.

1. More than 1 milliliter / Less than 1 milliliter
2. More than 1 liter / Less than 1 liter
3. More than 1 liter / Less than 1 liter
4. More than 1 liter / Less than 1 liter

2 Teach

Develop Skills and Concepts Explain to students that capacity, or the amount a container can hold, can also be measured in the metric system. Ask students to name types of containers that they have used that are measured in liters. (Possible answers: soda, bottled water, sports drinks) Show students the difference between a liter and a milliliter by showing a 1-liter bottle of water and a milliliter dropper. Students can use the liter bottle as a benchmark to compare other capacities.

3 Practice

Using page 275 Read the sentences at the top of the page with students. Call their attention to the drawings. Ask, *How many milliliters are in a liter of water?* (1,000)

- Work with students to complete Exercise 1. *Does a glass of juice have a greater capacity than a drop of water?* (yes) Have students trace the dashed circle around more than 1 milliliter. Have students complete the page independently.

Using page 276 Have students look at Exercise 1. Ask, *What does it mean for an object to contain 20 liters?* (It will have the same capacity as twenty 1-liter bottles of water.) *What does it mean for an object to contain 200 liters?* (It will have the same capacity as two hundred 1-liter bottles of water.) Have students choose their answer for Exercise 1 and then review with the class.

- Have students complete Exercise 2 and then review their answer with the class. Now, have students complete the page.

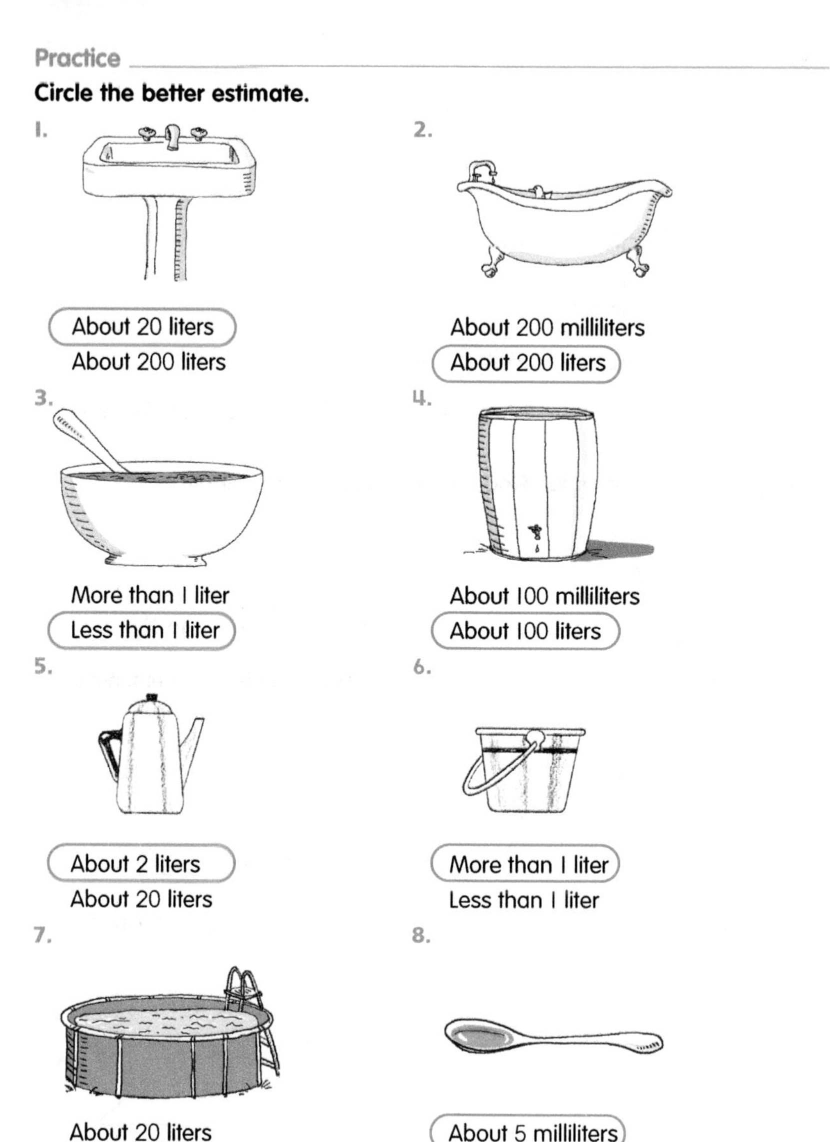

Practice

Circle the better estimate.

1. (About 20 liters) / About 200 liters
2. About 200 milliliters / (About 200 liters)
3. More than 1 liter / (Less than 1 liter)
4. About 100 milliliters / (About 100 liters)
5. (About 2 liters) / About 20 liters
6. (More than 1 liter) / Less than 1 liter
7. About 20 liters / (About 2,000 liters)
8. (About 5 milliliters) / About 5 liters

4 Assess

Ask students to name three containers that have a capacity that is less than 1 liter and three containers that have a capacity that is greater than 1 liter. (Possible answers: less—spoon, coffee mug, drinking glass; more—fish tank, bathtub, sink)

For Mixed Abilities

Common Errors • Intervention

Some students may think that when comparing milliliters and liters, the larger number is the correct measure. Remind students that 1,000 milliliters is equal to a liter, so any measure less than 1,000 milliliters is also less than 1 liter.

Enrichment • Measurement

Have students compare standard units of measurement with metric units of measurement. Ask, *Does a gallon container hold more or less than a liter container?* (more) *Which customary unit has about the same capacity as a liter?* (quart)

More to Explore • Measurement

In the metric system, prefixes are used to describe what part of a unit is being measured. Now that students have been exposed to centimeters, milliliters, and kilograms, have students describe what each prefix means. Have students create a picture glossary of the measurement terms they have learned.

ESL/ELL STRATEGIES

Write the following lists on the board: **List 1: capacity, length, weight**; **List 2: inches, centimeters, pounds, ounces, kilograms, grams, liters, milliliters**. Ask students to match each term in List 1 with appropriate units of measurement in List 2.

14-9 Perimeter

pages 277–278

1 Getting Started

Objective
- To measure to find the perimeter of a figure in centimeters

Vocabulary
perimeter

Materials
*straightedge; *square corner; *figures having sides in exact centimeters; centimeter ruler; ribbon cut to various sizes

Warm Up • Mental Math
Ask students to solve the following:

1. 100 + 6 (106)
2. 64 + 9 (73)
3. 6 + 6 + 6 (18)
4. 24 − 16 (8)
5. 40 + 50 (90)
6. 6 + 5 + 10 (21)
7. 50 + 70 (120)
8. 120 − 90 (30)

Warm Up • Measurement
Have students find the total length of two ribbons that are 8 cm and 5 cm long. (13 cm) Repeat for adding two lengths of various sizes using centimeters.

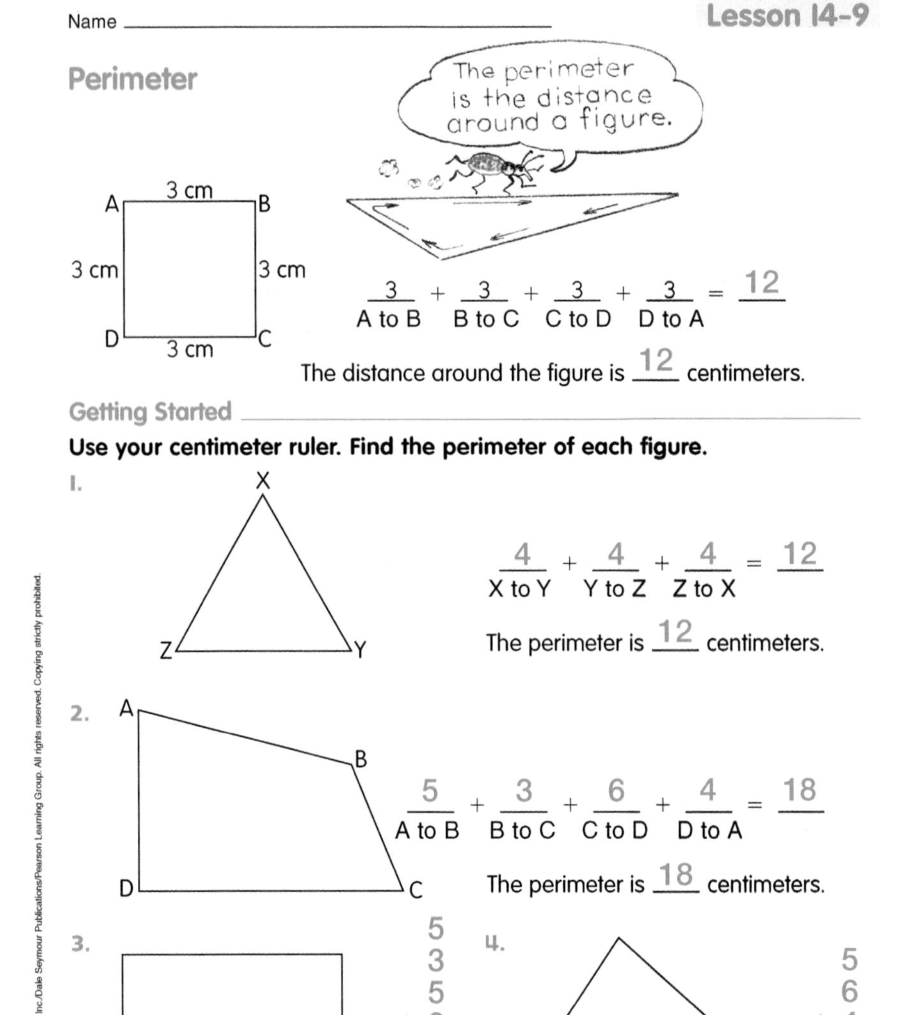

Name ______________________ Lesson 14-9

Perimeter

3 + 3 + 3 + 3 = 12
A to B, B to C, C to D, D to A

The distance around the figure is 12 centimeters.

Getting Started

Use your centimeter ruler. Find the perimeter of each figure.

1. 4 + 4 + 4 = 12 (X to Y, Y to Z, Z to X)
The perimeter is 12 centimeters.

2. 5 + 3 + 6 + 4 = 18 (A to B, B to C, C to D, D to A)
The perimeter is 18 centimeters.

3. 5 + 3 + 5 + 3 = 16
perimeter = 16 centimeters

4. 5 + 6 + 4 = 15
perimeter = 15 centimeters

Lesson 14-9 • Perimeter two hundred seventy-seven 277

2 Teach

Develop Skills and Concepts Use a straightedge and square corner to draw on the board a rectangle with sides of 8 centimeters and 4 centimeters. Label the corners **A, B, C,** and **D**. Write **Sides** on the board and the following under that: **A to B, B to C, C to D,** and **D to A**. Have a student use a centimeter ruler to measure the length from A to B and record the distance on the board. Repeat for the other sides. Tell students to find the total distance around the figure. Tell students that the perimeter is the total distance around a figure as you write **perimeter** on the board. Tell students that we must add all four lengths to find the perimeter as you write ____ + ____ + ____ + ____ = ____ **centimeters** on the board. Have a student write the measurements of the sides in the number sentence and find the sum. (8 + 4 + 8 + 4 = 24 centimeters) Display labeled figures that have sides measured in exact centimeters and have students find the perimeter of each.

3 Practice

Using page 277 Ask students to identify the shape at the top of the page. (square) Have one student read the caption aloud and tell what is to be found. (perimeter) Tell students that *cm* is the abbreviation for centimeter. Ask them the measure of each side. (3 cm) Have students fill in the measure of each side and then find the total. (12 cm) Then, have students complete the solution sentence.

- Help students complete Exercise 1. Then, assign the remaining exercises to be completed independently.

Using page 278 Tell students to measure each side in centimeters and then add the numbers to find the figure's perimeter. Tell students to record the sum on the answer line. Have students complete the page independently.

Practice

Use your centimeter ruler.
Find the perimeter of each figure.

1.

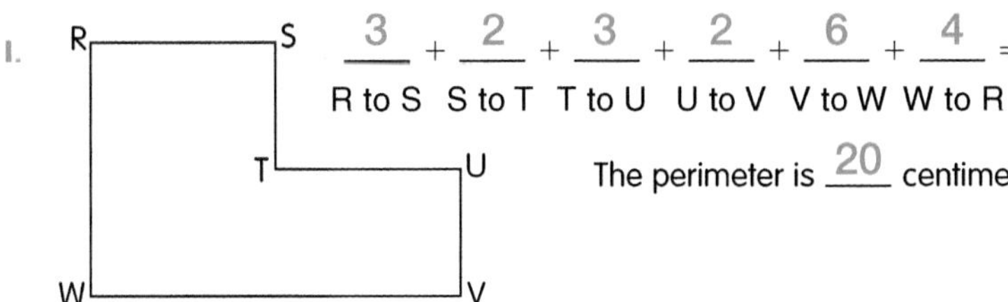

3 + 2 + 3 + 2 + 6 + 4 = 20

R to S   S to T   T to U   U to V   V to W   W to R

The perimeter is 20 centimeters.

2.

6
4
6
+ 4
20

perimeter = 20 centimeters

3.

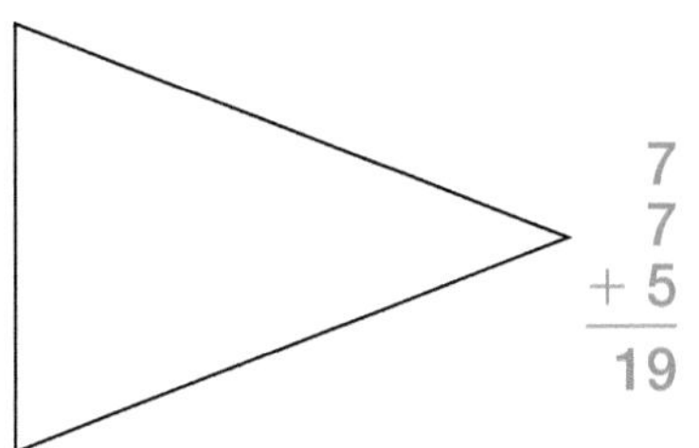

7
7
+ 5
19

perimeter = 19 centimeters

4.

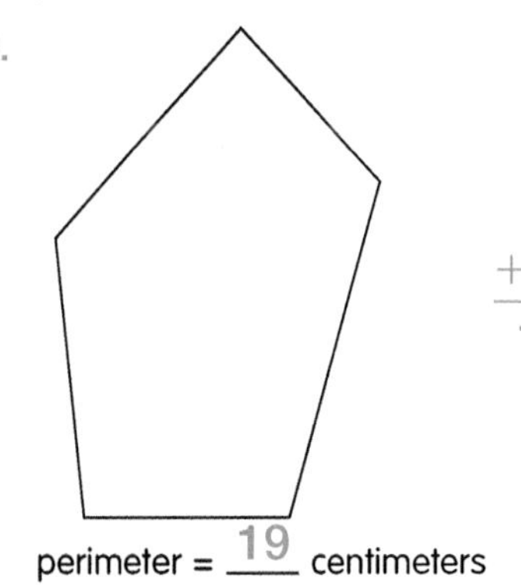

4
3
5
3
+ 4
19

perimeter = 19 centimeters

5.

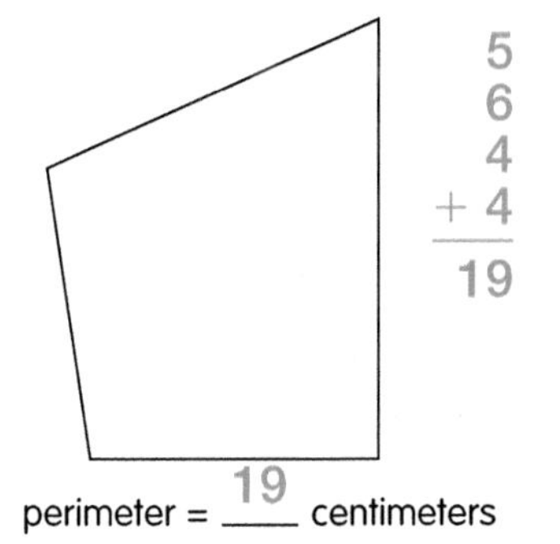

5
6
4
+ 4
19

perimeter = 19 centimeters

4 Assess

Have students find the perimeter of a 3-by-5 inch index card. (16 inches)

5 Mixed Review

1. 791 − 8 (783)
2. 303 + 28 (331)
3. 295 + 308 + 125 (728)
4. 408 + 390 (798)
5. 600 ◯ 60 (>)
6. 870, 880, 890, _____ (900)
7. $4.70 − $1.58 ($3.12)
8. 46¢ + 38¢ (84¢)
9. 391 − 68 (323)
10. _____ + 8 = 17 (9)

For Mixed Abilities

Common Errors • Intervention

Watch for students who forget to measure every side of a figure. Have them first count the number of sides on the figure and then make sure they have that number of measures, or addends, before they add.

Enrichment • Measurement

Tell students to draw three figures and find the length of each side to the nearest centimeter. Then, tell them to find the perimeter of each figure.

More to Explore • Measurement

Set up a fulcrum balance. Choose an object, such as a rock, to be the weight constant. Have each student bring in objects daily to compare with the constant. Each day, have students estimate whether the new object will weigh more or less than the constant. When all students have made an estimate, weigh the objects. Have students keep a chart and record both their estimate and the outcome. When finished, have students tally the number of correct estimates made.

14-10 Problem Solving: Try, Check, and Revise

pages 279–280

1 Getting Started

Objective

- To find the perimeter of figures by trying, checking, and revising

Warm Up • Mental Math

Have students find the sum or difference.

1. 20 + 44 (64)
2. 25 + 50 (75)
3. 58 + 30 (88)
4. 65 − 15 (50)
5. 42 − 22 (20)
6. 65 − 40 (25)

Warm Up • Paper and Pencil

Have students write the change they would receive if they gave a cashier a $1 bill for an item that cost the following:

1. 57¢ (43¢)
2. 79¢ (21¢)
3. 82¢ (18¢)
4. 22¢ (78¢)
5. 13¢ (87¢)
6. 46¢ (54¢)

Name ______________________

Problem Solving
Lesson 14-10

It's Algebra!

Problem Solving: Try, Check, and Revise

The perimeter of the square below is 8 centimeters. What is the length of each side?

What do I know?

The perimeter is __8__ centimeters.
A square has __4__ equal sides.

Try 1	Try 2	Try 3
1 + 1 + 1 + 1 = 4. 4 is less than 8. Too small.	3 + 3 + 3 + 3 = 12 12 is greater than 8. Too big.	2 + 2 + 2 + 2 = 8 8 is equal to 8. Each side has a length of 2 centimeters.

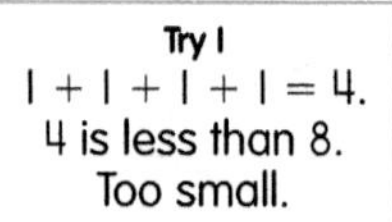

Try, check, and revise to solve.

1. The perimeter of the triangle is 12 centimeters.

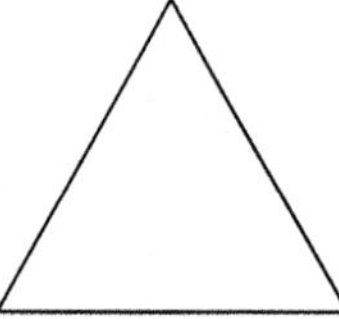

Each side of the triangle is the same length.
How long is each side?
__4__ centimeters

2. The perimeter of the square is 12 centimeters.

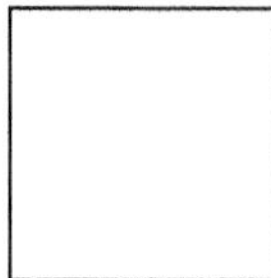

How long is each side?

__3__ centimeters

2 Teach

Develop Skills and Concepts Draw a square on the board and then read the following word problem to students: *Mike is building a fence for a dog run. Each side of the dog run will be the same length. If Mike buys 4 pieces of fence, how many will be on each side?* Now, allow students time to solve. (1 piece) Ask students what they were thinking about as you read the problem and how they solved it. (Possible answer: There are 4 pieces in all and 4 sides of the dog run. I needed to put an equal number of pieces on each side.) Show how they can use the try-check-and-revise strategy to solve the problem. *There are 4 sides and 4 pieces of fence, so try 1: 1 + 1 + 1 + 1 = 4. So, the answer is correct.*

It's Algebra! The concepts presented in this lesson prepare students for algebra.

3 Practice

Using page 279 Read with students the example at the top of the page.

- Now, apply the four-step plan. For SEE, ask, *What are you being asked to do?* (find how many centimeters each side of a square with a perimeter of 8 cm is) Then, *What information is given?* (The perimeter is 8 cm, there are 4 sides to a square.) For PLAN, ask students how they can go about finding the length of each side. (try a number, add it four times, and see if the sum is 8) For DO, have students solve the problem. For CHECK, ask, *Do you have four addends?* (yes) *Is the sum equal to 8?* (yes)
- Work with students to complete Exercise 1. Remind them that a triangle has three sides, so ask them how that will make the problem different from the example problem. Have students solve the problem and review as a class.

Practice

Try, check, and revise to solve.

1. The triangle has a perimeter of 18 centimeters. Each side is the same length.

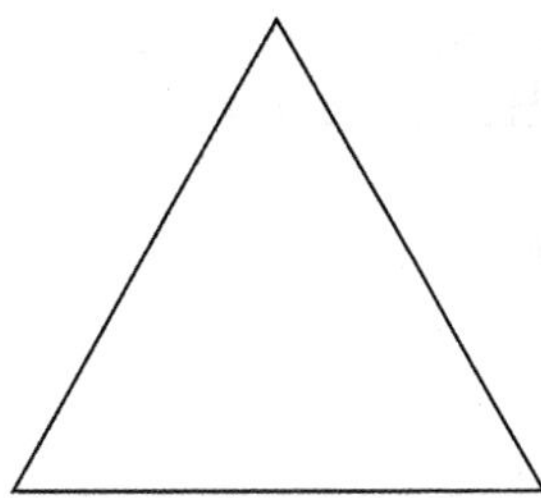

How long is each side?
__6__ centimeters

2. The square has a perimeter of 20 centimeters.

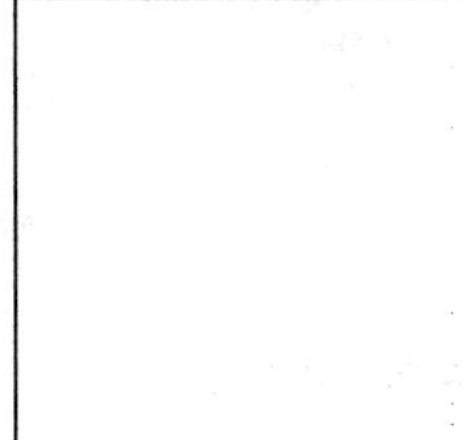

How long is each side?
__5__ centimeters

3. The rectangle has a perimeter of 16 centimeters. The longer side has a length of 5 centimeters.

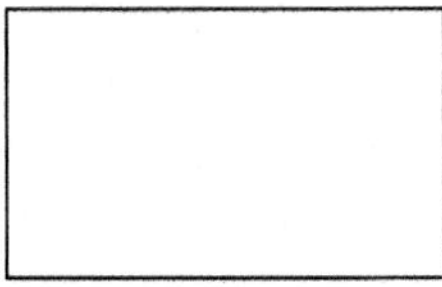

What is the length of each of the shorter sides?
__3__ centimeters

4. The triangle has a perimeter of 9 inches. Each side of the triangle is the same length.

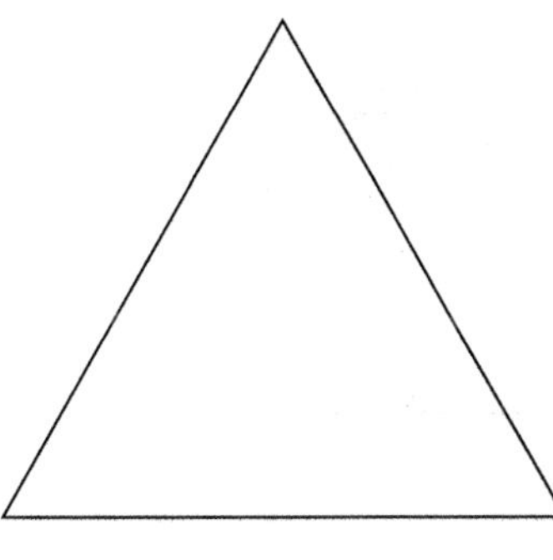

How long is each side?
__3__ inches

- Have students complete Exercise 2 independently.

Using page 280 Have students look at Exercise 1. Read the problem aloud while students read along. Ask students for the given information. (A triangle with all sides the same length has a perimeter of 18 centimeters.) Tell students to try a number that will add to 18 when added three times. If the number they chose does not work, tell them to try another number.

- Have students complete Exercise 2 independently. For Exercise 3, explain to students that a rectangle has four sides but not every side is the same length. Tell them that a rectangle will have two long sides and two short sides. Have students complete Exercise 4 independently.

4 Assess

Tell students the following: *I have a 5-sided figure and its sides are equal. The perimeter is 25 cm. How long is each side?* (5 cm)

For Mixed Abilities

Common Errors • Intervention

Students may have difficulty remembering which numbers they have already checked. After students have chosen a number, have them write down the number they have tried so that they can keep track and not lose time rechecking a number that does not work.

Enrichment • Geometry

Have students solve the following:

1. A pentagon with all 5 sides equal has a perimeter of 20 inches. What is the length of each side? (4 inches)
2. A pentagon with all 5 sides equal has a perimeter of 30 inches. What is the length of each side? (6 inches)

More to Explore • Geometry

Have students work in pairs. Give each student a centimeter ruler. Tell students that by using whole numbers only, they can find a number of different rectangles with perimeters of 20 centimeters. Have pairs work together to find how many different rectangles they can draw. Have them record the length and width of each rectangle. (1 cm by 9 cm, 2 cm by 8 cm, 3 cm by 7 cm, 4 cm by 6 cm, 5 cm by 5 cm) Have students share their findings.

14-11 Area

pages 281–282

1 Getting Started

Objective

- To find area by counting square units

Vocabulary

area, square centimeter

Materials

blank cards; centimeter graph paper; centimeter ruler; inch ruler; scissors

Warm Up • Mental Math

Tell students to name the number that equals the following:

1. days in a week + 1 dozen (19)
2. greatest 1-digit number − 3 (6)
3. minutes in 1 hour + your age
4. 1 dozen − your age
5. people in your family + all classmates
6. months in a year + 1 dozen (24)
7. wheels on a car − 2 flat tires (2)

Warm Up • Measurement

Draw lengths on the board for students to measure each to the nearest inch and to the nearest centimeter.

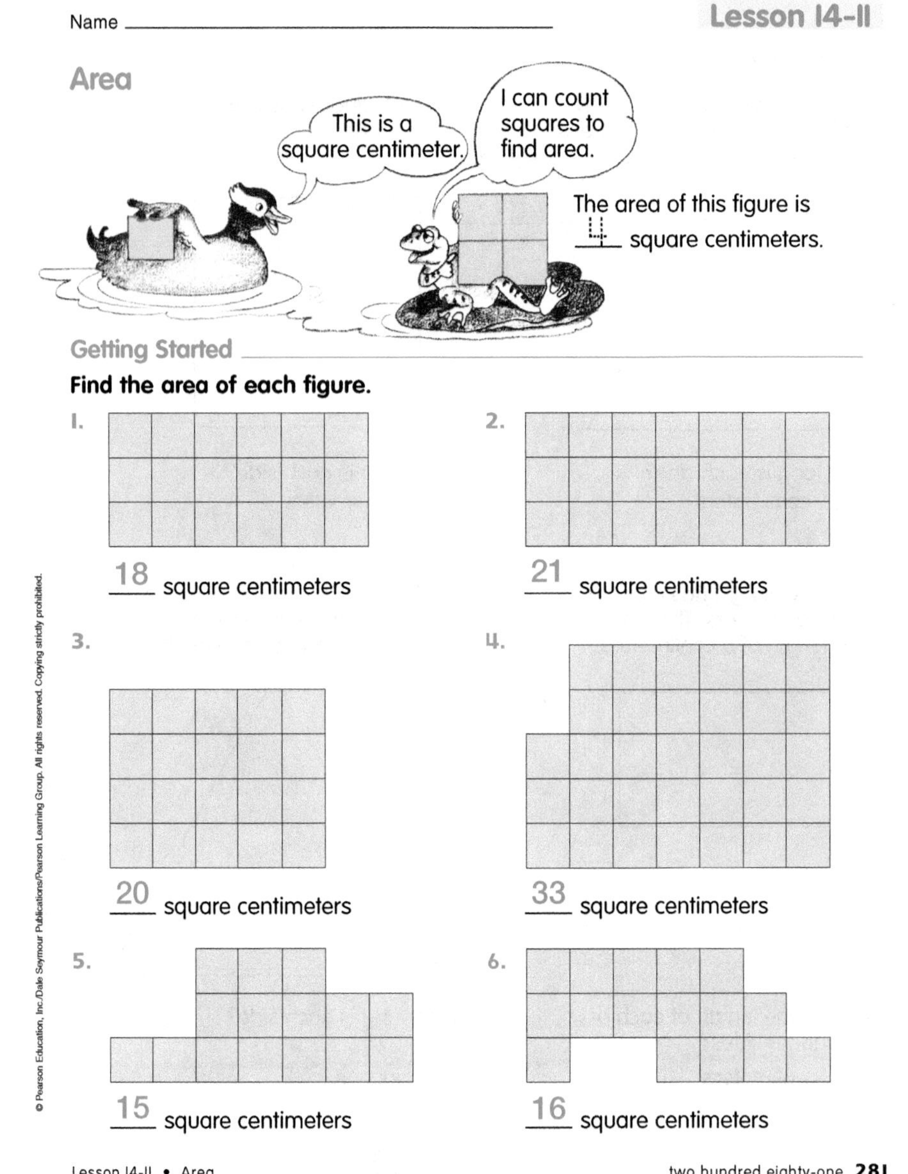

Name ______________________

Lesson 14-11

Area

The area of this figure is 4 square centimeters.

Getting Started

Find the area of each figure.

1. 18 square centimeters
2. 21 square centimeters
3. 20 square centimeters
4. 33 square centimeters
5. 15 square centimeters
6. 16 square centimeters

2 Teach

Develop Skills and Concepts Have students cut out 12 square centimeters from graph paper. Give each student a 3-by-3-centimeter card. Help students cover the card with square centimeters. Ask how many square centimeters it takes to cover the card. (9) Tell students that 9 square centimeters is called the area of the card. Repeat for more cards of various sizes. Now, have students mark an X on the first six squares across the top row of graph paper and continue to mark six Xs across on the next three rows. Have students outline the 6-by-4-centimeter rectangle and tell its area. (24 square centimeters) Continue for more squares and rectangles and then have students outline odd-sized figures and find each area by counting the square centimeters.

3 Practice

Using page 281 Have a student read the first caption aloud to learn about a square centimeter and then measure each side of the square to see that each is 1 centimeter long. Have a student read the second caption aloud to learn about area. Tell students to count the square centimeters in the figure to find the area. (4) Have students read and complete the solution sentence.

- Help students complete Exercise 1. Then, have them complete the remaining exercises independently.

Using page 282 Tell students to count the square centimeters in each figure and write the number under the figure. Have students complete the page independently.

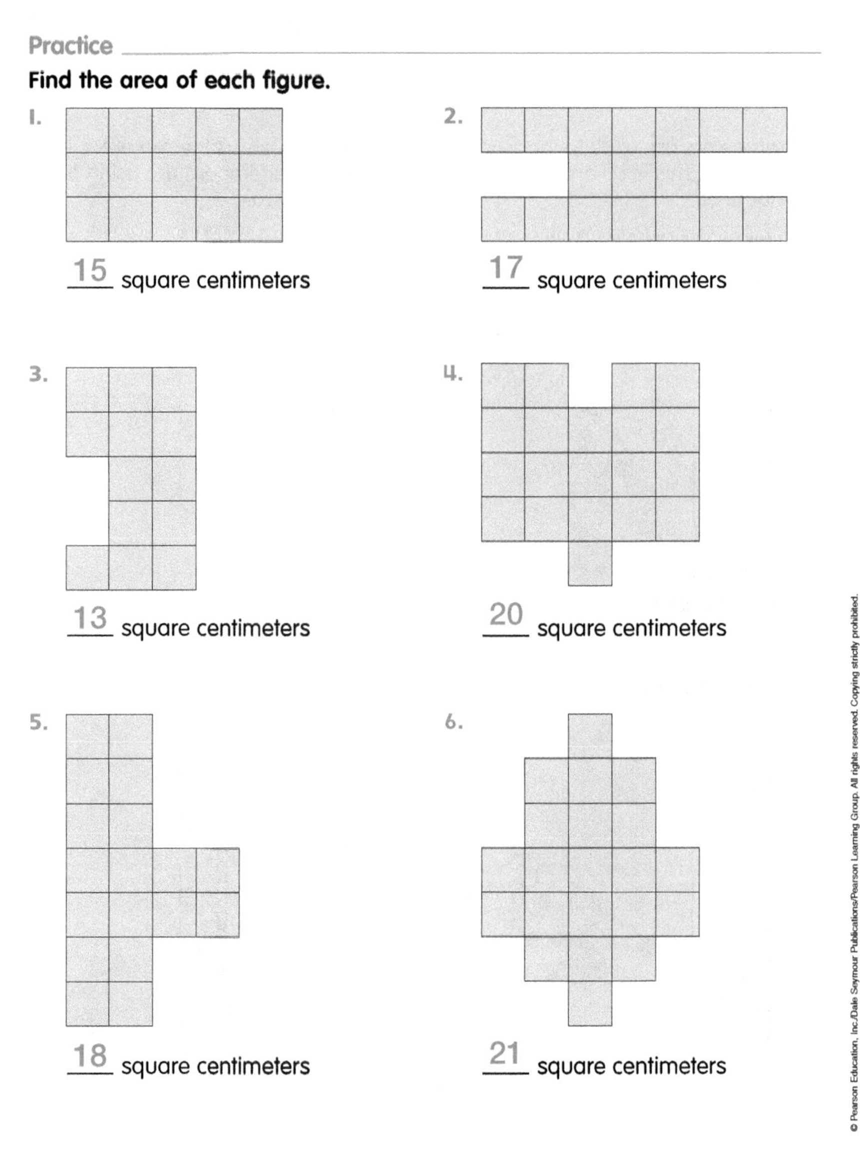

Assess

Give students pieces of graph paper cut into different sizes and shapes. Then, have them determine the area in square units.

For Mixed Abilities

Common Errors • Intervention

If students need additional work with area, have them work in small cooperative groups using centimeter grid paper. Have each member draw a polygonal figure with an area of 12 square centimeters. Then, have students compare their shapes to see that not all figures with the same area have the same shape.

Enrichment • Measurement

Tell students to use centimeter graph paper to draw a square that is 13 centimeters on all sides. Have them draw a square inside that square that has sides of 9 centimeters. Then, have them find the difference in the two areas.

More to Explore • Logic

Duplicate or draw the following on the board:

```
                              1.
        2.          3.        _
        _           _  _  _   _
4. _  _  _  _       _         _
        _ 6.    7. _      8.  _
5. _  _  _  _  _  _  _  _
   _     _     _        _
   _     _     _        _
   _     _     _
   _     _     _
                9. _  _  _  _  _  _  _
```

ACROSS

3. The distance between two points is a (line).
4. 35 is (more) than 27.
5. The side of a square is a (straight) line.
9. A foot is (smaller) than a yard.

DOWN

1. 256 is (less) than 526.
2. Twelve inches equal 1 (foot).
3. If your pencil is not short, it is (long).
5. The opposite of tall is (short).
6. You measure length with a (ruler).
7. (Inches) are smaller than feet.
8. There are (ten) digits from 0 to 9.

14-12 Temperature

pages 283–284

1 Getting Started

Objective
- To read Fahrenheit and Celsius thermometers

Vocabulary
temperature, thermometer, Fahrenheit, Celsius

Materials
*Fahrenheit and Celsius thermometers; cup, pint, and quart containers

Warm Up • Mental Math
Have students tell the change that would be received from $1 if they spent the following:

1. 15¢ (85¢)
2. 92¢ (8¢)
3. 75¢ (25¢)
4. 20¢ (80¢)
5. $1 (none)
6. 19¢ (81¢)
7. 50¢ (50¢)
8. 9¢ (91¢)

Warm Up • Measurement
Have students draw pictures to show how many cups are in 1 pint, cups in 1 quart, and pints in 1 quart. Allow students to use the cup, pint, and quart containers to remember the equalities.

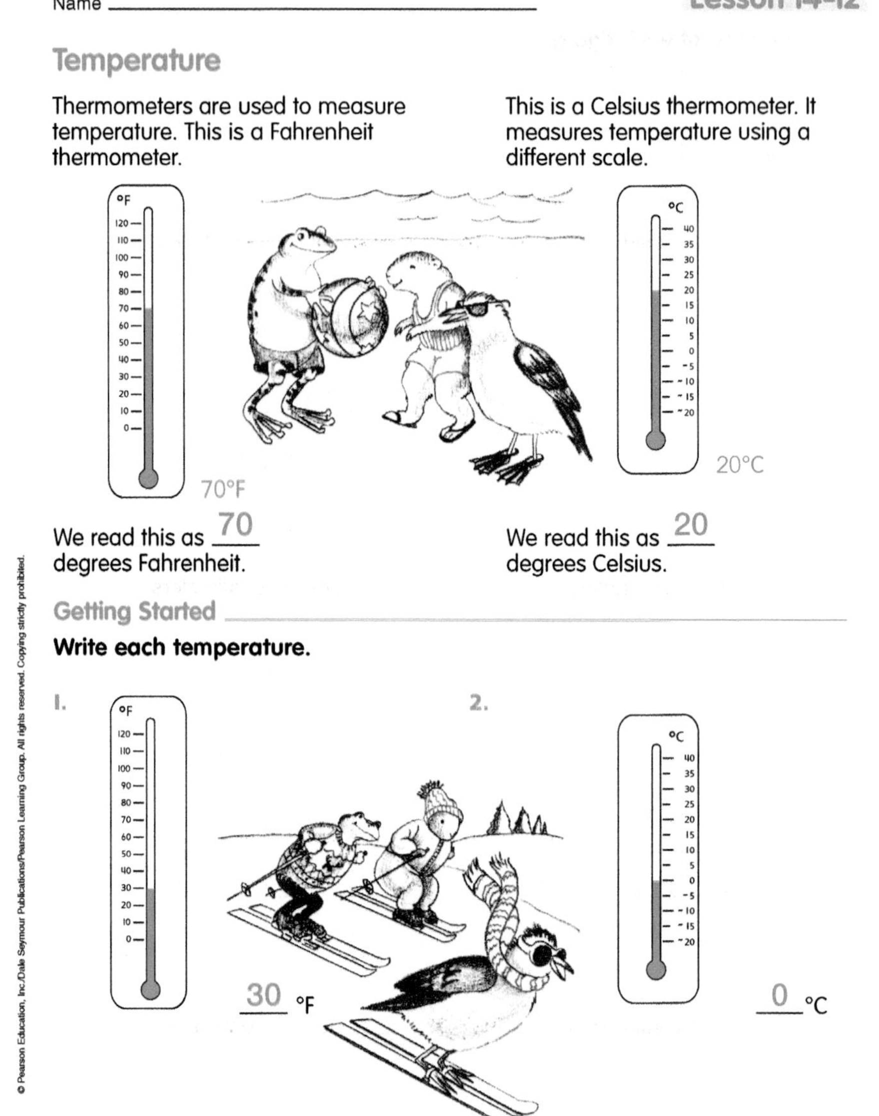

Name ______________________ Lesson 14-12

Temperature

Thermometers are used to measure temperature. This is a Fahrenheit thermometer.

This is a Celsius thermometer. It measures temperature using a different scale.

70°F

20°C

We read this as 70 degrees Fahrenheit.

We read this as 20 degrees Celsius.

Getting Started

Write each temperature.

1. 30 °F

2. 0 °C

2 Teach

Develop Skills and Concepts Display the Fahrenheit thermometer and tell students that the Fahrenheit thermometer is one of two kinds of thermometers used to measure temperature. Tell students that temperature is the amount of heat or cold in the air. Have a student find the zero on the thermometer. Tell students that zero degrees Fahrenheit is very cold weather and that the numbers below the zero are for showing even colder temperatures. Have a student find and read the highest number on the thermometer. Tell students that this number is for a very hot temperature. Have students find other temperatures. Display the Celsius thermometer and tell students that temperature can also be measured on a metric thermometer called a Celsius thermometer. Have a student find the zero as you tell students that a zero degree temperature is cold and the numbers below the zero are for even colder temperatures. Have a student find and read the highest number on the thermometer for an extremely hot temperature. Have students find other temperatures.

3 Practice

Using page 283 Have students tell about the picture. Have students read the sentences aloud with you. Ask a student to read the temperature on the Fahrenheit thermometer. Write **70°F** on the board and tell students that we write the number, the degree notation, and an *F* to tell the degrees as shown on a Fahrenheit thermometer. Tell students to write the temperature on the line before the degree notation and complete the solution statement. Be sure students understand that the °F is written out in words in the solution statement. Repeat this procedure for the Celsius example.

- Have students complete the Getting Started exercises independently.

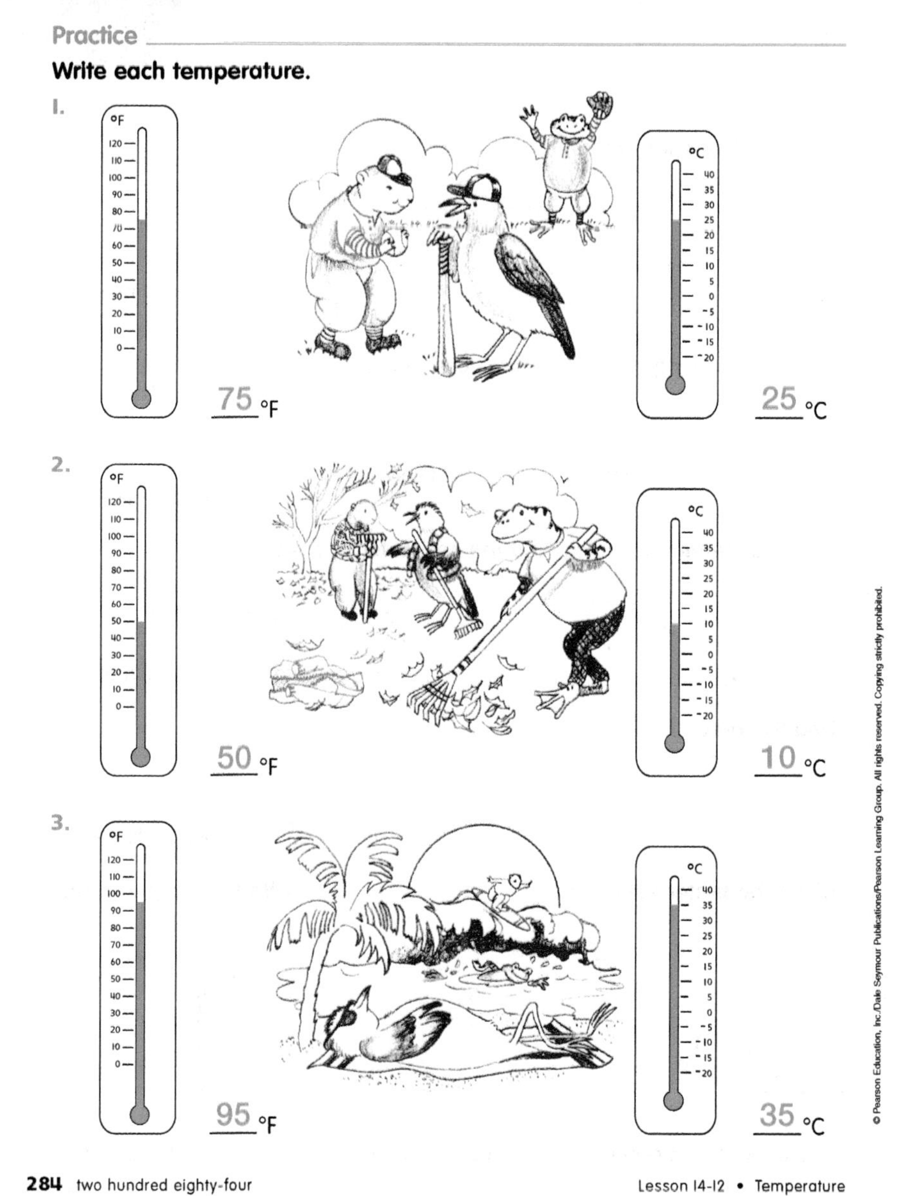

Using page 284 Assign the page to be completed independently. When all students have completed the page, discuss each picture and its corresponding temperature.

4 Assess

Set up a station with two containers of water, one cold and one room temperature. Have students use thermometers to determine the temperature in Fahrenheit and Celsius for each container.

5 Mixed Review

1. 38¢ + 92¢ ($1.30)
2. $4.00 − $2.68 ($1.32)
3. 96¢ − 47¢ (49¢)
4. 907 ◯ 790 (>)
5. 602 − 83 (519)
6. 573 − 161 (412)
7. 426 + 330 + 147 (903)
8. 667, 668, 669, _____ (670)
9. $4.28 + $3.95 ($8.23)
10. 401 − 320 (81)

For Mixed Abilities

Common Errors • Intervention

Some students may have difficulty relating temperature readings with events in their everyday lives. Have them work with partners and a list similar to the one shown below in which they circle the Fahrenheit temperature reading that they think is more appropriate.

EVENT	TEMPERATURE	
sledding	30°	80°
swimming	30°	80°
wearing shorts	30°	80°
skiing	30°	80°

Enrichment • Application

Tell students to draw a picture showing a hot day and a picture showing a cold day. Have them write a temperature in Celsius and Fahrenheit for each picture.

More to Explore • Logic

Have students solve this logic problem by encouraging them to look for nontraditional ways to arrive at a solution:

Ryan came to a bridge marked "Total weight 200 pounds." Ryan weighed 190 pounds, but he was carrying three pineapples, each weighing 5 pounds. He couldn't toss the pineapples across the river because they would break. How did Ryan cross the bridge with the pineapples? (Ryan was a juggler, so he juggled the pineapples while he was crossing the bridge.)

ESL/ELL STRATEGIES

When introducing temperature, pronounce the words *Fahrenheit* and *Celsius* in isolation and ask students to repeat. Then, model how to say several different temperatures using both scales and have students repeat. (e.g., 3 degrees Fahrenheit, 1 degree Celsius).

Chapter 14 Test

page 285

Items	Objectives
1	To measure length to the nearest inch (see pages 263–264)
2	To measure length to the nearest centimeter (see pages 271–272)
3	To measure the perimeter of a figure in centimeters (see pages 277–278)
4	To find area by counting square centimeters (see pages 281–282)
5	To estimate weight in pounds and ounces (see pages 265–266)
6	To estimate capacities of a cup, pint, and quart (see pages 267–268)
7	To read Fahrenheit thermometers (see pages 283–284)

Name ____________________

Chapter 14 Test

Estimate the length to the nearest inch.

1. 

It is between 3 and 4 inches. 3 nearest inch

Estimate the length to the nearest centimeter.

2. 

It is between 7 and 8 centimeters. 7 nearest centimeter

Use your centimeter ruler. Find the perimeter of the figure.

3. 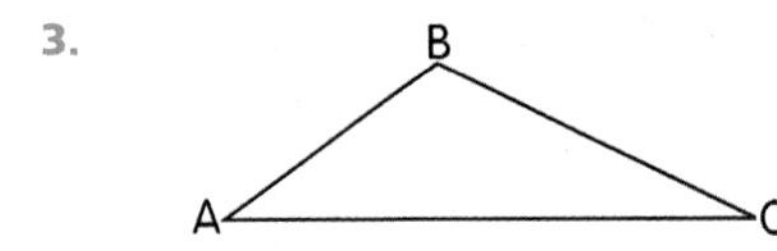

3 + 4 + 6 = 13
A to B, B to C, C to A

The perimeter is 13 centimeters.

Find the area.

4. 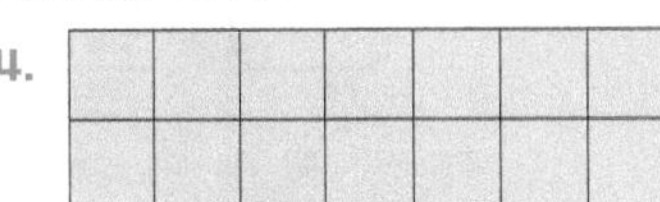

area = 14 square centimeters

Circle the better estimate.

5. 

5 ounces (5 pounds)

6. 1 cup (1 quart)

Write the temperature.

7. 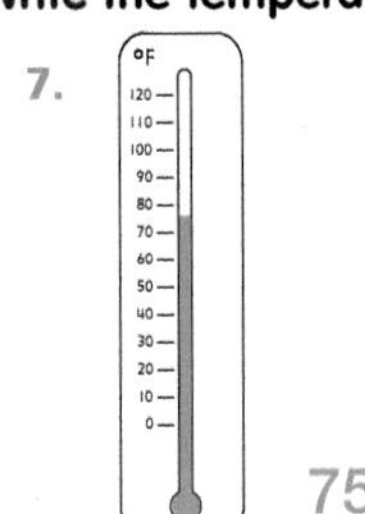

75 °F

Alternate Chapter Test

You may wish to use the Alternate Chapter Test on page 328 of this book for further review and assessment.

Cumulative Assessment

Circle the letter of the correct answer.

1. 7 + 5
   a. 2 (b.) 12 c. 13 d. NG

2. 17 − 8
   a. 8 b. 25 c. 11 (d.) NG

3. 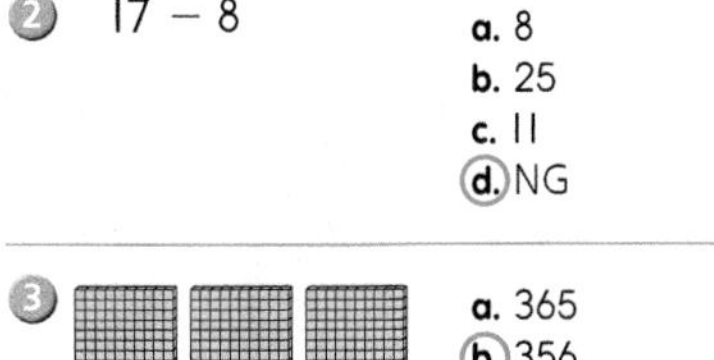
   a. 365 (b.) 356 c. 653 d. NG

4. 38 + 96
   a. 124 b. 62 (c.) 134 d. NG

5. 346 + 275
   (a.) 621 b. 611 c. 511 d. NG

6. 75 − 49
   (a.) 26 b. 34 c. 36 d. NG

7. 524 − 135
   a. 499 b. 411 (c.) 389 d. NG

8. Name this shape.
   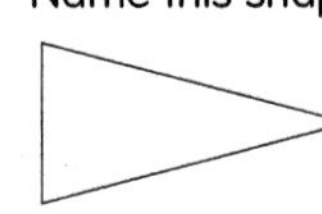
   a. square b. rectangle (c.) triangle d. NG

9. What part is blue?
   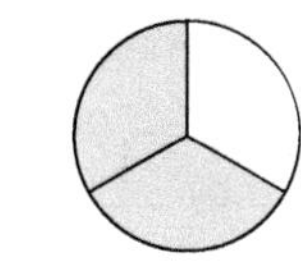
   (a.) $\frac{2}{3}$ b. $\frac{1}{3}$ c. $\frac{2}{4}$ d. NG

10. 3 pints = __?__ cups
    a. 2 (b.) 6 c. 4 d. NG

11. What part is blue?
    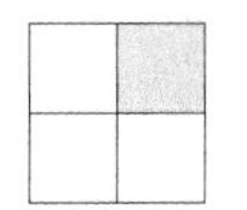
    a. $\frac{3}{4}$ (b.) $\frac{1}{4}$ c. $\frac{1}{3}$ d. NG

12. Which is the better guess?

    a. more than 1 pound (b.) less than 1 pound

score

STOP

Cumulative Assessment

page 286

Items	Objectives
1–2	To review addition and subtraction facts with sums and minuends through 18 (see pages 17–20, 23–28, 35–44, 53–56, 59–64)
3	To understand 3-digit numbers (see pages 71–74)
4	To add 2-digit numbers for a 3-digit sum (see pages 155–156, 221–222)
5	To add two 3-digit numbers for sums through 999 with regrouping (see pages 187–190, 221–223)
6	To subtract in a horizontal problem (see pages 163–164)
7	To subtract 3-digit numbers with regrouping (see pages 209–210, 225–226)
8	To identify plane figures (see pages 241–242)
9, 11	To identify fractional parts of a whole (see pages 247–252)
10	To compare the capacities of cups, pints, and quarts (see pages 267–268)
12	To estimate weight in pounds and ounces (see pages 265–0266)

Alternate Cumulative Assessment

Circle the letter of the correct answer.

1. 5 + 9
   a 12 b 13 (c) 14 d NG

2. 12 − 6
   (a) 6 b 7 c 8 d NG

3. 
   a 620 b 500 c 250 (d) NG

4. 17 + 74
   a 98 b 89 c 78 (d) NG

5. 247 + 366
   a 633 b 615 (c) 613 d NG

6. 85 − 59
   a 62 b 34 c 24 (d) NG

7. 637 − 261
   (a) 376 b 7476 c 496 d NG

8. Name the shape.
   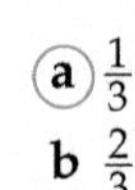
   a triangle (b) square c circle d NG

9. What part is blue?
   (a) $\frac{1}{3}$ b $\frac{2}{3}$ c $\frac{3}{3}$ d NG

10. 6 quarts = ? pints
    a 2 b 6 (c) 12 d NG

11. What part is blue?
    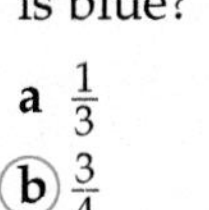
    a $\frac{1}{3}$ (b) $\frac{3}{4}$ c $\frac{1}{2}$ d NG

12. Which is the better guess?

    (a) more than 1 pound b less than 1 pound

CHAPTER 15

15-1 Multiplying by the Factor 2

pages 287–288

1 Getting Started

Objective

- To multiply by the factor 2 through 2 × 5

Vocabulary

multiply, factor, product

Materials

3-by-5-inch index cards; counters

Warm Up • Mental Math

Ask students to identify each.

1. I have 3 sides. (triangle)
2. I have 3 tens and 6 ones. (36)
3. I am 3 parts of 7 equal parts. ($\frac{3}{7}$)
4. I hold 2 cups. (pint)
5. I tell the distance around a figure. (perimeter)
6. I have 1 digit and mean none. (0)
7. I am used to find the total. (addition)
8. I am a mark halfway between two numbers on an inch ruler. (half-inch)

Warm Up • Number Sense

Have students count by 2s through 200 with each student saying five numbers in order and the next student counting on for the next five numbers.

Name ____________________

Chapter 15

Multiplication and Division Through 5

Lesson 15-1

Multiplying by the Factor 2

Rona put 2 buttons in each box. She has 4 boxes. How many buttons does she have?

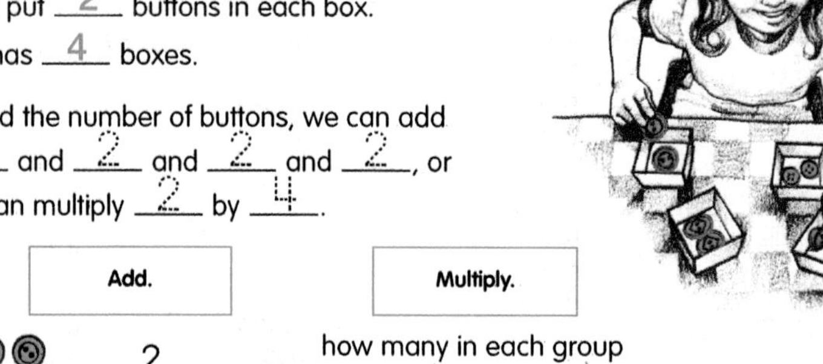

We are looking for the number of buttons.

Rona put __2__ buttons in each box.

She has __4__ boxes.

To find the number of buttons, we can add __2__ and __2__ and __2__ and __2__, or we can multiply __2__ by __4__.

Add. **Multiply.**

$$\begin{array}{r} 2 \\ 2 \\ 2 \\ +\,2 \\ \hline 8 \end{array}$$

or

how many in each group

$4 \times 2 = 8$ $\quad \begin{array}{r} 2 \\ \times 4 \\ \hline 8 \end{array}$

how many groups

Rona has __8__ buttons.

Getting Started

Use different ways to find the number of buttons.

1. 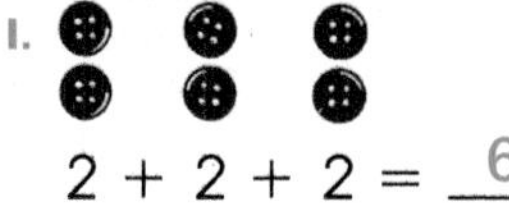

$2 + 2 + 2 =$ __6__

three 2s = __6__

$3 \times 2 =$ __6__

Multiply.

2. $\begin{array}{r} 2 \\ \times 4 \\ \hline 8 \end{array}$ 3. $\begin{array}{r} 2 \\ \times 2 \\ \hline 4 \end{array}$ 4. $\begin{array}{r} 2 \\ \times 1 \\ \hline 2 \end{array}$

2 Teach

Develop Skills and Concepts Tell students that an array is an arrangement of objects in equal rows. Then, draw 3 groups of 2 Xs each on the board. Ask students how many groups there are. (3) Ask how many Xs are in each group. (2) Tell students that we want to know how many there are in all. Tell students that adding three 2s is one way to find the total. Have a student write and solve the addition problem for a sum of 6.

- Tell students that there is another way to find the total of three 2s. Tell students that we can multiply 3 times 2 as you write **3 × 2** both vertically and horizontally on the board. Explain that 3 and 2 are factors, or numbers we are multiplying. The answer to a multiplication problem is called the product. Ask students to write the product to both problems. (6, 6) Write **three 2s =** _____ and have a student solve the problem. (6)
- Draw another group of two Xs on the board and repeat the procedure to multiply 4 × 2. (8) Repeat for 5 × 2 and 2 × 2.

3 Practice

Using page 287 Read the example aloud and ask what is to be found. (how many buttons Rona has in all) Ask what information is given. (Rona has 4 boxes with 2 buttons in each box.) Have students read and complete the information sentences. Work through the model with students and have them complete the solution sentence. Have students use counters to check their solution.

- Help students with the Getting Started exercises.

Using page 288 Remind students that adding 2 + 2 + 2 + 2 tells us the total of four 2s. Have students write the sum. (8) Have students read the two multiplication sentences aloud with you as they write 8 for each answer. Have students complete the page independently.

Practice

Use different ways to find the number of buttons.

1.

2 + 2 + 2 + 2 = 8

four 2s = 8

4 × 2 = 8

2. one 2 = 2

1 × 2 = 2

3. 2 + 2 = 4

two 2s = 4

2 × 2 = 4

4. 2 + 2 + 2 + 2 + 2 = 10

five 2s = 10

5 × 2 = 10

5. 2 + 2 + 2 = 6

three 2s = 6

3 × 2 = 6

Multiply.

6. 2 × 2 = 4 7. 3 × 2 = 6 8. 1 × 2 = 2

9. 4 × 2 = 8 10. 5 × 2 = 10 11. 4 × 2 = 8

12. 2 × 2 = 4 13. 2 × 4 = 8 14. 2 × 1 = 2 15. 2 × 3 = 6 16. 2 × 5 = 10

4 Assess

Have students make multiplication fact cards for the factor 2 through 5 × 2 . Have them write the problem on one side of an index card and the product on the other side. Then, organize the class into pairs and have students test each other using their flashcards.

5 Mixed Review

1. $3.27 − $1.56 ($1.71)
2. 308 − 36 (272)
3. 283 + 472 (755)
4. 657 − 421 (236)
5. 75 − 7 (68)
6. 323 ◯ 332 (<)
7. 63 + 21 + 38 (122)
8. $4.76 + $2.75 ($7.51)
9. 98 − 21 (77)
10. 7 dimes, 2 nickels, 9 pennies (89¢)

For Mixed Abilities

Common Errors • Intervention

Some students may not make the connection between multiplication and repeated addition. Have them work with counters to model arrays. For example, to find three 2s, or 3 × 2, have them lay out 3 sets of 2 counters and skip-count to find the total, e.g., 2, 4, 6.

Enrichment • Calculator Skills

Have students work in pairs. Give each pair a calculator and a sheet of graph paper. One student should complete the problem on the graph paper while the other student uses the calculator. After each problem is solved, have students switch roles.

Graph Paper

1. Color 2 rows of 4 boxes.
2. Color 2 rows of 2 boxes.
3. Color 2 rows of 5 boxes.
4. Color 2 rows of 3 boxes.

Calculator

1. Press on the calculator 2 × 4 =.
2. Press on the calculator 2 × 2 =.
3. Press on the calculator 2 × 5 =.
4. Press on the calculator 2 × 3 =.

Ask students what they notice about the two answers they got. (Answers are the same.)

More to Explore • Probability

Give each student a sheet of paper and a set of four objects, each a different color. Wooden cubes or beads in red, blue, green, and yellow would work well. Ask students to arrange the objects, two at a time, in all the possible paired combinations that they can. Have them illustrate each arrangement with crayons. Explain that if they make one arrangement, for example, red-blue, the opposite pair, blue-red, is different. Have students demonstrate and display all the possible arrangements as a volunteer writes them on the board. (12 combinations; if R = red, B = blue, Y = yellow, and G = green, then RY, YR, RG, GR, RB, BR, GY, YG, GB, BG, YB, and BY).

15-2 Multiplying by the Factor 3

pages 289–290

1 Getting Started

Objective
- To multiply by the factor 3 through 3 × 5

Materials
counters

Warm Up • Mental Math
Have students name the amounts.

1. 2 dimes (20¢)
2. 2 quarters (50¢)
3. two 2s (4)
4. 2 pennies (2¢)
5. two 3s (6)
6. 2 half-dollars ($1)
7. two 4s (8)

Warm Up • Number Sense
Draw 3 groups of 2 circles each on the board and have a student write and solve an addition problem to tell the total. (2 + 2 + 2 = 6) Have a student write and solve the multiplication problem. (3 × 2 = 6) Continue to draw groups of 2 circles for students to write and solve addition and multiplication problems.

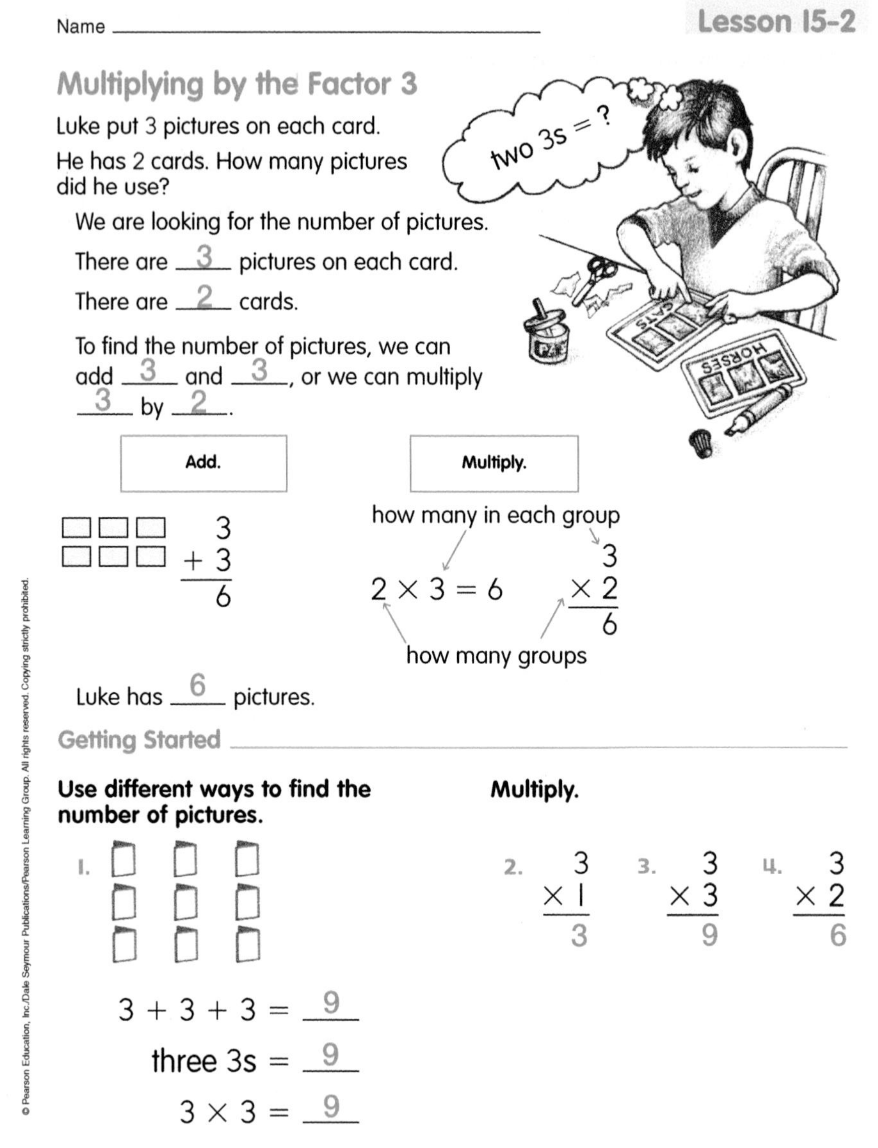

Name ____________

Lesson 15-2

Multiplying by the Factor 3

Luke put 3 pictures on each card.

He has 2 cards. How many pictures did he use?

We are looking for the number of pictures.

There are __3__ pictures on each card.

There are __2__ cards.

To find the number of pictures, we can add __3__ and __3__, or we can multiply __3__ by __2__.

Add.	Multiply.
3 + 3 = 6	how many in each group; 2 × 3 = 6; 3 × 2 = 6; how many groups

Luke has __6__ pictures.

Getting Started

Use different ways to find the number of pictures.

1. $3 + 3 + 3 =$ __9__
   three 3s = __9__
   $3 \times 3 =$ __9__

Multiply.

2. $3 \times 1 = 3$
3. $3 \times 3 = 9$
4. $3 \times 2 = 6$

2 Teach

Develop Skills and Concepts Have students lay out 3 counters in a group and then lay out another group of 3 counters. Ask if the groups are equal. (yes) Have students count to tell the total in both groups. (6) Write **two 3s = 6** and **3 + 3 = 6** on the board. Have students read the number sentences aloud with you. Now, write **2 × 3 = 6** on the board as you tell students that this is a multiplication fact. Repeat for students to lay out 4 groups of 3 each and 5 groups of 3. Help students write on the board and solve the multiplication facts for 3 through 5 × 3.

3 Practice

Using page 289 Have students tell about the picture. Have a student read the example and tell what is to be found. (how many pictures Luke has) Ask what information is known. (Luke has 2 cards with 3 pictures on each.) Have students read and complete the information sentences. Work through the model with students and then have them complete the solution sentence. Have students count the pictures shown on the cards to check their solution.

- Help students complete the Getting Started exercises.

Using page 290 Remind students that 4 × 3 means four 3s or 3 + 3 + 3 + 3. Encourage students to use counters when needed as they complete the page independently.

Practice

Use different ways to find the number of stickers.

1.    

$3 + 3 + 3 + 3 =$ 12

four 3s = 12

4 × 3 = 12

2. one 3 = 3

1 × 3 = 3

3.  

$3 + 3 + 3 =$ 9

three 3s = 9

3 × 3 = 9

4. 

$3 + 3 + 3 + 3 + 3 =$ 15

five 3s = 15

5 × 3 = 15

5. $3 + 3 =$ 6

two 3s = 6

2 × 3 = 6

Multiply.

6. $3 \times 2 = 6$
7. $3 \times 1 = 3$
8. $2 \times 2 = 4$
9. $2 \times 4 = 8$
10. $2 \times 1 = 2$
11. $3 \times 4 = 12$
12. $3 \times 5 = 15$
13. $3 \times 3 = 9$
14. $2 \times 3 = 6$
15. $2 \times 5 = 10$

4 Assess

Have students draw a diagram to show repeated addition of 3 + 3 + 3. Then, have them write the multiplication problem and solve.

5 Mixed Review

1. 308 + 36 (344)
2. 406 + 143 + 227 (776)
3. 3 hundreds 7 tens 4 ones (374)
4. 65 − 27 (38)
5. 78¢ + 17¢ (95¢)
6. 820 − 46 (774)
7. 570 − 126 (444)
8. 491 ◯ 501 (<)
9. $9.23 + $0.61 ($9.84)
10. $8.07 − $6.38 ($1.69)

For Mixed Abilities

Common Errors • Intervention

Watch for students who add instead of multiply when they see the multiplication fact. For example, when seeing 2 × 3, they think 2 + 3 = 5 instead of 2 × 3 = 6. Have them work with partners to draw arrays to model the problems.

Enrichment • Number Sense

Tell students to use multiplication fact cards for 2s and 3s to find two facts that use the same two numbers. Then, they should make a drawing to explain why the answers are the same.

More to Explore • Application

Ask students to think about all the different things they have for lunch. List the possibilities on the board. Try to limit the list to no more than ten items. Now, ask students to arrange the lunch foods into whole meals. For example, if they listed peanut butter sandwich, hard-boiled egg, apple, milk, and soup, these could be formed into different meal combinations. Have them check each other's work for duplicate meals. See who can find the most different lunches.

15-3 Multiplying by the Factor 4

pages 291–292

1 Getting Started

Objective

- To multiply by the factor 4 through 4 × 5

Materials

counters

Warm Up • Mental Math

Tell students to name the number.

1. 5 × 2 (10)
2. 2 + 2 + 2 (6)
3. 3 × 4 (12)
4. 5 × 3 (15)
5. 3 + 3 + 3 (9)
6. 3 + 5 (8)
7. three 5s (15)
8. three 3s (9)

Warm Up • Paper and Pencil

Have a student write and solve a multiplication problem to tell the number of fingers on 2 hands. (2 × 5 = 10) Repeat the activity to find the following: wheels on 3 bicycles (3 × 2 = 6), cents in 3 nickels (3 × 5 = 15¢), perimeter of a triangle whose sides are all 3 inches (3 × 3 = 9), tires on 3 cars (3 × 4 = 12), and so on.

Name ______________________

Multiplying by the Factor 4

Mary has 3 boxes. She put 4 shells in each box. How many shells does Mary have?

We want to know the number of shells.

There are __3__ boxes.

There are __4__ shells in each box.

To find the number of shells, we can add __4__ and __4__ and __4__, or we can multiply __4__ by __3__.

Add.	Multiply.
4 + 4 + 4 = 12	3 × 4 = 12; 4 × 3 = 12

how many in each group

how many groups

Marty has __12__ shells.

Getting Started

Use different ways to find the number of shells.

1. 4 + 4 + 4 + 4 + 4 = __20__

five 4s = __20__

5 × 4 = __20__

Multiply.

2. 4 × 2 = 8
3. 4 × 1 = 4
4. 4 × 5 = 20

2 Teach

Develop Skills and Concepts Have students lay out a group of 4 counters. Tell students to lay out 3 more groups of 4 counters each. Write **4 + 4 + 4 + 4** on the board for students to tell the sum. (16) Write **four 4s = _____ and 4 × 4 = _____** on the board and have students read and complete each. (16, 16) Remind students that the sum of 4 + 4 + 4 + 4 is the same as multiplying 4 × 4. Repeat for 4 × 5. Help students write and solve the multiplication facts for 4 × 1 through 4 × 5 on the board.

3 Practice

Using page 291 Have students tell about the picture. Have a student read the example and tell what is to be found. (how many shells Mary has) Ask what is known. (She has 3 boxes with 4 shells in each.) Ask students what operation needs to be done. (multiplication or addition) Have students read and complete the information sentences. Work through the model with students and then have them complete the solution sentence and count the boxes in the picture to check their work.

- Help students complete the Getting Started exercises.

Using page 292 Tell students to write the answers to the multiplication problems for the factors 2, 3, and 4 on this page. Assign the page to be completed independently.

Practice

Use different ways to find the number of shells.

1. 

$4 + 4 + 4 + 4 =$ 16

four 4s = 16

$4 \times 4 =$ 16

2. $4 + 4 =$ 8

two 4s = 8

$2 \times 4 =$ 8

3. one 4 = 4

$1 \times 4 =$ 4

Multiply.

4. $3 \times 2 =$ 6
5. $2 \times 2 =$ 4
6. $1 \times 3 =$ 3
7. $4 \times 3 =$ 12
8. $4 \times 5 =$ 20
9. $4 \times 2 =$ 8
10. $3 \times 5 = 15$
11. $2 \times 5 = 10$
12. $3 \times 3 = 9$
13. $4 \times 1 = 4$
14. $4 \times 4 = 16$

Problem Solving

Solve.

15. A farm has 3 pens. There are 4 pigs in each pen. How many pigs are there?

12 pigs

16. Stacy made 5 stacks of books. There are 4 books in each stack. How many books does she have?

20 books

4 Assess

Have students use counters to model multiplication problems with the factor 4.

For Mixed Abilities

Common Errors • Intervention

Some students may have difficulty with facts of 4. Have them work with partners and make multiplication fact cards for 1×4 through 5×4. Then, write **4 + 4** on the board and have students show the multiplication fact for this addition problem. (2×4) Have students give the answer. (8) Repeat for the following:

$4 + 4 + 4$
($3 \times 4 = 12$)

$4 + 4 + 4 + 4$
($4 \times 4 = 16$)

$4 + 4 + 4 + 4 + 4$
($5 \times 4 = 20$)

Enrichment • Number Sense

Have students lay out multiplication fact cards for the factors 2, 3, and 4. Tell them to make a list of all the facts that use the same numbers. Tell them to then make a list of all the other facts.

More to Explore • Logic

Arrange desks in your room to form gates like the boxes below: the first gate indicating red one way and blue the other; the next two showing smiling one way, frowning the other; and the last showing boys one way, girls the other.

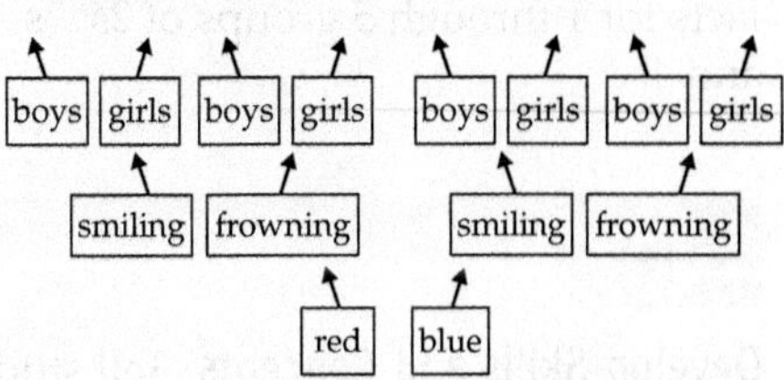

Make a number of cards coloring half red, half blue, half with a smiling face, and half with a frowning face. Ask students to line up at the first gate and have one student pass out the cards. As students receive a card, they should start through the gates. At each gate, they will have to choose the right direction. When all students have negotiated this maze, they should be divided into eight groups: smiling red boys, smiling red girls, frowning red girls, and so on.

15-4 Multiplying by the Factor 5

pages 293–294

1 Getting Started

Objective
- To multiply by the factor 5 through 5×5

Materials
counters; multiplication fact cards for factors 2, 3, 4, and 5

Warm Up • Mental Math
Tell students to name a multiplication fact for the following:

1. 16 (4×4)
2. 20 (4×5 or 5×4)
3. 12 (3×4 or 4×3)
4. 6 (2×3 or 3×2)
5. 4 (2×2)
6. 8 (2×4 or 4×2)
7. 9 (3×3)
8. 10 (5×2 or 2×5)

Warm Up • Number Sense
Lay out 3 groups with 3 counters in each group and a group of 4 counters. Ask students if the groups are equal. (no) Remove 1 counter from the group of 4 counters and ask if the groups are equal. (yes) Ask a student to write a multiplication fact on the board to tell about the number of counters in all. ($4 \times 3 = 12$) Repeat to review multiplication facts for 1 through 5 groups of 2s, 3s, and 4s.

Name ____________________

Multiplying by the Factor 5

Pablo has 4 bags. He put 5 rocks in each bag. How many rocks does Pablo have?

We are looking for the number of rocks.

There are __4__ bags.

There are __5__ rocks in each bag.

To find the number of rocks, we can add __5__ and __5__ and __5__ and __5__, or we can multiply __5__ by __4__.

Add.

○○○○○ 5
○○○○○ 5
○○○○○ 5
○○○○○ + 5
20

Multiply.

how many in each group

$4 \times 5 = 20$

$$\begin{array}{r} 5 \\ \times 4 \\ \hline 20 \end{array}$$

how many groups

Pablo has __20__ rocks.

Getting Started

Use different ways to find the number of rocks.

1. 

$5 + 5 + 5 =$ __15__
three 5s $=$ __15__
$3 \times 5 =$ __15__

Multiply.

2. $\begin{array}{r} 5 \\ \times 2 \\ \hline 10 \end{array}$ 3. $\begin{array}{r} 5 \\ \times 1 \\ \hline 5 \end{array}$ 4. $\begin{array}{r} 5 \\ \times 4 \\ \hline 20 \end{array}$

2 Teach

Develop Skills and Concepts Tell students that the total number in several groups of 5 objects can be found by multiplying the number of groups by 5 or by writing an addition problem. Lay out 5 groups of 5 counters and ask a student to write and solve a multiplication problem to find the total number of counters. ($5 \times 5 = 25$) Tell students that counting by 5s is another way to remember that $5 \times 5 = 25$. Have a student write and solve an addition problem to find the total number of counters. ($5 + 5 + 5 + 5 + 5 = 25$) Repeat the procedure for finding two 5s, three 5s, and four 5s using addition. Now, have students write and solve the problems for one 5 through five 5s using multiplication on the board.

3 Practice

Using page 293 Have a student read the example aloud and tell what is to be found. (total number of rocks Pablo has) Ask what information is known. (Pablo has 4 bags of 5 rocks each.) Have students read and complete the information sentences. Work through the addition and multiplication models with students and then have them complete the solution sentence. Tell students to count the rocks in the picture to check their solution.

- Help students complete the Getting Started exercises.

Using page 294 Have students solve the exercises on this page independently.

Practice

Use different ways to find the number of rocks.

1. 

$5 + 5 + 5 + 5 + 5 =$ 25

five 5s = 25

$5 \times 5 =$ 25

2. one 5 = 5

$1 \times 5 =$ 5

3. $5 + 5 =$ 10

two 5s = 10

$2 \times 5 =$ 10

Multiply.

4. $2 \times 5 =$ 10
5. $2 \times 2 =$ 4
6. $4 \times 5 =$ 20
7. $3 \times 4 =$ 12
8. $3 \times 5 =$ 15
9. $3 \times 3 =$ 9
10. $1 \times 2 =$ 2
11. $2 \times 4 =$ 8
12. $5 \times 4 =$ 20
13. $4 \times 3 =$ 12
14. $5 \times 5 =$ 25
15. $3 \times 2 =$ 6
16. $2 \times 2 =$ 4
17. $5 \times 4 =$ 20
18. $4 \times 2 =$ 8
19. $3 \times 3 =$ 9
20. $2 \times 5 =$ 10
21. $5 \times 5 =$ 25
22. $4 \times 3 =$ 12
23. $5 \times 2 =$ 10
24. $5 \times 3 =$ 15
25. $2 \times 4 =$ 8
26. $5 \times 1 =$ 5
27. $4 \times 4 =$ 16

4 Assess

Use multiplication fact cards to hold a class math bee for factors through 5.

5 Mixed Review

1. $8 + 5 + 7$ (20)
2. 3×7 (21)
3. \$9.53 − \$7.28 (\$2.25)
4. $602 - 248$ (354)
5. $93 - 46$ (47)
6. 2×7 (14)
7. 105 ◯ 510 (<)
8. $490 - 103$ (387)
9. \$2.78 + \$4.08 (\$6.86)
10. 6 hundreds 2 tens 8 ones (628)

For Mixed Abilities

Common Errors • Intervention

If students have difficulty multiplying with 5, have them work with partners and use counters to model the problem. For example, to find 3×5, they should think "three 5s," put out 3 sets of 5 counters each, and skip-count to find the total, that is, 5, 10, 15.

Enrichment • Number Sense

Tell students to write numbers by 5s through 25. Then, tell them to write a multiplication fact for each number they wrote. Ask if they can write the facts for the next four numbers when counting on to 45 by 5s.

More to Explore • Number Sense

You will need counters of three different colors. Draw this conversion chart on the board:

one red = three blues
one blue = two yellows

Now, arrange a display of simple objects that students can buy with the counters you will give them. Label each item with a price. (one blue and one yellow, or two blues, or one red and one yellow, for example) Give students two red counters each. Explain that before they can buy anything, they must visit the exchange counter to get the correct change. Have students act as shopkeepers and bankers, often exchanging roles. Give each student an opportunity to exchange counters and to purchase an item.

15-5 Order in Multiplication

pages 295–296

1 Getting Started

Objective
- To understand the Order Property in multiplication

Materials
*multiplication fact cards through 2×5, 3×5, 4×5, and 5×5; counters; real or play nickels and pennies

Warm Up • Mental Math
Ask students the following riddles:

1. 4 of me equals 20. (5)
2. 3 of me equals 12. (4)
3. 2 of me equals 6. (3)
4. 5 of me equals 20. (4)
5. 3 of me equals 15. (5)
6. 4×4 equals me. (16)
7. Me $\times$ me equals 9. (3)
8. $5 \times 5 =$ me. (25)

Warm Up • Number Sense
Have students give answers for multiplication fact cards as you show them in random order. Help students work to increase their speed of recall.

Name ______________________ **Lesson 15-5**

Order in Multiplication

Here is an important idea that makes multiplication easy.

We can multiply in any order. The answers will always be the same.

two 3s
$2 \times 3 = 6$

three 2s
$3 \times 2 = 6$

Getting Started

Multiply.

1. $3 \times 4 =$ 12
   $4 \times 3 =$ 12
2. $2 \times 5 =$ 10
   $5 \times 2 =$ 10
3. $2 \times 4 =$ 8
   $4 \times 2 =$ 8
4. $1 \times 3 =$ 3
   $3 \times 1 =$ 3
5. $2 \times 3 = 6$; $3 \times 2 = 6$
6. $5 \times 4 = 20$; $4 \times 5 = 20$
7. $3 \times 5 = 15$; $5 \times 3 = 15$

Find each total cost.

8. 2 [3¢ stamp] 3¢ × 2 = 6¢
   Total cost 6¢
9. 3 [2¢ stamp] 2¢ × 3 = 6¢
   Total cost 6¢

---

2 Teach

Develop Skills and Concepts Have students lay out 8 counters. Tell students to place the counters into groups of 2 and tell how many groups there are. (4) Ask the total of 4×2. (8) Write **4 × 2 = 8** on the board. Ask students to group the 8 counters into groups of 4 and tell how many groups there are. (2) Ask the total of 2×4. (8) Write **2 × 4 = 8** on the board. Have students note that the same three numbers are in both facts and that the answer is still 8 whether there are 2 groups of 4 or 4 groups of 2.

- Repeat for 20 counters to show that $5 \times 4 = 20$ and $4 \times 5 = 20$. Continue for 3×1 and 1×3 and then 3×5 and 5×3. Now, have students work with coins to work similar problems. Remind students that the cent sign must be written in all problems using cents.

3 Practice

Using page 295 Have a student read aloud the sentences about order in multiplication. Talk through the two examples. Then, have students complete the Getting Started exercises independently.

Using page 296 Have students complete the page independently.

Practice

Multiply.

1. $5 \times 4 = $ 20
   $4 \times 5 = $ 20

2. $1 \times 5 = $ 5
   $5 \times 1 = $ 5

3. $4 \times 1 = $ 4
   $1 \times 4 = $ 4

4. $3 \times 5 = $ 15
   $5 \times 3 = $ 15

5. $\begin{array}{r} 5 \\ \times 2 \\ \hline 10 \end{array}$ $\begin{array}{r} 2 \\ \times 5 \\ \hline 10 \end{array}$

6. $\begin{array}{r} 4 \\ \times 2 \\ \hline 8 \end{array}$ $\begin{array}{r} 2 \\ \times 4 \\ \hline 8 \end{array}$

7. $\begin{array}{r} 3 \\ \times 4 \\ \hline 12 \end{array}$ $\begin{array}{r} 4 \\ \times 3 \\ \hline 12 \end{array}$

Find each total cost.

8. 5 

Total cost 15¢

9. 3 

Total cost 15¢

10. 3 

Total cost 12¢

11. 4 

Total cost 12¢

12. 4 

Total cost 20¢

13. 5 

Total cost 20¢

4 Assess

Have students use counters to model two multiplication problems with a product of 15. (3 groups with 5 counters in each group, 3 × 5; 5 groups with 3 counters in each group, 5 × 3)

For Mixed Abilities

Common Errors • Intervention

To help students who have difficulty believing the Order Property, have 6 students go to the front of the classroom. Separate them into groups of 2 and ask, *How many groups are there?* (3) *How many are in each group?* (2) Write **3 × 2 = 6** on the board. Then, separate the group of 6 students into groups of 3 and ask, *Now how many groups are there?* (2) *How many are in each group?* (3) Write under the sentence, 3 × 2 = 6 this sentence, **2 × 3 = 6.** Ask, *What is different and alike about 3 × 2 and 2 × 3?* (The order of the factors is different; the products are the same.)

Enrichment • Number Sense

Tell students to cut and paste pictures from catalogs showing that the order of numbers in multiplication does not change the answer. Have them use these facts for their illustrations: 3 × 4 and 4 × 3, 2 × 5 and 5 × 2, 4 × 5 and 5 × 4, and 3 × 5 and 5 × 3.

More to Explore • Probability

A common source of combinations and permutations is the grocery store. Tell students to go to the grocery store with a parent. Ask them to record all the different kinds of cola they find there. In addition to differences in the brand of cola, they will find a variety of kinds of cola, for example, regular, diet, and caffeine-free. They should also find various packaging possibilities. For example, cola comes in glass bottles, aluminum cans, and plastic bottles. Tell students to keep a tally while they go through the store. Help them tabulate their results, listing all the types and bottling strategies on the board. Have all students report their findings to the class, and make a combined tally of findings on the board.

15-6 Problem Solving: Choose an Operation

pages 297–298

1 Getting Started

Objectives

- To choose an operation to solve problems
- To multiply to solve problems

Warm Up • Mental Math

Ask students what operation to use to find the following:

1. the number of tires on 4 cars (multiplication or addition)
2. how much more (subtraction)
3. the sum (addition)
4. the difference (subtraction)
5. 4 groups of 5 (multiplication or addition)
6. the number of wheels on 5 bikes (multiplication or addition)
7. how much change (subtraction)

Warm Up • Number Sense

Tell students a story of 5 groups of 3 children in each. Have a student draw stick figures to show the problem on the board. Have a student write and solve a multiplication fact to find the total number of children. (15) Have students draw and solve more story problems using multiplication facts through 5×5.

Name ______________________

Problem Solving
Lesson 15-6

It's Algebra!

Problem Solving: Choose an Operation

Solve.

1. 2 chairs have 8 legs.
2. 5 chairs have 20 legs.
3. 3 chairs have 12 legs.
4. 4 chairs have 16 legs.

5. 3 birds have 6 legs.
6. 1 bird has 2 legs.
7. 2 birds have 4 legs.
8. 5 birds have 10 legs.
9. 4 birds have 8 legs.

10. 2 hands have 10 fingers.
11. 4 hands have 20 fingers.
12. 3 hands have 15 fingers.
13. 1 hand has 5 fingers.
14. 5 hands have 25 fingers.

---

2 Teach

Develop Skills and Concepts Write the following on the board:

There are 5 children in Mrs. Julie's class. Each child has read 4 books this week. How many books did the entire class read?

Ask which operations could you use to solve this problem. (addition and multiplication) Then, have students solve the problems using addition ($4 + 4 + 4 + 4 + 4 = 20$) and multiplication ($5 \times 4 = 20$). Ask which is the quicker way to find the solution. (multiplication)

It's Algebra! The concepts presented in this lesson prepare students for algebra.

3 Practice

Using page 297 Have students look at Exercise 1.

- Now, apply the four-step plan. For SEE, ask, *What are you asked to do?* (find how many legs 2 chairs have) Then, *What information are you given?* (Each chair has 4 legs.) For PLAN, ask students how they will solve the problem. (add 4 + 4 or multiply 2 and 4) For DO, have students use their plan to find an answer. (8 legs) For CHECK, have students use addition to check their multiplication or multiplication to check their addition.
- Have students complete the page independently.

Using page 298 Tell students to decide if addition or multiplication is the quickest way to find any answer to each exercise. Work through the first problem together and then have students complete the page independently. Remind students to write each answer in the solution sentence.

Practice

Write a multiplication sentence for each. Solve.

1.

How many buttons are there in all?

2 × 4 = 8

There are 8 buttons.

2.

How many birds are there in all?

3 × 5 = 15

There are 15 birds.

3.

How many flowers are there in all?

2 × 5 = 10

There are 10 flowers.

4.

How many tires are there in all?

4 × 4 = 16

There are 16 tires.

5.

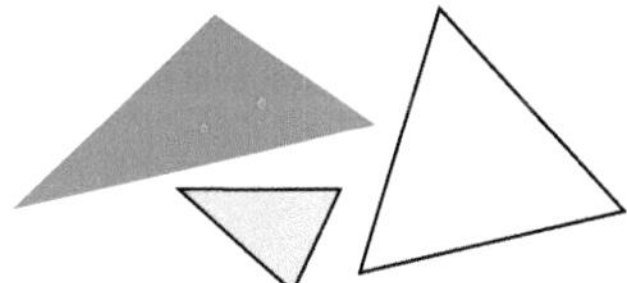

How many sides are there in all?

3 × 3 = 9

There are 9 sides.

6.

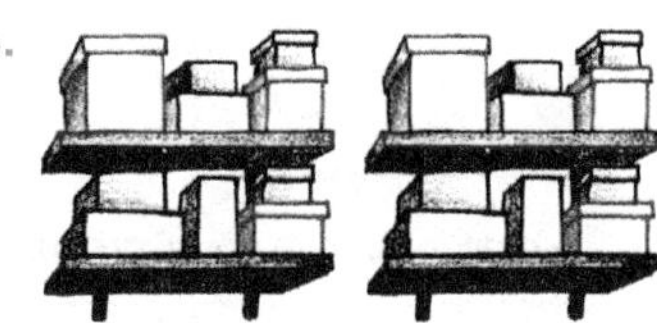

How many boxes are there in all?

4 × 5 = 20

There are 20 boxes.

4 Assess

Draw 3 squares on the board. Ask, *How many corners are there in all?* (12) Have students say whether they used addition or multiplication. Then, have them write the problem and answer.

For Mixed Abilities

Common Errors • Intervention

Some students may have difficulty understanding when multiplication can be used to solve a problem. Have these students work with partners to create a word problem that requires multiplication. For example, How many panes are there in 3 windows of our classroom? They then can write the multiplication fact that can be used to solve it, recognizing that an addition sentence with equal addends also could be used.

Enrichment • Number Sense

Tell students to draw a picture of a rectangular table with 4 chairs on each of the long sides and 3 chairs on each shorter side. Have them write and solve problems to find out how many legs are on each side of the table. Then, tell them to find out how many legs are on all the chairs plus the table.

More to Explore • Measurement

Give each student 10 toothpicks. Have students glue the toothpicks onto paper to form various shapes that have the same perimeter. Broken toothpicks may be used to make interesting shapes without changing the perimeter. Have students use a centimeter ruler to measure the perimeter of each figure and compare the results. Display their toothpick creations on the bulletin board.

15-7 Dividing by 2

pages 299–300

1 Getting Started

Objective
- To divide numbers by 2

Vocabulary
dividend, divisor, divide, quotient

Materials
counters

Warm Up • Mental Math
Have students find the product.

1. 3 × 5 (15)
2. 2 × 5 (10)
3. 4 × 4 (16)
4. 5 × 2 (10)
5. 4 × 3 (12)
6. 5 × 5 (25)

Warm Up • Paper and Pencil
What is the difference?

1. 25 − 16 (9)
2. 20 − 12 (8)
3. 35 − 24 (11)
4. 42 − 28 (14)
5. 36 − 16 (20)
6. 28 − 12 (16)

Name ______________________

Lesson 15-7

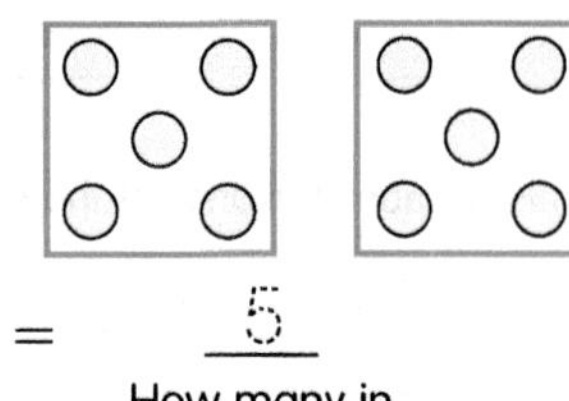

It's Algebra!

Dividing by 2

There are 10 children at the playground. They are going to form 2 teams. How many children will be on each team?

To find the answer, we can use counters to make equal groups.

We can find how many children will be on each team by dividing 10 by 2. The division sentence is 10 ÷ 2.

10	÷	2	=	5
How many in all?		How many groups?		How many in each group?

There will be 5 children on each team.

Getting Started

Draw a picture to show equal groups.

1. 8 pennies in two equal groups

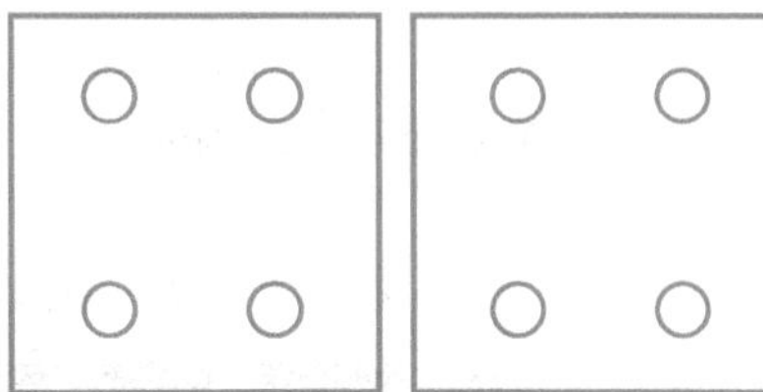

2. 6 crayons in two equal groups

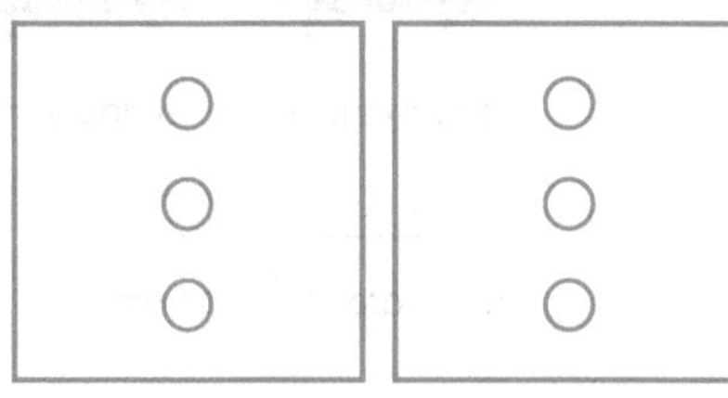

2 Teach

Develop Skills and Concepts Read the following word problem to students: *Tim baked 8 cookies. He wants to give each of his 2 best friends an equal number of cookies. How many cookies will each friend get?* Give students 8 counters each and have them divide the counters into two equal groups. Ask how many counters are in each group. (4)

- Now, write the outline of a division problem on the board. Tell students that another way to find out how many cookies each friend will get is to use division. Place the 8 before the division sign and explain that 8 is the dividend. Say, *8 is the number of cookies in all.* Place the 2 after the division sign and explain that 2 is the number you are dividing by.

It's Algebra! The concepts presented in this lesson prepare students for algebra.

3 Practice

Using page 299 Read with students the example at the top of the page.

- Ask, *What are you being asked to find?* (how many players will be on a team if 10 children are divided into 2 groups) Give students 10 counters and have them divide the counters into 2 equal groups. Ask how many counters are in each group. (5)
- Tell students that another way to solve the problem is to divide 10 by 2. Write the division sentence on the board. Explain that 10 is the number of children in all and that 2 is the number of teams. Five is the number of children that will be on each team.
- Have students complete the Getting Started exercises independently. If necessary, allow students to work with counters to create equal groups.

Using page 300 Read the instructions with students. Then, complete Exercise 1 as a class. Have students draw the equal groups. Relate the drawing to the structure of a division sentence. Then, have students trace the division sentence.

- Have students complete the remaining exercises independently.

Practice

Draw a picture to show equal groups. Then write a division sentence for each.

1. 8 cupcakes divided between 2 boxes

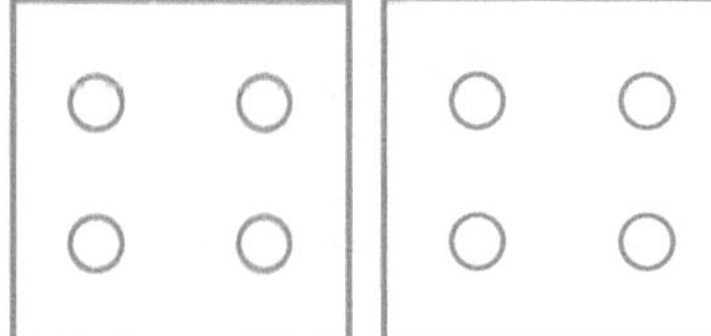

8 ÷ 2 = 4

2. 2 slices of pizza divided between 2 plates

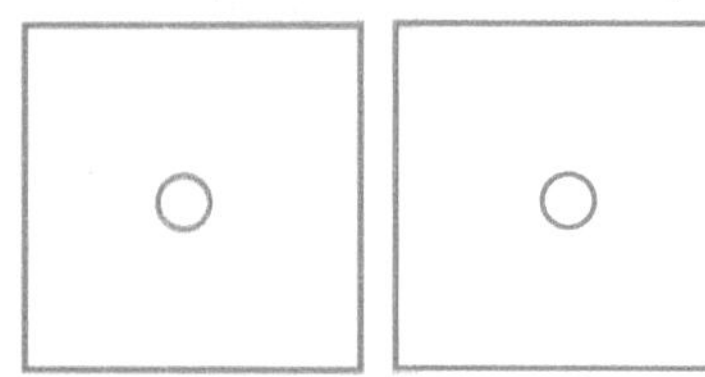

2 ÷ 2 = 1

3. 10 people divided between 2 cars

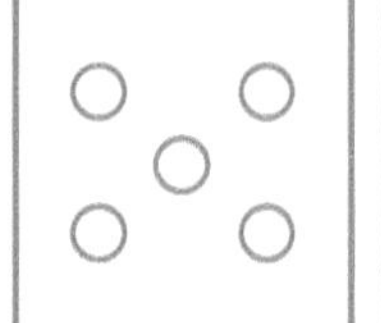
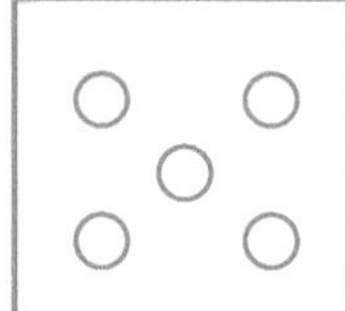

10 ÷ 2 = 5

4. 6 cookies divided between 2 plates

6 ÷ 2 = 3

For Mixed Abilities

Common Errors • Intervention

Some students may add or multiply the numbers in a division fact instead of dividing. Have them work with partners with 8 counters. Have them arrange the counters into 2 equal groups. Ask, *How many counters are there?* (8) *How many groups are there?* (2) *How many counters are in each group?* (4) Write **8 ÷ 2** on the board. Follow the same procedure for other division facts.

Enrichment • Number Sense

Have students name phrases that indicate that they should divide. (Possible answers: share equally, cut in half, split equally)

More to Explore • Number Sense

Have students work in pairs. One partner can write multiplication facts using 2 as one of the factors. The other partner can write related division facts using 2 as the divisor. When the partners have finished, one of the partners can make a copy of the sheet for their notebooks.

4 Assess

Give each student 10 counters. Have students divide the counters into 2 equal groups and then write a division sentence showing how they divided the counters. (10 ÷ 2)

5 Mixed Review

1. 495 + 42 (537)
2. 2 × 8 (16)
3. 450 + 127 + 203 (780)
4. 220, 230, 240, _____ (250)
5. 108 − 89 (19)
6. 4 nickels, 8 pennies (28¢)
7. $6.50 − $2.84 ($3.66)
8. 2 × 5 (10)
9. 695 − 108 (587)
10. 409 ◯ 490 (<)

15-8 Dividing by 3

pages 301–302

1 Getting Started

Objective
- To divide numbers by 3

Materials
counters

Warm Up • Mental Math
Have students find the product.

1. 4 × 4 (16)
2. 3 × 3 (9)
3. 5 × 4 (20)
4. 4 × 3 (12)
5. 5 × 5 (25)

Warm Up • Paper and Pencil
Have students copy the following items and find the quotient:

1. 4 ÷ 2 (2)
2. 8 ÷ 2 (4)
3. 10 ÷ 2 (5)
4. 6 ÷ 2 (3)
5. 2 ÷ 2 (1)

2 Teach

Develop Skills and Concepts Read the following word problem to students: *Sarah made 12 cards. She wants to give each of her 3 cousins an equal number of cards. How many cards will each cousin get?* Give students 12 counters each and have them divide the counters into 3 equal groups. Ask how many counters are in each group. (4)

- Now, write the outline of a division problem on the board. Remind students that division is another way to organize objects into equal groups. Have students tell where the 12 and the 3 should go. Then, work with students to find the quotient. (4)

It's Algebra! The concepts presented in this lesson prepare students for algebra.

3 Practice

Using page 301 Read with students the example at the top of the page.

- Ask, *What are you being asked to find?* (how many cookies each friend will get if 15 cookies are shared equally by 3 friends) Give students 15 counters and have them divide the counters into 3 equal groups. Ask how many counters are in each group. (5)
- Tell students that another way to solve the problem is to divide 15 by 3. Write the division sentence on the board. Explain that 15 is the number of cookies in all and that 3 is the number of friends the cookies are to be divided among. Five is the number of cookies each friend will get.
- Have students complete the Getting Started exercises independently. Allow them to use counters if needed.

Using page 302 Read the instructions with students. Then, complete Exercise 1 as a class. Have students draw the equal groups. Relate the drawing to the structure of a division sentence. Then, have students trace the division sentence.

- Have students complete the remaining exercises independently.

Name ____________________

Lesson 15-8

It's Algebra!

Dividing by 3

Lonnie has 15 cookies to give to 3 friends.
How many cookies will each friend get?

You can put counters into equal groups to find the answer.

We can find how many cookies each friend will get by dividing 15 by 3.
The division sentence is 15 ÷ 3.

15	÷	3	=	5
How many in all?		How many groups?		How many in each group?

Each friend will get __5__ cookies.

Getting Started

Draw a picture to show equal groups.

1. 9 cats in three equal groups

2. 6 pencils in three equal groups

Practice

Draw a picture to show equal groups.
Then write a division sentence for each.

1. 3 pies divided among 3 boxes

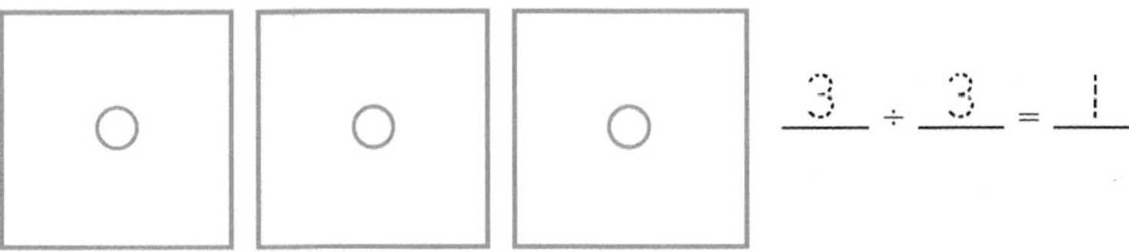

3 ÷ 3 = 1

2. 12 slices of pizza divided among 3 plates

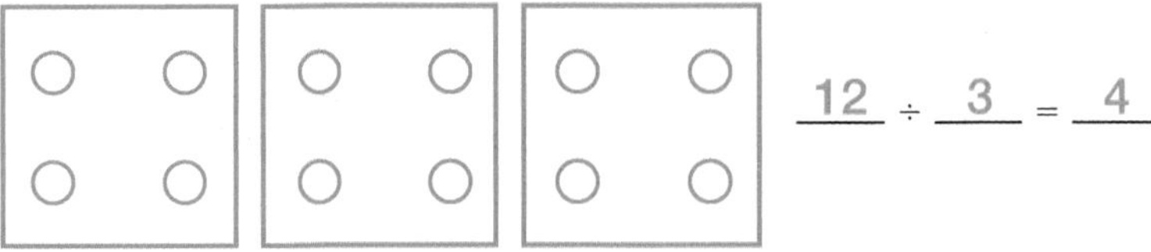

12 ÷ 3 = 4

3. 9 quarters divided among 3 groups

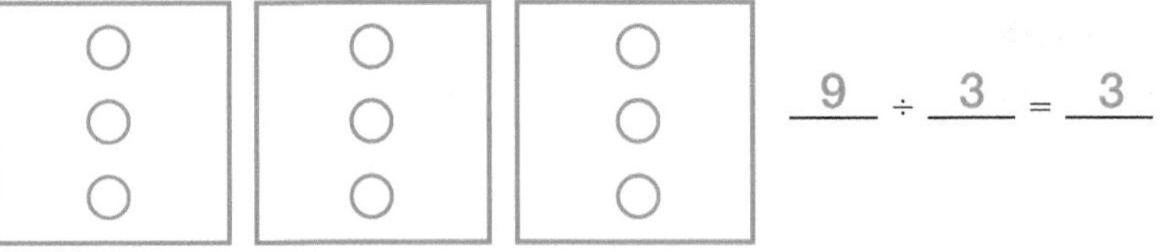

9 ÷ 3 = 3

4. 15 hats divided among 3 groups

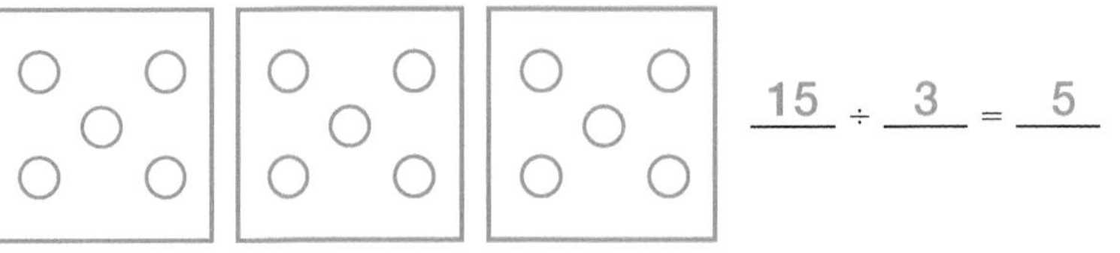

15 ÷ 3 = 5

4 Assess

Write the following on the board: **9 cars divided into 3 groups.** Have students draw a picture to show the problem. Then, have them write and solve the division problem.

For Mixed Abilities

Common Errors • Intervention

Some students may have difficulty understanding division by 3. Have them work with partners and counters. Have them arrange 15 counters so that there are 3 groups with the same number of counters in each group. Ask, *How many counters are there?* (15) *How many groups are there?* (3) *How many counters are in each group?* (5) Write **15 ÷ 3 = 5** on the board. Follow the same procedure for other division facts in which the divisor is 3.

Enrichment • Number Sense

Have students use counters to determine which numbers less than 30 can be divided by 3 equally. (3, 6, 9, 12, 15, 18, 21, 24, 27)

More to Explore • Number Sense

Have students work in pairs. One partner can write multiplication facts using 3 as one of the factors. The other partner can write related division facts using 3 as the divisor. When the partners have finished, one of the partners can make a copy of the sheet for their notebooks.

15-9 Dividing by 4

pages 303–304

1 Getting Started

Objective

- To divide numbers by 4

Materials

counters

Warm Up • Mental Math

Have students find the product.

1. 5 × 5 (25)
2. 4 × 3 (12)
3. 5 × 4 (20)
4. 3 × 3 (9)
5. 5 × 2 (10)
6. 4 × 4 (16)

Warm Up • Paper and Pencil

Have students copy the following problems and find the quotient:

1. 10 ÷ 2 (5)
2. 9 ÷ 3 (3)
3. 12 ÷ 3 (4)
4. 15 ÷ 3 (5)
5. 3 ÷ 3 (1)
6. 6 ÷ 2 (3)

Dividing by 4

It's Algebra!

Josh has 16 quarters. 4 quarters are equal to 1 dollar. How many dollars does Josh have?

To find the answer, use quarters to make equal groups.

We can find how many dollars Josh has by dividing 16 by 4. The division sentence is 16 ÷ 4.

16	÷	4	=	4
How many quarters in all?		How many quarters in a dollar?		How many dollars?

Josh has 4 dollars.

Getting Started

Draw a picture to show equal groups.

1. 12 marbles in four equal groups
2. 8 crayons in four equal groups

2 Teach

Develop Skills and Concepts Read the following word problem to students: *Ted has 20 books that he wants to put on 4 shelves. How many books will go on each shelf?* Give each student 20 counters and have students organize the counters into 4 equal groups. Ask how many counters are in each group. (5)

- Now, write the outline of a division problem on the board. Have students tell where the 20 and the 4 should go. Then, work with students to find the quotient. (5)

It's Algebra! The concepts presented in this lesson prepare students for algebra.

3 Practice

Using page 303 Read with students the example at the top of the page.

- Ask, *What are you being asked to find?* (how many dollars Josh has if he has 16 quarters) Give students 16 counters and have them organize the counters into 4 equal groups. Ask how many counters are in each group. (4)
- Tell students that another way to solve the problem is to divide 16 by 4. Write the division sentence on the board. Explain that 16 is the number of quarters in all and that 4 is the number of quarters in a dollar. Four is the number of dollars Josh has.
- Have students complete the Getting Started exercises independently. Allow them to use counters if needed.

Using page 304 Read the instructions with students. Then, complete Exercise 1 as a class. Have students draw the equal groups. Relate the drawing to the structure of a division sentence. Then, have students trace the division sentence.

- Have students complete the remaining exercises independently.

Practice

Draw a picture to show equal groups.
Then write a division sentence for each.

1. 4 cookies divided among 4 plates

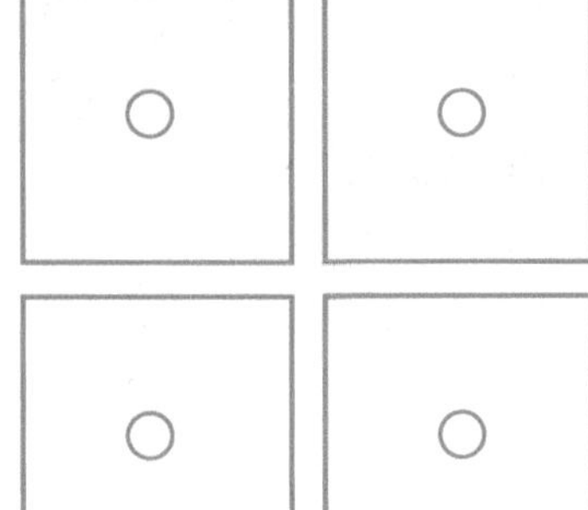

$4 \div 4 = 1$

2. 16 pencils divided among 4 boxes

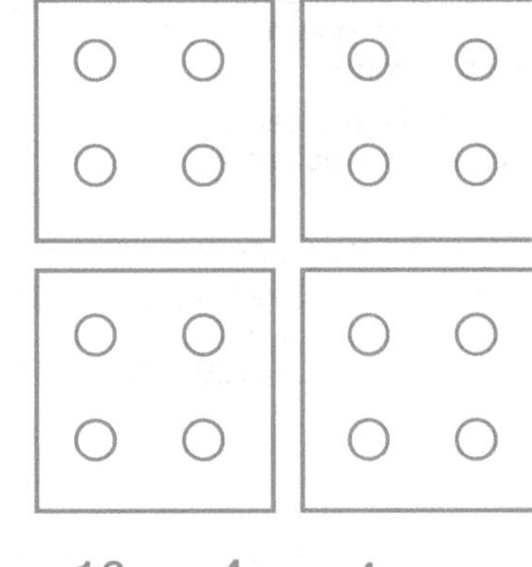

$16 \div 4 = 4$

3. 20 dogs divided among 4 groups

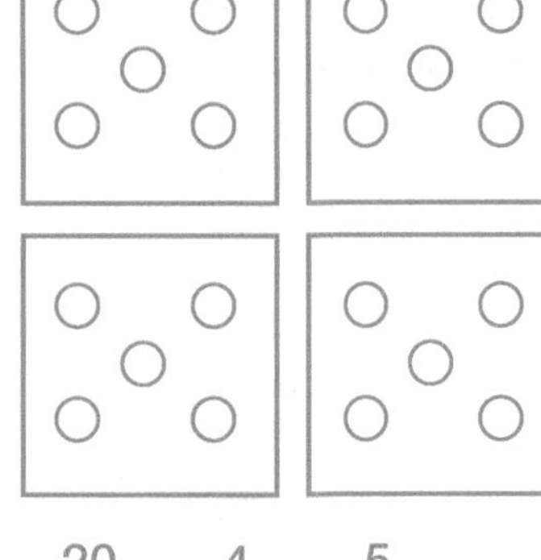

$20 \div 4 = 5$

4. 8 cupcakes divided among 4 boxes

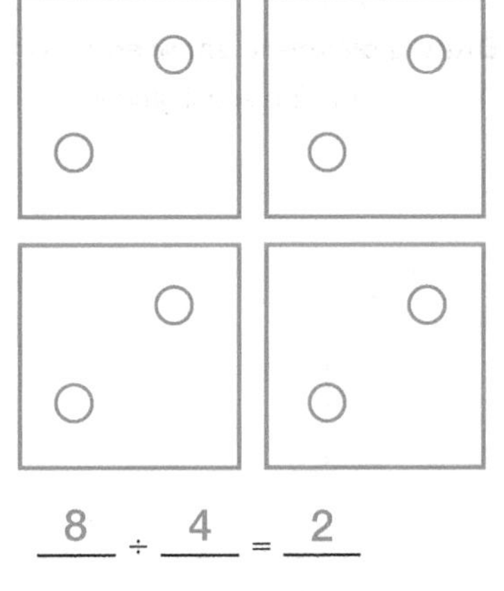

$8 \div 4 = 2$

4 Assess

Have students draw a picture to show how to divide 16 by 4. Then, have them write the division sentence below their picture.

5 Mixed Review

1. 471 + 153 (624)
2. 208 + 315 + 194 (717)
3. 80 − 23 (57)
4. 4 × 8 (32)
5. 702 − 501 (201)
6. 3 × 8 (24)
7. 308 ◯ 316 (<)
8. \$9.09 − \$3.26 (\$5.83)
9. 5 × 7 (35)
10. 7 hundreds 7 tens 6 ones (776)

For Mixed Abilities

Common Errors • **Intervention**

Some students may have difficulty understanding division by 4. Illustrate by giving each student 4 counters. Ask two students to put their counters on a tray. Ask, *How many counters are on the tray?* (8) *How many students put their counters on the tray?* (2) Write **8 ÷ 4 = 2** on the board. Clear the tray, giving students their counters back. Have three other students put their counters on the tray and repeat the activity. Continue until you have illustrated facts through 20 ÷ 4.

Enrichment • Number Sense

Have students work in groups of three. Have students make flashcards with the basic division facts that use 4 as a divisor. One partner can hold the card and a second partner can answer the facts. The third partner can record how many of the facts were answered correctly. After one partner has finished answering the facts, mix up the cards and change roles.

More to Explore • Number Sense

Ask students, *When you divide an even dividend by an odd divisor, is the quotient odd or even?* Have students give an example. (even, 12 ÷ 3 = 4) *When you divide an odd dividend by an odd divisor, is the quotient odd or even? Give an example.* (odd, 9 ÷ 3 = 3)

15-10 Dividing by 5

pages 305–306

1 Getting Started

Objective
- To divide numbers by 5

Materials
counters

Warm Up • Mental Math
Have students find the product.
1. 5 × 5 (25)
2. 5 × 4 (20)
3. 2 × 4 (8)
4. 5 × 1 (5)
5. 3 × 4 (12)
6. 3 × 5 (15)

Warm Up • Paper and Pencil
Have students copy the following problems and find the quotient:
1. 16 ÷ 4 (4)
2. 15 ÷ 3 (5)
3. 8 ÷ 2 (4)
4. 12 ÷ 4 (3)
5. 12 ÷ 3 (4)
6. 20 ÷ 4 (5)

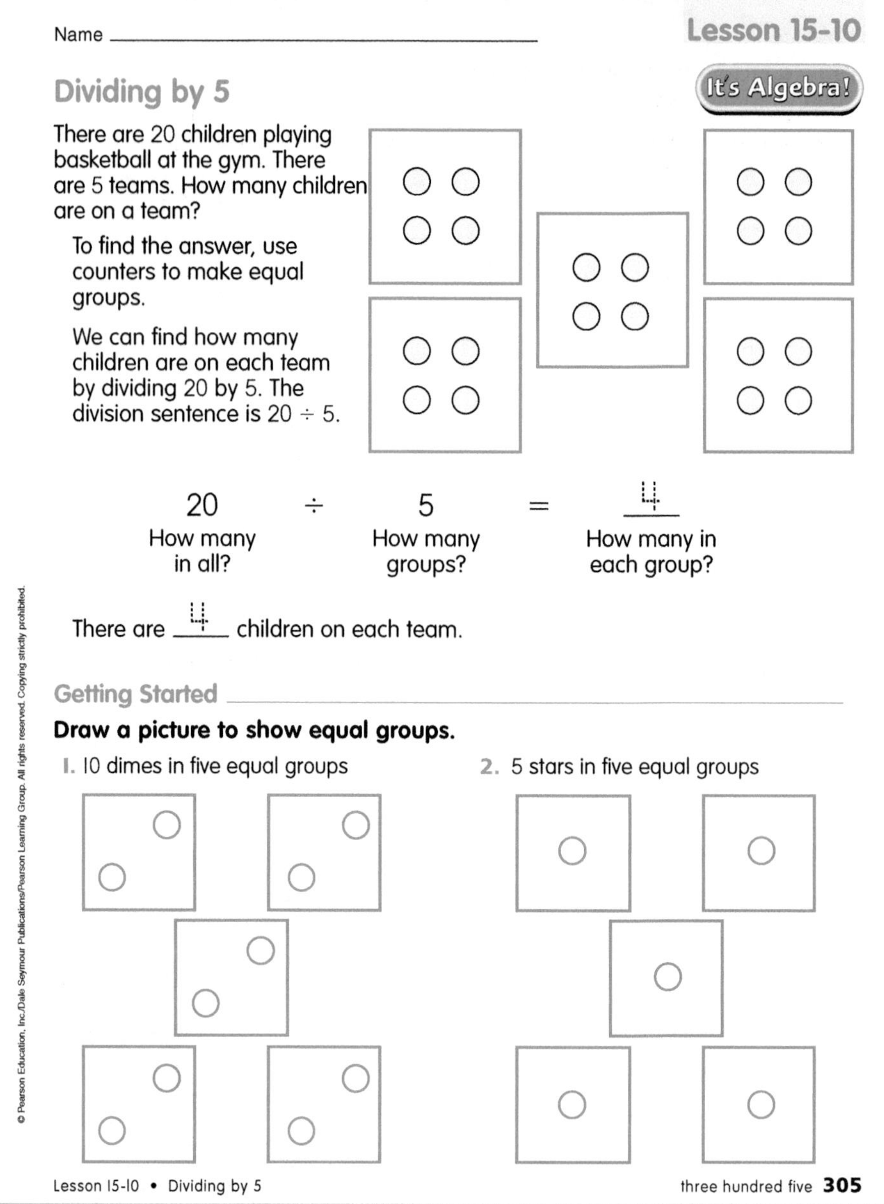

Name ______________________ Lesson 15-10

It's Algebra!

Dividing by 5

There are 20 children playing basketball at the gym. There are 5 teams. How many children are on a team?

To find the answer, use counters to make equal groups.

We can find how many children are on each team by dividing 20 by 5. The division sentence is 20 ÷ 5.

20	÷	5	=	4
How many in all?		How many groups?		How many in each group?

There are 4 children on each team.

Getting Started

Draw a picture to show equal groups.

1. 10 dimes in five equal groups
2. 5 stars in five equal groups

2 Teach

Develop Skills and Concepts Read the following word problem to students: *Madison has eaten 15 meals in the last 5 days. How many meals does she eat each day?* Give students 15 counters and have them organize the counters into 5 equal groups. Ask how many counters are in each group. (3)

- Now, write the outline of a division problem on the board. Have students tell where the 15 and the 5 should go. Then, work with students to find the quotient.

It's Algebra! The concepts presented in this lesson prepare students for algebra.

3 Practice

Using page 305 Read with students the example at the top of the page.

- Ask, *What are you being asked to find?* (how many teams are playing basketball if 20 children are playing) *What information do you know?* (There are 20 children playing and there are 5 players on each team.) Give each student 20 counters and have them divide the counters into 5 equal groups. Ask how many are in each group. (4)

- Tell students that another way to solve the problem is to divide 20 by 5. Write the division sentence on the board. Explain that 20 is the number of children in all and that 5 is the number of players on a team. Four is the number of teams.

- Have students complete the Getting Started exercises independently. Allow them to use counters if needed.

Using page 306 Read the instructions with students. Then, complete Exercise 1 as a class. Have students draw the equal groups. Relate the drawing to the structure of a division sentence. Then, have students trace the division sentence.

- Have students complete the remaining exercises independently.

Practice

Draw a picture to show equal groups.
Then write a division sentence for each.

1. 20 crayons divided among 5 boxes

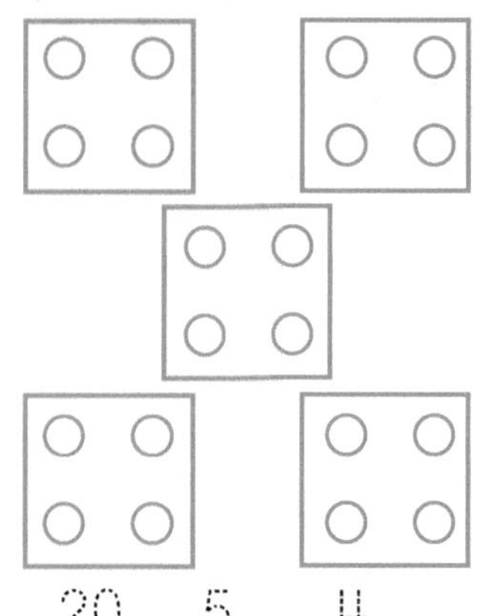

20 ÷ 5 = 4

2. 15 pencils divided among 5 boxes

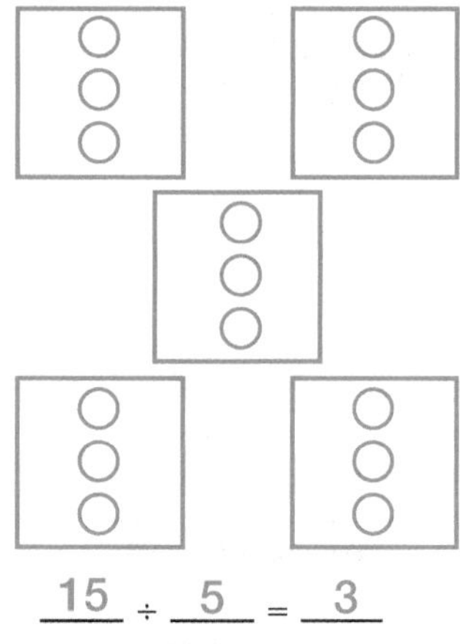

15 ÷ 5 = 3

3. 25 buttons divided among 5 groups

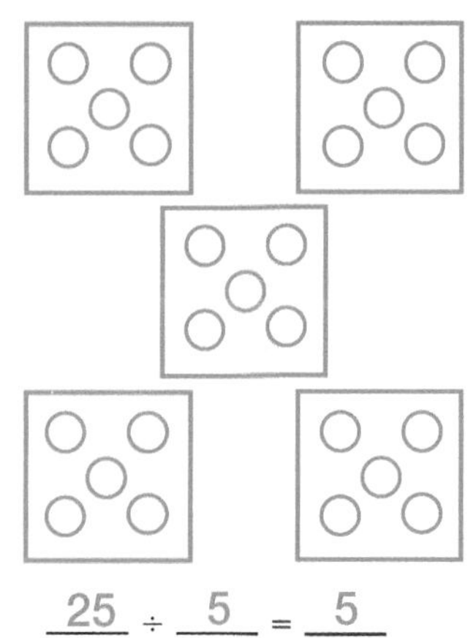

25 ÷ 5 = 5

4. 5 slices of pizza divided among 5 plates

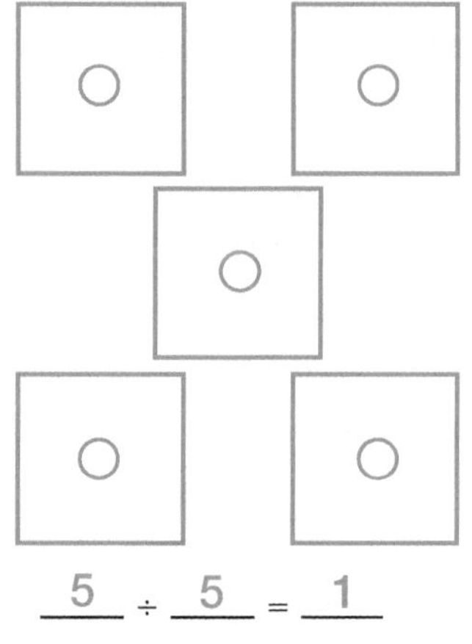

5 ÷ 5 = 1

4 Assess

Give students 25 buttons. Have them organize the buttons into 5 equal groups and write the division sentence.

For Mixed Abilities

Common Errors • Intervention

Some students may have difficulty understanding division by 5. Practice by relating division to finding the missing factor, using a form as shown below.

? 5s = 15	15 ÷ 5 =
? 5s = 20	20 ÷ 5 =
? 5s = 25	25 ÷ 5 =

Enrichment • Number Sense

Ask students, *Suppose you are making a tally table and you count 20 of an item. How many tally marks showing 5 would you need?* (4)

More to Explore • Number Sense

Have students work in groups of three. Have students make flashcards with the basic division facts that use the numbers 2 through 5 as a divisor. One partner can hold the card and a second partner can answer the facts. The third partner can record how many of the facts were answered correctly. After one partner has finished answering the facts, mix up the cards and change roles.

15-11 Problem Solving: Make and Use a Picture Graph

pages 307–308

1 Getting Started

Objectives
- To interpret picture graphs using multiplication
- To solve problems using graphs

Vocabulary
pictograph

Materials
*multiplication fact cards through 2 × 5, 3 × 5, 4 × 5, and 5 × 5

Warm Up • Mental Math
Ask students how many
1. cups in a pint (2)
2. eggs in a dozen (12)
3. wheels on 3 tricycles (9)
4. sides on 3 doors (6)
5. hands on 5 people (10)
6. wheels on 4 bicycles (8)
7. days in 1 week (7)
8. sides on 4 squares (16)

Warm Up • Number Sense
Have students give answers to multiplication fact cards randomly shown. Have students place cards in pairs when possible to show that the answer is the same regardless of the order of the two factors.

Name ______________________

Problem Solving: Make and Use a Picture Graph

Mary made a picture graph to show the books she read in January. Another name for a picture graph is pictograph.

Books Read in January	
First week	📖 📖
Second week	📖 📖 📖 📖
Third week	📖 📖 📖
Fourth week	📖 📖 📖 📖 📖

Each 📖 stands for 2 books.

How many books did Mary read

the first week? 4 — the third week? 6

the second week? 8 — the fourth week? 10

Getting Started

Write each answer on the lines.

1. Mary read the most books during the fourth week.
2. She read the fewest books during the first week.
3. How many more books did Mary read the fourth week than the first week?
   10 − 4 = 6
4. How many books did Mary read the first two weeks?
   4 + 8 = 12

2 Teach

Develop Skills and Concepts Ask students to vote on their favorite ice-cream flavor, chocolate or vanilla. Use tally marks to keep a record of the results on the board. Then, use the results to draw a simple pictograph, using an ice-cream cone to represent 5 students. Walk through how to read the graph with students. Then, ask students questions about the information in the graph.

3 Practice

Using page 307 Have students look at the pictograph in the example. Ask students what information is presented in the graph. (the number of books Mary read in January)

- Now, apply the four-step plan to the example. For SEE, ask, *What are you being asked to do?* (read a pictograph to determine how many books Mary read each week in January) Then, *What information is given?* (One book icon represents 2 books.) For PLAN, ask students how they will find the number of books Mary read each week. (multiply the number of book icons by 2) For DO, have students answer the questions. For CHECK, have them check the information in the chart.

- Have students complete the Getting Started exercises independently.

Using page 308 Have students read the first sentence aloud. Tell students that 4 tally marks are crossed by a fifth tally mark to make it easy to count the tallies by 5s. Have students count by 5s to tell how many shells each child found. (Del, 10; Jennifer, 15; Rosa, 25; Joseph, 20; Rodney, 5) Have students read the directions for the pictograph aloud. Ask students how many shells each picture represents. (5) Ask how many shells will be colored for Del. (2) Repeat for the other names on the graph. Have students color the necessary shells.

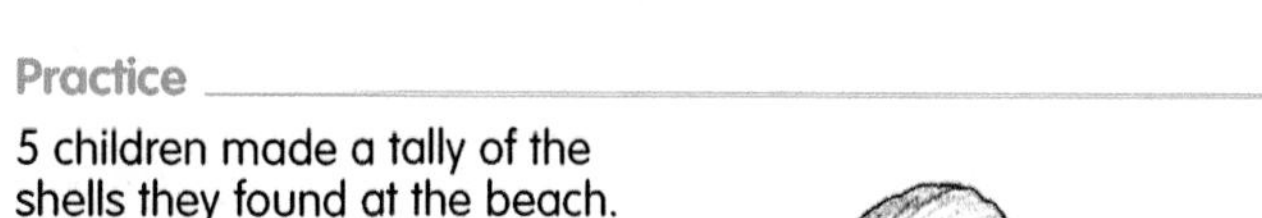

Practice

5 children made a tally of the shells they found at the beach.

Color the number of shells to show how many shells each child found.

1.	Del					
2.	Jennifer					
3.	Rosa					
4.	Joseph					
5.	Rodney					

Each shell stands for 5 shells.

Answer each question.

6. Who found the most shells? Rosa
7. Who found the fewest shells? Rodney
8. How many shells were found by Del and Jennifer? 25
9. How many shells were found by Joseph and Rodney? 25
10. How many more shells were found by Rosa than Rodney? 20

- Have students answer the questions at the bottom of the page independently.

4 Assess

Have students keep track of how many glasses of water they drink each day over the period of 1 week. Then, have them use this information to create a pictograph.

For Mixed Abilities

Common Errors • Intervention

Watch for students who always think that a symbol on a pictograph represents 1. Correct students by having them write the number that a symbol represents on each symbol on the graph.

Enrichment • Number Sense

Tell students to use the pictograph on page 307 to find out how many books in all were read in the 4 weeks.

More to Explore • Measurement

Make up a scavenger hunt that requires students to find things in your classroom by measuring linear distance accurately.

Give students a direction sheet and a meter- or yardstick. Create directions that refer to specific things in your room. Tell students they must complete each measurement and record the name of each object as they locate it. This could be done as a timed activity. Directions might include the following:

1. Two yards from the pencil sharpener you will find a blue _____.
2. There are five _____ lying 2.5 centimeters from the upper right corner of the teacher's desk.
3. _____ is hanging 1 meter from the tip of the flag.

Have a small reward or prize at the end of the hunt that students can find if they solve the last clue correctly.

15-12 Coordinate Graph

pages 309–310

1 Getting Started

Objective
- To locate and name points on a coordinate grid

Vocabulary
coordinate graph

Warm Up • Mental Math
Have students find the product.

1. 4 times 3 (12)
2. 5 times 4 (20)
3. 5 times 2 (10)
4. 5 times 1 (5)
5. 3 times 2 (6)
6. 2 times 4 (8)

Warm Up • Geometry
Have students name the number of sides each figure has.

1. triangle (3)
2. square (4)
3. rectangle (4)

Name ______________________________

It's Algebra!

Coordinate Graph

A coordinate graph is used to show where objects are located.

This graph shows where places are located in a town. Find the mall.

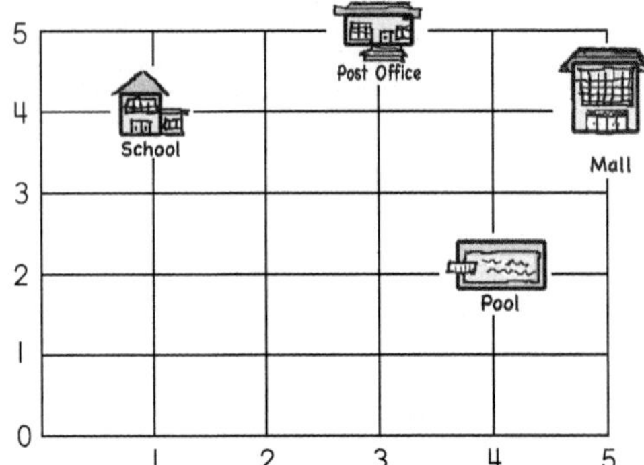

Always start at 0.

First, count to the right →. The mall is __5__ units to the right.

Then, count up ↑. The mall is __4__ units up.

To find the mall, go to the right __5__ and up __4__.

Getting Started

Use the graph to find each of the following.

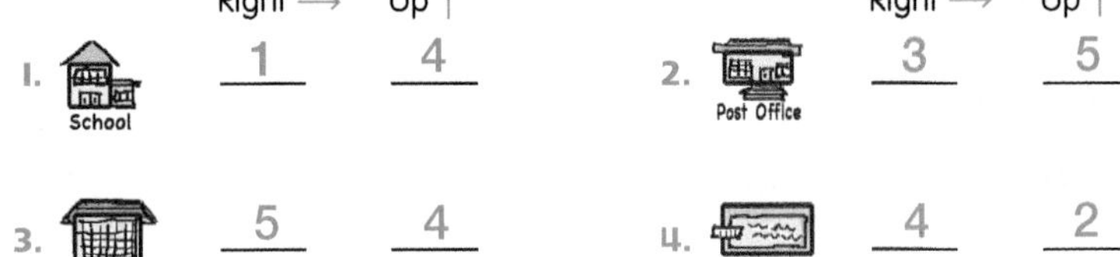

	Place	Right →	Up ↑
1.	School	1	4
2.	Post Office	3	5
3.	Mall	5	4
4.	Pool	4	2

2 Teach

Develop Skills and Concepts On the board, draw a coordinate grid that is 5 units by 5 units. Draw a small square at (2, 3). Ask students how many units to the right of 0 the square is located. (2) Then, ask how many units above 0 the square is located. (3) Explain to students that 2 units to the right and 3 units up describes the location of the square. Tell students that when reading a coordinate grid, the location to the right of 0 is read first and then how many units above 0 is read second.

It's Algebra! The concepts presented in this lesson prepare students for algebra.

3 Practice

Using page 309 Read the example at the top of the page with students.

- Ask students, *For which building are you trying to find the location?* (mall) *How many units to the right of 0 is the mall?* (5) *How many units above 0 is the mall?* (4)
- Work through Exercise 1 with students if necessary. You may wish to repeat the questions you used to elicit the location of the mall from students. Then, have students complete the page independently.

Using page 310 Have students look at Exercise 1. Ask, *What do you need to do to write the location of the banana?* (count how many units to the right of 0 and how many units above 0 the banana is) Have students count the units and then review their answers with the class.

- Have students complete the page independently.

Practice

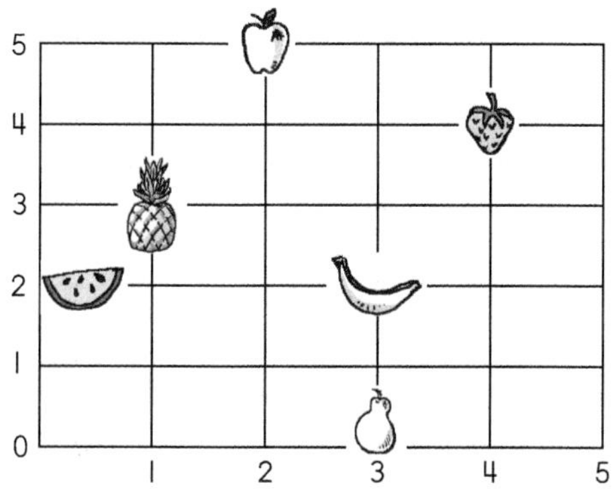

Use the graph to find each of the following.

		Right →	Up ↑
1.		3	2
2.		2	5
3.		0	2
4.		4	4
5.		3	0
6.		1	3

4 Assess

Give students a point such as (2, 6) and have them point to it on a coordinate graph.

For Mixed Abilities

Common Errors • Intervention

Some students may have difficulty counting the correct number of spaces. Remind those students to start at 0 but do not count 0 as one of the spaces.

Enrichment • Geometry

Have students draw a coordinate grid that is 4 units to the right of 0 and 4 units above 0. Tell them to start at 0 units to the right of 0 and 4 units above 0 and write the letter *A*. Then, have them write each of the letters of the alphabet from left to right from top to bottom. Ask, *At which points are your initials?*

More to Explore • Geometry

Have students work in groups of four. Divide the groups into two teams. Each team should draw a 5-by-5 grid and then draw a square, a rectangle, a triangle, and a circle on one point each. Teams should not show the other team their points. Then, one member of the team can name a point such as 3 to the right of 0 and 2 above 0 to see if their point matches their partner's drawing. The other partner will be responsible for answering the other team's questions.

ESL/ELL STRATEGIES

Explain that the word *coordinate* means "using two measurements." Point out that the first measurement on a coordinate graph is always a horizontal one (from left to right like handwriting) and that the second measurement is always vertical (up from the bottom, the like an elevator).

Chapter 15 Test

page 311

Items	Objectives
1–9	To multiply through factors of 5 (see pages 288–294)
10–12	To divide by 2, 3, 4, and 5 (see pages 299–306)
13–16	To multiply by the factors 2, 3, 4, and 5 (see pages 288–294)

Alternate Chapter Test

You may wish to use the Alternate Chapter Test on page 329 of this book for further review and assessment.

Name ____________________

Chapter 15 Test

Multiply.

1. 

$3 \times 4 =$ 12

2.

$2 \times 4 =$ 8

3.

$3 \times 5 =$ 15

4. 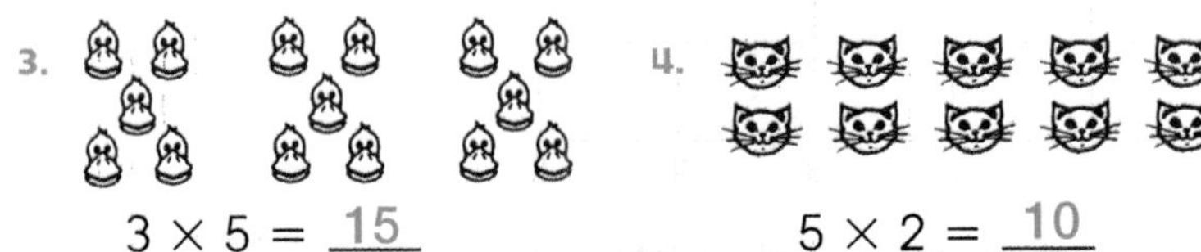

$5 \times 2 =$ 10

5. $5 \times 4 = 20$
6. $4 \times 5 = 20$
7. $3 \times 3 = 9$
8. $3 \times 4 = 12$
9. $5 \times 2 = 10$

Divide.

10. $10 \div 5 =$ 2
11. $9 \div 3 =$ 3
12. $8 \div 2 =$ 4

Solve.

13. Calvin bought 3 bunches of carrots. There are 5 carrots in each bunch. How many carrots does he have?

15 carrots

14. There are 16 wheels. Each car has 4 wheels. How many cars are there in all?

There are 4 cars.

Find the total cost.

15. 5 

Total cost 10¢

16. 3 

Total cost 9¢

Cumulative Assessment

Circle the letter of the correct answer.

1. 7 + 8
   a. 16
   b. 1
   (c.) 15
   d. NG

2. 13 − 6
   (a.) 7
   b. 13
   c. 19
   d. NG

3. [clock]
   a. 3:45
   (b.) 8:15
   c. 8:03
   d. NG

4. [coins]
   (a.) 85¢
   b. 80¢
   c. 75¢
   d. NG

5. 37 + 54
   a. 23
   b. 81
   c. 83
   (d.) NG

6. 356 + 575
   (a.) 931
   b. 921
   c. 821
   d. NG

7. 81 − 55
   a. 36
   (b.) 26
   c. 34
   d. NG

8. 623 − 298
   (a.) 325
   b. 335
   c. 435
   d. NG

9. What part of the figure is blue?
   a. $\frac{2}{4}$
   b. $\frac{1}{4}$
   (c.) $\frac{3}{4}$
   d. NG

10. 5 × 3
   a. 8
   (b.) 15
   c. 2
   d. NG

11. $8.35 − 4.26
   a. $4.11
   b. $4.19
   (c.) $4.09
   d. NG

12. 8 ÷ 4
   a. 1
   (b.) 2
   c. 3
   d. NG

score

STOP

Cumulative Assessment

page 312

Items	Objectives
1–2	To review addition and subtraction facts with sums of and minuends through 18 (see pages 23–28, 35–44, 53–56, 59–64)
3	To tell time in 5-minute intervals (see pages 95–96)
4	To count money through 99¢ (see pages 107–208)
5	To add two 2-digit numbers with some regrouping (see pages 125–126)
6	To add two 3-digit numbers with regrouping (see pages 187–190, 221–223)
7	To subtract two 2-digit numbers (see pages 137–146, 159–160)
8, 11	To subtract 3-digit numbers, including money, with regrouping (see pages 209–210, 225–226, 231–232)
9	To identify fractional parts of a whole (see pages 247–252)
10	To multiply through factors of 5 (see pages 288–294)
12	To divide by 4 (see pages 303–304)

Alternate Cumulative Assessment

Circle the letter of the correct answer.

1. 4 + 9
   (a) 13
   b 14
   c 15
   d NG

2. 15 − 8
   a 6
   (b) 7
   c 8
   d NG

3. 
   a 5:35
   b 4:42
   (c) 4:35
   d NG

4. 
   a 55¢
   b 61¢
   (c) 60¢
   d NG

5. 47 + 74
   a 111
   (b) 121
   c 123
   d NG

6. 742 + 178
   a 910
   (b) 920
   c 830
   d NG

7. 37 − 18
   a 29
   b 25
   c 35
   (d) NG

8. 625 − 267
   (a) 358
   b 442
   c 312
   d NG

9. [circle]
   a $\frac{2}{5}$
   b $\frac{2}{3}$
   (c) $\frac{3}{4}$
   d NG

10. 5 × 3
   a 8
   (b) 15
   c 20
   d NG

11. $6.75 − 2.76
   a $3.39
   (b) $3.99
   c $4.01
   d NG

12. 20 ÷ 5
   (a) 4
   b 5
   c 6
   d NG

Glossary

A

add to put numbers together to find the total amount; for example, $2 + 4 = 6$

after next; for example, 45 is after 44.

area the amount of space in a figure

B

bar graph a graph that compares the number of two or more objects

before ahead of; for example, 44 is before 45.

C

calendar a table that shows the days, weeks, and months of a given year

cent (¢) one penny

centimeter (cm) a metric unit of length

congruent figures figures that are exactly the same size and shape

cup (c) a customary unit of capacity

cylinder a space figure with two bases that are circles

D

day 24 hours

degrees (°) units used to measure temperature

digit any one of the ten number symbols: 0, 1, 2, 3, 4, 5, 6, 7, 8, 9

dime a coin that is worth 10 cents

dollar ($) paper money that is worth 100 cents

divide to separate into equal parts

dividend the number to be divided

E

edge the line where two plane faces on a solid figure meet

elapsed time the amount of time that has passed between two given times

estimate to quickly find an answer that is close to an exact answer

F

face the flat part of a solid figure

factors numbers that are multiplied

foot (ft) a unit of measurement equal to 12 inches

fraction a form of a number that shows parts of a whole

G

greater than more than; for example, 65 is greater than 33.

H

half-dollar a coin that is worth 50 cents

half-hour 30 minutes

hour 60 minutes

I

inch (in.) a customary unit of length

K

kilogram (kg) a metric unit of mass

L

length how long an object is

less than fewer than; for example, 33 is less than 65.

line of symmetry a line that divides a figure into two parts that are exactly the same

liter (L) a metric unit of capacity

M

meter (m) a metric unit of length

minute 60 seconds

mixed number a number made up of a whole number and a fraction

month a period of time equaling almost 4 weeks

multiples possible products of a given number

multiply to add a number to itself one or more times

N

nickel a coin that is worth 5 cents

O

ordinal numbers a number used to tell order or position; for example, first, second

P

perimeter the distance around a figure

pint (pt) a customary unit of capacity that is equal to 2 cups

place value hundreds, tens, or ones

pound (lb) a customary unit of weight

product the answer to a multiplication problem

Q

quart (qt) a customary unit of capacity equal to 2 pints

quarter a coin that is worth 25 cents

R

regroup (in addition) to rename and then carry a tens digit to the place on the left when adding

regroup (in subtraction) to rename and then carry a tens digit to the place on the right when subtracting

S

subtract to take away one number from another

V

vertex a point where three faces of a solid figure meet

W

week 7 days

Y

year 12 months

Name ______________________________

Match.

6	four
4	six

Add.

$$\begin{array}{r} 2 \\ +\,2 \\ \hline \end{array} \quad \begin{array}{r} 4 \\ +\,1 \\ \hline \end{array} \quad \begin{array}{r} 3 \\ +\,4 \\ \hline \end{array} \quad \begin{array}{r} 5 \\ +\,0 \\ \hline \end{array} \quad \begin{array}{r} 2 \\ +\,6 \\ \hline \end{array} \quad \begin{array}{r} 5 \\ +\,4 \\ \hline \end{array} \quad \begin{array}{r} 1 \\ +\,9 \\ \hline \end{array}$$

Subtract.

3

$$\begin{array}{r} 5 \\ -\,2 \\ \hline \end{array} \quad \begin{array}{r} 8 \\ -\,6 \\ \hline \end{array} \quad \begin{array}{r} 10 \\ -\,5 \\ \hline \end{array} \quad \begin{array}{r} 9 \\ -\,7 \\ \hline \end{array} \quad \begin{array}{r} 6 \\ -\,0 \\ \hline \end{array} \quad \begin{array}{r} 8 \\ -\,8 \\ \hline \end{array} \quad \begin{array}{r} 7 \\ -\,4 \\ \hline \end{array}$$

Solve.

Joe had 8 blocks. He gave Mike 4. How many blocks are left?

____ blocks

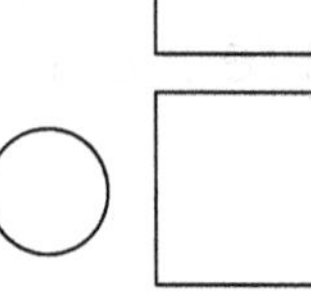

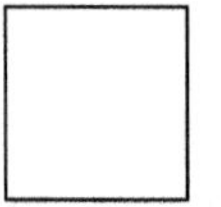

Sally made 3 cards. Kim made 4 cards. How many cards were made?

____ cards

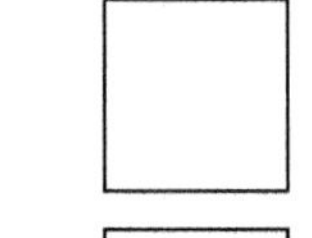

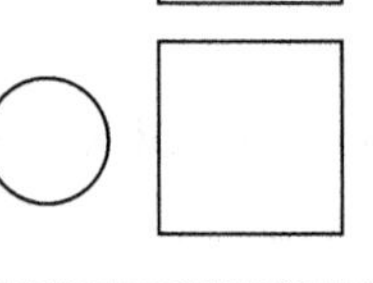

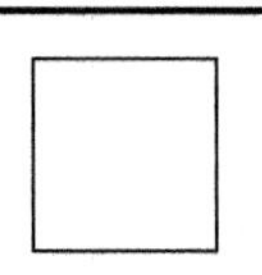

Name ______________________________

Add.

1.

7	6	2	8	1	4	6
+ 5	+ 4	+ 8	+ 3	+ 9	+ 7	+ 6

2.

9	3	6	9	5	5	4
+ 2	+ 7	+ 5	+ 3	+ 7	+ 5	+ 8

Subtract.

3.

10	11	12	12	11	10	11
− 2	− 7	− 6	− 9	− 5	− 4	− 3

4.

11	10	12	10	11	12	10
− 2	− 9	− 4	− 3	− 4	− 5	− 5

Solve.

5. Bob had 12¢.
He spent 5¢.
How much money does he have left?

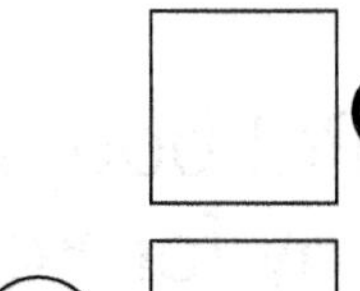

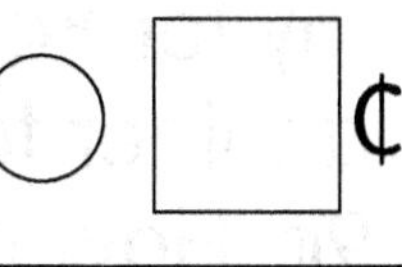

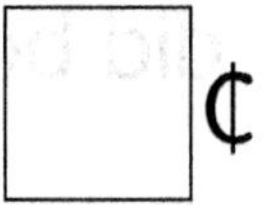

____ ¢

6. Mary bought a pencil for 6¢ and a sticker for 3¢.
How much money did she spend?

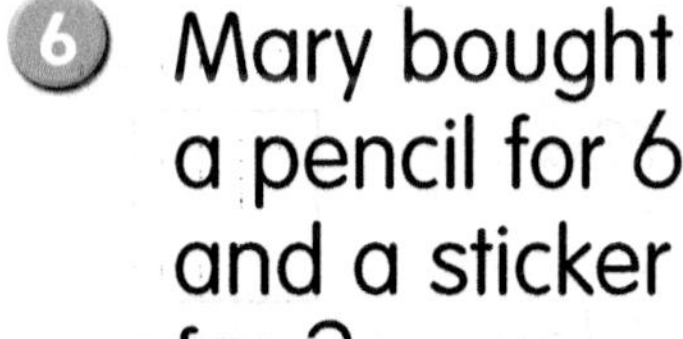

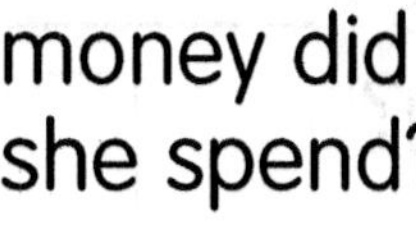

____ ¢

Name ________________________________

Add.

1. | 7 | 8 | 5 | 7 | 8 | 6 | 8 |
|---|---|---|---|---|---|---|
| + 3 | + 9 | + 6 | + 7 | + 5 | + 9 | + 8 |

2. | 4 | 9 | 7 | 9 | 6 | 9 | 8 |
|---|---|---|---|---|---|---|
| + 7 | + 5 | + 8 | + 3 | + 7 | + 7 | + 2 |

3. | 9¢ | 8¢ | 4¢ | 7¢ | 6¢ | 6¢ | 7¢ |
|---|---|---|---|---|---|---|
| + 9¢ | + 3¢ | + 9¢ | + 5¢ | + 6¢ | + 8¢ | + 4¢ |

Add. Look for a ten.

4. | 7 | 6 | 8 | 5 | 5 | 2 | 7 |
|---|---|---|---|---|---|---|
| 3 | 5 | 3 | 5 | 3 | 7 | 8 |
| + 6 | + 4 | + 2 | + 4 | + 4 | + 8 | + 3 |

Solve.

5. There are 5 red marbles and 9 green marbles in a bag. How many marbles are in the bag?

_____ marbles

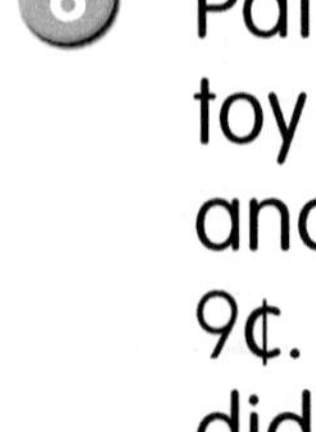

6. Pat bought one toy for 8¢ and another toy for 9¢. How much did both cost?

_____ ¢

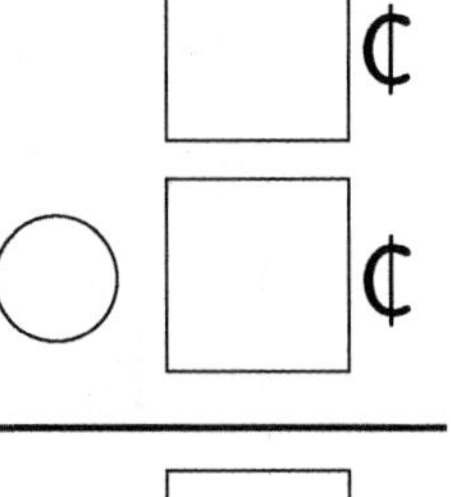

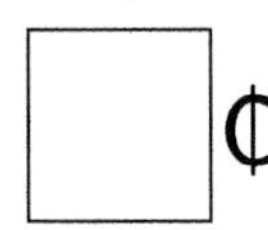

Name ______________________________

Subtract.

1	13 − 7	17 − 9	12 − 5	9 − 0	10 − 6	14 − 5	15 − 7
2	16 − 7	11 − 4	18 − 9	12 − 6	13 − 8	11 − 5	14 − 7
3	13 − 9	16 − 8	14 − 6	10 − 2	12 − 9	15 − 6	11 − 8
4	15 − 8	11 − 9	8 − 8	12 − 4	10 − 3	13 − 6	17 − 8

Solve.

5. Ray is 13 years old. Sue is 8 years old. How much older is Ray?

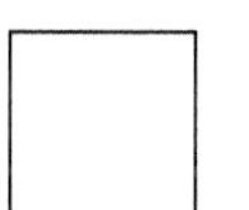

_____ years older

6. Joe has 16 cars. Tim has 9 cars. How many more cars does Joe have?

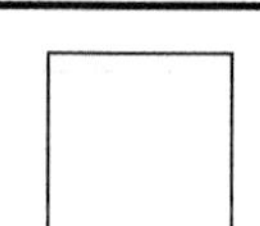

_____ cars

7. Sandy has 14¢. She spent 5¢. How much money does she have left?

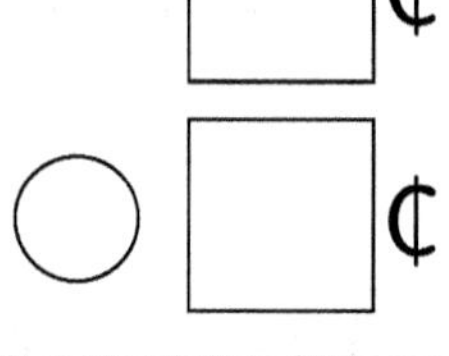

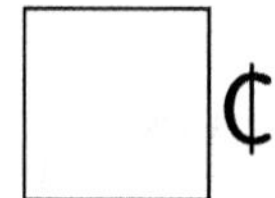

_____¢

8. Judy had 15 stickers. She used 6. How many does she have left?

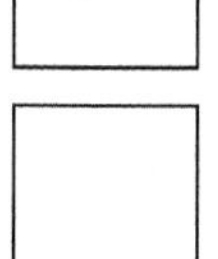

_____ stickers

Name ______________________________

How many hundreds, tens, and ones are there? Write the number.

 1.

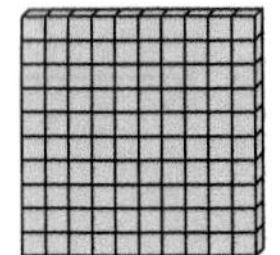 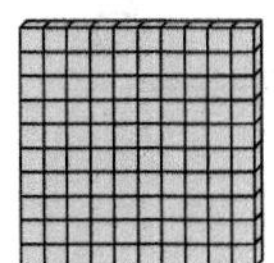 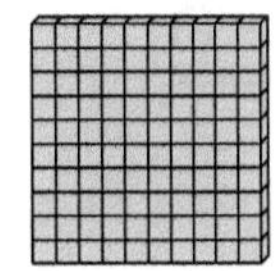 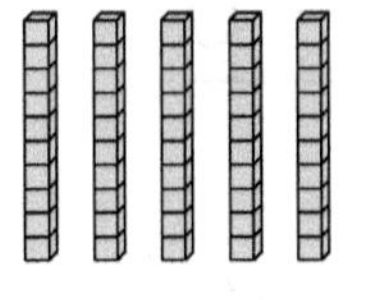

____ hundreds ____ tens ____ ones ______

Write the amount in two ways.

 2.

______

____ . ________

Write each missing number.

3. 256, 257, 258, _____, _____, _____, _____

4. 30, 40, 50, _____, _____, _____, _____

Write the number of hundreds, tens, and ones.

5. 427

____ hundreds ____ tens

____ ones

6. 309

____ hundreds ____ tens

____ ones

Write each missing number before and after.

7. _____, 451, _____

8. _____, 689, _____

Write >, <, or = in each ◯.

9. 876 ◯ 678

10. 381 ◯ 318

11. 295 ◯ 295

12. 199 ◯ 200

Name ____________________

Write each time.

1 

_____ o'clock

_____:_____

2 

_____ minutes

after _____

_____:_____

3 

The time is

_____

José played for 3 hours. What time did he stop playing? Draw the hour hand.

He stopped at _____.

4 What day comes before Tuesday?

_____

5 What month comes before May?

_____

6 **Count the money. Write the amount.**

_____ _____ _____ _____ _____

_____ _____

_____ ¢

Count the money. Check the money spent. Solve.

Mike had _____.

He spent 63¢.

He has _____ left.

8 

Tim had _____.

He spent $1.15.

He has _____ left.

Name ______________________________

Add. Regroup if needed.

1. $43 + 6$
2. $65 + 9$
3. $76 + 7$
4. $70 + 40$
5. $20 + 90$
6. $50 + 60$
7. $53 + 45$
8. $83 + 9$
9. $27 + 77$
10. $59 + 50$
11. $45 + 6$
12. $98 + 61$
13. $28 + 27$
14. $69 + 74$
15. $88 + 5$
16. $36 + 36$
17. $17 + 44$
18. $64 + 8$
19. $40 + 87$
20. $55 + 98$
21. $91 + 71$
22. $73 + 68$
23. $54 + 53$
24. $87 + 8$

Add. Then write each answer in dollar notation.

25. 57¢ + 8¢ ______
26. 80¢ + 50¢ ______
27. 74¢ + 13¢ ______
28. 85¢ + 22¢ ______
29. 97¢ + 7¢ ______

Solve.

30. There were 72 girls and 69 boys in the swimming pool. How many children were swimming?

_____ children

31. Tony has 99¢.
Young Mi has 85¢.
How much money do they have in all?

_____

Name ______________________________

Subtract. Regroup if needed.

1. $47 - 3$	2. $85 - 9$	3. $76 - 7$	4. $61 - 5$
5. $70 - 20$	6. $90 - 50$	7. $40 - 10$	8. $55 - 31$
9. $74 - 15$	10. $92 - 45$	11. $67 - 38$	12. $75 - 45$
13. $91 - 15$	14. $87 - 69$	15. $48 - 19$	16. $56 - 38$
17. 64¢ − 25¢	18. 71¢ − 54¢	19. 38¢ − 29¢	20. 95¢ − 56¢

Solve.

21. Jason saved 57 marbles. He gave Sonja 18 of them. How many marbles did he have left?

_____ marbles

22. The pet store had 84 hamsters. They sold 39 of them. How many did they have left?

_____ hamsters

Chapter 9 Alternate Test

Name ______________________________

Add or subtract.

1. $63 + 9$
2. $58 + 31$
3. $23 + 76$
4. $41 + 48$
5. $57 + 34$
6. $62 + 19$
7. $26 + 45$
8. $83 + 38$
9. $63 + 77$
10. $14 + 88$
11. $45 + 46$
12. $98 + 61$
13. $76 - 22$
14. $52 - 31$
15. $91 - 47$
16. $65 - 58$
17. $74 - 19$
18. $86 - 68$
19. $44 + 15 + 26$
20. $58 + 21 + 43$
21. $72 + 16 + 33$
22. $27 + 35 + 68$
23. $54 + 62 + 19$
24. $67 + 26 + 55$
25. $16 + 69 + 8$
26. $32 + 21 + 49$
27. $47 + 43 + 14$
28. $86 + 33 + 28$
29. $63 + 68 + 53$
30. $27 + 19 + 42$

Add or subtract. Then write each answer in dollar notation.

31. 57¢ + 18¢ = ______
32. 82¢ + 59¢ = ______
33. 74¢ − 27¢ = ______
34. 85¢ + 36¢ = ______
35. 97¢ − 18¢ = ______

Name ______________________________

Add. Regroup if needed.

1. $543 + 6$

2. $646 + 7$

3. $432 + 9$

4. $715 + 5$

5. $136 + 5$

6. $329 + 60$

7. $455 + 16$

8. $376 + 29$

9. $528 + 73$

10. $409 + 54$

11. $48 + 333$

12. $26 + 178$

13. $77 + 460$

14. $143 + 109$

15. $321 + 538$

16. $177 + 304$

17. $326 + 176$

18. $265 + 416$

19. $531 + 199$

20. $428 + 275$

21. $\$2.37 + 0.42$

22. $\$3.42 + 1.39$

23. $\$4.11 + 3.69$

24. $\$5.28 + 3.72$

Solve.

25. Kathy spent \$3.74. Matt spent \$4.33. How much did they spend altogether?

____

26. The Jacksons drove 313 miles on Tuesday. They drove 178 miles on Wednesday. How many miles did they drive altogether?

_____ miles

Name ______________________________

Subtract. Regroup if needed.

1. 432 − 6	2. 833 − 7	3. 715 − 10	4. 168 − 50	5. 917 − 60
6. 329 − 81	7. 456 − 92	8. 376 − 35	9. 528 − 38	10. 401 − 78
11. 177 − 89	12. 326 − 27	13. 265 − 174	14. 534 − 243	15. 428 − 278
16. 483 − 365	17. 258 − 179	18. 734 − 585	19. 672 − 433	20. 916 − 558
21. \$2.75 − 0.24	22. \$5.64 − 2.42	23. \$7.17 − 1.58	24. \$4.12 − 3.23	25. \$3.45 − 2.98

Solve.

26. The music store had 765 CDs. Lucy sold 177 of them. How many CDs are left?

_____ CDs

27. Sam had \$8.42. He bought a book for \$3.85. How much money does he have left?

____

Name ______________________________

Add or subtract.

1. $\begin{array}{r} 465 \\ +\ 34 \\ \hline \end{array}$

2. $\begin{array}{r} 638 \\ +\ 38 \\ \hline \end{array}$

3. $\begin{array}{r} 313 \\ -\ 49 \\ \hline \end{array}$

4. $\begin{array}{r} 752 \\ +\ 139 \\ \hline \end{array}$

5. $\begin{array}{r} 278 \\ +\ 610 \\ \hline \end{array}$

6. $\begin{array}{r} 329 \\ 143 \\ +\ 333 \\ \hline \end{array}$

7. $\begin{array}{r} 251 \\ 227 \\ +\ 295 \\ \hline \end{array}$

8. $\begin{array}{r} 406 \\ 118 \\ +\ 276 \\ \hline \end{array}$

9. $\begin{array}{r} 593 \\ +\ 248 \\ \hline \end{array}$

10. $\begin{array}{r} 888 \\ -\ 359 \\ \hline \end{array}$

11. $\begin{array}{r} 656 \\ -\ 447 \\ \hline \end{array}$

12. $\begin{array}{r} 451 \\ -\ 167 \\ \hline \end{array}$

13. $\begin{array}{r} 923 \\ -\ 278 \\ \hline \end{array}$

14. $\begin{array}{r} \$6.95 \\ +\ 2.24 \\ \hline \end{array}$

15. $\begin{array}{r} \$4.37 \\ +\ 3.33 \\ \hline \end{array}$

16. $\begin{array}{r} \$6.14 \\ -\ 2.69 \\ \hline \end{array}$

17. $\begin{array}{r} \$8.21 \\ -\ 3.54 \\ \hline \end{array}$

Subtract. Then check your answers.

18. $\begin{array}{r} \$3.49 \\ -\ 1.67 \\ \hline \end{array}$

19. $\begin{array}{r} 852 \\ -\ 564 \\ \hline \end{array}$

20. $\begin{array}{r} \$6.21 \\ -\ 2.45 \\ \hline \end{array}$

Solve.

21. Soo had \$5.35. She spent \$4.58. How much money does she have now?

Soo has ________.

22. Mike had \$3.42. He spent \$1.58. How much money does he have left?

Mike has ________ left.

Name ______________________________

How many of each shape are there? Write the number.

1. _____ triangles

2. _____ rectangles

3. _____ circles

4. _____ squares

Write the number for each.

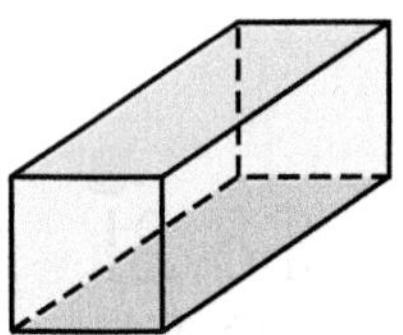

5. _____ faces

6. _____ vertices

7. _____ edges

Is the line a line of symmetry? Circle yes or no.

8. 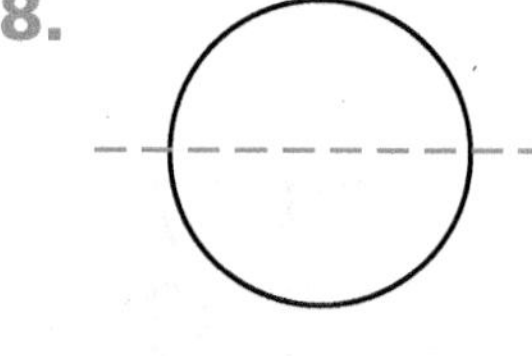

yes no

9. 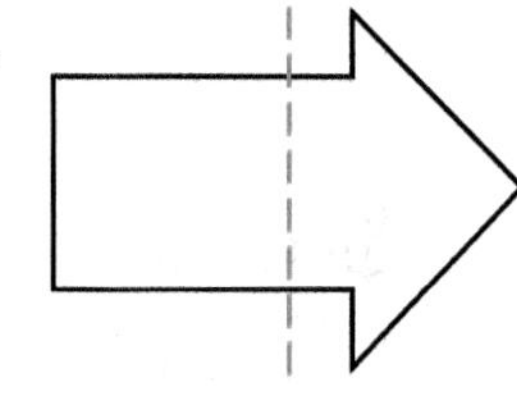

yes no

Write the fraction for each.

10. 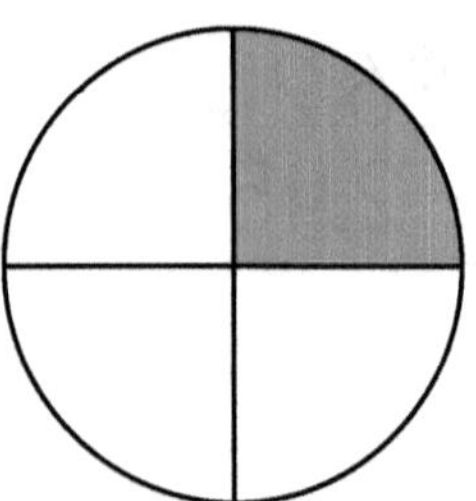

_____

11. 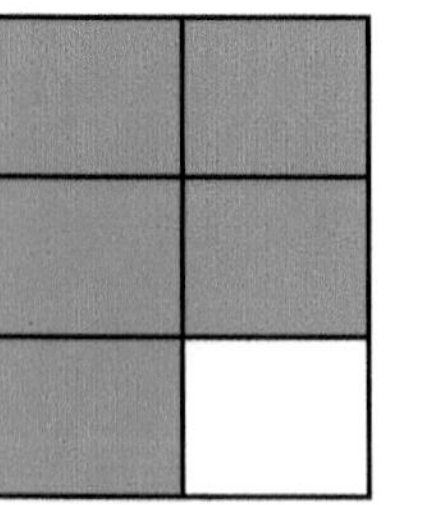

_____

12. 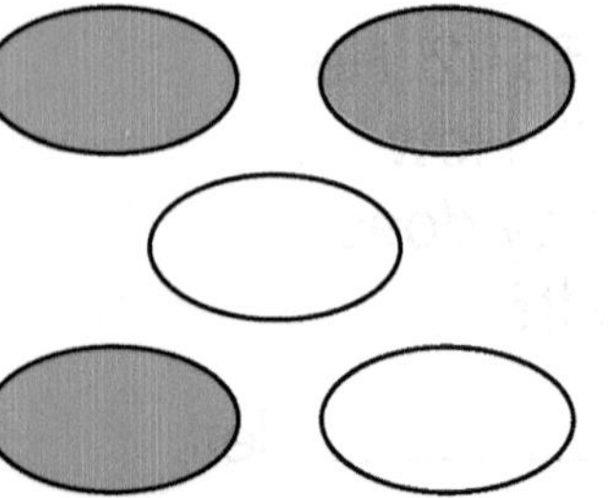

_____

13. 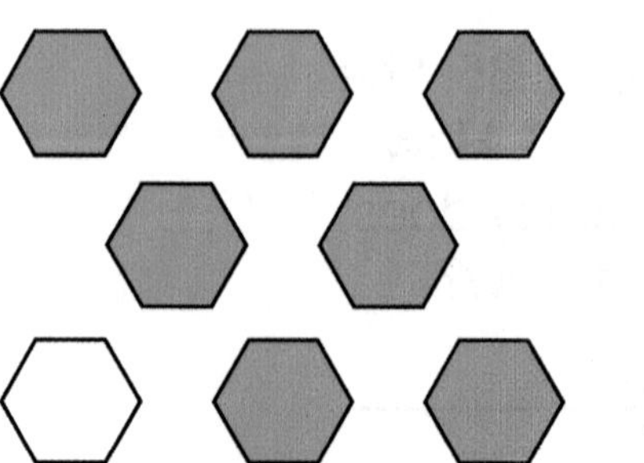

_____

Name ____

Estimate the length to the nearest inch.

1. 

It is between ____ and ____ inches. ____ nearest inch

Estimate the length to the nearest centimeter.

2. 

It is between ____ and ____ centimeters. ____ nearest centimeter

Use your centimeter ruler. Measure around the figure.

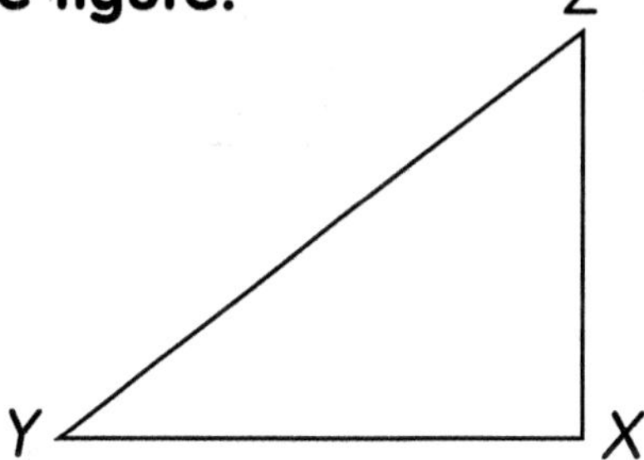

3. 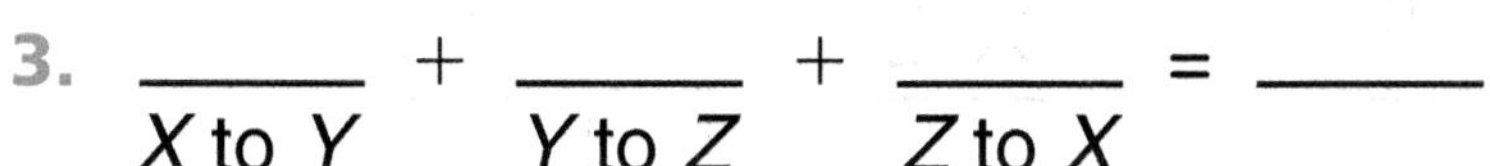

______ + ______ + ______ = ______
X to *Y* *Y* to *Z* *Z* to *X*

The perimeter is ____ centimeters.

Estimate the area.

4. 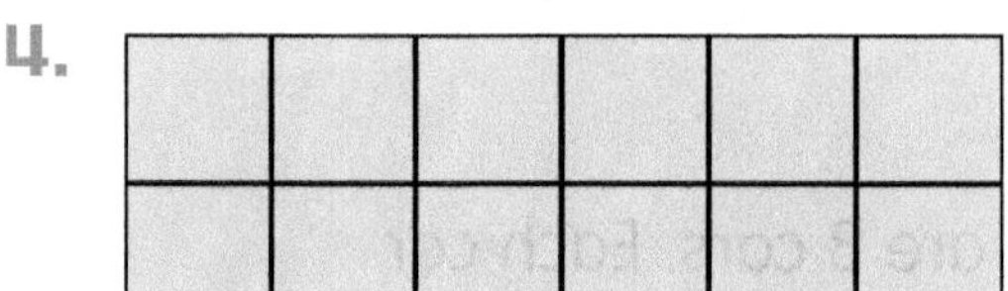

area = ____ square centimeters

Circle the better estimate.

5. 

4 ounces 4 pounds

6. 

I cup I quart

Write the temperature.

7. 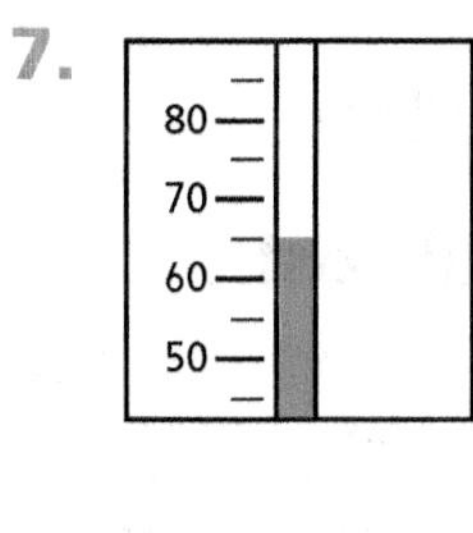

____°F

Name ______________________________

Multiply.

1.  

$3 \times 3 =$ ____

2.   

$2 \times 3 =$ ____

3.   

$3 \times 4 =$ ____

4.    

$4 \times 2 =$ ____

5. $\begin{array}{r} 2 \\ \times 4 \\ \hline \end{array}$

6. $\begin{array}{r} 5 \\ \times 5 \\ \hline \end{array}$

7. $\begin{array}{r} 3 \\ \times 5 \\ \hline \end{array}$

8. $\begin{array}{r} 4 \\ \times 3 \\ \hline \end{array}$

9. $\begin{array}{r} 2 \\ \times 2 \\ \hline \end{array}$

Divide.

10. $8 \div 2 =$ ____

11. $25 \div 5 =$ ____

12. $12 \div 4 =$ ____

Solve.

13. Peter bought 4 bunches of grapes. There are 5 grapes in each bunch. How many grapes does he have?

____ grapes

14. There are 3 cars. Each car has 4 wheels. How many wheels are there in all?

There are ____ wheels.

Find the total cost.

15. 5 

Total cost ____

16. 3 

Total cost ____

Alternate Chapter Test Answer Key

Chapter 1

1. top picture, 4, four; bottom picture, 6, six
2. 4, 5, 7, 5, 8, 9, 10
3. 3, 2, 5, 2, 6, 0, 3
4. $8 - 4 = 4$, 4 blocks
5. $3 + 4 = 7$, 7 cards

Chapter 2

1. 12, 10, 10, 11, 10, 11, 12
2. 11, 10, 11, 12, 12, 10, 12
3. 8, 4, 6, 3, 6, 6, 8
4. 9, 1, 8, 7, 7, 7, 5
5. 12¢ − 5¢ = 7¢, 7¢
6. 6¢ + 3¢ = 9¢, 9¢

Chapter 3

1. 10, 17, 11, 14, 13, 15, 16
2. 11, 14, 15, 12, 13, 16, 10
3. 18¢, 11¢, 13¢, 12¢, 12¢, 14¢, 11¢
4. 16, 15, 13, 14, 12, 17, 18
5. $5 + 9 = 14$, 14 marbles
6. 8¢ + 9¢ = 17¢, 17¢

Chapter 4

1. 6, 8, 7, 9, 4, 9, 8
2. 9, 7, 9, 6, 5, 6, 7
3. 4, 8, 8, 8, 3, 9, 3
4. 7, 2, 0, 8, 7, 7, 9
5. $13 - 8 = 5$, 5 years older
6. $16 - 9 = 7$, 7 cars
7. 14¢ − 5¢ = 9¢, 9¢
8. $15 - 6 = 9$, 9 stickers

Chapter 5

1. 3 hundreds 5 tens 6 ones, 356
2. 422¢, $4.22
3. 259, 260, 261, 262
4. 60, 70, 80, 90
5. 4 hundreds 2 tens 7 ones
6. 3 hundreds 0 tens 9 ones
7. 450, 452
8. 688, 690
9. >
10. >
11. =
12. <

Chapter 6

1. 1 o'clock, 1:00
2. 10 minutes after 8, 8:10
3. 10:00, 1:00
4. Monday
5. April
6. 62¢
7. 93¢, 30¢
8. $1.42, 27¢

Chapter 7

1. 49 2. 74 3. 83 4. 110 5. 110
6. 110 7. 98 8. 92 9. 104 10. 109
11. 51 12. 159 13. 55 14. 143
15. 93 16. 72 17. 61 18. 72
19. 127 20. 153 21. 162 22. 141
23. 107 24. 95 25. 65¢, $0.65
26. 130¢, $1.30 27. 87¢, $0.87
28. 107¢, $1.07 29. 104¢, $1.04
30. 141 31. $1.84

Chapter 8

1. 44 2. 76 3. 69 4. 56 5. 50
6. 40 7. 30 8. 24 9. 59 10. 47
11. 29 12. 30 13. 76 14. 18
15. 29 16. 18 17. 39¢ 18. 17¢
19. 9¢ 20. 39¢ 21. 39 22. 45

Chapter 9

1. 72 2. 89 3. 99 4. 89 5. 91
6. 81 7. 71 8. 121 9. 140 10. 102
11. 91 12. 159 13. 54 14. 21
15. 44 16. 7 17. 55 18. 18 19. 85
20. 122 21. 121 22. 130 23. 135
24. 148 25. 93 26. 102 27. 104
28. 147 29. 184 30. 88
31. 75¢ $0.75 32. 141¢ $1.41
33. 47¢ $0.47 34. 121¢ $1.21
35. 79¢ $0.79

Chapter 10

1. 549 2. 673 3. 441 4. 720
5. 141 6. 389 7. 471 8. 405
9. 601 10. 463 11. 381 12. 204
13. 537 14. 252 15. 859 16. 481
17. 502 18. 681 19. 730 20. 703
21. $2.79 22. $4.81 23. $7.90
24. $9.00 25. $8.07 26. 491

Chapter 11

1. 426 2. 826 3. 705 4. 118
5. 857 6. 248 7. 364 8. 341
9. 490 10. 323 11. 88 12. 299
13. 91 14. 291 15. 150 16. 118
17. 79 18. 149 19. 239 20. 358
21. $2.51 22. $3.22 23. $5.59
24. $0.89 25. $0.47 26. 588
27. $4.57

Chapter 12

1. 499 2. 676 3. 264 4. 891
5. 888 6. 805 7. 773 8. 800
9. 841 10. 529 11. 209 12. 284
13. 645 14. $9.19 15. $7.70
16. $3.45 17. $4.67 18. $1.82
19. 288 20. $3.76 21. $0.77
22. $1.84

Chapter 13

1. 2 2. 2 3. 3 4. 4 5. 6 6. 8
7. 12 8. yes 9. no 10. $\frac{1}{4}$
11. $\frac{5}{6}$ 12. $\frac{3}{5}$ 13. $\frac{7}{8}$

Chapter 14

1. 2, 3, 2
2. 8, 9, 9
3. 4, 5, 3, 12, 12
4. 12
5. 4 pounds
6. 1 quart
7. 65

Chapter 15

1. 9 2. 6 3. 12 4. 8 5. 8 6. 25
7. 15 8. 12 9. 4 10. 4 11. 5
12. 4 13. 20 14. 12 15. 10¢ 16. 9¢